the
South London
HANDBOOK

Celie Parker

First Published 1986

© The Stockwell Press, 1986
London SW9 Tel 733 7040

Printed in Great Britain by
The Guernsey Press Company Limited
PO Box 57, Braye Road
Vale, Guernsey

Designed by David Brancaleone
Illustrated by Damon Burnard

ISBN 0 9511022 0 6

CONTENTS

chapter one
ADULT EDUCATION 1

chapter two
ART 9

chapter three
CHILDREN 27

chapter four
DANCE 53

chapter five
DISABILITY 67

chapter six
ELDERLY 101

chapter seven
ETHNIC MINORITIES 125

chapter eight
FESTIVALS & EVENTS 161

chapter nine
FILM & VIDEO 169

chapter ten
HEALTH 181

chapter eleven
HOUSING 187

chapter twelve
LESBIAN & GAY 201

chapter thirteen
LIBRARIES 211

chapter fourteen
LOCAL HISTORY 233

chapter fifteen
LOCAL SERVICES 263

chapter sixteen
MARKETS 277

chapter seventeen
MUSEUMS 289

chapter eighteen
NIGHTLIFE 301

chapter nineteen
PARKS 315

chapter twenty
POETRY & PROSE 323

chapter twenty-one
RESTAURANTS 331

chapter twenty-two
SCHOOL 341

chapter twenty-three
SPORT 345

chapter twenty-four
THEATRE 375

chapter twenty-five
WOMEN 393

chapter twenty-six
YOUNG PEOPLE 407

chapter twenty-seven
WHOOPS! 431

chapter twenty-eight
EMERGENCY 433

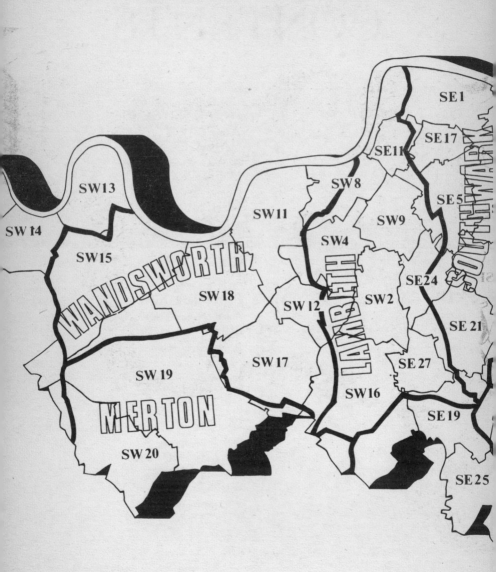

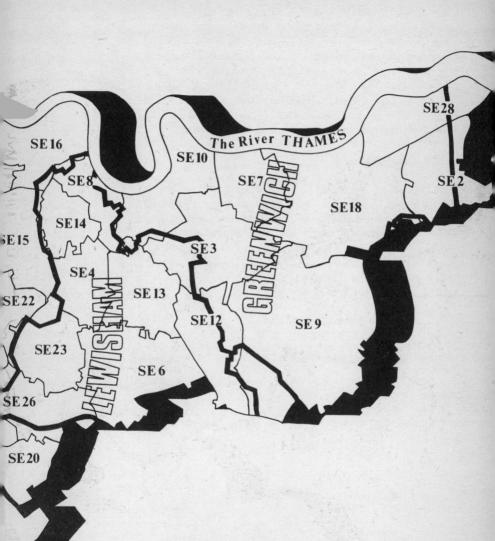

writing and research

Tricia Anderson, Paul Beasley, Terry Brian, Colin Bumstead, David Burbidge, Marlene Burridge, Chris Cresswell-Jones, Andrew Crowe, Julie Curran, Henry Dopson, Maureen Gallagher, Nanette Greenblatt, Carl Harrison, Chris Harrison, Graham Jackson, Sue Jones, Seymour Kelly, Pauline de Laine, Lambeth Archives Department, Mary Marshall, Richard Milward, Sean Moore, Veronica Moore, Jennifer Murray, Celie Parker, Isabel Plumbly, Reg and Joan Prescott, Joel Stewart, Paul Tomlin, Trevor Toussaint and Fid Warman.

additional thanks to

Dith Banbury, Tissa Davis, The English Tourist Board, Jane Funnell, Steph Kay, Abbey Monkhouse, Nigel Montagu, Georgia Morgenstern, Patricia Norris, Origin Design, Geoffrey and Betty Parker, Freda Rodgers, the South London Press, Southwark Local Studies Library, Sarah West, William Wilding, and all the many other groups and people of South London who have contributed so much to the project.

How The Book Was Made

A community and arts handbook to South London had been on my mind for many years. I had often talked of it to my friend Mike Carter and in a foolhardy moment in the late summer of '84, he agreed to sponsor the project through his company, Stockwell Travel. We naively planned a six-month production period and I started work at the beginning of November. During the first few months of research, I struggled with the new technology provided and wondered if word processors were like food processors (ie basically destructive). Only with the help of another friend, Nanette Greenblatt, did the beast get tamed. She came in from time to time whenever she was free and offered me a bundle of practical and moral support. By August '85 my weeks had merged into weekends. That month, Jennie Murray came to work on the project and Nanette slipped into full-time gear too. Over the next months, a band of wonderful people (whose names you'll find under Writing and Research) came to contribute their talents and knowledge. Every room in the house had someone busy at a typewriter, computer or telephone. Drinking mugs of Revival tea and watching the dawn rise over Stockwell from my living room window was by now a regular feature of life. Just one year (and four days) since the project began, I am writing this, Mike is pasting up in the kitchen, and tomorrow it'll all be over and we can get back to normality . . . except that now we have to sell the book. (If you have a shop or any other potential outlet, perhaps you could stock a few copies?)

My special thanks go to Mike, for taking the risk and sticking by me as he watched the project grow out of all proportion in size and cost, and to Nanette, for the quality of her work, friendship and support over very many months.

Celie Parker

How The Book Works

The Handbook covers six London boroughs — Greenwich, Lambeth, Lewisham, Merton, Southwark and Wandsworth (see the map at the front of the book). We talked long and hard about where to draw the line and eventually decided to concentrate on the boroughs south of the river that have London postal codes. Having made our decision we discovered that the whole of London is an ill-fitting jigsaw. Postcodes and neighbourhoods cross borough boundaries and Merton, for instance, goes right outside the inner London area. Even worse than that, ILEA and the Health Authorities all have their own quite different boundaries that bear no relation to the boroughs'. This affects essential matters like where you go to school and which hospitals or doctors' surgeries you can attend. No wonder we're all confused! As far as the Handbook's concerned, next time round we intend to rationalise further and hope to include areas like Croydon. We have spent months and months researching, talking to people, and checking and re-checking facts in an attempt to find out what's on tap for one and all. However, despite our efforts, there will inevitably be some items that are out of date or inaccurate by the time the book gets to you. For this we take no responsibility but we do apologise. Please let us know if you spot any errors or omissions. We hope the organisation of most chapters will be self-evident. In the case of chapters that aren't so easy to get around, we have included a note in the introduction, explaining how the contents are arranged. When listing venues, we have included local neighbourhood names to give you some idea of where they are. In a few parts of South London local names don't really exist and, in these instances, we've had to plump for neighbouring ones.

We are planning a second edition in a year or so's time and already have lots of new chapters in mind. If you think you're doing something we should know about or have any other suggestions, do let us know. This is a community handbook so we need ideas and help from you lot out there!

ADULT EDUCATION

This chapter covers part-time day and evening study in South London. The listings of colleges are divided into two sections – Adult Education Institutes followed by Colleges and Polytechnics. We thought it was important to make a distinction since these establishments do have a slightly different approach and emphasis. All of them, of course, offer marvellous opportunities. Read on!

General Advice

If you need any individual help in choosing a course or working out a programme of study, contact your nearest Education Advice Service below. If you live in **Lewisham**, contact either the Greenwich or Southwark branch. **Merton** is outside the ILEA area and doesn't have quite the same system, but you can get general advice and help at Merton Adult Education Institute below.

Greenwich Education & Training Advice (GRETA)
12-14 Wellington Street
Woolwich   SE18
Tel 854 2993/2030

Lambeth Educational Opportunities
Lambeth Institute
Strand Centre
Elm Park
Brixton   SW2
Tel 671 2961

Merton Adult Education Institute
Whatley Avenue
Raynes Park   SW20
Tel 543 9292

Information & Advice Network on Southwark Education & Training
175 Rye Lane
Peckham   SE15
Tel 635 9111

Wandsworth Education Shop
86 Battersea Rise
Battersea SW11
Tel 350 1790

Back to Study?

The Open College of South London
Manor House
58 Clapham Common Northside
Clapham SW4
SW4
Tel 228 2015
The Open College of South London is
a network of ten colleges that
provides courses for mature students
(19+) who wish to return to study.
No formal qualifications are
necessary and many different levels
are offered in each subject. The
colleges (Adult Education Institutes
and Colleges of Further and Higher
Education) are based in
Wandsworth, Lambeth and
Southwark but are open to anyone.
Four different courses are offered:
Access, Return to Learning, New
Technology and Flexible Learning
Opportunities. (How sad that the
names of the courses in this
wonderful scheme should be so
obscured by jargon. We will try to
demystify!) Access prepares mature
students without qualifications for
degree and diploma courses in a range
of subjects (from Architecture to
Social Work); Return to Learning

offers students the chance to study
many subjects so that they may
improve their learning ability and
explore new career possibilities; New
Technology is for people who want to
understand new technology and
develop skills in Computing, Modern
Office Technology, Word Processing,
Information Technology, Electronics
and Communications; Flexible
Learning Opportunities permits
people to study a range of subjects
either at home with tutorial support
or at a centre at times to suit. Fees are
charged at the usual ILEA rates for
all Open College courses. Part-time.
Access students do not qualify for
concessionary rates but discretionary
grants are available to full-time
students. The Open College student
card offers many benefits.

Adult Education Institutes

Part-time day and evening classes are
available in a host of different
subjects at Adult Education Institutes
throughout South London. At some,
it's possible to follow a syllabus of
study leading to a conventional
examination but for the most part
classes are geared towards those
wishing to take up a new interest just
for the fun of it or pursue an old one
in an informal setting and easy-going
atmosphere. Classes range from fairly
traditional subjects to inventive new
ones. We have tried to reflect both of
these aspects in our listings below but
do bear in mind that the subjects we
have mentioned represent only a tiny
sample of those on offer. Most colleges
are committed to working alongside
the community and welcome ideas for
courses from local people, so contact
the institute for your area if you have
any suggestions. You may enrol for
classes at any college within the ILEA
area. To find out where you can study
the subject of your choice be sure to
get a copy of Floodlight (ILEA's

London-wide guide to adult education), which is usually published around August of each year. Floodlight also contains details of fees. Unemployed people are charged a fee of £1 for any number of courses. Merton's fees are higher than ILEA courses. To obtain further information about an institute or a prospectus (usually out in August also) you should phone or write to the main branch listed below. Enrolment dates vary but tend to take place in September and courses usually follow the pattern of the academic year, starting in September and going through to the end of June. Depending on the subject it's often possible to join classes mid-session. Some institutes offer summer and short or intensive courses.

Clapham-Battersea Institute
Headquarters
6 Edgeley Road
Clapham   **SW4**
Tel 622 2965
Variety of part-time and evening classes. Well-established Art Department offering good studio space and range of courses including two year part-time City & Guilds Art Certificate. Ceramics, Stained Glass, and craft classes in Patchwork, Applique, Jewellery and Enamelling. Courses for Playgroup Leaders, Women-Only Sports Nights, New Games (non competitive anti-sexist and anti-racist), Family Music and Movement classes, Afro-Caribbean Hair Braiding and Make-up, Circus Skills, several classes for people with special needs and many other traditional courses.

Lambeth Institute
Headquarters
Strand Centre
Elm Park
Brixton   **SW2**
Tel 671 1300

Lambeth offers the usual range of classes with a particularly well-equipped Computer Department providing courses in Home Computers, Micros and other areas of Information Technology. There is also a professional-style dance practice room. Screen Printing classes use the colour zeroxing and offset-litho facilities of a local printing firm, the Film-Making and Animation Department have links with the Ritzy Cinema and there is a good Ceramics Department. Other classes include Rasta Keep-Fit, Balcony Gardening, Caribbean Cookery, Music Business, Pop Singing and Composing, and Reggae Workshops. Some classes are held in the community rather than in the colleges. One of Lambeth's main aims is to cater for the needs of local people. Groups are encouraged to set up their own programmes using the institute's facilities. Volunteer support is provided for people with special needs.

Merton Adult Education Institute
Headquarters
Whatley Avenue
Raynes Park
SW20
Tel 543 9292
Merton offers a programme of basic education leading to RSA exams, GCE O Levels (these can be done as part correspondence courses or by flexi-study), pre TOPS courses and English as a Foreign Language. Other

available courses are Business Studies, Keep Fit and Health, History of Art (concentrating on the Renaissance), Painting, Pottery, Woodcarving and other arts and crafts. Liberal Studies include a part-time two year Royal Horticultural Society gardening course and two courses on National Trust properties. Daytime creche facilities.

Morley College
Headquarters
61 Westminster Bridge Road
Lambeth North SE1
Tel 928 8501
Established in South London for a hundred years and able to boast Gustav Holst and Michael Tippett as past directors of music, The Morley has an extensive range of courses to offer (including a summer programme) and a considerable reputation in its Music, Art, Literature and Languages Departments. Intensive language courses are particularly popular. On offer also is a programme of Fresh Start Return-to-Study courses designed to build confidence in people starting or returning to study. The Morley holds several of its courses in the local community rather than in the college. There's a well-stocked library for staff and students and an excellent gallery (see Art).

Putney & Wandsworth Adult Education Institute
Headquarters
Manresa House
Holybourne Avenue
Roehampton SW15
Tel 789 8255/6
Putney and Wandsworth provide a wide choice of day as well as evening courses often with childcare provision for the under-5s. As well as traditional classes there are many more flexible and informal family workshop sessions, a large variety of art and related courses (in a well-

equipped art school), and a programme of English and Return-to-Study classes. Other subjects include Arabic, Japanese, Black Studies, Alternative Medicine, Philosophy, and Meditation. The Institute welcomes requests for courses from the local community.

Morley College

Ravensbourne Institute
Headquarters
Lewisham School
Ewhurst Road
Brockley SE4
Tel 690 0720
Keep-Fit and Health classes, Swimming, Squash, Ski-Training, Indoor Golf, Football, Archery and Fencing are all available at Ravensbourne. There is also a well-equipped Art Department offering Painting and Sculpture classes, Ceramics, Stained Glass and Design. You can learn Chair Caning, Basketry, Upholstery and how to make cushions, soft toys and lampshades. The fashion department has courses in Design and Pattern Drafting, Dressmaking, Sewing Machine Maintenance, Embroidery, Soft Tailoring, Millinery and Machine Knitting. There are family workshops in Languages and Cookery and a Chinese Language day every Sunday. Most European languages plus Urdu and Turkish are taught. Computers and Electronics, Indian and Chinese Cookery, a range of classes for people

with special needs and some short summer courses are also on offer.

South Greenwich Institute
Headquarters
Haimo Road
New Eltham   SE?
Tel 850 3632/3503
South Greenwich runs special PE classes for handicapped people, mother and toddler workshops in the community, and craft classes for the elderly in old people's homes. Other unusual courses are held on Radio Theory, Producing a Newspaper, Horse Care, Dog Training, Mexican Cooking, Machine knitting, Clock Repairs, Silversmithing, Bookbinding, Appreciation of Antiques, Astronomy, Medau, Fitness Testing and Ski Training. Pottery, Calligraphy, Photography and Abstract Sculpture are all available too, plus a range of music and language courses.

South Lewisham Institute
Headquarters
Malory School
Launcelot Road
Downham
Bromley
Tel 698 4113
A whole range of conventional and unusual courses are available at South Lewisham including Dressmaking, Tailoring, and Sewing For Young People; Angling, Aviation, Gymnastics, Netball, and Archery; Animal Illustration, Cartoon Drawing, Calligraphy and Lettering; Lacemaking, Basketry and Chair Caning; Bee-keeping, Bird-watching, Botany and Field Archeology; Clock-making and Jewellery (gold casting, gem setting and costume jewellery); Computers and Electronics; Buying Your Own Home, Home Maintenance and Starting Your Own Business; Modern Languages and Family Workshops; Homeopathy and a Self-Help Coronary Club for coronary thrombosis sufferers.

Southwark Institute
Headquarters
Queen's Road Centre
St Mary's Road
North Peckham   SE15
Tel 639 1178
Southwark has a Return-to-Study course in Food Studies (cookery and related skills) and in Fashion (cutting, drawing and design, the construction of a garment and the history of fashion). There are good creche facilities, mother and toddler clubs, and educational home visiting schemes when staff visit mothers and children at home. There are the usual art courses, a good pottery centre, craft and badminton classes for disabled people, Car Maintenance, Home Decoration, Self Defence for Women and special courses for people who have had mental or emotional difficulties. A range of summer courses includes Holiday Greek, Jewellery Box Making, an Introduction to Bobbin Lacemaking, Life Saving, and Picnic and Summer Fruit Cookery.

Streatham & Tooting Adult Education Institute
Headquarters
The Adare Centre
Mount Earl Gardens
Leigham Court Road
Streatham   SW16
Tel 677 3522
An exciting and varied range of day and evening classes can be enjoyed in many centres throughout a large part of Wandsworth and a smaller part of Lambeth. On offer are numerous traditional classes and an expanding programme of Basic Education, English as a Second Language and Family Education. Streatham & Tooting also do a considerable amount of work among old people and people with severe learning difficulties.

Thamesside Adult Education Institute
Headquarters
Burrage Grove
Plumstead SE18
Tel 855 9044
Some of the more unusual courses that Thamesside has to offer are Nautical Studies (with Sunday morning sailing classes), excellent domestic science opportunities (with Cake Decoration as a specialist subject), 'Gateway to Skills' courses for people with special needs, and Family Cookery and Language Workshops. Also available are general courses on Computers and Typing, English as a Foreign Language and a variety of the more traditional part-time day and evening classes.

Colleges & Polytechnics

In addition to adult education institutes, there are many South London-based colleges and polytechnics that are primarily involved in providing full-time academic, business and technical education but also offer a useful range of part-time day and evening courses. These colleges are geared towards those wishing to improve their knowledge of a craft or skill or gain a professional or academic qualification in art, commerce, technology or management. They offer general education courses as well, both for people wishing to sit exams and for those wanting to improve their level of general education. Some fascinating, unusual and highly specialised courses are also to be found at these colleges. Most prospectuses are printed in June or July but there are some exceptions - check individual listings below.

Brixton College
56 Brixton Hill
Brixton SW2
Tel 737 1166
Multi-cultural college offering a wide range of part-time and evening courses: Computing, Word Processing, Electronics, Telecommunications and other new technology subjects; Return-to-Study courses for those out of education for some time, and evening as well as part-time day BTEC National courses.

Goldsmiths College
(University of London)
School of Adult and Community Studies
Lewisham Way
New Cross SE14
Tel 692 7171
The School of Adult & Community Studies caters for the extra-mural subjects of Goldsmiths College. Part-time courses are available in Art in London Galleries, Art Therapy (foundation), Film Studies, TV Studies, Community Radio, Drama and Dance and Writing for the Theatre. A few of the courses lead to exams and qualifications but the majority are designed for general interest.

London College of Printing
Elephant & Castle SE1
Tel 735 8484
The college offers a wide range of courses in all aspects of Printing Studies and in Design, Media and Business Studies. Prospectus available from the end of March.

Polytechnic of the South Bank
Borough Road
Elephant & Castle SE1
Tel 928 8989
The Language Centre offers courses at all levels in eight languages

including English as a foreign language. Other evening and part-time courses lead to degrees, diplomas or higher education qualifications in the faculties of Social Sciences, Building, Administration, Science & Technology and Engineering. Prospectus available from the end of March.

South East London College
Lewisham Way
Lewisham   SE4
Tel 692 0353
Part-time courses for adults in Engineering, Business and Office Studies, Catering, Construction, GCE, General Education, English as a Foreign/Second Language. Special courses for women in non-traditional areas are being developed.

South London College
Knights Hill
West Norwood   SE27
Tel 670 4488
Part-time day and evening courses in Business and Secretarial Studies, Computing, Dental Technology, Electronics, Food Technology, GCE O and A Level, Geology, Horticulture, Photography, Return-to-Study and Sciences.

South Thames College
Wandsworth High Street
Wandsworth   SW18
Tel 870 2241
A wide range of full and part-time vocational courses. Engineering, Business Studies, Secretarial and Commercial studies, Audio-visual Technology and Science. General education courses are offered in many GCE O and A Level subjects and in pre-vocational courses. Short courses in most subjects. The college also has a large specialist EFL and ESL section and considerable involvement in new technology. Prospectus available from January.

Southwark College
The Cut
Waterloo   SE1
Tel 928 9561
33 O Level and 24 A Level subjects in Science, Art, Humanities and Business. Day release BTEC General Certificate and a variety of BTEC National Certificate day and evening courses together with day and evening classes in Shorthand, Typewriting, Audio Typewriting and Word Processing. Also Floristry, Horticulture, Computer

Programming, Computer Awareness, Information Technology, EFL & ESL, drop-in classes for non-exam Maths and English, and several courses for those wishing to return to learning, eg: Access and Return-to-Study.

South West London College
Tooting Broadway
Tooting   SW17
Tel 672 2441
The ILEA specialist business college, which works on all-through principle, enabling students to join courses without formal entry qualifications and progress to the final examinations of the main professional bodies. A comprehensive range of courses in Management, Business Studies, Accountancy, Counselling, Computer Programming, Secretarial Skills and GCE O and A Level.

Vauxhall College of Building & Further Education
Belmore Street
Wandsworth Road
Stockwell   SW8
Tel 928 4611
A wide range of GCE O and A Levels. Other courses include Art, Sciences, Computing, Recreation, Community Care, Basic Literacy, Typing, Shorthand, Word Processing, Construction Technician Work and City & Guilds courses in Building Crafts, eg Sign-Writing, Glazing (including Leaded Light Work), Graining and Marbling. Special courses include Black Culture Hair & Beauty, Book-in Word Processing (ie you choose a schedule that suits) and a Women's Introductory Course in Computing.

Westminster College
Wye Street
Battersea   SW11
Tel 871 7471
This college also has branches north of the river. Courses include Wider Opportunities for Women, an MSC funded six-week full-time course for women (over 19) who have been out of employment for two or more years; a special ACCESS preparatory BEd in Home Economics for mature students (22+) interested in becoming Home Economics teachers (no qualifications necessary) and Fashion, a course for mature students leading to City & Guilds qualificatons. Also, part-time courses in Civil Engineering, Computer Studies, Word Processing and many O & A Level subjects. Prospectus available from the end of May.

Woolwich College
Villas Road
Plumstead
SE18
Tel 855 1216
A community college offering a wide range of full-time, part-time and evening courses in Business Studies, Commerce and Secretarial Studies, Engineering, Science, Maths, Arts and the Humanities. Besides the traditional courses, the college offers an Open Access course for adults (19+), a women-only course - Women and New Technology (WANT), ESL courses, computing facilities and YTS courses. Prospectus available from the end of May.

ART

History was made in South London in 1814 when the Dulwich Picture Gallery opened as the country's first public art gallery (it pre-dated the National Gallery by about ten years). South London continues to break new ground in the art world and is well populated by artists and new and exciting venues. Many galleries (Battersea Arts Centre, Brixton Gallery and Cafe Gallery, in particular,) are working hard to break down the barriers between art and the community and are not afraid to take risks by showing unusual, experimental, less mainstream art (such as mixed media, performance and video) and the work of unestablished artists. Brixton and Cafe have been organised by groups of artists who have found funding through grants and subsidies and who have made an effort to create galleries that are less dependent on the usual commercial pressures and freer to experiment with shows. Coracle Press has managed highly successfully to involve a body of artists within the structure of a commercial gallery.

Specialist South London galleries abound. There are several thousand works of maritime art at The National Maritime Museum, fine pre-Raphaelite paintings at Old Battersea House, theatrical paintings at The National Theatre, book arts at Book Works, Japanese, Australian and other prints at Intaglio, ceramics at Ceramics 7, and do-it-youself art at Wood Wharf. At the other end of the scale, South London also has The Hayward Gallery, offering major international art shows.

There are works of art in some pretty unusual places in South London. In the arches under Hungerford Bridge there is Feliks Topolski's important and personal 'Memoir of The Century'. If you go there on a Friday (see listings under Feliks Topolski for times), you can visit the painter himself in his studio in a neighbouring arch. A fine Barbara Hepworth sculpture and the marvellous Peace Pagoda can be enjoyed in Battersea Park and there are many other sculptural pieces and countless murals throughout South

London (see the borough sections of this chapter for some examples). Another unexpected setting for pleasing works of art is St Thomas's Hospital. Here patients, visitors and hospital staff can enjoy paintings, sculptures and prints in the wards and corridors of the hospital along with about thirty 19th century locally made Doulton tile panels depicting nursery rhyme scenes. Works of art are increasingly finding their way into places not traditionally used for art, such as community and leisure centres, libraries and even swimming pools and there are countless community arts workshops and projects in South London. If you want to find out about activities in your area, contact the organisation listed under your borough (below).

There are some important art colleges in South London and galleries are attached to three of them. Camberwell has links with The South London Art Gallery and Goldsmiths and Morley College have their own galleries. Camberwell, Wimbledon and Goldsmiths all have Fine Art degree courses. Wimbledon is one of only two London colleges to have a Theatre Design department, Goldsmiths offers a degree course in Photography and Camberwell has excellent Ceramics and Textiles departments. If you're interested in viewing and perhaps buying new work, take a look at the

degree shows of these colleges, which usually take place between May and July.

If you yourself want to study art part-time or wish to build up a pre-foundation portfolio, try an adult education institute. There are several in South London with highly professional art departments, such as Morley College, Clapham-Battersea and Putney (see Adult Education).

Art in Your Borough

Greenwich

Visual art is organised within the Leisure Services Department of Greenwich Council and the council assists art groups through its Entertainments Department and Greenwich Arts Council. One of the groups to benefit from funding from Leisure Services and from the Arts Council is the Greenwich Mural Workshop, who have done some striking murals in the borough, including the one at the end of Creek Road. Woodlands Art Gallery is run by Greenwich Council.

Greenwich Entertainment Service & Greenwich Arts Council
25 Woolwich New Road
SE18
Tel 854 8888 or 317 8687 (Box Office)
Open 10-4.45(Mon-Fri)
The Entertainment Service consists of an Arts & Entertainments Manager, an Entertainments Officer and four Arts Assistants, one of whom is specifically responsible for Community Art. The Greenwich Entertainment Service produces a monthly diary of events (covering visual and other arts and entertainments) which is available in libraries and local community centres. If you have difficulty obtaining one, you can ask to be put on the mailing

list. By visiting the Entertainment Service during box office hours, you can also pick up leaflets or news of any unscheduled events and obtain general information about exhibitions, events and entertainments in the borough. The Entertainment Service also advises and services The Greenwich Arts Council, an independent, voluntary body which co-ordinates many arts events in the borough (particularly during Greenwich Festival) and offers small-scale grants to local individuals and organisations. Applications should be made in writing to The Arts & Entertainments Manager at the above address.

Lambeth

Lambeth's visual arts are organised within the Amenity Services of the council and there are two Arts Officers, who cover the arts generally in the borough. The council hopes to expand its already vast community arts programme, and is particularly concerned that all art forms should be enjoyed and created by local people, particularly by those with special needs, such as the unemployed, the low waged, women, the Black and Asian communities and other ethnic groups.

It certainly is well known as a borough for its community art. It has wonderful murals and had its own muralist-in-residence, Gordon Wilkinson, from 1979 to 1982. There are now about forty murals in Lambeth, the most famous of which are perhaps Nuclear Dawn by Brian Barnes (in Coldharbour Lane) and a mural in Dexter Road by Gavin Jantjes and Thomas Joseph, commissioned by the GLC and completed in July 1985. The mural depicts immigrants arriving in a strange country and dispersing throughout Britain. It ends with a representation of the Notting Hill

riots in 1956. One of its creators says that it addresses itself to the reality of the people of the area, to their history and creative potential, invoking a new vision of the future reality. There are exhibitions at many community venues such as Brixton Recreation Centre (used by local artists and groups like Creation for Liberation), Clapham Pool (where there are also several arts workshops) and West Norwood Library (which has to be booked by local artists at least a year in advance - such is its popularity). The noticeboard at Brixton Art Gallery is one of the best places to find out what's going on in Lambeth as far as visual art is concerned.

Lambeth Arts Council
c/o Lambeth Amenity Services
164 Clapham Park Road
SW4
Tel 622 6655
653 2105 (Lambeth Arts Council Administrator)
Lambeth Arts Council helps develop the arts generally in the borough by giving small-scale grants to individual artists, groups, performers and community arts festivals and events.

Every other month, it produces a lively magazine called Lambeth Arts which contains reviews of arts events and news and views of people involved in the arts generally in the borough. Free copies are available at libraries, other council outlets and local arts venues. Individuals and organisations involved in local arts can become affiliated to the Arts Council and be put on the mailing list. The Arts Council also produces The Lambeth Arts Guide, a bi-monthly general events guide, which lists exhibitions and other arts events and entertainments in the borough. This is available along with odd leaflets about other events in libraries, community centres and other council outlets.

Lewisham

The council department responsible for art in Lewisham is Leisure Services. There is no public art gallery in the borough but the council helps distribute the Garden Gallery's publicity material and is very active generally in the visual arts. Lewisham is making a positive effort to encourage the use of non gallery spaces for art shows, eg Ladywell Swimming Baths, and has funded posters for leisure centres and community buildings. One of the borough's main aims is to bring art to the community and it is the only borough in South London to have adopted in principle a "Percentage for Arts" scheme. The principle of this scheme (which originated in the USA) is that visual art should be an integral part of the environment and that a percentage (usually 1%) of a borough's capital funding on public works (on anything from highway work to bus shelters) should be spent on enhancing the environment through visual art. Lewisham is also unique in South London in having an artist-in- residence. This scheme is partly funded by Lewisham and partly by The Greater London Arts. The present artist-in-residence, Conrad Atkinson, has been in post since February 1984 and is based at Old Mill Studios in Molesworth Street. He works with groups and individual artists, giving general assistance, including funding advice. He has, for instance, attracted funding to a print workshop in the borough. He is also trying to get the 'Percentage for Arts' scheme underway. During his stay in Lewisham, he has exhibited at Lewisham Library, Ladywell Baths and Telegraph Hill Neighbourhood Council. He serves on a GLC Community Arts committee which advises on visual arts and has judged a competition of anti-racist greetings cards. He is working on a number of paving stones (to be located around the borough) enscribed with the word PEACE in a dozen diferent languages and he will be providing a permanent piece for the borough before his contract comes to an end in February 1986. It is hoped that the scheme will continue in Lewisham. Sculptures of note in the borough include a wood sculpture in Bell Green, Sydenham which was created by the late artist, Terry Scott, as part of an Art in Public Places scheme a few years ago. There is also a more recent national project, (funded jointly by Lewisham, GLA and The Arts Council in consultation with the Public Art Development Trust) awarded to a New Zealand artist, Hamish Horsley, who made a piece in Portland stone called 'Sunstone' (an abstraction on a sundial), which stands in the new Bellingham Green Park.

Lewisham Arts & Entertainments Service
Lewisham Theatre
Rushey Green
SE6
Tel 690 4343

Lewisham has a community arts team consisting of a Communuty Arts Officer, an Ethnic Arts Officer, a Visual Arts Assistant and a Community Arts Assistant (at the above number). They advise and answer queries from both the general public and from local artists. A monthly Lewisham Diary of events is distributed to council estates and to libraries, community and leisure centres. If you have any difficulty obtaining a copy, ring The Public Relations Office at the above phone number and ask to be put on the mailing list. As with other boroughs, leaflets of one-off events are usually available from local libraries.

Merton

Merton is lucky to have not only the

beautiful Cannizaro Park in its borough but also the excellent Wimbledon School of Art. The park and school join forces for 2-3 weeks at the beginning of June when sculptures by degree students and staff are put on show in Cannizaro Park. Wimbledon's other degree shows take place in June and July. News of exhibitions and events in the borough, such as the ones promoted by Merton Arts Council (see below), are detailed in a monthly blue newsheet which is distributed to libraries and community centres throughout the borough. There is no mailing list.

Merton Arts Council
Wimbledon Library
Wimbledon Hill Road
SW19
Tel 947 6545
Merton Arts Council promotes a yearly exhibition, called 'Vision', which takes place at The Canons Leisure Centre, Madeira Road, Mitcham. 'Vision 86' will be taking place in June and is expected to include paintings, photographs, collage and other work. Affiliated to the Arts Council are two local art societies which each have two main exhibitions a year. The Merton Arts Society usually holds exhibitions in April and October in Morden Library Lecture Room, and The Wimbledon Sketch Club has a spring and a winter show in Wimbledon Library Exhibition Room.

Dulwich Picture Gallery

Southwark
At present, Southwark has a Visual Arts Officer and an Arts Officer, who deals with matters relating to all the other arts in the borough. The Arts Officer is also involved in the BIF scheme, in which GLA identified Southwark and a few other London boroughs as being ready for development in the arts. The first thing to come out of BIF was The Live Arts for Southwark report which was published in the spring of 1984. This report made a number of recommendations about the establishment of an arts team, community arts projects and a community arts festival in Southwark. All of these recommendations have been implemented apart from the staffing of the team. The current arts co-ordinating team in Southwark consists of the Entertainments & Halls Manager, the Arts Officer, the Visual Arts Officer and Assistant Borough Librarian & Curator. A new Leisure and Recreation Department is in the process of being agreed, which may involve a move of premises early in 1986. As a borough, Southwark is committed to making performing and visual arts more accessible to the local community. Libraries are beginning to develop small displays of work and there's a lot of mural work going on in local schools and in the community generally to improve areas such as the North Peckham Estate. There's a particularly interesting mural outside Brunel's Engine House and, opposite it, a series of knot sculptures. Other sculptures in Southwark include a depiction of Minerva (also known as Pallas Athena), Goddess of War, Wisdom and the Liberal Arts, in a rather splendid river-fronted square at the back of Southwark Cathedral and outside Grindley's Bank. She is portrayed traditionally in armour, with a shield and spear, but her armour shields her face to signify her defensive but aggressive nature.

**Southwark Entertainments &
Southwark Arts Council**
28 Peckham Road
SE5
Tel 703 2917 (direct line 24 hrs)
or 703 6311
The Live Arts for Southwark report is
available from the above address or
from the reference library. A few
copies are still available of another
more recent publication, The
Southwark Directory of Community
Artists and Arts Professionals
(produced as part of Southwark's
ongoing arts programme), and it is
also available in the reference library.
The findings of two further reports,
one on the media and one on venues
in the borough should be available
some time in 1986. There is a monthly
'What's On in Southwark' leaflet,
which features local organisations
free of charge. This is available in
libraries, information centres, the
Town Hall and from Southwark
Entertainments. The Southwark Arts
Council is an independent body of
affiliated arts organisations, which
receives an annual grant from
Southwark Council. Its role is to
assist the community arts groups and
organisations in its membership in a
general way or by giving grant aid or
guarantee against losses. The grants
given are small amounts. The
Southwark Arts Council also
promotes events such as the
Southwark Community Arts Festival
and gives grant advice to the council
about arts organisations. Every other
month it produces a publication called
'Scan' which contains reviews,
interviews and comment on the
community arts events in the
borough. At present, Scan is mailed
only to members of the Arts Council.
A charge to non members may be
introduced.

Wandsworth

Wandsworth's arts team comes under
the umbrella of Leisure and Amenities
and was decentralised in 1985 to
enable the three Arts Officers to be
more in touch with the community.
The Arts Officers are based at Putney
and Balham Libraries and The
Courthouse Community Centre.
There is, additionally, an Arts
Development Officer for Ethnic
Minorities who is based at
Courthouse. Together, they are trying
to build up an information resource
for artists and interested members of
the public. The overall aim in
Wandsworth is to try and encourage
more arts events and entertainments
at community and sports centres.
Latchmere Sports Centre has an
indoor hall which has great
possibilities for performance and
visual arts. Arts events take place in
libraries intermittently though there
is almost always something going on
at Earlsfield Library. There are
interesting murals in Thessally Road
(near the junction with Wandsworth
Road), on Elspeth Road (near
Lavender Hill), in Plough Road and in
other parts of the borough. There are
a number of community arts projects
(as well as events and entertainments
in Battersea Park) which
Wandsworth will probably inherit
from the GLC.

**Wandsworth Arts &
Entertainment Section**
The Court House Community Centre
11 Garratt Lane
SW18.
Tel 871 7037
Wandsworth has an Arts Officer
with overall responsibility for the
arts in the borough who will answer
enquiries from both artists and
members of the public. He and his
colleagues are in the process of
building up an information resource
for artists and members of the public.
There are no special arts publications
produced by the borough but the
monthly What's On In Wandsworth
is available from libraries and other

council outlets or you can arrange to be put on the mailing list by contacting the Press and Publicity Officer at the Town Hall on 871 6362.

Galleries & Other Spaces

Abbot and Holder
73 Castelnau
Barnes   SW13
Tel 748 2416
Open 9-5(Mon-Fri by appointment only) 9-5(Sat)
Wheelchair access assisted to part of gallery only (ring first)
Admission free
Permanent shows of 18th, 19th and 20th Century watercolours, drawings and paintings.

Adam Gallery
62 Walcott Square
Kennington   SE11
Tel 582 1260
Open 2-5.30(Wed-Sat) till 8(Thur)
Wheelchair access assisted to greater part of gallery
Admission free
Shows of contemporary work (any media) approximately every month. Usually closed for a week between exhibitions.

Anthony Dawson
41 Lillian Road
Barnes   SW13
Tel 748 1306
Open 10-5.30(Mon-Fri) 10-1(Sat)
At other times by appointment
Wheelchair access assisted to part of gallery
Admission free
Artists' agent. Modern international original prints and paintings representing over fifty contemporary artists. Gallery exhibitions usually in March and November and touring exhibition every year.

Bankside Gallery
48 Hopton Street
Blackfriars   SE1
Tel 928 7521
Open 10-5(Tue-Sat) 2-6(Sun)
Closed between exhibitions
Wheelchair access entry ramps available on request access inside
Admission £1(adults) £50p(unwaged children students OAPs)
Free for Friends of Bankside and for members of affiliated societies
Bankside commands a stunning

Bankside Gallery

riverside position and is a modern gallery with a traditional feel. Regarded as the national centre for the appreciation and promotion of watercolours, prints and drawings, it is also the home of The Royal Society of Painters in Watercolour (founded in 1804) and The Royal Society of Painter-Etchers and Engravers (founded in 1880). Ten exhibitions are held every year of watercolours, etchings and engravings, some of which are for sale. Both societies have spring and autumn shows and permanent collections of past and present work which are shown occasionally. Many of the works in the watercolour collection have been damaged by acid in the mounting and backing materials or by over-exposure to light so Bankside has introduced an 'Adopt a Picture' campaign whereby individuals and companies can contribute towards the conservation of a favourite painting. Lists of pictures and the sums required are available from the gallery. There is a small gallery shop selling postcards and a selection of art books. Bankside administers The Old Watercolour Society's Club, a Print Collectors' Club and a Friends of Bankside scheme, all of which offer special activities and privileges.

Battersea Arts Centre Gallery

Old Town Hall
Lavender Hill
Clapham Junction　　　　SW11
Tel 223 6557
Open 11-9(Wed-Sun)
Wheelchair access to entire building
Admission free
Battersea Arts Centre's gallery is

Battersea Arts Centre

located in the small bar area and two adjoining rooms on the first floor of the fine Old Town Hall building. One of the rooms is large and can cope with vast pieces of work, the other is a good size and the bar area is fairly small. An additional exhibition space, known as 'On The Balcony', is used for a variety of different shows and whenever extra hanging space is required for the main exhibition. Gallery policy is to exhibit imaginative and experimental new pieces in 2-D, 3-D, video and film, and to give unknown and young artists

(as well as established artists) an opportunity to show their work. Shows are monthly and often conform to a theme or have a community interest (although work isn't usually confined to local artists). The Women Artists Slide Library (see Libraries – Specialist Libraries) has two shows a year, workshops within BAC and the community also use the gallery, and there are some open submissions. Artists are welcome to submit slides for consideration and, as there are always lots of people milling around, there's a good chance of work being well viewed. The bookshop on the ground floor has a selection of art books and magazines.

Bedford Hill Gallery

50 Bedford Hill
Balham　　　　SW12
Tel none
Open 12-5.30(Mon-Fri) 10-6(Sat)
Wheelchair access to gallery
Admission free
A fine art gallery in a disused shop. Monthly exhibitions of contemporary (often local) artists. The aim of the gallery is to help local artists gain recognition without heavy commission charges on sales. 20% of all proceeds go to Save The Children Fund's Ethiopian famine appeal.

Blackheath Gallery

34a Tranquil Vale
Blackheath　　　　SE3
Tel 852 1802
Open 10-6(Mon Tue Wed Fri Sat)
Wheelchair access to ground floor
Admission free
Exhibitions every 5-6 weeks of contemporary paintings, drawings, prints, sculptures and pottery mainly by local and London-based artists.

Bookworks

Arch 3
Green Dragon Court
Borough Market
London Bridge　　　　SE1

Tel 378 6799
Open 1-6(Wed-Sat)
Wheelchair access to ground floor
only
Admission free
Tucked away in a railway arch
overlooking Southwark Cathedral,

Book Works is quite hard to find but
well worth the effort. Started by four
bookbinders, it has taken initiative,
commitment and a lot of hard work to
set up the gallery. It is a unique
exhibition space which celebrates the
arts involved in the creation of the
Book and the many people working in
the book arts field - writers, artists,
designers, typographers, printmakers,
paper makers and bookbinders. There
is a lively programme of exhibitions
on the art and craft of making books,
and work is exhibited in two smallish
rooms and on free standing display
stands. Shows vary in length and the
gallery sometimes closes between
exhibitions. A series of seminars and
events are arranged to encourage
comment and discussion about the
work on show and there are plans to
run courses and set up a reference
library of book works, catalogues and
slides. Friends of Book Works receive
a newsletter, are given opportunities
to exhibit and are encouraged to use
the workshop facilities, to contribute
ideas and slides and be actively

involved in the running of the
gallery.

Brixton Art Gallery
21 Atlantic Road
Brixton   SW9
Tel 733 7757
Open 11-6(Mon-Sat)
Closed for one week between shows
Wheelchair access to gallery
disabled toilets close by
Admission free

Alongside the shops in Brixton's busy
market area, Brixton Art Gallery has
become an established venue for the
local and art communities. Although
it is divided into three arched
sections, it is open and light and has
good wall space. Run by The Brixton
Artists Collective (a group of artists,
craftworkers and helpers), it shows a
regular turnover of art, craftwork,
objects, fabrics and mixed media
mainly by unestablished artists.
Exhibitions usually either conform to
a theme (for example, Black Women's
Art, 1984, Art in the Playground,
Roadworks and Seeing Diversity), or
feature the work of a group of artists.
Much of the work to be seen at the
gallery is exciting and inspiring. Open
submissions are accepted four times a
year and often contain interesting
work. The Brixton Artists Collective
welcomes ideas from other artists. The
gallery is there for artists to use and
for the rest of us to enjoy. It is a
unique place.

Cafe Gallery
By the Pool
Southwark Park
Bermondsey   SE16
Tel 232 2170
Open 11-6(Wed-Sun in summer)
10-5(Wed-Sun when clocks change)
Wheelchair access
Admission free
It is a real pleasure to come across the
Cafe Gallery while strolling through
Southwark Park. Although from the
outside the building doesn't look too
inviting, inside it is cool and spacious.

One window overlooks the fountain of
the lido and the remaining walls have
been used for hanging space. The
gallery was founded in 1984 by
members of the Bermondsey Artists
Group, who hope to put on shows that
interest and involve local people.
They are open to suggestions from the
community and from other artists and
they also have their own shows.
Southwark Council helped to
refurbish the building and the
gallery's daily running costs are
covered by various grants. Shows
cover a wide range of themes and past
exhibitions have included Masks (an
open invitation show), Circus and
Clowns (children's ceramics,
paintings and drawings), People and
Places (photographs of the local area)
and Blooming Bermondsey (pictures
of the wild flowers of Bermondsey).
Also shown is a wide range of
contemporary and experimental
works, paintings and sculpture,
plaster with neon, prints and
assemblages. Video shows are planned
for the future and maybe some
theatre.

Ceramics 7 Gallery

7 Turnpin Lane
Off Nelson Road
Greenwich   SE10
Tel 858 2290
Open 11-5(Tue Wed Fri Sat Sun)
Wheelchair access none
Admission free
Continuously changing exhibitions
of contemporary ceramics by
members of Ceramics 7 and by
visiting potters. All works for sale.

Coracle Press

235 Camberwell New Road
Camberwell   SE5
Tel 703 5201
Open 10-6(Mon-Sat)
Wheelchair access limited to ground
floor only
Admission free
Coracle Press has been established at
233 Camberwell New Road for the past

Coracle Press

nine years and is now next door at no
235. Previously a shop, the gallery has
retained the original window so that
the largish front room has an open
view both ways. This and the smaller
back room have a spacious feel due to
high ceilings, minimal decoration and
natural light. Coracle is an
interesting and unusual gallery that
shows a range of contemporary work -
paintings, drawings, prints,
photographs, sculpture and objects -
by individuals and groups of artists.
The artists who run Coracle are
always happy to receive slides from
people who feel the gallery would suit
their work. Exhibitions are monthly.
The artists who show at Coracle are
encouraged to become involved in
presenting and talking about their
work and to participate in the gallery
in much the same way as writers
might choose to contribute to a
favourite literary magazine. The
gallery produces a range of books,
cards and catalogues of exhibtions
and their house style is one of quality
and visual integrity. These
publications are also on sale at
Whitechapel Art Gallery and at
Coracle's Cambridge shop in Kettle's
Yard.

Dulwich Picture Gallery

College Road
Dulwich   SE21
Tel 693 5254
Open 10-1 2-5(Tue-Sat) 2-5(Sun)
Wheelchair access by prior
arrangement

Admission 60p(adults) 30p(students unemployed OAPs) free(children under 16)

The country's first public art gallery, designed by the neo-classical architect, Sir John Soane, in 1814, and set in beautiful gardens containing a tulip tree, two mulberries, a gingko and a Judas tree. A stunning collection of 17th century paintings including works by Poussin, Rubens, Murillo, Rembrandt, Van Dyck and other Dutch old masters. Also a collection of important 18th century paintings by Hogarth, Reynolds, Lawrence, Gainsborough, Watteau, Canaletto, Tiepolo and others. About 300 pictures in all.

Edwin Pollard Gallery
23 Church Road
Wimbledon   SW19
Tel 946 4114
Open 10-6(Tue-Sat)
Wheelchair access to ground floor only
Admission free
Exhibitions every two weeks of living professional artists working in a representational style.

Feliks Topolski's Memoir of the Century
Hungerford Railway Arches
close to rear of RFH
Concert Hall Approach
South Bank   SE1
Open 5-8(Mon-Sat)
Wheelchair access assisted at entrance access inside
Admission free
This is an adventure both for the visitor and the artist, who describes it as 'a panoramic summary of his life's work'. The images in and around the arches beneath Hungerford Bridge reflect Topolski's life and travels around the world. Some carry sadness, some outrage and others joy. The arches are divided into small passages containing several pieces and large areas in which walls, ceilings and floor may display one work.

Projection and mechanics are employed in some parts. The overall effect is one of a total panaroma while individual portraits of the unrecognisable and the well-known (such as Tom Stoppard and Iris Murdoch) invite the viewer to close and intimate study.

Feliks Topolski's Open Studio Arch
Hungerford Railway Arches
Concert Hall Approach
opposite rear of RFH
South Bank   SE1
Tel 928 3405
Open 5-8(Fri)
Wheelchair access to arch but space is cluttered
Admission free
Here Feliks can be found surrounded by hundreds of canvasses. The environment and atmosphere owe their inspiration to the working, selling and live-in studios of the old masters, and are friendly and calm, as is the man himself. There are several pieces of work on display and sometimes the chance of a chat too.

Garden Gallery
26 Monson Road
New Cross Gate   SE14
Tel 732 0307
Open 10.30-4.30(Tue-Sat) 1-4(Sun)
Wheelchair access to ground floor
Admission free
Three-weekly exhibitions by contemporary artists working in mixed media. Artists wishing to exhibit should contact the gallery.

Goldsmiths College Gallery
Lewisham Way
New Cross   SE14
Tel 692 7171
Open 12-5(Mon-Fri during term-time exhibitions)
Wheelchair access none
Admission free
6-9 shows per year during term time. Work asociated with that of the college. Fine Art, textiles, photographs, ceramics. Also permanent collection of past and contemporary work.

Greenwich Gallery
23 Nelson Road
Greenwich   SE10
Tel 858 9713
Open 10-1.30 2.30-5.30(Mon-Wed
Fri-Sat) 1.30-2.30) 10-1.30(Thur)
Wheelchair access none
Admission free
Changing stock of period paintings
on early English watercolours. Also
some pieces of furniture.

**Greenwich Printmakers
Association**
1 The Market
off College Approach
Greenwich   SE10
Tel 858 1569
Open 11-5(Tue-Wed Fri-Sun)
Wheelchair access to gallery
Admission free
Marketing co-op of 43 printmakers.
Four exhibitions a year of original
prints, drawings and watercolours
mostly by members. Gallery manned
by members of the Association.

Greenwich Theatre Art Gallery
Crooms Hill
Greenwich   SE10
Tel 858 4447
Open 10-6(Mon-Sat during evening
performances)
Wheelchair access none
Admission free
Monthly shows usually by local
artists. Exhibited work has included
painting, drawing, photography,
prints, sculpture and textiles.

Hayward Gallery
South Bank
South Bank   SE1
Tel 928 3144
Open 10-8(Mon-Thur) 10-6(Fri-Sat)
12-6(Sun)
Closed between exhibitions
Wheelchair access to gallery
Admission varies (Mon & some eve
reductions)
The Hayward takes its name from Sir

Isaac Hayward who was leader of the
GLC from 1947-65, during which time
the South Bank complex was
conceived. The building was designed
in consultation with the Arts Council
of Great Britain (used primarily for
touring exhibitions). It is also a
showcase for changing major
international exhibitions of all
periods with an emphasis on 19th &
20th century European art in all
media. Past shows have included a
retrospective of Matisse, Van Gogh's
drawings and paintings, frescoes from
Florence, an Anglo-American survey
of pop art, photographs by Bill Brandt,
Soviet art and design since 1917, the
arts of Islam, 2000 years of North
American Indian art, early Celtic art
and an international survey of kinetic
art. The Hayward also holds a
prestigious annual summer exhibition
of contemporary British art.

Hayward Gallery

Major exhibitions in 1986 include
14 Nov 1985-16 Feb: Homage to
Barcelona (the art & architecture of
Barcelona including the early work of
Torres Garcia) with a separate
exhibition of Garcia's later work.
9 April-15 June: The Hayward
Annual (three British artists working
in a European context).
10 July-5 Oct: Scandinavian Painting
at the turn of the century and
L'Amour Fou (surrealism and
photography).
30 Oct-25 Jan 1987: Rodin, also Mark
Boyle.

Imperial War Museum
Lambeth Road
North Lambeth   SE1
Tel 735 8922
Open 10-5.50(Mon-Sat) 2-5.50(Sun)
Possible closures in 1985/6 due to
major reconstruction *Wheelchair*
access by prior arrangement
Admission free
Permanent collection of many
powerful 1st and 2nd World War
paintings, drawings and sculptures by
artists such as Wyndham Lewis,
Stanley Spencer, Paul Nash, Dame
Laura Knight, J D Fergusson, Henry
Moore, John Piper and Graham
Sutgerland. Also large poster
collection and some special
exhibitions. Many of the works of art
are temporarily in store during the
museum's extensive building
programme.

Intaglio Printmakers
20-22 Newington Causeway
Borough   SE1
Tel 403 6585
Open 10-6(Mon-Fri) 10-3(Sat)
Wheelchair access by prior
arrangement
Admission free
Across the road from the law courts,
in amongst the offices and businesses
of Newington Causeway, Intaglio is a
friendly, relaxed place which offers
expertise and quality service to
printmakers and collectors. The
gallery is available for hire to
printmakers and is a good size and
well lit by daylight. It is often used by
colleges for student shows, and
Japanese and Australian printmakers
sometimes exhibit there. Shows vary
in length and, even when there isn't
anything special on, there's always a
stock of prints to sift through and
look at on the walls. Next to the
gallery Intaglio has a framing service
and a huge range of materials for most
kinds of printmaking. The plan is to
set up a print workshop with a
resident technician and make the
workshop facilities available to

printmakers, thus creating a total
print centre with facilities for buying
materials, making prints, framing and
exhibiting.

Morley Gallery
61 Westminster Bridge Road
Lambeth North   SE1
Tel 928 8501
Open 10-6(Mon-Fri)
Wheelchair access to greater part of
gallery by prior arrangement
Admission free
It comes as no surprise that The
Morley College (whose Art
Department is so respected) should
have a gallery of comparable quality.
The two adjoining rooms are a
reasonable size, the wall space is good
and the shows are always interesting,
informative and often lively. The
gallery operates as an independent
body and is organised by a committee
of art critics, dealers and two or three
students. Exhibitions run for two to
three weeks and can include painting,
prints, sculpture and photography.
They cover a broad range of work,
featuring established and lesser
known artists, international artists
and occasionally a historical show or
one that links with a Morley College
art course, with an emphasis on skills
as well as ideas. There is also an
annual show of work by Morley art
students. Artists are welcome to send
in slides for consideration. If they are
offered a show they must provide
their own costs for publicity and
private views. There is a small art
shop within the gallery.

Museum of Garden History
St Mary-at-Lambeth
next to Lambeth Palace
Lambeth Palace Road
Lambeth Palace   SE1
Tel 261 1891(between 11 & 3)
Open 11-3(Mon-Fri) 10.30-5(Sun)
1st Sun in March until 2nd Sun in
Dec
Wheelchair access to church & garden
Admission free

Changing theme exhibitions featuring plants gardens, herbs or some other botanical subject in this permanent home of The Museum of Garden History (see Museums).

National Maritime Museum (including The Old Royal Observatory)
Romney Road
Greenwich   SE10
Tel 858 4422
Open 10-5(Mon-Fri) 10-5.30(Sat) 2-5(Sun) winter
10-6(Mon-Sat) 2-5.30(Sun) summer
Wheelchair access difficult
Admission £1(adults) 50p(children over 7 OAPs & unwaged) to each museum or £1.50 & 75p respectively to both Prices expected to change in 1986
Thematic exhibitions from vast permanent collection of maritime art. Approx 75,000 paintings, also drawings, watercolours and prints and some portraits and paintings of local historical interest.

National Theatre
South Bank   SE1
Tel 928 2033
Open 10-11(Mon-Sat)
Wheelchair access to theatre
Admission free
On permanent show in the foyers is Somerset Maugham's collection of 18th and 19th Century theatrical paintings, including many works by Samuel de Wilde and Johan Zoffany. Also six-weekly exhibitions of contemporary painting, drawing, photography and jewellery.

New Grafton Gallery
49 Church Road
Barnes   SW13
Tel 748 8850
Open 10-5.30(Tue-Sat)
Wheelchair access to gallery
Admission free
Contemporary and earlier 20th

Century British figurative painting and drawing. Portraits and heads can be commissioned through their Portrait Centre, which represents the work of fourteen painters and sculptors.

North Peckham Exhibition Gallery
North Peckham Civic Centre
600-608 Old Kent Road
Old Kent Rd   SE15
Tel 639 1255 (or South London Art Gallery 703 6120 for details of forthcoming exhibitions)
Open 9.30-8(Mon Tue Thur Fri) 9.30-5(Sat)
Wheelchair access to gallery
Admission free
About eleven exhibitions a year, often with a local interest. Contemporary paintings, drawings, prints and photographs.

Old Battersea House
Requests to visit should be made in writing only to
The Visit Organiser
De Morgan Foundation
21 St Margaret's Crescent
Battersea   SW15
Open strictly by prior appointment
Wheelchair access by prior arrangement in writing (as above)
Admission free
Old Battersea House is the finest example of 17th century domestic architecture in present day Battersea. Once the home of Sir Christopher Wren and built to his own design, it remains a private house, saved from demolition and beautifully restored by its tenant, and home too of part of the De Morgan Foundation's collection of pre-Raphaelite paintings, pottery and porcelain. On show are a few crayon and chalk drawings and about thirty paintings by Evelyn De Morgan (1855 - 1919). May Morris (William's daughter) described the latter as being noteworthy for their "beauty of drapery design, for drawing both vigorous and delicate, for sumptuous

colour, and for great enjoyment of texture". Also to be seen are six painting's by Evelyn's uncle and mentor, John Roddam Spencer Stanhope (1829 - 1908) and a few by other artists, including one by Evelyn's husband, William De Morgan (1839 - 1917). Although he took to writing in his later years, William De Morgan was, first and foremost, a potter and decorator whose work contained a unique richness of colour and pattern. His early designs show strongly the influence of William Morris (with whom he worked as a young man) but he was particularly renowned for the colour and glazes in his work. He learnt how to produce the rich blue and turquoise glazes of 13th Century Islam and medieval Persian lustre - an extremely complicated process involving three firings at crucial temperatures. The last of these deposits a fine metallic film over the design which reflects the light in tones of gold, silver and copper. Several of his pieces are on show at Battersea House.

Rangers House
Chesterfield Walk
Blackheath   SE10
Tel 853 0035
Open 10-5(daily Feb-Oct) 10-4(daily Nov-Jan)
Wheelchair access to ground floor only
Admission free
Rangers House is a handsome redbrick villa built in 1688 on the edge of Greenwich Park. The south wing, built of yellow brick and containing a splendid bow windowed gallery, was designed by Isaac Ware and completed in 1750. The house had many illustrious occupants including Philip, fourth Earl of Chesterfield (statesman and author) and The Duchess of Brunswick (mother of George IV's unfortunate wife, Queen Caroline). From 1815 it became the official residence of the Ranger of Greenwich

Park until it was converted into an art gallery by the GLC in 1974. The gallery houses the Suffolk Collection, part of the family collections of the Earls of Suffolk and Berkshire, which is particularly renowned for a magnificent series of full-length Jacobean portraits by William Larkin, the Royal Portraits by Lely, and many old masters. Also to be seen is the Dolmetsch collection of antique musical instruments (belonging to Arnold Dolmetsch, grandfather of today's Dolmetsch musical family).

Royal Festival Hall
South Bank   SE1
Tel 928 3641
Open 10-10(daily)
Wheelchair access to exhibitions
Admission free
Theme exhibitions – often linked to various festivals. Also some shows of contemporary painting, prints, and photography, at times including work by children and young people.

Royal Naval College
King William Walk
Greenwich   SE10
Tel 858 2154
Open 2.30-5(Mon-Wed Fri-Sun)
Wheelchair access by prior arrangement
Admission free
Included for its magnificent baroque painted ceiling (by Sir James Thornhill, 1701-1717) depicting William and Mary attended by the Cardinal Virtues. The Wren Chapel is also stunning.

South London Art Gallery
Peckham Road
Camberwell   SE5
Tel 703 6120
Open 10-6(Tue-Sat) 3-6(Sun) Closed between exhibitions
Wheelchair access assisted by prior arrangement
Admission free

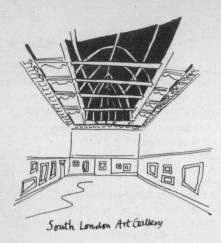

South London Art Gallery

The South London Art Gallery is housed in a fine late 19th Century building, which was partially restored in 1949 following severe bomb damage. Although its elegance and quiet reverence can be a little daunting for some exhibits, its natural light and large wall space ensure that everything is shown well and with respect. Works displayed cover a wide range of art - painting, drawing, sculpture, craftwork and photography. The nine exhibitions a year include annual shows by The South London Artists, The South East London Art Group and neighbouring Camberwell Art School students. At other times of the year there are theme shows or exhibitions featuring the work of one or more artists (some local, some not).

The gallery has a number of permanent collections which are kept in store and occasionally brought out in part and shown in the gallery. The most significant of these is a collection of about 300 paintings of the Victorian period, including works by Ford Maddox Brown, Val Prinsep, Lord Leighton and G F Watts. There is also a collection of 20th Century original British prints which is available for reference (see Libraries – Specialist Libraries). Michael Ayrton, Patrick Heron, David

Hockney, John Piper and Graham Sutherland are among the artists represented. The third collection contains 23 British paintings by John Piper, Martin Bloch, Alan Reynolds, Duncan Grant, Christopher Wood and others. There are a number of topographical paintings and drawings of Southwark (including works by Sir Gerald Kelly, Russell Reeve and S R Badmin) and a small collection of mid-19th century pottery with a selection of 80 Martin ware vessels of the Victorian and Edwardian periods. None of these collections are on display but they are available for reference on application to the Keeper.

The Stable Gallery
22b Bellevue Road
Wandsworth Common　　　**SW17**
Tel 767 4688
Open 9-4(Mon-Tue Thur-Fri) 9-5(Sat)
Wheelchair access
Admission free
Period and contemporary paintings and prints including the ballet paintings of Robert Heindel. Changing stock. Two mixed exhibitions a year. Also mounting and framing service and range of greetings cards.

Stanley Unwin Gallery
National Book League
Book House
45 East Hill
Wandsworth　　　**SW18**
Tel 870 9055
Open for occasional exhibitions phone for dates & times
Wheelchair access none
Admission free
Occasional exhibitions about books and the book trade. An exhibition of Children's Books of the Year is held each summer.

Tudor Barn
Well Hall Pleasaunce
Well Hall Road
Eltham   SE9
Tel 850 2340
Open usually 11-4.30(Sun-Fri) Phone
to check
Wheelchair access none
Admission free
Monthly shows mainly by artists of
contemporary watercolours, prints
and paintings. Linked to The
Woodlands Art Gallery.

Unit 7
rear of 36-38 Peckham Road
Camberwell   SE5
Tel 703 0818
Open 12-6(Mon-Sat)
Wheelchair access none
Admission free
2-3 weekly exhibitions of work by
local artists. A wide range of
paintings, sculpture, ceramics, and
paper making is shown. The artists
working in the studios attached to the
gallery occasionally have "open
studio".

The Woolwich Pottery
2a Parry Place
Woolwich   SE18
Tel 855 1871
Open 10-3(Thur-Fri) 10-5(Sat)
2.30-5(Sun)
Wheelchair access
Admission free
Not strictly a gallery but a working
studio and adjoining yard belonging
to two potters. A wide variety of
terracotta pots in spring and
summer. At other times, functional
stoneware and purely decorative and
sculptural forms.

Woodlands Art Gallery
90 Mycenae Road
Blackheath   SE3
Tel 858 4631
Open 10-7.30(Mon-Tue Thur-Fri) 10-
6(Sat) 2-6(Sun)
Wheelchair access assistance required
at entrance access inside

Admission free
Monthly exhibitions of contemporary
art mostly by London-based artists.
Also (view by appointment) a
permanent collection of watercolours
and drawings of historical interest
depicting local areas of Greenwich.

Wood Wharf Gallery
28-30 Horseferry Place
Greenwich   SE10
Tel 853 4766
Open 12-6(Wed-Sun April-Sept)
Wheelchair access by prior
arrangement
Admission free
1/2-weekly shows in space hired by
artists for do-it-yourself exhibitions.
Mainly local artists' watercolours,
prints and photographs. Attached to
music rehearsal studio and record
company.

If you really want to keep in touch
with gallery activities, take a yearly
subscription (six issues a year for
£2.50) to 'New Exhibitions of
Contemporary Art', which lists
exhibitions at all London galleries.
The addresss to write to is NECA, 152
Narrow Street, Limehouse, E14, Tel
515 6036. Alternatively, you can pick
up free copies of NECA at most
galleries.

CHILDREN

This chapter contains information about some of the services and activities available locally for children and young people (up to the age of about 15). If you are at the end of this age range you will also find items of interest in the Young People's chapter.

If your child has special needs, you will find that local facilities and activities are featured throughout the chapter. You should also look at the Special Needs section. The other chapter that will be of interest to you is Disability (in particular the sections on Schooling, National Organisatons and Societies and Clubs).

This chapter is arranged in four main sections:

- What Is Available?
- A Borough Guide
- Special Needs
- Something For Everybody

What Is Available?

When we started to research this chapter we discovered a new 'child provision' language and found it quite difficult to understand what the various schemes had to offer. Hence, we list below our own glossary of terms.

Adventure Playgrounds

Adventure playgrounds are for young people of school age and are open after school and during holidays. They are always supervised and offer lots of activities like games, art and craft workshops, cookery projects, camping trips and other outings.

After School Schemes/Latchkey

These schemes tend to vary but basically children aged 5-11 are collected from school and looked after until their parents arrive to fetch them. Some provide snacks or a hot meal. There is often a long waiting list and priority is given to children of working parents. There is often a nominal charge but many are free.

Childminders

These are people who are registered and approved by the council and provide care for other people's children in their own homes, usually between 8am and 6pm. They are encouraged to provide a variety of activities for the children in their care and sometimes take them to playgroups or nursery schools. Details of registered minders are available from your social services department which is also the place to contact if you want to become a childminder yourself. The fees per child (about £25-30 a week) are arranged between parents and minders.

Creches

These are places (often adult education institutes, health or community centres) where babies and children under 5 are looked after (at no charge) for up to two and a half hours while their parents are away. They may stay longer if the parents are on the premises. There is a nominal charge sometimes. Private creches must be approved by the council. (See also Mobile Creches.)

Gateway Clubs

These are youth and social clubs that provide after-school, evening and weekend activities for mentally handicapped children and young people. They also run competitions and sports activities and organise outings and holidays. There are many branches in South London. Ring Mencap (Tel 250 4105) for details of your nearest clubs.

Holiday Play Schemes

The councils run lots of exciting play schemes during the school holidays, especially in the summer. Activities include inflatables, sports, games, face painting, theatre performances and outings. Playleaders are employed to run them and the cost is about 25p a day. Call in at your local library to pick up leaflets or ring the council and find out what's in store.

Home Visiting Schemes

Home visitors offer support to parents at home by listening, talking, bringing toys and equipment to the home, and generally helping out. They aim to help lessen the isolation parents with under 5s at home often experience. Contact your social services department or local under 5s' group if you feel you would like to know more about this service.

Mobile Creches

Most boroughs have a team of creche workers, toys and equipment and a vehicle to make the service mobile. Their aim is to give single parents and others the chance to participate in local activities outside the home. By providing a multi-cultural, anti-sexist creche, they hope to increase awareness of racism and sexism. Demand is heavy so book well in advance. (See also Creches.)

Nurseries (community)

Community nurseries are subsidised so they tend to be cheaper than private nurseries, although the fees do vary a lot. You can find out about community nurseries in your catchment area by contacting your social services department.

Nurseries (council)

Council nurseries are for working people who have no-one to look after their pre-school age children during the day. Parents who want their children to go to a council nursery usually go through their health visitor or social worker. There are very few places. Details of local nurseries are available from social services. Fees are about 75p a day (free to single parents and people receiving certain state benefits).

Nurseries (private)

These nurseries have to be registered with the council and have qualified staff in attendance. They are usually open from 8am to 6pm and offer full day care and play experience for all or most of the year. Average prices range from about £16 to £40 a week (for five full days) although sometimes the fees are very much higher. Details of local groups are available from the library or the council. Apply direct to the nursery.

Nursery Classes/Schools (ILEA)

Run by ILEA, these provide education for 3-5 year olds during school hours. Admission is free but there are long waiting lists. Nursery classes are held at primary schools which children usually join when they reach school age. Nursery schools serve exactly the same function but are in separate buildings of their own. Your local library or your ILEA Divisional Office will give you information about local nursery schools and classes. Once you have selected a suitable one you should make contact with the school or class direct.

Nursery Schools (private)

Private nursery schools are similar to private nurseries (see above) but they only run during school term time, usually between 9am and 3pm. The children who attend nursery schools are aged 3 to 5. Prices vary considerably. Find out about local nurseries from the council or your local library.

One O'Clock Clubs

These are free and run by the council. Parents stay with their children (aged 0-5) and trained staff are in attendance. There is generally a good supply of play equipment and the clubs provide an opportunity for children to play and parents to meet and chat in a friendly environment. They usually run between 1 and 4.30 during the week (sometimes during term time only).

Parent and Toddler Groups

These are often set up by community groups and offer an informal meetig place for parents and their toddlers (usually 0-3). Parents must stay with their children. Details of groups are available from libraries. Apply direct to the group you have selected.

PHAB Clubs

These are meeting places for physically handicapped children and adults and others without a disability. Ring the PHAB main office for details of your nearest club (Tel 388 1963).

Playgroups

Playgroups aim to encourage young children (usually 2–5) to interact with other children and explore activities through play. They are equipped to provide a wide range of play activities and trained staff supervise the children. Painting, jigsaws, cooking, sand and water play, and storytelling are just some of the activities children get up to. Parents may stay or leave. The charge for attendance at all playgroups is 40p a session, which generally lasts from 9.30 to 12.30. Ring the Pre-School Playgroups Association (Tel 828 2417) for details of groups in your borough and then apply direct to the playgroup.

Play Parks

These are playgrounds with swings, slides, roundabouts located in many local parks.

Portage Scheme

A home visiting scheme for children with special needs. Educational toys are brought to the home to aid the child's intellectual development. The service is not statutory so there isn't one in every borough. You can find out if your borough has a scheme by contacting your social services department, the health authority or the National Portage Association (Tel 278 9441).

Respite Care/Family Link

These are schemes whereby volunteer families have handicapped children to stay for short, regular periods so that the children's families can have some time to themselves. There are schemes in most boroughs (see the Borough Guide).

Toy Libraries

Toy libraries are run by an organisation called Play Matters (also known as the National Toy Libraries Association). They provide

Toy Library

a chance for children and parents to meet one another and explore the range of toys on offer. Most libraries have a toy loan service and many provide a play space for children. Some offer a special service to children with special needs, with a stock of carefully designed toys and games and sometimes the chance for children to play on a one to one basis with a volunteer. Children of any age are welcome at toy libraries. We are told that new toy libraries are opening up all the time so keep in touch with Play Matters (Tel 387 9592).

Youth Centres

Youth centres are based in schools or community centres. They offer social, recreational and skills activities to young people. Most have a junior section.(11-15). Facilities tend to vary from one centre to another. The fees are £1 per term.

Youth Clubs

Youth clubs are usually based in the community and offer almost exactly the same activities as youth centres. They cost about 10p a visit.

A Borough Guide

Several different council departments are involved in care and activities for children and young people and there are a number of other organisations involved in allied work. Sometimes the services they offer overlap. In the first part of each borough section we have listed the key advice and service-providing organisations, which are generally open during normal office hours. Following this there is a short section called Some Local Activities. This is by no means comprehensive and should be regarded as a mere taster of what's available locally. We have used a   to help you find the age group in which you are interested though most organisations are very happy to deal with others who are not quite within this range.

Greenwich

Area Youth Office
20 Passey Place
Eltham   SE9
Tel 859 4236
●School age
The Youth Office has a department that deals with activities for 5-15 year-olds. They can tell you about any local youth clubs, youth centres and play centres that are registered with ILEA. They will also give you the address of your nearest branch of the Brownies, Cubs, Scouts, Guides et al.

Community Leisure Department
London Borough of Greenwich
29-37 Wellington Street
Woolwich   SE18
Tel 854 8888
●Over 5s
There are several supervised after school clubs for 5-11 year-olds whose parents are working. They are collected from school and taken to local community centres where they can join in activities until their parent(s) pick them up after work. There are four schemes in Greenwich and more are expected to open.Contact the above department

for further details. ILEA also runs similar schemes.

Greenwich Childcare Campaign
East Greenwich Community Centre
Christchurch Way
Greenwich   SE10
Tel 858 8272
●All ages
This organisation was formed by a group of women whose aim is to improve childcare and play facilities in the borough of Greenwich by promoting anti-racist, anti-sexist practice in existing provision. It also hopes to open up more centres where children can be cared for, and offers an information, advice and resource service.

Greenwich Play Association
c/o Play Department
London Borough of Greenwich
29-37 Wellington Street
Woolwich   SE18
Tel 854 8888
●All ages
The Greenwich Play Association receives a grant from the council and from ILEA and is an umbrella organisation which assists local voluntary groups to run holiday schemes, usually in halls or community centres. One of the most successful schemes in 1985 enabled 350 local children to go to a YMCA holiday centre in Southampton where they took part in outdoor activities like canoeing and riding. Another group is hoping (subject to funding) to acquire a double-decker bus with a mobile creche, soft play room and toy library. If you are interested in setting up a play scheme in the area contact the GPA for a grant aid application form.

ILEA Divisional Office (Division 6)
Riverside House
2nd Floor
Tower Block
Beresford Street
Woolwich   SE18

Tel 855 3161
●All ages
This department will give you advice
and information about local
nurseries, primary and secondary
schools. (For details about how the
state and independent school systems
work see the chapter called School.)

Play Department
London Borough of Greenwich
29-37 Wellington Street
Woolwich SE18
Tel 854 8888
●All ages
The emphasis in this department is
on fun. Broadly speaking, if there is
no local voluntary group to run a
play scheme, this council department
will do it. It organises staffed one
o'clock clubs for the under 5s and
their parents and has recently
opened a new one on the Ferrier
Estate which currently has room for
more parents and children. The
department also runs adventure
playgrounds and play centres for
school age children and young
people. Most of these activities are
out of doors in local parks. Lots of
inter-school sports projects are
arranged and countless special
holiday play schemes are organised
and publicised in council literature.
All play centres offer more or less the
same facilities and the same can be
said of adventure playgrounds. One
example is Plumstead Common

Adventure Playground in Blendon
Terrace which always has lots going
on – discos, arts and crafts
workshops, cookery projects and
seasonal festivities.

Pre-School Section
Greenwich Social Services
Nelson House
50 Wellington Street
Woolwich SE18
Tel 854 8888 Ext 3038
●Under 5s
This department deals with all
aspects of care for the under 5s and
provides leaflets, called Facilities for
the Under Fives, for the five areas of
Greenwich. Services covered in the
leaflets include council-run day
nurseries, creches, one o'clock clubs,
nursery classes and schools, council-
run playgroups, mother and toddler
groups, pop-ins, facilities for
handicapped children and
information about childminders.
These services include voluntary and
independent groups registered with
the council. The leaflets are available
at health centres, libraries, social
service area offices and community
centres. Greenwich is currently
running a pilot extended day care
scheme from an ILEA nursery school
in Woolwich. This is for children
who have working parents. The
children can stay on at school until
their parents collect them from work
at about 5.30.

Sports Department
London Borough of Greenwich
Plumstead Pools
High Street
Plumstead SE18
Tel 854 9217
●All ages
This is where you can get details of
coaching courses which take place all
the year round at various venues and
cover a whole range of sports from
athletics to rollerskating. One
scheme being run by the department
is Gentle Gymnastics for the under

5s. (See the chapter on Sport for other local sports activities and centres.)

Some Local Activities

Charlton Toy Library
Dutch Room
Charlton House
off Charlton Park Road
Charlton   SE7
Tel 856 3951
Open 10-4(Mon during term time)
Wheelchair access by lift to 2nd floor where toys are brought down, also special toilets
●Under 5s
This is a lending toy library open to all under 5s. There is also play space at the library.

Community Mental Handicap Team
Lodge Hill
Abbey Wood   SE2
Tel 311 3370
Contact Dominic O'Hara
The Community Mental Handicap Team will provide information and support to parents of mentally handicapped children.

Cycle Training
Greenwich Road Safety Officer
Peggy Middleton House
50 Woolwich Road
Woolwich   SE18
Tel 854 8888
●Over 9s
Contact this department about cycle training schemes for the over 9s.

Family Link
28 Climpsing Green
Erith Kent
Tel 311 7966
Contact Maggie Morgan
Despite the address, this is the Greenwich branch of Family Link, which offers a respite care service to parents of children with special needs.

Greenwich Creche Project
217 Maryon Road
Charlton   SE7
Tel 855 0577
●Under 5s
This project (the first mobile creche in the country) has a team of workers, toys, equipment and a minibus. They provide regular and one-off creches throughout the borough and operate a strong anti-racist, anti-sexist approach to childcare.

Greenwich Toy Library
Clockhouse Community Centre
Defiance Walk
Woolwich   SE18
Tel 855 7188
Open 10.30-12.30(Tue Thur)
Wheelchair access throughout with special toilets
●All ages
A toy library and play space for children with disabilities. Also an opportunity group whereby volunteers play on a one-to-one basis with children.

Greenwich Young People's Theatre
Burrage Road
Plumstead   SE18
Tel 854 1316
●Age 7 upwards
GYPT has been around since the 1960s and includes a youth theatre (with two youth theatre groups) and a professional theatre-in-education which visits ILEA schools in Greenwich, Lewisham and Southwark. Examples of some of the concepts and issues tackled at schools include justice, education, the family and gender roles, the General Strike and cultural conflict. It also runs a number of arts workshops for young people and for those with special needs. Theatre, dance, music and the visual arts are all offered. The two theatre groups each present an annual production at GYPT and then go on tour nationally. They present

Blackheath Kite Festival

the centres. Tea is provided as well as games and activities. Service is of special use to working parents or in times of emergency. The centres are open until 6, and there is no charge for the service. For details and application forms contact the head teacher at your child's school. Many schools run their own after school schemes. If one doesn't exist at your school try and get the approval of the head teacher and start your own. Many local community centres run after school clubs also.

work at the National Youth Theatre Festival and sometimes do exchanges with groups from other countries. Based in what was once a church, GYPT has two fully-equipped studio spaces, facilities for photography, video and sound, several technical workshops and a coffee bar. GYPT is there to be enjoyed by anyone over 7, with or without experience. Give them a ring to find out what's going on or just just drop by and join in the fun.

Parents as Partners
24 Glenhouse Road
Eltham   SE9
Tel 850 9298
Contact Mrs Edwards
This is a scheme which introduces parents to other parents of children with disabilities.

Lambeth

After School Care Organisers
Lambeth Social Services
91 Clapham High Street
Clapham   SW4
Tel 720 0220
●Age 3-7
After school care is provided for children aged 3-7 at centres serving particular schools. The children are collected from school by the staff of

Area Youth Office
1-3 Brixton Road
Oval   SW9
Tel 582 5656
●School age
ILEA runs the Youth Office so this is where you can find out about all registered local youth clubs, youth and play centres. They will also be able to put you in touch with the right people if you want to find out about sports coaching, entertainments and arts activities as well as local facilities and projects.

Day Care & Playgroup Organisers
Lambeth Social Services
91 Clapham High Street
Clapham   SW4
Tel 720 0220
●Under 5s
This is where you can find out about playgroups for pre-school age children. You can also get information about day nurseries and Lambeth's childminding service.

ILEA Divisional Office (Division 9)
50 Acre Lane
Brixton   SW2
Tel 274 6288
Information about local nursery, primary and secondary schools can be obtained from this office. (For details about how the school system works see the chapter on School.)

Lambeth Under 5s Campaign
22 Kendoa Road
Clapham   SW4
Tel 627 3686
Wheelchair access to part of building
but no special toilets
Campaign for anyone who cares
about the needs of the under 5s in
Lambeth. They hold regular meetings
to decide which issues to concentrate
on. Creche work, special needs,
racism and sexism, day care and
council policy are some of the topics
of interest. They produce a regular
newsletter to keep everyone
informed about things that are
happening for the under 5s in the
community, and eight very useful
area guides to put you in touch with
facilities in your area. They provide
support and help to anyone wanting
to set up a new project such as a
community day nursery.

Latchkey
Latchkey Administrator
Clapham Manor School
Stonhouse Street
Clapham   SW4
Tel 627 1743
●School age
This is a referral service provided at
particular schools usually for
children aged 3-10 and at some
schools for 3-5s. It is aimed at
children who need care from 8 in the
morning while the parent is at work
or college. The children are looked
after by two care workers who bring
them to school from the centre and
back to the centre after school. There
they provide tea and activities until
the parents collect them at 6. During
holidays children are at the centre
between 8 and 6. The centres are
very like play schemes, with
organised activities and outings. The
service costs £25 per year
membership. Apart from that there is
no charge. If your child's school is in
the Latchkey scheme you can apply
to join it.

Slade Gardens

Play Section
Lambeth Amenities Services
164 Clapham Park Road
Clapham   SW4
Tel 622 6655
●All ages
The Play Section at Lambeth runs a
number of schemes for under 5s in
the borough. Your local community
centre probably has a parent and
toddler club where you can go and
relax while the children play
together with toys and equipment,
sand and water, painting, slides and
climbing frames. A mixture of indoor
and outdoor activities are on offer.
One o'clock clubs are also for anyone
under 5 and offer similar activities.
Most are open 1-4.30 Monday to
Friday all year round. Just drop by
whenever you like. The department
also runs adventure playgrounds and
play centres for school age children
and young people. Most of these
activities are outdoors in local parks.
Lots of sports projects are arranged
as well as special holiday play
schemes with outings and trips away.

Some Local Activities

**Charlie Chaplin Adventure
Playground**
Kennington Park
Bolton Crescent
Oval   SE5
Tel 735 1819
Wheelchair access throughout

●All ages
A special fun place for handicapped children with lots of things to play on, electric go-karts, an outdoor sandpit and pool. There are some small animals too. There's also a heated building for arts and crafts, music making and other activities. The playground is used by special schools and groups during the week and is open for families on Saturdays from 10 to 4.30.

Clapham & Larkhall Under 5s Organisation
22 Kendoa Road
Clapham   SW4
Tel 622 0786
Wheelchair access to ground floor only
●Under 5s
Advice, pressure and action group that looks at welfare policy for the under 5s and campaigns for improved facilities. They also offer a No Strings Attached Home Visitors Scheme, providing support and information to parents.

Clapham Pool
10 Clapham Manor Street
Clapham   SW4
Tel 622 2786
Open 8-7(Mon Wed Fri) 8-8(Tue) 8-5 8-9 (Thur family swim 6.15-7.45) 10-5(Sat) 8-2.15(Sun)
●All ages
Apart from the expected sports and swimming activities, there are pottery workshops and classes in art, jive and photography. The pottery workshops cover basic throwing on a Monday evening, general ceramics with an emphasis on handbuilding and modelling techniques on a Tuesday evening, a women only group on Wednesday at noon at which there is a creche, an afternoon group on Thursday to which everyone is welcome and on Saturday afternoon there is a family session. The art workshops which are run on Saturday morning for

children are at present doing projects using scrap materials. There are also a series of six jive classes for beginners on Saturday morning. Photography sessions are for beginners on a Wednesday evening and on Monday afternoon and evening for women only. There is a small charge for some of the classes while others are free. Phone for more details of this new venture.

Contact a Family
10 Bernays Grove
Brixton   SW9
●All ages
A local self-help group for families who have children with special needs. Mutual support, practical help and lots of lively activities are offered.

Family Link
10 Bernays Grove
Brixton   SW9
Tel 326 5149
Contact Nick Wareham
Scheme which puts families with handicapped children in touch with local volunteers who will care for their children for a short while allowing them the chance of a break.

Kendoa Road Opportunity Group
20 Kendoa Road
Clapham   SW4
Tel 720 1410
Wheelchair access to ground floor only
●All ages
Drop-in and family support centre with an open and welcoming atmosphere and lots of different activities. A special opportunity playgroup allows disabled children to play with others. There is a creche for children for whom English is a second language and a childminding creche. Teenage activities take place in the afternoon and evenings. Members of the group are always willing to visit any parents before they come for the first time.

Lambeth Toys
Co-op Centre
11 Mowell Street
Oval   SW9
Tel 735 6618
Open 9-4(Mon-Fri)
Lambeth Toys make multi-cultural
toys, jigsaws, and dressing-up clothes
in the workshop. The co-op was set
up three years ago and now sells
mainly to schools and play centres.

Mobile Creche
130-146 Ferndale Road
Clapham North   SW4
Tel 274 9886
●Under 5s
This project organises creches for
low-funded groups throughout
Lambeth. Sessions last 2& hours and
cater for groups of 3 to 20 children.

Playbox
22 Kendoa Road
Clapham   SW4
Tel 622 0786
Wheelchair access to ground floor
●Under 5s
A toy library which provides a
complete set of toys suitable for
playgroups, creches and parent and
toddler groups.

Women & Children's Health Bus
Tel 737 7151
●Under 5s
A converted double decker bus which
has a creche for under 5s downstairs
and a health and advice service
upstairs. Visits estates throughout
Lambeth providing information
about health issues. Phone for details
about routes and stops.

Lewisham

Area Youth Office
Capital House
47 Rushey Green
Catford   SE6
Tel 697 7031
●School age

You can find out about registered
youth centres, clubs and play centres
here.

ILEA Divisional Office (Division 6)
Capital House
47 Rushey Green
Catford   SE6
Tel 698 4633
●All ages
There is information and advice
available here about local nursery,
primary and secondary schools. See
the chapter called School for details
about state and independent schools.

Play and Recreation Services
Lewisham Council
Riverdale Office
68 Molesworth Street
Lewisham   SE13
Tel 852 9121
●All ages
This is where you can find out about
the fun things that happen in
Lewisham as well as places where
your child can go to after school. Ask
about play clubs for the under 5s in
parks and the three adventure
playgrounds in the borough. Holiday
time (this includes easter and
summer) is when a lot of things are
organised for children so find out
here about workshops, shows, fun
days, festivals and events. Phone the
Action Sport team to find out about

participation in a range of activities
from trampolining to canoeing.

Play Leadership Centre
Ladywell Road
Lewisham SE13
Tel 852 9121
Open 1-4(Mon) 10-4(Tue-Fri)
●All ages
There is information here about
under play clubs for the under 5s and
five play centres where school age
children can enjoy sports or arts and
crafts.

Pre-School Playgroups Association
Tel 852 4245
●Under 5s
Go here to find out about the 50 or
more local playgroups. You can also
contact this organisation to find out
about parent and toddler groups.
Some in Lewisham are places where
parents meet for a chat and a coffee
while their children play, while
others offer keep-fit and crafts. Be
sure to ask what each club does. The
Pre-School Playgroups Association
offers advice and information if you
would like to start a group. The
organisation is a charity and staffed
largely by volunteers so if your
interest is in helping to improve care
for the under 5s then phone and offer
your help.

Social Services Department
Lewisham Council
Eros House
Brownhill Road
Catford SE6
Tel 698 6121
●Under 5s
If you need someone to look after
your baby or young child during the
day contact the social services
department to find out about day
nurseries and centres. Places are in
demand and your application will
have to be made through a health
visitor or a social worker. You will
also be able to find out about
registered voluntary and community

nurseries here. Contact the
Childminding Section for
information about childminders.
Information is also available about
local playgroups.

Some Local Activities

Bunbury Project
Old Coach House
Rushey Green
Catford SE6
Tel 859 4304
●Under 5s
This project organises drop-in
centres equipped with play facilities
for childminders and the children in
their care. Phone the project worker
for details of the centre nearest to
you.

Contact a Family
Ladywell Buildings
Peter Pan Block
23 Slagrove Place
Lewisham SE13
Tel 870 9567
●All ages
A self-help group for families and
their special needs children. Mutual
support, practical help, friendship
and activities are the ingredients of
the group. They also produce a guide
to useful local facilities called Who
Can Help?

Lewisham Childminders Association
2 Wolfram Close
Lewisham SE13
Tel 852 1067
●Under 5s
An organisation which belongs to
the National Childminders
Association and is run on a
voluntary basis. Meetings are held
once a month. It is largely a support
group but volunteers also involve
themselves in fundraising events and
organise holiday outings.

Lewisham Mobile Creche
Tel 469 0834
●Under 5s
The Mobile Creche goes to areas
where there are few facilities and
provides play space and toys.
Community groups who wish to
make a booking should phone for
details.

Lewisham Playbus
Tel 692 3653
●Under 5s
The bus is based at Clyde Nursery
School and travels across the
borough. Educational toys are taken
into places where few facilities exist.
Parents are supported who wish to
start their own groups or nurseries.
Don't miss the bus – contact them for
times and places.

Lewisham Toy Library
The Old Coach House
41 Rushey Green
Catford   SE6
Tel 698 7433
Wheelchair access to the Library
Open 1-3(Mon)
●All ages
Provides toys on loan for pre-school,
handicapped and foster children and
to childminders.

**Lewisham Neighbourhood Visiting
Scheme**
Tel 699 4815
●Under 5s
This is a scheme that offers friendly
support in the home for families with
children under 5. They will visit you
for a chat and offer help and advice
as well as give you information about
local facilities available to you. They
can also offer advice about any
family problems you may be having.
The scheme is organised by the Pre-
school Playgroups Association.

New Cross Playbus
Tel 692 4908
●Under 5s
The bus moves around estates in New

Cross and Deptford providing play
facilities for children under 5 with
their parents. Available for one-off
visits to nurseries, schools and
playgroups.

Ravensbourne Toy Library (HQ)
Grove Park Hospital
Manvilles Lane
Lewisham   SE12
Tel 851 2762
Open 9-12.30(Tue-Fri)
●All ages
Provides toys on loan to people who
have or work with handicapped
children.

**Ravensbourne Toy Library
(branch)**
Salvation Army Hall
Albion Way
Lewisham   SE13
Open 10.30-12(Mon)
●All ages
On Monday morning the
Ravensbourne Toy Library operates
from the Salvation Army Hall.

Merton

Merton Children's Scheme
226 London Road
Mitcham
Tel 640 4814
●All ages
Start finding out about facilities here
if you have young children and live
in Merton. The scheme was started
in 1983 and runs activities as well as
giving advice and information to
those working with children under 5.
Drop in for a cup of tea and have a
chat while the children play in the
creche. For children with special
needs there is an Opportunity Group
on Friday between 10 and 12. On
Wednesday between 10 and 12.30
there is a group for parents and
children with impaired hearing.
There is also a mobile creche which
can be used by any organisation. A
booklet called What's Available for

Under Fives in Merton is useful so contact them if you would like a copy. If you have older children you might find the after school care scheme helpful. Children can be cared for from 3.30 to 6. There are courses like sewing, cooking, art and crafts and games to join and a light meal is given for a small charge (40p per day). In the holidays schemes based at community centres and schools provide a range of activities for children which can keep them occupied for most of the day. The Merton Children's Scheme is also active in supporting groups like playgroups, nurseries, parent and toddler groups and family workshops.

Merton Education Department
Crown House
London Road
Morden
Tel 545 3262
●All ages
Merton is not part of ILEA so its educational system is arranged slightly differently. You can find out about local schools (whatever the stage). Bear in mind that some primary schools in Merton have part-time nursery classes for children who are over 3 years old.

Merton Pre-School Playgroups Association
203 Sanderstead Road
Sanderstead
Tel 651 5347

●Under 5s
The Association was started to help parents understand and provide for the needs of their young children. Also involved are people who work in playgroups, parent and toddler groups, and day nurseries in the borough.

Social Services Department
Crown House
London Road
Morden
Tel 543 2222
●Under 5s
Contact the Social Services Department to find out about day nurseries. Three are run by the borough and an additional three are registered. There are waiting lists for places and allocation is according to the degree of necessity. You can also find out about one o'clock clubs and parents and toddlers groups. Childminders have to be registered with social services so contact them if you're looking for someone to look after your children in the day time.

Youth Office
Merton Education Department
Crown House
London Road
Morden
Tel 543 2222
●All ages
Information about youth centres and clubs in Merton is available here.

Some Local Activities

Home From Home
Merton Personal Services Department
Crown House
London Road
Morden
Tel 543 2222
●All ages
A respite care scheme for local families who have mentally handicapped children.

Merton Community Bus
226 London Road
Mitcham
Tel 648 5588
●Under 5s
Merton community bus is a mobile
play place for children under 5.
Parents and childminders can relax
while the children play safely. There
is also a space for under 5s groups to
have meetings.

Merton Toy Loan Scheme
St Theresa's School
Montacute Road
Morden
Tel 543 3221
Open 1-3(Thur during term time)
The toy loan library provides toys
and equipment for playgroups,
nurseries, childminders and other
community groups in the borough.
Toys can be borrowed for up to six
months at a time. The scheme also
has a bus available for groups to use.
All they ask is a donation towards
running cost.

YMCA
220 The Broadway
Wimbledon   **SW19**
Tel 542 3129/540 7255
Open 2-10(daily)
●School age
There are facilities available here for
badminton, basketball, bridge, chess,
circuit training, table tennis,
volleyball, yoga, keep fit, board
games, drama, films and weight
training.

Southwark

Area Youth Office
83 Peckham Road
Peckham
Tel 701 8559
●School age
This is the place to find out about
local youth centres, clubs and play
centres. Get in touch if you want
information on local facilities and
projects, sports coaching,
entertainment and arts activities.

ILEA Divisional Office (Division 8)
Camden Square
Peckham   **SE15**
Tel 703 0855
●All ages
There are five nursery schools and
many nursery classes attached to
infant and primary schools in the
borough. For more information about
schools see the chapter called School.

Play Office
Starters Road
Peckham Rye Common
Peckham Rye   **SE15**
Tel 299 2860
●All ages
There is information here about play
schemes, parent and toddler groups,
one o'clock clubs, junior clubs and
adventure playgrounds.

Pre-School Playgroup Association
173 Choumert Road
Peckham   **SE15**
Tel 639 5072
Contact Janet Heatley
●Under 5s
If you want to find out about
playgroups in your area contact this
organisation.

Social Services Department
Castle House
27-29 Camberwell Road
Camberwell   **SE5**
Tel 703 0941
●Under 5s
The day care section can help you
find out about local nurseries. Bear
in mind that there are waiting lists
and admission is allocated according
to need. Ask the childminding
section for information about
childminders in your area.

Southwark Childcare Campaign
96 Camberwell Grove
Camberwell SE5
Tel 701 7535

●All ages
This is a borough-wide pressure group which is campaigning for a wider and better planned range of childcare facilities and educational services to meet the needs of children and parents. They are fighting for more nurseries, more full-time nursery classes, more holiday and after school schemes and for housing development schemes to include nursery and childminding facilities. They offer support to local groups trying to improve facilities. The Campaign also publishes a newsletter.

Southwark Under 5s Forum
Southwark Council For Voluntary Services
135 Rye Lane
Peckham   SE15
Tel 732 3731
●Under 5s
At this office you can find a useful booklet called Under Fives in Southwark which gives details of local facilities. These are the people who campaign for the needs of under 5s in the borough.

Some Local Activities

Charterhouse Toy Library
The Rainbow Building
32 Crosby Row
Southwark   SE1
Tel 407 1123
Wheelchair access NONE
Open 10-5(Wed)
●Under 5s
This toy library has been open since 1978 and offers children a selection of multi-cultural toys to play with at the library or to take home on loan. The Wednesday drop-in is at present used in the morning by the local childminders' group and in the afternoon by the playgroup. Anyone is welcome to join in the relaxed and cheerful atmosphere. Parents can also buy, at low cost, powder paints and sheets of drawing and tissue

paper. There are some toys and games available for older children. Phone to find out about the range of activities Charterhouse-in-Southwark offer parents and children. They are a registered charity who have been working in Southwark for the last hundred years (1985 was their centenary).

Copleston Children's Centre
Copleston Road
Peckham   SE15
Tel 732 2544
●All ages
This community project, an example of local intiative, provides a multi-purpose centre for children. The Centre provides day care facilities, after school provision, a childminder scheme for local residents and a toy library. They are already flooded with applicants for places on the scheme but phone if you would like to find out how the scheme was set up.

Home Visitors Scheme
Adult Education Institute
Queen's Road Centre
St Mary's Road
Peckham   SE15
Tel 639 1178
●Under 5s
A co-ordinator and eight home visitors work in Southwark, Peckham, Walworth, Bermondsey and Rotherhithe. Home visitors visit families with pre-school age children and bring a variety of toys, books, paints and play material. They can show and discuss aspects of how children learn to play. Home visitors also have a knowledge of other facilities in your area so you can find out about these too.

Hummingbird Peckham Project
183-185 Glengall Road
Peckham   SE5
Tel 639 8550
●Under 5s

This is a nursery centre which caters for 33 children. Twenty of these places are allocated by the council while thirteen are taken up privately. Fees are partly subsidised if parents work in health, education, social services or the voluntary sector. There is also a toy library and holiday playschemes and childminders are organised.

John Donne School
Woods Road
Harders Road
Peckham   SE15
Tel 639 0594
Open 3.30-6
Wheelchair access to school
●Age 5-11
The School provides a scheme where children of working parents are looked after in the afternoons. Six full time staff run activities like games, dancing, art and table tennis.

New Parent Infant Network (NEWPIN)
Sutherland House
Sutherland Square
Walworth   SE17
Wheelchair access none
Tel 703 5271
●All ages
NEWPIN is a charity which offers support to local mothers by local mothers who befriend them (after a period of training) for as long as is needed. The scheme helps prepare people to take responsibility for their own lives in a caring and secure environment.

Share a Family
First Floor
Battersea Town Hall
Battersea   SW11
Tel 228 0069
Contact Jo Anthony
Respite care scheme for families who have a mentally handicapped child and need an occasional break.

Time and Talents Centre
The Old Mortuary
St Mary Church Street
Rotherhithe   SE16
Tel 231 7845/237 4277
Open daily
Membership £1.50
●All ages
At this community centre there are a variety of classes, workshops and clubs for children. There are violin and cello lessons in the afternoons during the week except on Thursday when there is a computer and technology class. Junior and senior clubs in the evenings have activities like drama, arts and crafts and computer studies. The Centre has a reputation for having top table tennis coaches. There are parent and toddler classes every morning and there are some music therapy and adult computer groups. Phone for timings.

Wandsworth

Area Youth Office
92 St John's Hill
Clapham Junction   SW11
Tel 228 6693
●School age
Contact this office for information on youth centres, clubs and play centres.

ILEA Divisional Office (Division 10)
78 Garrett Lane
Wandsworth   SW18
Tel 874 7262
●All ages
Here you can find out about nursery schools and nursery classes at many infant schools and the whole range of schooling in the borough. For more information about the state and independent systems see the chapter on School.

Play Section
Leisure and Amenities
Wandsworth Town Hall
Wandsworth High Street
Wandsworth SW18
Tel 874 6464/6374
●All ages
The Play Section has information on
one o'clock clubs, junior clubs and
adventure playgrounds in the
borough. They also have six sport
and play centres which are organised
after school from Tuesday to Friday
and all day on Saturday. In the
summer they fund up to sixty holiday
play schemes and about thirty at
Easter. Other holiday events are also
organised and look out for their
broadsheet called Sport and Play
which has lots of information on
what's going on locally.

Pre-School Playgroup Association
Battersea Town Hall
Theatre Street
Battersea SW11
Tel 228 7024
●Under 5s
The PPA in Wandsworth have
decided to run groups with longer
hours to suit working parents. They
have also tried to concentrate on the
whole 0 to 5 age range rather than
break it down into parent and
toddler clubs and 3 to 5 age groups.
Their emphasis is on flexibility in
childcare facilities.

Social Services Department
Welbeck House
Wandsworth High Street
Wandsworth SW18
Tel 871 6060/6529/6260
●Under 5s
Here you can find information on
day nurseries and day care facilities
for children under 5. Applications
have to be made through a health
visitor or social worker for the
council run facilities. They can also
give you information on voluntary
and community nurseries in your
area. Find out about the playbuses
which tour local estates with
playgroup facilities.

Wandsworth Childcare Campaign
Tel 622 9231(day) 228 4368(eve)
Contact Sarah Rackham
●Under 5s
The Campaign was formed by local
parents and childcare workers who
were concerned at the lack of
facilities for working parents. Many
of the original group members have
moved on to related work with the
under 5s and the Campaign is going
through a quiet patch. If you have
enthusiasm and ideas for working
with under 5s contact them and offer
your help.

Wandsworth Education Shop
86 Battersea Rise
Clapham Junction SW11
Tel 350 1790
Wheelchair access to Shop
●All ages
If you're studying in Wandsworth
and need childcare facilities ask
about the Students Guide to
Childcare.

**Working for Children in
Wandsworth**
Office of Popular Planning Unit
Old Chesterton Centre
116 Battersea Park Road
Battersea SW11
Tel 622 1457
●All ages

A useful booklet, Wandsworth Child Care Guide, is available from this organisation. The unit was formed to provide support for parents and workers campaigning for childcare facilities. It works in conjunction with social services, ILEA, the health authority, voluntary groups and the private sector. It also has information on local childcare facilities and campaigning groups.

Some Local Activities

Battersea Boatyard
Old Chesterton School
110-116 Battersea Park Road
Battersea SW11
Tel 622 9231
●School age
A large project which involves clearing land around five railway arches set in the Wandle Basin. Two boat projects are being set up. One will be involved with the restoration of historic river boats and the other will repair and maintain smaller boats. There are plans to set up a small river museum, have a Thames sailing barge and a community narrowboat. School groups are going to be involved in all aspects of the scheme. (See ILEA DISCO Scheme in the last section of this chapter).

Battersea Toy Library
28 West Hill
Battersea SW18
Tel 870 7592
Open Wed (phone for times)
●All ages
The toy library has been set up because it has been recognised that stimulating toys are necessary to a child's development. Childminders can borrow toys on Wednesdays and the rest of the week the two workers go out to childminders' groups where other minders can borrow toys.

Contact a Family
170 Garratt Lane

Wandsworth SW18
Tel 870 9282
●All ages
A local self-help group for families who have children with special needs. The group offers practical help, mutual support, activities and gatherings. A guide to facilities for local special needs children under 5 has been produced by the group.

Family Education Unit
Adult Education
110-116 Old Chesterton Building
Battersea Park Road
Battersea SW11
Tel 622 6787
●All ages
Family workshops are run by local adult education institutes. Activities vary from week to week. These are usually run at schools and there are tutors who concentrate on working with the under 5s. Many workshops organise schemes which are open to adults and children all week during holidays.

Oasis Children's Venture
407 Wandsworth Road
Vauxhall SW8
Tel 720 4276
●All ages
Oasis supports, organises and sometimes funds activities like playschemes, festivals and holiday events. It is an active, respected organisation.

Oasis Karting Project
407 Wandsworth Road
Battersea SW8
Tel 720 4276
●School age
Run by Oasis Children's Venture this project is a place where community, school and youth groups can have some fun with go-karts. Groups pay a hire charge of about £15 and for the first hour they learn how to maintain a go-kart. After that they can take to the track.

Wandsworth One-Parent Family Group
102 Earlsfield Road
Wandsworth   SW18
Tel 870 3207
Open 10-6(Mon-Fri)
●All ages
A drop-in advice centre which also
has a latchkey service attached to
local schools. On Monday evening
there is a group for one-parent
families which has creche facilities.
They also organise for children to be
looked after in the school holidays.

Special Needs

If you have a young child with
special needs, one of the people you
should turn to for support and
information is your health visitor.
Health visitors have a lot of
experience about play activities for
children and if you ask they will
probably bring some interesting toys
to your home for you and your child
to play with. Your health visitor will
also know about lots of schemes and
support services which may be of
help. When it comes to play, all the
play activities for the under 5s that
we have already mentioned in this
chapter are designed for all children,
whatever their needs. Toy libraries
are particularly important places (see
Play Matters in the listing that
follows).
Pre-school age children with special
needs are the only children who have
a statutory right to a place in a
nursery, and you may be able to take
your child along to one at quite a
early age. When your child is about 5,
an arrangement will be made for you
to visit your local ILEA Divisional
Office so that you can discuss his/her
educational needs. A careful
assessment will then be carried out
by an educational specialist. The 1981
Children's Act recommends that
children with special needs should be
educated in the same school setting

as other children and slowly special
schools are being phased out. When
you are considering various schools,
enquire about after-school activities
as this is an important bonus for
children. Lots of other organisations
are involved in leisure activities for
children and young people with
special needs. You may have already
found some interesting local schemes
in the previous Borough Guide but
there are definitely more than we
have had room to list. The Scouts,
the Brownies and the Guides all run
special groups and there are lots of
other organisations like Riding for
the Disabled as well as special sports
and leisure activities organised by
the council. You could also ring some
of the national charities (see the
chapter on Disability – national
organisations). We list below some
useful organisations and support
groups which may have local
activities close to home.

Parents Campaign for Integrated Education in London
25 Woodnock Road
Streatham   SW16
Tel 677 9828
Contact Margaret Gault
This organisation aims to support all
parents of children with special
needs so that they get the best
possible education for their children.
They are working towards the
ultimate integration of all children
into mainstream schools. Local
groups meet in Wandsworth,
Lambeth, Southwark and Lewisham
and new groups are being set up in
Merton and Greenwich. Ring the
above number to find out where your
nearest group is.

Play Matters
68 Churchway
NW1
Tel 387 9592
●All ages
Play Matters publishes a useful
factsheet called Play for Handicapped

Children and a series of nine illustrated booklets called Ready to Play which are aimed at people caring for a child with a mental handicap or learning difficulties. Titles include In the Bath, Going to Bed, Getting Dressed, Time to Eat and Out and About. Play Matters is the umbrella organisation for toy libraries throughout the UK so this is where you can find out about local toy libraries. Some libraries are for all children and some are concerned in particular with children who have special needs. Any toy library will welcome you and your child

(regardless of age) and they are usually pleasant meeting places for parents and children. Some special toy libraries have Opportunity Groups when volunteers run play sessions with individual children. We are told that new toy libraries are opening up all the time so keep in touch with Play Matters. Active is another scheme within Play Matters which brings together disabled people (of all ages) and their relatives with designers and technicians. The aim is to produce aids for communication, teaching, leisure and play. The aids are designed to suit individual needs, where nothing commercially produced is available or suitable. Active publishes a series of worksheets which provide clear DIY instructions on how to make up the designs at home. If you are interested in starting your own Active group for local special needs children or young people ring the above number. Play Matters are there to be used and their excellent work should be supported.

Something For Everybody

As its title suggests, this section does not pretend to include everything of interest to everybody. Alas, we do not have the space, so we have selected some projects and

organisations which we hope you will find interesting.

Award Schemes

Duke of Edinburgh's Award Scheme
●Age 14-25
The Scheme began in 1956 since when nearly two million young people have taken part, many of whom have a physical or mental handicap. It is run by volunteers from schools, youth organisations, award centres and local firms and offers young people a programme of leisure activities and the chance of winning a bronze, silver or gold award. The activities cover four sections – service, expeditions, skills and physical recreation. Ring your Area Youth Office (see the Borough Guide) to find out what's going on in your area.

Books

Take a look at the many special collections listed in the Libraries chapter and don't miss all the wonderful collections at the Centre for Children's Books detailed in the Specialist Libraries section. There are also some interesting children's book publishers and storytellers in the chapter on Poetry and Prose. Other local book organisations follow.

Bookboat
PO Box 347
Greenwich   SE10

Tel 853 4383
Wheelchair access none
Open 10-5(Mon-Wed Fri-Sat)
●All ages
A floating bookshop which has books for children of all ages.

Bookspread
58 Tooting Bec Road
Tooting   SW17

Tel 767 6377
Wheelchair access to building
Open 10-5(Mon-Wed) 10-9(Fri) 10-3(Sat)
●Under 5s
This is an active children's book centre run in a private home. A group of ex-teachers give advice to parents and children about books. They are particularly concerned about non-sexist, non-racist books. They have an activity room in which they run a busy programme of events. Story telling for 0 to 3 year olds happens on Monday, Tuesday and Wednesday. Sessions last about an hour. For 3 to 5 year olds there is story telling on Monday afternoon and on Wednesday afternoon there is reading and writing for 4 to 5 year olds. On Thursday afternoon there is dance, counting and rhythm for 3 to 5 year olds. Once a month on a Friday there's a session called Tune Time which allows handicapped children to enjoy music. The Chess Mate Club meets on Saturdays and is for beginners as well as players.

City Farms

City farms provide a slice of farm life in the city where children can get to know farm animals and see how plants are grown and harvested. Older children can volunteer to help and get a chance to look after the animals, join in the harvest or do small repairs. If you wish to know more about city farms contact The City Farms Advisory Service, Old Vicargage, 66 Fraser Street, Bedminster, Bristol B53 4L7.

Elm Farm
Gladstone Terrace
Battersea   SW8
Tel 627 1130
Open Tue-Fri(phone for appointment)
●All ages
A thriving community city farm which has goats, hens, ducks, and

City Farm

land to plant and harvest. Volunteers get involved in building fences, milking goats, taking plant cuttings and looking after the animals.

Surrey Docks Farm
Commercial Dock Passage
Gulliver Street
Surrey Docks   SE16
Tel 231 1010
Open 10-5(Tue-Sun) Closed on Fri during school holidays
●All ages
There are goats, chickens, donkeys, pigs, sheep and bees here. There is a farm shop where you can buy honey from the farm's bees. Volunteers are welcome to partake in the many farm activities, there is a classroom and a teacher to cater for visits from schools.

Vauxhall City Farm
24 St Oswalds Place
Vauxhall   SE11
Tel 582 4204
Open 10.30-5(Tue Wed Thur Sat Sun)
Membership 50p(under 16)
●All ages
Animals to enjoy here are sheep, goats, rabbits, donkeys and ponies. There are also donkey and pony rides. Volunteers can help with feeding, cleaning and looking after the animals.

Dance

See the chapter called Dance. The section you will probably find most helpful is Education which has information on dance schools, studios and classes and youth dance.

Family Classes

A few adult education institutes have started running family days or sessions. Here is one that is especially successful.

Morley College
61 Westminster Bridge Road
Waterloo   SE1
Tel 928 8501
Wheelchair access none
Admission 70p(adult) 35p(child)
●All ages
The Saturday Morning Family Concerts at Morley College are a series of six family concerts held every month from October to March. Each one covers a different kind of music and they have had steel bands, brass bands, symphony orchestras, violin recitals, chamber groups, sitar recitals and children's choirs. The event is divided into two contrasting sections and often the audience is asked to participate. The atmosphere is very informal and young babies are welcome. People can come and go as they wish. Do find out about the programme of concerts and take the

family along to join in the experience. Since the family concerts have been such a success they have started running other family activities classes at the Morley. There are classes on pottery, natural history, astronomy, family music making, and family languages (French, Spanish and German). There is also a music workshop for families with handicapped children.

Film

Local cinemas and clubs that have special slots for children are detailed in the Film and Video chapter. Of particular interest are the Wandsworth Cinema Club, Battersea Arts Centre, the National Film Theatre (Junior NFT) and the summer season at the Ritzy.

Holidays

Children's Country Holiday Fund
1 York Street
W1
Tel 935 8371
●Age 5-13
This organisation provides summer holidays every year for about 3000 children who otherwise wouldn't have the chance of a holiday. The younger ones go to stay with host families in the country or by the seaside and the older ones go on camping holidays. If you would like your child to be considered, contact your local social services, family service unit or education welfare officer.

Music

There is music to be enjoyed at the South Bank complex and The Purcell Room, in particular, often has concerts for children. See also the Family Classes entry in this section.

Phone Lines

Children's London
Tel 246 8007
●All ages
A recorded weekly diary of events
and competitions.

Kidsline
Tel 222 8070
●All ages
A personal telephone service offering
advice, information and details about
what's on for children. A commercial
advertisers' medium (a bit like
Teledata).

Leisureline
Tel 246 8041
●All ages
A guide to entertainment and events
in London.

Storyline
Tel 246 8000
●All ages
Bedtime stories every night from 6.

Play

Play Matters
68 Churchway
NW1
Tel 387 9592
Play Matters (sometimes known as
the National Toy Libraries
Association) is concerned with
everything that has to do with toy
libraries and play needs. Amongst its
many activities it produces the Good
Toy Guide (700 toys described),
booklists and factsheets on the
importance of play. It also runs the
Active scheme for children and
young people with special needs.
Membership offers additionally a
thrice-yearly magazine called ARK,
toy catalogues and toy library
information, entry with your
child(ren) to the Toy Display Room
(of toys recommended in the Good
Toy Guide), and free tickets to the
annual Toy and Hobby Fair at Earls
Court.

Save the Children Fund
Children's Centre
Castlemead
Camberwell Road
Camberwell   SE5
Tel 701 4418
●Under 5s
Save the Children Fund runs
playgroups in many areas. These
include two to three hourly sessions,
all-day sessions, groups that only run
during term time and others that run
all year.
Phone to find the one that's nearest
to you.

The South London Scrap Scheme
Between 161 Verdant Lane and
Hither Green Cemetry
Catford   SE6
Tel 698 9280
This project supplies clean industrial
waste material to other projects and
schemes for educational play. Things
like paper, card, buttons, beads,
leather, fabrics, wallpaper, wood,
plastic, boxes and chalk are kept in
store. The stock is replenished
constantly and is free to members.
Membership is given to non-profit
making organisations only and they
will only supply to paid up members.
Phone for prices of membership.
Sometimes workers from the scheme
visit playgroups and demonstrate the
wonders of scrap as they

manufacture objects like dragons or buildings. This workshop activity is unfortunately limited by time and money.

Puppets

If you're interested in puppets be sure to visit the Polka Children's Theatre Museum. You will find a brief description of it in the chapter on Museums.

Battersea Arts Centre
Old Town Hall
Lavender Hill
Clapham Junction   SW11
Tel 228 5335
Wheelchair access throughout
Open 2-6(Mon-Fri)
●School age
This is an active puppet centre for viewing and making with an information service, a library and a small exhibition space. There are also courses, workshops and exhibitions. On Wednesday afternoon after school there is a workshop at the centre where you can make your own puppets and work on a production. The charge for this is 20p a session. There are special holiday projects so phone for more details. If you are interested in a puppet company to entertain at a child's party then contact BAC for their directory of puppet companies.

School Projects

ILEA DISCO Scheme
c/o ILEA Divisional Office (see Borough Guide above)
●3rd/4th year and some younger
This is an ILEA run scheme which is very active in South London. (Indeed, it grew out of a Wandsworth scheme called WISP.) Based in each ILEA Divisional Office is a Divisional Industry Schools Co-ordinator (hence the name DISCO), who is concerned with enabling young people at school to become

aware of industry and to become actively involved as part of the school curriculum in the local working community. The emphasis is on active learning. Students visit local industries and representatives from local firms visit schools. Projects might include a look at the fast food industry as part of a home economics or health & safety course, the study of how trade unions work in relation to a social studies course or, as part of a maths or economics course, students might do a project on a local building society. Hospitals, local voluntary agencies and factories are all involved. Battersea Boatyard in Wandsworth is to be the focus of a future project for local young people. In the third year, before students choose their O levels, girls are given a wide range of opportunities in non-traditional subjects such as sciences and engineering and boys have access to the caring professions. There is also a Mini-Enterprise scheme whereby groups of students devise projects that they feel will be of use to the local community. They might offer a much needed new service or manufacture and sell a project they have designed. Alternatively, they might take on board a project for a local industry, thus offering a two-way service. Sometimes work experience comes out of the DISCO scheme. DISCO works with a small

turn over for more !

Children's zoo, Crystal Palace

number of schools for 1-2 years aiming at high quality work and it hopes that afterwards teachers will continue the scheme themselves. 3rd and 4th year students tend to be most involved although some primary school children have participated in the scheme. Local business people who would like their firms to be involved in the scheme should contact DISCO at the ILEA Divisional Office (see Borough Guide) and young people interested in DISCO should tell their teachers about it.

Support

Children's Legal Centre
20 Compton Terrace
N1
Tel 359 6251
●All ages
National organisation which gives children and young people advice on legal matters and their rights in relation to parents, statutory parents (if they are in care) and teachers. Young people are welcome to write or phone for advice. The Centre has produced a really useful publication called At What Age Can I? which costs 40p including postage and packing.

National Association of Young People in Care (NAYPIC)
20 Compton Terrace
N1
Tel 359 6251
●All ages
The London office of a national organisation which is run by and for those who are or have been in care. Pressure group which works towards better conditions for young people in care. Ring for the address of your local group.

Theatre

There are lots of theatres and theatre companies mentioned in our Theatre chapter that are of specific interest to children. One theatre for whom children have always come first is the Polka Children's Theatre. Pantomimes are presented every year at Lewisham Theatre, Wimbledon Theatre and Lambeth Town Hall.

Things to Do

The chapters on Museums and Festivals are well worth looking at if you can't decide how to spend a day out. The one called Parks has details of children's zoos, nature trails, walks and other outdoor projects. A useful place to get to know is your local library. They all have junior sections and special library projects and competitions are frequently arranged. The library staff should also have details about any holiday projects and play schemes in the area. One organisation that co-ordinates holiday activities is ILEA,

which produces a wonderful booklet called Holiday Fun (one for every borough), packed with summer holiday activities. You should check City Limits and Time Out for one-off events and some of the phonelines in this listing can be helpful too.

DANCE

This chapter is organised in four sections as follows: People (Choreographers, Dancers and Dance Companies), Venues, Special Events, Education (Dance Schools, Studios and Classes, and Youth Dance).

People

The dance image is often referred to as 'ephemeral' and the very same might be said of dancers and dance companies. Dance people are hard to pin down anywhere, but in South London where professional and semi-professional dance has only recently begun to flourish, they are nearly invisible. Nearly, but not totally. Thanks are due in large measure to Arts Officer, Katie Venner in Lambeth, Vaughan Aston in Southwark and Dance Development Workers like Bronwyn Williams in Lambeth and Beverley Glean at the Albany Empire, who work hard to make audiences aware of dance, and dance artists aware of one another. It is because of Lambeth's ambitious Dance Brolly

and other festivals (see Special Events below) that dance is beginning to gain a sense of community. Incongruous dance spectacles like the Tokyo Classical Ballet's performance of Swan Lake at Wimbledon Theatre a few years ago are being replaced by dance events that have an organic feel to them, that have taken root in community which feeds them. Slowly, South London is ceasing to be a neighbourhood dance artists just pass through. The list which follows contains only those artists and companies who work on a professional or semi-professional level and perform to an audience.

Kirsty Alexander
81 Kerrin Point
SE11
Tel 735 4668
●Dancer Choreographer
A contemporary dancer-choreographer who has worked with Rosemary Butcher among others, Kirsty Alexander is the primary dance component of the multi-media

performing group, Jugnost. She is also active in SHAPE, an organisation which creates opportunities for disabled people to participate in arts activities. She has worked as a Dance Development Officer at the Albany and is currently studying full-time at the Laban Centre.

Roland Alexander
31 Deodar Road
Putney
SW15
Tel 788 7274
●Dancer
Born and trained in Canada, Roland Alexander has worked in ballet, Graham-based modern dance and musical comedies. He was the original Rumpuscat in Andrew Lloyd Webber's Cats.

Artlink Dance
Clockhouse Community Centre
Defiance Walk
Woolwich Dockyard Estate
Woolwich
SE18
Tel 854 1576
Directors Mark Harris & Miriam Bird
●Company
In their professional work, the six-strong Artlink Dance follows the gentle and meditative way of American modern dance pioneer Erick Hawkins, for whom dance was not an angst-ridden journey of self-searching (unlike his great mentor Martha Graham), but a means of both discovering and revealing inner harmony. As in Hawkins' dance, specially commissioned scores and décors play an important part in Artlink's creative process. One thing Artlink has reacted against in Hawkins is what Mark Harris refers to as 'the white, hairless look'. For a description of Artlink's other activities, see Education (Studios and Classes and Youth Dance) below.

Miriam Bird
see Artlink Dance

Black Tulip
c/o Courthouse Community Centre
Arndale Community Project
Garratt Lane
Wandsworth
SW18
Tel 874 1094
Director Caroline Nembhard
●Company
A semi-professional contemporary dance company of six women.

Carl Campbell
28 St James Walk
Camden Estate
Peckham
SE15
Tel 703 2388
●Dancer Director
Carl Campbell is the founder-director of Dance Co 7, a performing group specialising in Afro-Caribbean dance. Considered by many to be the hottest exponent of Afro-Caribben dance in London, he was trained at the London School of Contemporary Dance, the Jamaica School of Dance and the Hilde Holder School of Creative Dance. He tutors for ILEA and the Rose Bruford School of Speech and Drama and lectures at Middlesex Polytechnic. With his company, he works actively on local community arts projects to try and develop a strong appreciation for Afro-Caribbean dance.

Scott Clark
13C Gautrey Road
New Cross
SE15
Tel 635 8395
●Dancer Choreographer
American-born and trained, Scott Clark has been teaching technique at the Laban Centre since autumn 1984. He trained at Ohio State University and danced for a time with Bebe Miller's company before accepting teaching posts in New York and then California. In London he appeared with Jackie Wilford (see this listing) and Nelson Fernandez at the

Southwark Community Arts Festival in 1985, and for the 1985 Dance Umbrella he choreographed a duet. A programme of his work will be presented at the Laban Centre in early 1986.

Coreoteatro
see Andreas Demetriou

Dance Co 7
see Carl Campbell

Dancing Union
Flat F
Bowyer House
15 Voltaire Road
Clapham
SW4
Tel 627 3096
●Company
A relatively new performance company headed by Nicola Childs which deals in highly theatrical imagery. One of the highlights of the 1984 Dance Days festival at Battersea Arts Centre was a collaboration between Dancing Union and sculptor Deborah Thomas.

Andreas Demetriou
98 Railton Road
Brixton
SE24
Tel 274 2246
●Dancer Choreographer
A Cypriot by birth, Andreas Demetriou is the mastermind behind the outrageous Coreoteatro, a gay dance-theatre group which, like Dancing Union, specialises in theatricalism. Trained in Graham-based modern dance at the London School of Contemporary Dance as well as in jazz and ballet, he received a degree in performance from Middlesex Poly. At Oval House he has conducted dance workshops where his highly-touted dance adaptation of Genet's violent drama of illusion, The Maids, was first seen. Entitled Rumbasambatango, the work followed Genet's wishes by having men portray the three female characters. The score (a musical collage) and décor were also created by the choreographer. These days, Demetriou claims to be particularly interested in contact improvisation and Tai Chi (which he teaches).

Paul Farquharson
see Strawberry All Stars

Debbie Green
59A Jeffrey's Road
Clapham
SW4
Tel 622 1358
●Dancer Choreographer
Debbie Green was trained at Ballet Rambert and danced in Germany with a ballet company for several years before returning to England and forming her own company called Ibis. Along the way she became interested in the fluid, curvaceous classical dance form of North-east India, known as Odissi, and studied with acclaimed Odissi dancer Sanjeevini Dutta in North London. Today her choreography bears the influence of Odissi. Indeed, she likes to see her choreographic work for Ibis as an effort to bridge the gap not only between ballet and contemporary dance but also between East and West. Recent work includes the choreography for a one-woman show presented by singer-songwriter

Elaine Koster, and a dance piece on
the career of Cortez' mistress, the
enigmatic La Malinche, seen at
Dance Brolly '85.

Philip Grosser
55 Holden House
Deptford Church Street
SE8
Tel 691 4927
●Dancer Choreographer
For the past three years, Philip
Grosser has taught technique,
choreography and repertory at the
Laban Centre where he has also
presented his own dances. Born in
New York, he trained (and for a brief
time appeared) with Martha Graham
and then at the State University of
New York in Purchase. He graduated
from Teachers College, Columbia
University. In addition to his work
at the Laban Centre, his British
activities have involved him as a
dancer in several Dance Umbrellas
and as a choreographer for such
companies as the Welsh-based
Diversions (formerly Jumpers).

Mark Harris
see Artlink Dance

Ibis
see Debbie Green

Sarah Jones
59 St George's Road
SE1
Tel 582 7433
●Dancer
As a contemporary dancer and mime
artist, Sarah Jones has appeared at
Oval House and Croydon Warehouse.
She combines her involvement in
dance with a passion for
photography. Exhibitions of her
photographs have appeared in South
London's more adventurous
galleries.

Rosemary Lehan
see Manoeuvres

London Festival Ballet
Royal Festival Hall
SE1
Tel 928 3191
Director Peter Schaufuss
●Company
The resident big ballet company of
South London presents a Christmas
spectacle (so far, The Nutcracker)
and a summer season of repertoire at
the RFH every year. Under the
relatively new leadership of Danish-
born superstar Peter Schaufuss, the
LFB's repertoire has broadened
considerably. These days seemingly
incompatible works like Béjart's
Songs of a Wayfarer and Alvin
Ailey's Night Creatures might very
well turn up on either side of a Don
Quixote pas de deux. The LFB corps
are now of a reasonably high
standard and the ranks of soloists
and principals have swelled with an
increasing number of foreign
dancers. Many of them are extremely
talented (Maurizio Bellezza, Patrick
Armand and Mireille Bourgeois to
name but three). However,
Schaufuss's own performances and
those of his glittering array of guest
stars (Makarova, Patrick Dupond,
Eva Evdokimova) remain the chief
attraction. Some home-grown
company dancers are up in arms and
even resigning because their chances
of dancing the leading roles are being
taken away under the company's
new policy.

Manoeuvres
Longfield Hall
Knatchbull Road
SE5
Tel 733 3503
Director Rosemary Lehan
●Company
Manoeuvres is a 5-6 member dance
company which concentrates on
community-based activities, such as
school projects and workshops.
However, it is also gaining a

reputation for performance in South London's alternative dance circles. It has taken part in the Brixton Festival, two Dance Brollies, the 1985 Albany dance festival, One Step Beyond, and several other events.

Don McClure
71 Kellet Road
SW2
Tel 737 5420
●Dancer
A member of the contemporary dance troupe, Mantis (based north of the river), Don McClure also teaches and conducts workshops in South London.

Original Phoenix
126 Abbeville Road
SW4
Tel 627 1291
Director Richard Myers
●Company
An award-winning body popping and break dancing group that appears frequently at South London venues and festivals.

Parallax Dance Company
45 Canterbury Grove
SE27
Tel 670 7203

Director Augustus Hamilton
●Company
An intermittently active contemporary dance company.

Peter Schaufuss
see London Festival Ballet

Françoise Sergy
48 Morat Street
SW9
Tel 735 1640
●Dancer Choreographer
'To dance as feminists is to talk about how we see ourselves, how we let other people see us, how we enjoy our body, communicate with other people. It is about challenging traditional ways of experiencing physical contacts and relationships. It is about feeling real, strong and active: connected.' Thus wrote Françoise Sergy in a 1985 issue of Spare Rib. Though presently engaged in exploring the organic, pro-body, fluid techniques of Aikido, Tai Chi, and Contact Improvisation, Swiss-born Françoise Sergy has had considerable exposure to more formal movement techniques, including Graham-based modern, Limon, and Cunningham. As one of sixteen directors of Brixton Art Gallery, she is engaged in the Women's Work exhibitions there where she finds plenty of opportunity to explore feminist themes. Works like The Fish and The Bicycle, and The Silent Roof are interesting too for her collaboration with artists in other media. She has worked with artists (Gail Bourgeois, Sally Dawson), musicians (Pomme Clayton and Diamanda Galas) and poets (Diana Scott).

Shamwari
137 Lafone House
New Park Road
SW2
Tel 671 4464

Director Peta Rose
●Company
An African dance-drumming group.

Rosamund Shreeves
148 Stockwell Road
SW9
Tel 737 5235
●Dancer Choreographer
Formerly a dancer-in-residence in
Hounslow, Rosamund Shreeves has
been very involved in children's
workshops, but this is by no means
the sum of her work. Recently, she
has expressed a deep concern about
the wholesale destruction of the
environment. As she herself wrote in
New Dance (no 33), '... through
movement we can *be* more vividly.
Maybe this awareness of both self
and surroundings will increase our
responsibility for the conservation of
the human being.'

Mala Sikka
210 Amelia Street
SE17
●Dancer
Mala Sikka is a dancer trained in
Kathakali who has also performed in
Western dance styles. She recently
collaborated with Debbie Green (see
above) on La Malinche.

Strawberry All Stars
34 Albon House
Neville Gill Close
SW18
Tel 870 4346
Director Paul Farquharson
●Company
A very slick break dancing/body
popping group that has performed
around London. Members of the
company have taught at Pineapple,
the Dance Centre and, in South
London, at the Courthouse
Community Centre and at Dance
Attic (see Studios and Classes under
Education below).

Clarence Thompson
Strand Centre
Elm Park
SW2
Tel 671 1300
●Dancer
This popular instructor of Afro-
Caribbean dance at the Strand
Centre, is also a dynamic performer
in his own right.

Uprock
50 Lewisham Hill
SE13
Tel 852 4601
●Company
Formerly the Uprock Girls, a trio of
female break dancers and body
poppers, Uprock now consists of two
women and one man. Really fresh top
hip hop.

Zig Zag Dance Company
Flat C
8 Nevern Place
SW5
Tel 370 1798
Director Jackie Snow
●Company
This gymnastic-dance trio (two
women and one man) work at the
Courthouse Community Centre
opposite the Arndale Shopping
Centre in Wandsworth.

Zodiac
c/o Academy Theatre
211 Stockwell Road
SW9
Tel 274 1525
Director Peter Wharrie
●Company
Zodiac or, as it used to be known, the
Academy Dancers, comprises six
dancers (five boys and one girl)
between the ages of seventeen and
twenty. It is arguably the most
sophisticated and ambitious break
dance and body popping troupe in
South London and its star dancer,

Michael Forsythe, has to be seen to believed. Plans are currently underway to move to Clapham North where the company hopes to open a school for hip hop devotees.

Zuriya African Performers
38 Brixton Road
SW9
Tel 582 9479
●Company
Zuriya's aim is to introduce the cultures of Africa and the Caribbean to young people through story-telling, drumming, singing and dancing. There are currently five members in the group.

Venues

Today, you no longer have to go to a traditional venue like a theatre to see dance. Performances take place just as often in art galleries, parks, schools, hospitals, community, civic and shopping centres, and even at swimming pools. Nowhere is this more true than in South London where traditional performance space is at a premium anyway. What follows is a list of the South London venues most commonly used for theatrical dance performances.

Details of ticket prices and wheelchair access are included in this listing for any venue which doesn't appear elsewhere in the Handbook. For information about other venues see Theatre.

Albany Empire
Douglas Way
Deptford   SE8
Tel 691 3333
The Albany has long included dance in its programming. Much of it is community-based (groups like Manoeuvres perform here – see People above). In recent times,

however, 'imported' companies like the Leeds-based Phoenix Dance Company and the Joel Hall Dancers from Chicago, have made appearances at the Albany. Local response to the dance activity has encouraged the Albany's managers to increase the dance component in the season's programming with the result that it now offers mini dance festivals every year. One of the 1985 festivals was called One Step Beyond and featured everything from capoeira to contemporary dance and break dancing to tap. The seating is informal in this theatre-in-the-round for 250-300 people.

Battersea Arts Centre
Old Town Hall
Lavender Hill
Battersea   SW11
Tel 223 8413

Like the Albany, Battersea Arts Centre is not primarily a dance venue, but dance has long played an important part in BAC's programming. Companies from around the country and abroad perform here. The highlight of the season's dance activity is undoubtedly the annual summer dance festival, called Dance Days (see Special Events). Two performing spaces are available to dancers, the main theatre and a studio ideal for workshops.

The Big Top
Battersea Park
Battersea   SW11
Wheelchair access to Big Top and
special toilets on site
Admission varies
Robert Fossett's splendid 1200-seat
variation on a theatre (it is a circus
tent) offers ballet audiences the
opportunity to see mainly ballet at
substantially less cost than at the
Royal Opera House or Sadler's Wells.
The principal tenants of The Big Top
over the last ten summers have been
The Royal Ballet, The Sadler's Wells
Royal Ballet and Ballet Rambert.
Though the atmosphere is chummier
than that of its West End
counterparts, the Big Top does not
cut back on the quality of its
productions. If the Royal Ballet
mounts Manon or Romeo and Juliet,
audiences in Battersea Park can be
sure they're getting the West End
versions. Attached to the tent are
full backstage facilities including
units for orchestra, wardrobe,
physiotherapy, a stage door canteen
and thirty dressing rooms. At the
time of going to press, there are no
definite Big Top dates for 1986.

Laban Centre
Laurie Grove
Goldsmiths College
New Cross   SE14
Tel 692 4070 Ext 27
Wheelchair access arrive early for
assistance over steps into foyer and
theatre
Admission £3 Concessions
The generously equipped Studio
Theatre in the Laban Centre complex
is the scene for student and faculty
dance concerts as well as
performances by visiting artists
during term time. Seats 150.

Nettlefold Hall
West Norwood Library
1 Norwood High Street
West Norwood   SE27
Tel 670 6212

A popular venue with local and
visiting artists. The wing space isn't
ample, but the stage is wooden (not
sprung), the auditorium is raked and
the sight lines are good. The 200 or so
seats are retractable so a larger
performance space can be created
when necessary. Nettlefold sees a lot
of action during Lambeth's Dance
Brolly.

Norwood Hall
38 Knight's Hill
West Norwood   SE27
Tel 670 5030
Wheelchair access with ramp to hall
and special toilets being installed
Admission £3 maximum Concessions
An alternative venue to Nettlefold
Hall during Dance Brolly when it is
often used for workshops. The home
of Lambeth Youth Dance (see Youth
Dance under Education in this
chapter). Flexible seating for
maximum of 264 people.

Oval House
52-54 Kennington Oval
Oval   SE11
Tel 735 2786
Since the 1960s, this 19th century
building has served as an educational
arts centre and experimental theatre
venue. It has two performing spaces,
both of which have been used by
dancers and performance artists in
the past. Not all of the dance activity
can be described as experimental (the
English Dance Theatre for instance)
but most of it plays in an area where
the borders between dance, theatre,
mime and performance overlap. Oval
House has been used by Dance Brolly,
and dance workshops given by both
local and visiting artists are offered
from time to time. The upstairs space
seats between 60 and 80, the
downstairs 100.

The South Bank Concert Halls
South Bank   SE1
Tel 928 3191
The Queen Elizabeth Hall, Purcell
Room and Royal Festival Hall offer a

fair amount of dance activity during the year. The Queen Elizabeth Hall and the Purcell Room generally feature small (often ethnic minority) companies. The London Festival Ballet (see People above) is the resident company of the RFH where it presents Christmas and summer seasons. There are often free performances by dancers in the foyer of the RFH and dance-related painting, designs and sculpture are occasionally featured in the gallery section. In 1985, the GLC, RFH and London Festival Ballet sponsored a festival of dance (appropriately named Festival Dance 1985), which presented free foyer performances by a wide variety of international groups as well as workshops, classes, demonstrations and slide talks.

Stanley Halls
South Norwood Hill
South Norwood   SE25
Tel 653 3630
This has been a venue for GLA touring artists, but presently is used by Asian dancers and dance companies for occasional performances. See also Education – Studios and Classes below.

Tara Arts Centre
356 Garratt Lane
Earlsfield   SW18
Tel 871 1458
Recently reopened after 18 months of renovation and expansion, the Tara Arts Centre specialises in the presentation of contemporary Asian artists. As such it has played host to dancers Valli Subbiah, Astad Deboo (whose movement style utilises everything from Kathakali to Pina Bausch), Flora Gatha (Odissi-trained mime artist and dancer), Journeywomen (Debbie Green, Mala Sikka and Sue Weston), and the breathtaking Kathak dancer Alpana Sengupta and her students. Caribbean and Latin American dance styles have also been seen in the 50-

seat studio theatre. Though small, the theatre is handsomely equipped and the stage is more than adequate to meet the needs of the dance forms usually seen there. Membership (£5pa or £7.50pa family membership) entitles visitors to a substantial discount for each event plus priority booking and invitations to special previews and open rehearsals. Ticket prices for dance events rarely rise above £3.

Special Events

With interest in theatrical dance on the rise everywhere, it's not surprising to find dance showing up with increasing regularity on the programmes of South London borough arts festivals. Gone is yesterday's tokenism. Dance is as actively represented at these events as music or even theatre. Not only that, there are now in South London several festivals devoted to nothing but dance. Some of these are regular features of South London's dance life and they are listed below. One of the great advantages of these events is that they give local dance audiences the chance to see dancers and companies who do not often stray south of the river. This is an enlightening experience which can only have a positive effect on the growth of dance in the south. Some of these artists have become great favourites with South London audiences and show up at festivals with the regularity of local artists. Among these are American jazz hoofer Will Gaines and the extraordinary Kathak dancer Alpana Sengupta (she has taught in South London, too), groups like Rebecca Wilson's popular youth dance group, Rare Earth, and that highly acrobatic quartet of performers directed by Michael Merwitzer called The Kosh. Others, like Ian Spink's brilliant Second Stride, have a rather smaller following, but around Oval House and Brixton that following is an intense one. The best-loved of the constant visitors is almost certainly the all-male black Leeds-based group known as The Phoenix Dance Company. Their athletic concerts (always described as 'dynamic' and 'powerful' in the papers) sell out whenever the company appears.

Not included in the listing below are one-off events and those previously GLC sponsored festivals on the South Bank, whose future is unclear at the time of going to press.

Albany Empire Dance Festivals
Douglas Way
Deptford SE8
Tel 691 8016/3333
Festival Co-ordinator Beverley Glean
1986 dates unconfirmed
The Albany can offer as many as two festivals a year devoted entirely to dance. Not infrequently, these are built around a theme – for instance, One Step Beyond (in 1985) took advantage of the London-wide American Festival to present several American artists. Beverley Glean is also interested in current dance trends (capoeira, break dancing etc), and the Albany events are popular with young and Black audiences. The performances feature visiting and local artists, sometimes appearing on the same bill (which can make for a highly eclectic evening of dance). Master classes with performers are usually offered as part of the festival for very low fees. Seats for evening performances rarely exceed £3.50.

Dance Brolly
c/o Lambeth Amenity Services
164 Clapham Park Road
Lambeth SW4
Tel 622 6655 Ext 355
Director Katie Venner
1986 probably mid Nov-mid Dec
Easily the most ambitious of the South London dance festivals, Dance Brolly, which celebrated its fourth anniversary in the autumn of 1985, was originally set up to provide an alternative to the more mainstream events on show at Dance Umbrella which takes place at the same time of the year. (Ironically, Dance Umbrella was introduced as an event that would provide an alternative to the kind of dance at Sadler's Wells). Dance Brolly usually runs for a month and features an incredible range of artists from Odissi dancers to body poppers, ballerinas to jazz hoofers and Second Stride. Master classes, seminars, workshops, film screenings and children's activities complete the fare offered by the Brolly. Most ambitious of all, in 1985 Lambeth set aside an evening for South London dance for which it commissioned works by local dance artists. If nothing else could, Dance Brolly would make a believer out of the scoffer who says there's no dance life south of the river. Top ticket price £3. Not to be missed.

Dance Days
Battersea Arts Centre
Old Town Hall
Lavender Hill
Battersea SW11
Tel 223 8413
Festival Programmer Diana Warden
1986 probably 1st two weeks of July
Like the Albany's events, Battersea

Arts Centre's annual summer festival of dance features a mixture of local and visiting artists with plenty to engage young people and ethnic minority audiences. Where Battersea is different is in its programme of additional festival activities. There are cabaret and musical events, dance films for both children and adults, special classes conducted by artists from the big London ballet and contemporary companies as well as intensive workshops and seminars for young dancers (aged 14-21). The title Dance Days has been adopted for the summer festival and each year a different element is developed. Dance Days '85 (which marked the fourth summer dance festival at BAC), emphasized the fusion of music and dance.

Education

The variety of dance instruction offered in South London is remarkable. Commercial studios, adult education institutes, youth, community and civic centres, as well as highly specialised dance schools, all contribute to this variety. In addition to formal training for performance, there are classes that specialise in international and British folk dance and countless others to suit all ages and tastes in dance. South London's dance festivals (see Special Events above) also provide opportunity for study with professional dancers.

No attempt has been made here to list all the dance classes available (see Adult Education for your nearest institute and Young People for youth dance workshops). Under **Studios** and **Classes**, you will find only a handful of entries, selected for their association (even if it's only the quality of the studio) with the professional dance world. South London is notable, too, for its commitment to youth dance activity. In fact, the five resident youth dance groups listed below might make South London a leader in this field.

Dance Schools

Laban Centre for Movement and Dance
University of London
Goldsmiths College
New Cross   SE14
Tel 691 5750
Director Marion North
Head of Dance Theatre Bonnie Bird
Founded in the 1940s by Rudolf Laban (1879-1958), the great German pioneer of dance and movement study in the UK, the Centre moved to its present site in 1976. Here, in a dance studio building, a new extension which includes a specialist dance library, seminar rooms, a wardrobe department and nine studios, and a Studio Theatre (see Venues above), a broad programme is offered. Full-time dance-theatre studies, one year and one term courses and advance degree courses (MA, MPhil, PhD research degrees) encompass all levels of training from beginner to professional. Evening classes, workshops and community-based activities, which keep close links with neighbouring youth clubs, theatre groups, arts centres, schools and colleges, are also part of the

Laban programme. During term time, visits from leading dancers, choreographers and lecturers often lead to master classes and performance events. Other special features of the Centre include a full-time course in Labanotation, a method of recording dance movement devised by Laban himself, which is highly regarded internationally, and the publication of Dance Theatre Journal, a quarterly survey of contemporary and historical dance edited by Chris De Marigny and Alastair Macaulay. The Centre boasts 200 students a year, 25% of whom come from abroad.

Royal Academy of Dancing
48 Vicarage Crescent
Battersea SW11
Tel 223 0091
Patron Her Majesty the Queen
President Dame Margot Fonteyn de Arias
From its beginnings in 1920 as the brainchild of five leading European ballet dancers (Adeline Genee, Tamara Karsavina, Edouard Espinosa, Lucia Cormani and Phyllis Bedells), the RAD has seen itself as a guardian of dance teaching standards throughout the world. Indeed, it is the largest and most influential examining body for classical ballet in existence. Its course of study and related syllabuses are taught in 50 countries and every year more than 135,000 students around the world are examined by over 200 official RAD examiners. The College of the RAD offers one year and three year teacher training courses, a professional dancers' teaching course, a new classical ballet training programme as well as international and children's summer school schedules and an annual dance-training seminar known as Assembly.

Studios and Classes

Albany Empire
Douglas Way
Deptford SE8
Tel 691 8016
Dance Development Officer Beverley Glean
Though hardly proper studios, two rooms in the Albany complex function as dance classrooms. Weekly classes are held in jazz, contemporary dance, Caribbean and breaking and body popping (for girls only). Also, in conjunction with theatre appearances by dancers and dance companies, master classes and workshops are occasionally offered. Fees by the class.

Battesea Arts Centre
Old Town Hall
Lavender Hill
Battersea SW11
Tel 223 8413
BAC runs regular six-week seasons of classes throughout the year. A wide variety of dance styles are taught, but among the most frequently scheduled are jazz, contemporary and children's ballet. Tutors are very often professional dancers. In addition to regular classes, dance workshops are offered. Subjects range from choreography to Bhartha Natyam. All classes and workshops take place in BAC's large studio. Fees per class.

Brixton Recreation Centre
Brixton Station Road
Brixton SW9
Tel 274 7774
Perhaps the most beautifully appointed dance studio in South London (dancers would adore its sprung floor), the room at the top of Brixton's new recreation centre is at present not being used to its full capacity. At the time of going to press, only a weekly contemporary dance class was being offered (in

addition to the ubiquitous keep-fit classes). Fees by the class.

Clockhouse Community Centre
Defiance Walk
Woolwich Dockyard Estate
Woolwich　　　　　　　　SE18
Director Sargeat Singh-Gill
Director of Dance Miriam Bird
Artlink Dance (see People) presents a programme of weekly classes here which mixes contemporary, jazz and a bit of Erick Hawkins' meditative, non-stressful technique. Membership.

Club of Dance and Self-Defence
Paragon School
Searles Road
Elephant & Castle　　　　　SE1
Tel 703 3360
Director Michael Jacques
Twenty-two rooms and three halls including one dance studio. Keith Hodiak (formerly Ballet Rambert) teaches classes in jazz ballet and Tai Chi (one of the eight varieties of martial arts taught at the Club) and Gloria Hamilton teaches contemporary dance for children. The studio is available for rehearsals. Membership.

Courthouse Community Centre
Arndale Community Project
Garratt Lane
Wandsworth　　　　　　　SW18
Tel 874 1094
Director Ivor Fry
Two studios, one of which serves as a theatre space. Classes are offered in ballet and gymnastic dance to children, aged 5 to 11. Courthouse is also the home of two dance companies, Zig Zag Dance Company and Black Tulip (see People). Members of Zig Zag teach here.

Dance Attic
214 Putney Bridge Road
Putney　　　　　　　　　SW15
Tel 785 2055
Directors Andrew Corbet Burcher and Deedee Wilde
This is as much a rehearsal studio and performance venue for theatre groups (The Old Vic, Theatre of Wales, National Theatre and others) as a dance centre. Dance Attic nevertheless offers a wide range of classes including RAD, ISTD and Russian variants of ballet, tap, jazz, contemporary and even belly dancing, jive and rock 'n' roll. Four studios comprising 7000 square feet of space make for an impressive operation. The directors (Deedee Wilde was a founder of Pan's People in the 1960s) estimate that some 2000 students pass through the doors each year, many of them professional actors and musicians looking for a non-competitive environment in which to develop body-awareness. Among the dancers and choreographers who use Dance Attic as a rehearsal space is Matthew Hamilton. Fees by the class plus a daily, yearly or half-yearly membership (students under 15 are not charged membership).

The Gymini Club
(aka Gymini Gymnastics Club and Dance Centre)
Southwark Municipal Dance Centre
Warwick Hall
Kimpton Road
Camberwell　　　　　　　SE5
Tel 703 1078
Directors Rhona Hill and Katy Sime
Hill and Sime, former students of London School of Contemporary Dance, have set up a full and varied curriculum which includes ballet, contemporary, jazz and gymnastic dance classes. The Club is open seven days a week. Fees by the hour.

Stanley Halls
South Norwood Hill
South Norwood　　　　　　SE25
Tel 653 3630
Director Keith Lancing
A public hall where, on Friday evenings, instruction in the classical Indian dance form, Bharata Natyam,

is given by Sitakumari. Fees by the class.

Tara Arts Centre
356 Garratt Lane
Earlsfield   SW18
Tel 871 1458
Director Jatinder Verma
Wandsworth's Asian arts centre frequently presents dance workshops and master classes taught by visiting artists. Regular classes in Asian dance forms will undoubtedly be added to TAC's already impressive list of commitments.

Youth Dance

Artlink Youth Dance
Clockhouse Community Centre
Defiance Walk
Woolwich Dockyard Estate
Woolwich   SE18
Tel 854 1576(Artlink)
855 7188(Clockhouse)
Directors Miriam Bird and Mark Harris
A weekly class (Saturday afternoon) for 14 to 21 year-old students that tends to be more technically oriented than those of other youth dance groups. An intensive week of dance training and a performance by the students completes the year's work.

Contemporary Youth Dance
c/o Danuta Todryk
34 Culverhouse Gardens
Streatham   SW16
Tel 677 0568
Director Danuta Todryk
Formed in 1979 by Danuta Todryk, CYD has earned a reputation for highly polished performances. Classes are weekly and technically more demanding than most.

Greenwich Youth Dance
Eaglesfield Youth Centre
Red Lion Place
Shooters Hill   SE18
Tel 850 1155
Director Linda Bird

Linda Bird and theatre designer, Ray Slater, work with 10 to 19 year-olds on Saturday mornings developing their understanding of the theatrical aspects of dance. The dance work itself is largely non-technical. The students present an annual concert at Trident Hall Theatre in Greenwich.

Inner London Schools Dance Group
Strand Centre
Elm Park
Brixton   SW2
Tel 671 1300
Directors Jill Henderson and Veronica Jobbins
The ILSDG uses the professionally-equipped studio of Lambeth Institute's Strand Centre as its headquarters. Students are divided into two groups according to age (13 plus and 15 plus) and come from schools around Lambeth where Jill Henderson works as a dance tutor/animateur. The classes are weekly and 'by invitation only'.

Lambeth Youth Dance
Norwood Hall
38 Knight's Hill
West Norwood   SE27
Tel 670 5030
Director Bronwyn Williams
Bronwyn Williams' approach is non technical and she concentrates on the development of dance consciousness rather than training. Her own dance background in ballet (RAD intermediate) and Graham-based modern, is complemented by an MA in Theatre Studies from Leeds and two years experience with the Northern Black Light Theatre in York. Not surprisingly, her work with LYD makes the most of her theatre training. Two classes (one for 6 to 12 year-olds and one for over 13s) are held on Thursday nights. Participation is rewarded with the chance to perform.

DISABILITY

This chapter aims to inform you about what is going on in your area for people with disabilities. We've concentrated on organisations which give advice, support and information; on how to go about claiming benefits; on where to go to meet other people; and on how to get the practical help you may need.

Borough Advice Centres

These associations cover the borough in which they are based. They work with disabled and able bodied people in voluntary organisations and the statutory field who are concerned in the quality of life of disabled people. They provide guidance and information to individual disabled people and make sure the local authority is aware of the needs of disabled people when making decisions in such areas as services, facilities, planning, housing, transport and traffic control.

Greenwich

Greenwich Association of the Disabled
St Mary's Church
Greenlaw Street
Woolwich　　　　　　　　SE18
Tel 854 7289
Open 9.30-1 Mon 1-4.30 Wed
(answerphone at other times)
Wheelchair access good

Lambeth

Lambeth Association for the Disabled
91 Clapham High Street
Clapham　　　　　　　　SW4
Tel 720 0220 ext 500 (Mon-Thur)
Wheelchair access good

Lewisham

Lewisham Association for the Handicapped
Room 302
Eros House
Brownhill Road
Catford   SE6
Tel 698 6121 ext 49
Wheelchair access assisted

Merton

Merton Association for the Disabled
43 Heath Drive
Raynes Park   SW20
Tel 540 5188(9-12 Mon-Thur)
Wheelchair access none

Southwark

Southwark Disablement Association
Room 48
Aylesbury Day Centre
Boyson Road
Bradenham   SE17
Tel 701 1391
Wheelchair access good

Wandsworth

Wandsworth Disablement Association
c/o London Production Centre
Broomhill Road
Wandsworth   SW18
Tel 871 618
Wheelchair access ring beforehand

Other Advice Centres

The Advisory Centre for Education
18 Victoria Park Square
E2
Tel 980 4596

Information and advice on all aspects of education.

Breakthrough Trust
The Hall
Peyton Place
Greenwich   SE10
Tel 853 5661
Self-help group offering advice and information on all aspects of hearing impairment. They run communication courses and opportunities for volunteers, especially people who are themselves deaf. There is a working display of aids and equipment at the centre.

Disability Alliance Educational & Research Association
25 Denmark Street
WC2
Tel 240 0806
Researches and publishes reports on disability and publishes the Disability Rights Handbook, a guide to benefits and services for disabled people, price £2.40.

Disabled Living Foundation
380-384 Harrow Road
W9
Tel 289 6111
For information and advice on all those aspects of ordinary life which present particular problems to disabled people. There's information on aids, clothing, incontinence, physical recreation, visual handicap and music. They have a permanent exhibition of aids for disabled people and will advise on their use and where to get them. They also publish several useful pamphlets.

Disablement Advice Service (DIAL)
Tel 870 7437
Phone-in service for legal and general advice on disability. Will make referrals where necessary.

Greater London Association for
Disabled People (GLAD)
336 Brixton Road
Brixton   SW9
Tel 274 0107
Advice and information on all issues
relating to disabled people. Researches
and campaigns to improve conditions
and facilitites for disabled people and
publishes useful information on
disability. It is the umbrella
organisation for London disability
groups.

Lambeth Accord
336 Brixton Road
Brixton   SW9
Tel 274 2299
Wheelchair access yes
Group of disabled and able-bodied
people campaigning for better
provision for those with disabilities in
such areas as employment, education,
transport, housing and planning.

Network
16 Princeton Street
WC1
Tel 831 8031
Law and general advice for disabled
people and their families. You can
make an appointment to see a solicitor
or home visits can be arranged for
housebound people. Many queries are
also dealt with over the phone.

Royal Association for Disability &
Rehabilitation (RADAR)
25 Mortimer Street
W1
Tel 637 5400
Advice and information on all aspects
of disability. They have specialist staff
concerned in the following areas:
education, access, employment,
holidays, communication aids, general
welfare, benefits, housing and social
services. They produce many
publications relevant to disabled
people (you can get a publication list
from them). They are the umbrella
group for most national disability
organisations.

Benefits

Many of the organisations listed
above can help you with queries about
benefits and other welfare rights. The
Disability Alliance Educational and
Research Association (see Other
Advice Centres above) publishes the
Disability Rights Handbook which
costs £2.40, the Greater London
Association for Disabled People (see
Other Advice Centres above) has a
free leaflet on social security benefits,
and the GLC Welfare Rights Advice
Line will answer queries on claiming
benefits (dial 100 and ask for
freephone 2838 between 9-4.30
Monday to Friday). If you are an old
age pensioner there is useful
information on benefits in the Elderly
chapter. You will find your local
Social Security office by looking for
your borough below and then finding
the office which deals with your
postcode.

Greenwich

SE2 SE3 SE7 SE18 SE28
Crown Buildings
Woolwich New Road
Woolwich   SE18
Tel 854 2276

SE10 SE12
110 Norman Road
Greenwich   SE10
Tel 858 8070

SE9
40 Welling High Street
Welling
Tel 301 3322

SE9 SE12
62 Well Hall Road
Eltham   SE9
Tel 850 2102

Lambeth

SW2 SW9 SE24
246 Stockwell Road
Brixton
Tel 274 7777

SW9

SE5 SW4 SW9
6 Camberwell New Road
Kennington
Tel 582 4511

SE5

SE27 SW16
Crown House
Station Approach
Streatham
Tel 677 8122

SW16

Lewisham

SE19 SE20 SE25 SE26
9 Cargreen Road
Norwood
Tel 653 8822

SE25

SE10 SE12
110-112 Norman Road
Greenwich
Tel 858 8070

SE10

SE6 SE13 SE23
9-19 Rushey Green
Catford
Tel 698 6144

SE6

SE9 SE12
62 Well Hall Road
Eltham
Tel 850 2102

SE9

SE9
40 Welling High Street
Welling
Tel 301 3322

SE3 SE7 SE18
Crown Building
48 Woolwich New Road
Woolwich
Tel 854 2274

SE18

Merton

SW19 SW20
Ravensbury House
3 Palmerston Road
Wimbledon
Tel 543 6211

SW19

SW19 SW20
30-32 St George's Road
Wimbledon
Tel 947 6531

SW19

Southwark

SE1 SE16
Wedge House
32 Blackfriars Road
Blackfriars
Tel 928 4949

SE1

SE11 SE17
206-210 Kennington Park Road
Kennington
Tel 735 8747

SE11

SE5 SE15 SE21 SE22
1-15 Bournemouth Road
Peckham
Tel 639 2040

SE15

SE5 SE15
3 Blenheim Grove
Peckham
Tel 732 1091

SE15

Wandsworth

SW4 SW12 SW16 SW17
Irene House
218 Balham High Road
Balham   SW12
Tel 673 7722

SW8 SW11
40 Parkgate Road
Battersea   SW11
Tel 228 6454

SW15 SW18
Arndale House
Arndale Walk
Wandsworth   SW18
Tel 8701451/8

SW13 SW14
Parkshot House
Richmond
Tel 940 6011

SW13 SW14
3 Brook Street
Kingston-upon-Thames
Tel 549 1400

Invalidity Pension

Who Qualifies?
People who have been unable to work
for at least 28 weeks because of
disability or infirmity and who have
paid enough national insurance
contributions.

How Much?
£38.30 a week (single person)
£23 a week (spouse or other adult
dependant)
£8.05 a week (for each dependent
child)
●If you have not paid enough
national insurance contributions you
will receive less than the basic
pension in which case you will
probably qualify for Severe
Disablement Allowance or
Supplementary Benefit (see below).

●If the adult dependant is your wife
or a woman living with you as your
wife and looking after your children
then the rate for her will be reduced
proportionately if she earns more
than £45 a week.
●If the dependent adult is your
husband or any other adult the extra
rate will not be paid if that person
earns more than £23 a week.

How Do I Claim?
Ask for leaflet and application form
NI 16A from your Social Security
office (see above). Also get a
statement from your doctor saying
that you are incapable of work and
send them both to your local Social
Security office. You may be asked to
have a medical examination by a
DHSS doctor before you receive the
benefit.

Invalidity Allowance

Who Qualifies?
The same criteria apply as for
Invalidity Pension (see just above).
Invalidity Allowance and Invalidity
Pension are usually paid together
and make up what is called your total
Invalidity Benefit.

How Much?
£8.05 a week (if you were under 40
when you first became incapable of
work)
£5.10 a week(if you were between 40
and 50 when you first became
incapable of work)
£2.55 a week (if you were between 50
and 55 if you're a woman, or 50 and
60 if you're a man, when you first
became incapable of work)

How Do I Claim?
Fill in form NI 16A (it is the same
one as for Invalidity Pension) which
you will get from your local Social
Security office (see above) and return
it to them making sure you enclose
the letter from your doctor saying

you are incapable of work and have been so for the last 28 weeks.

Severe Disablement Allowance

Who Qualifies?
People who are incapable of work and have been so for 196 consecutive days. If you are aged 20 or over you must also be at least 75% disabled. You must be aged between 16 and 60 (if you're a woman) and 65 (if you're a man).

How Much?
£23 a week (single person)
£13.75 a week (wife or other dependent adult)
£8.05 a week (each dependent child)
●The extra rate for a dependent wife will be reduced proportionately if she earns more than £45 a week.
●The extra rate will not be paid if the adult dependant earns more than £13.75 a week.
●The extra rate for each dependent child will not be paid if your partner earns more than £85 a week.
●Whether you are entitled to Severe Disablement Allowance or not you may also be eligible for Supplementary Benefit (see below).

How Do I Claim?
Fill in form NI 252 which you will get from your local Social Security office (see above). Send it back to them together with a letter from your doctor saying you are incapable of work and have been so for at least the past 196 days.

Supplementary Benefit

Who Qualifies?
People who have less than £3000 in savings and a low income or none at all. If you are aged 16-19 and still at school you could receive supplementary benefit provided that you are unlikely to be able to find work because of your disability if you were not at school.

How Much?
This depends on your circumstances. You may be able to claim for additional expenses on top of your basic Supplementary Benefit:
●If you already receive mobility or attendance allowance (see below) you will automatically be eligible for a heating allowance of £5.45 a week.
●If you don't receive mobility or attendance allowance but your circumstances require you to spend more on heating you may be eligible for the higher rate of £5.45 or a lower rate of £2.20 a week.
●You may also be entitled to financial help with laundry, dietry or other weekly expenses (see How Do I Claim? just below).
●You may be entitled to Single Payments for certain one-off expenses. For instance if your disability means you wear out clothes or shoes faster than usual or incontinence means that bedlinen has to be bought more often than usual.

How Do I Claim?
Fill in form SB1 from your Social Security office (see above) and return it. If you feel you need extra financial help because of your disability then write to your Social Security office telling them what kind of assistance you require. Someone will then visit you at home to consider your claim.

Housing Benefit

Who Qualifies?
●If you have less than £3000 in savings and a low income or none at all and you are entitled to Supplementary Benefit then you

should get the full amount to cover your rent (or mortgage interest) and rates.

●If you are not entitled to Supplementary Benefit then you may still be able to get part of your rent (or mortgage interest) and rates paid.

●If you do not receive help with the full amount of your rent or mortgage interest payments and rates you may still be entitled to Housing Benefit Supplement.
(Benefit for private and council tenants comes from the local authority. Help for homeowners with mortgage interest payments comes from the DHSS).

How Much?
This depends on your circumstances.

How Do I Claim?
●If you are a council or private tenant on Supplementary Benefit your Social Security office should forward your application for Housing Benefit to the local authority housing benefit office.

●If you are a council or private tenant not entitled to Supplementary Benefit you should contact your local authority housing benefit office yourself (see Housing Benefit Offices below).

●If you are a homeowner your Social Security office should deal with your application for help with mortgage interest payments.

●You may be entitled to Housing Benefit Supplement as well because of your disability. Get the relevant form from your local Social Security office (see above). Fill in the form and send it to your local authority housing benefit office (see Housing Benefit Offices just below).

Housing Benefit Offices

Greenwich

Housing Benefit Section
Directorate of Housing
Peggy Middleton House
Woolwich New Road
Woolwich   SE18
Tel 854 8888
For council tenants only.

Housing Benefit Section
Borough Treasurer's Department
29-31 Wellington Street
Woolwich   SE18
Tel 854 8888
For private tenants only.

Lambeth

Housing Benefit Section
Directorate of Housing & Property Services
Hambrook House
Porden Road
Brixton   SW2
Tel 274 7722
For council tenants only.

Housing Benefit Section
Directorate of Finance
18 Brixton Hill
Brixton   SW2
Tel 274 7722
For private tenants only.

Lewisham

Housing Benefit Office
Cantilever House
Burnt Ash Road
Lee Green   SE12
Tel 852 4391
For council tenants only.

Town Hall
Housing Benefit Section
Catford Road
Catford   SE6
Tel 690 4343
For private tenants only.

Merton

Housing Department
Crown House
London Road
Morden   **Surrey**
Tel 543 2222
For council and private tenants

Southwark

Housing Department
38 Rye Lane
Peckham   SE15
Tel 693 4353
For council and private tenants

Wandsworth

Town Hall
Wandsworth High Street
Wandsworth   SW18
Tel 871 6000
For council and private tenants.

Attendance Allowance

Who Qualifies?
People who are severely disabled or
sick and have needed someone to look
after them byday and /or by night for
at least the last six months.

How Much?
£20.45 week if you need attention

either by day or by night.
£30.60 a week if you need attention
both day and night.
●This payment does not affect any
benefits based on national insurance
contributions that you may be
receiving.

How Do I Claim?
Fill in form NI 205 which you can get
from your Social Security office (see
above). Send it back to them and a
doctor will then examine you to see if
you are entitled to any financial
assistance.

Invalid Care Allowance

Who Qualifies?
If you receive an Attendance
Allowance (see just above) and live
with someone who looks after you for
at least 35 hours a week and
therefore cannot go out to work,
then that person may be eligible for
Invalid Care Allowance. But if you
are receiving at least £23 a week
from other benefits (not counting
Mobility Allowance – see below, or
Attendance Allowance – see above),
then your carer will not be eligible. A
married woman cannot usually get
the allowance, but she can claim
national insurance contributions in
order to protect her retirement
pension (see How Do I Claim? just
below).

How Much?
£23 a week

How Do I Claim?
Your carer should get form DS700
from the local Social Security office,
fill it in and send it back to them. A
married woman carer should ask the
Social Security office for the relevant
form to have her national insurance
contributions paid so that her
retirement pension is protected.

Mobility Allowance

Who Qualifies?
A person who is unable or virtually inable to walk and you became so before your 65th birthday. You must apply before your 66th birthday. The allowance is intended to help you get out and about.

How Much?
£21.40 a week.
●This is paid until you reach the age of 75.
●This allowance does not affect any other benefits based on national insurance contributions you may be receiving.

How Do I Claim?
Fill in form NI 211 which you will get from your Social Security office (see above). Send it back to the address on the form. A doctor may come to your home to examine you.

Social Services Departments

Greenwich

Nelson House
50 Wellington Street
Woolwich SE18
Tel 855 9711

Lambeth

Mary Seacole House
91 Clapham High Street
Clapham SW4
Tel 720 0220

Lewisham

Eros House
Brownhill Road
Catford SE6
Tel 698 6121

Merton

Crown House
London Road
Morden
Tel 543 2222

Southwark

Castle House
2 Walworth Road
Elephant & Castle SE1
Tel 703 6363

Wandsworth

Welbeck House
Wandsworth High Street
Wandsworth SW18
Tel 871 6060

Social Services Area Offices

Greenwich

If you're not sure which office deals with your area, then contact your borough social services department (see just above). In the case of an emergency outside normal office hours ring 854 0396.

Area Office 1
Greenwich Mini Town Hall
17-23 Woolwich Road
Woolwich SE10
Tel 858 3210

Area Office 2
Nelson House
50 Wellington Street
Woolwich SE18
Tel 855 9711

Area Office 3
Plumstead Mini Town Hall
256 Plumstead High Street
Plumstead SE18
Tel 855 9651

Area Office 4
Kidbrooke Mini Town Hall
1a Birdbrook Road
Kidbrooke   SE3
Tel 856 0011

Area Office 5
Eltham Mini Town Hall
Eltham High Street
Eltham   SE9
Tel 859 0031

Lambeth

If you're not sure which office deals
with your area contact your Social
Services department (see just above).
Out of office hours in case of an
emergency phone 274 7722.

Area Office 1
188-198 Kennington Lane
Kennington   SE11
Tel 735 7255

Area Office 2
44-46 Offley Road
Stockwell   SW9
Tel 735 7307/735 8277

Area Office 3
2 Herne Hill Road
Loughborough Junction   SE24
Tel 737 1441

Area Office 4
35 Clapham Park Road
Clapham   SW4
Tel 7205051

Area Office 5
86-88 Acre Lane
Brixton   SW2
Tel 737 1331

Area Office 6
240-250 Ferndale Road
Brixton   SW9
Tel 274 0671

Area Office 7
Bentley House
225 Streatham High Road

Streatham   SW16
Tel 677 2631

Area Office 8
38 Knights Hill
Norwood   SE27
Tel 761 1911

Lewisham

If you're not sure which office deals
with your area contact your Social
Services department (see above). In
an emergency out of office hours
phone 690 4343.

Northern District
St Paul's House
125 Deptford High Street
Deptford   SE8
Tel 692 1288

Southern District
Ballantyne
Lushington Road
Bellingham   SE6
Tel 698 9112

Eastern District
8-12 Eltham Road
Lee Green   SE12
Tel 852 4391

Western District
1-3 Ashby Road
Brockley   SE4
Tel 692 1288

Central District
1 Eros House
Brownhill Road
Catford   SE6
Tel 698 6121

South West District
Kingswear House
Dartmough Road
Forest Hill   SE23
Tel 699 0111

Merton

If you're not sure which office covers

your area contact your Social
Services department (see above).
Outside office hours in an emergency
phone 661 5000.

Wimbledon Area Office
42-44 Russell Road
Wimbledon   SW19
Tel 540 8791

Mitcham Area Office
Worsefold House
Chapel Orchard
Church Road
Mitcham   Surrey
Tel 640 1171

Morden Area Office
Gifford House
67c St Helier Avenue
Morden   Surrey
Tel 640 3431

Southwark

If you're not sure which office covers
your area contact your Social
Services department (see above). In
an emergency outside office hours
phone 703 6311.

Area Office 1
Municipal Offices
151 Walworth Road
Walworth   SE17
Tel 703 5464

Area Office 2
283 Tooley Street
Bermondsey   SE1
Tel 407 5344

Area Office 3
Lady Gomm House
58 Hawkstone Road
Rotherhithe   SE16
Tel 237 6644

Area Office 4
Kingsbury House
777 Old Kent Road
Peckham   SE15
Tel 732 8881

Area Office 5
4 Heaton Road
Peckham   SE15
Tel 639 7861

Area Office 6
47b East Dulwich Road
East Dulwich   SE22
Tel 693 3399

Area Office 7
Georgian House
64 Camberwell Church Street
Camberwell   SE5
Tel 701 4281

Area Office 8
27 Camberwell Road
Camberwell   SE5
Tel 703 0941

Wandsworth

If you're not sure which office covers
your area contact your Social
Services department (see above). In
an emergency outside normal office
hours phone 871 6000.

Balham Area Office
114 Balham High Road
Balham   SW12
Tel 871 7201

Battersea North Area Office
207 Lavender Hill
Battersea   SW11
Tel 871 6060

Battersea South Area Office
207 Lavender Hill
Battersea   SW11
Tel 871 7372/7373

Putney Area Office
125 Upper Richmond Road
Putney   SW15
Tel 871 6060

Tooting Area Office
234 Upper Tooting Road
Tooting   SW17
Tel 871 6060

Wandsworth Central Office
Welbeck House
Wandsworth High Street
Wandsworth   SW18
Tel 871 6060

Help in the Home

The amount of help in the home
available varies from borough to
borough, and so does the cost. (Many
of the services are free, however).
Below we give you an idea of the
kind of help which is offered if you
live at home. Mostly it is provided by
your Social Services department. To
find out where to contact Social
Services look under Social Services
Departments and Social Services
area offices (see above).

Home Helps

If you are finding difficulty in coping
with household tasks, contact your
local Social Services area office (see
above) to see if they can provide a
home help. This person will help with
shopping, cooking, cleaning and
other tasks around the home which
seem necessary.

Meals on Wheels

Meals can be brought to your home if
you are having difficulty doing your
own cooking. There is a small charge.
Contact your Social Services area
office (see above).

Aids & Adaptations

A variety of aids such as wheelchairs
and walking frames are available on
loan from the Social Services
department. Adaptations can also be
made to your home if necessary such
as handrails, ramps and stair lifts.
Financial assistance may be available
for large scale adaptations such as a
ground floor bathroom or specially
adapted kitchen. (For more
information on adaptations to your
home see Housing below). The
Disabled Living Foundation (see
Other Advice Centres above) has a
permanent display of aid and
equipment for people who are
disabled and produce information
sheets on topics such as wheelchairs,
transport and specialist aids. The
Royal National Institute for the
Blind (RNIB) (see National
Organisations below)displays and
sells special aids for blind and
partially sighted people.
Breakthrough Trust (see Societies &
Clubs below) displays and gives
advice on aids and equipment on all
aspects of hearing impairment.
RADAR (see Other Advice Centres
above) operate a mobile aids and
equipment centre which visits groups
and institutions at their request.

Laundry

You may be able to have your laundry collected, cleaned and delivered if you suffer from incontinence. Contact your doctor or Social Services area office (see above).

Bathing

Someone may be able to assist you in bathing if you find this difficult or impossible. Tell your doctor or contact your Social Services area office (see above).

Chiropody

There are chiropody clinics which offer a free service to physically and mentally handicapped people. Home visits can also be arranged for people who are housebound. Contact your doctor or disability association (see Advice Centres above) to find out more.

Hairdressing

Some boroughs offer a home hairdressing service. Contact your disability association (see Advice Centres above) for more details.

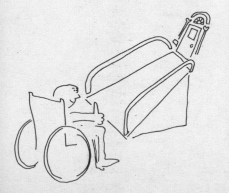

Volunteers

Your local disability association (see Advice Centres above) will be able to tell you if there are any volunteers who would be willing to do a job around the house or garden for you.

District Nurses

If you need frequent medical and nursing help tell your doctor and it can be arranged that a district nurse visits you regularly.

Health Visitor

If you have been ill and your doctor thinks it's a good idea that someone calls to check that you are all right, a health visitor will visit you at home.

Telephone

In certain circumstances, and depending on your income, you may be able to have a telephone installed free of charge and the quarterly rental paid. Contact your Social Services area office (see above). You will be responsible for paying for your own telephone calls, however.

Housing

Disabled Persons' Units

Your Social Services department runs council accommodation which has been either specially designed or adapted to suit the needs of disabled people. This kind of accommodation is available to those who are eligible for council housing. You should apply to your Social Services area office (see above) and an occupational therapist will visit you at your home to find out what your requirements are. It is only fair to say that there is a long waiting list for housing of this type.

Adaptations to your Home

Whether you are a council or private tenant or own your home it may be possible to have it adapted to your own special needs. The Centre on Environment for the Handicapped produces a guide for home owners called Buying or Adapting a House or Flat – A Consumer Guide for Disabled People. You can get a copy from them at 126 Albion Street NW1, price 50p. Rate rebates and improvement grants are available to people with disabilities who need to have their homes adapted. You can get further details from your Housing Department if you are a council tenant or Social Services area office if you are a private tenant or home owner.

Hostels

All boroughs run hostels for disabled people. They are usually for people of similar age and/or type of disability. Your Social Services area office will tell you more about the hostels in your borough.

Transport

On the whole public transport does not meet the needs of disabled people who are therefore reliant on 'special needs' transport schemes. Valuable though these schemes are, they are often over subscribed or do not operate at all times to suit the users. Getting your own car (if you can afford it) is not necessarily an answer. Even assuming that a disabled person can afford the necessary adaptations for a vehicle and pass the medical test – not to mention the driving test – the whole business is fraught with problems which never affect the abled-bodied person. This can be very discouraging. Below we list some schemes which won't make the transport problem go away but will alleviate it a little.

Dial-a-Ride

Schemes vary from borough to borough as far as times of operation and distances are concerned, but on the whole the charge is equivalent to fares on London Transport buses. To be eligible you should get a letter from your doctor or social worker saying that you are unable to use public transport for reasons of disability or infirmity.

Greenwich Dial-a-Ride
St Mary's Church
Greenlaw Street
Woolwich   SE18
Tel 854 9500

Lambeth Dial-a-Ride
245a Coldharbour Lane
Brixton   SW9
Tel 326 1052

Lewisham Dial-a-Ride
35 Brownhill Road
Catford   SE6
Tel 461 1169

Southwark Dial-a-Ride
Portakabin
42 Braganza Street
Walworth   SE17

Wandsworth Dial-a-Ride
1b Yukon Road
Balham   SW12
Tel 675 4046

Trains

British Rail runs a service which gives special consideration to disabled people. Trains from Victoria to Gatwick airport have carriage doors and gangways wide enough for wheelchair users. Victoria station has a separate waiting lounge for air passengers where wheelchairs are available on loan and trained staff are at hand to help. For more information contact British Rail.

Buses & Coaches

Community Transport
1b Yukon Road
Balham   SW12
Tel 675 3812
Hire of mini-buses for people with special needs including those with disability.

Fleet Systems Ltd
Unit 2
Aldington Road
Westminster Industrial Estate
Woolwich   SE18
Tel 854 1115
Tail-lift coaches able to accommodate up to ten wheelchair passengers are available for hire either on a self-drive basis or with a driver. A commercial rate is charged.

London Crusader Ltd
Western House
Argyll Street
237-239 Oxford Street
W1
Tel 437 4208
Arranges hire of converted National Bus Company vehicles. A commercial rate is charged.

Taxis

At the time of going to press the GLC taxi card system is still in operation.

To be eligible you must either be receiving mobility allowance (see Benefits above), or have a letter from your doctor saying your disability is long term and makes travel on public transport difficult, or be registered blind. You can get an application form from your post office. For a taxi fare up to £6 you pay £1 and 20p for each passenger. If the fare comes to more than £6 you pay the difference.

Driving

Anyone receiving mobility allowance (including parents of children receiving mobility allowance can apply to Motability which offers both a vehicle leasing scheme and hire purchase scheme to help disabled people buy or lease a car. Contact them at Boundary House 91-93 Charterhouse Street EC1. Driving lessons will cost you about £9.50 an hour. The following driving schools have specially adapted vehicles or you can use your own car if you have one. Within certain areas they will pick you up before the lesson and take you back afterwards.

British School of Motoring
Disability Training Centre
119 Broadway
Wimbledon   SW19
Tel 543 5554
Lessons cost £9.50-£9.75 weekdays and weekends.

British School of Motoring
Disability Training Centre
81 Hartfield Road
Wimbledon   SW18
Tel 540 8262
Lessons cost £9.50-£9.75 weekdays and weekends.

British School of Motoring
Disability Training Centre
212 Rye Lane
Peckham   SE18
Tel 639 5135

Lessons cost £9.50-£9.75 weekdays and weekends.

Wandsworth School of Motoring
7 West Hill
Wandsworth   SW18
Tel 874 9202
For people living in SW11 SW15 SW17 SW18 SW19. They do a pick up service within the borough of Wandsworth. Lessons cost £8.50 during weekdays and £9 for evenings and weekends.

Other Transport

If you have difficulty travelling and you want to go to a day centre, for instance, it should be possible for your Social Services area office (see above) to arrange transport for you. If you need to get to hospital for an appointment contact your doctor or the hospital to arrange for an ambulance to pick you up. There may be a voluntary transport organisation in your area. To find out contact your borough disablement association (see Advice Centres above).

Schooling

The 1981 Children's Act recommends that children with special needs should be educated in the same schools as other children. Putting this into practice has so far been slow however. The Fish Report called Equal Opportunities for All? published by the ILEA in July 1985 also recommends a policy of integration which if implemented would mean an end to all special schools in inner London. The Parents' Campaign for Integrated Education in London is setting up self-help groups all over the city which are working toward the integration of all children into mainstream schools. You can contact them at 25 Woodnock Road SW16 (Tel 677 9828). Children with special needs who are under five have a statutory right to a place in a nursery school and you should therefore have no difficulty in placing your child either in a state

nursery or voluntary nursery. The health authority also has a statutory obligation to inform the education authority so that a disabled child is properly assessed to see what kind of education will best suit his or her needs. The Advisory Centre for Education (ACE) has information on educational opportunities for children with disabilities of all ages. You will find them at 18 Victoria Park Square E2 (Tel 980 4596). You will find further useful information in the School chapter.

Employment

One of our researchers on this chapter suggested calling this section Unemployment – for obvious reasons. There is no doubt that disabled people are discriminated against when it comes to opportunities for employment. A few organisations are trying to change the situation. Disablement resettlement officers are based in jobcentres (see Local Services) to help disabled people to find jobs and training for employment. They can arrange special assistance such as adaptations to employers' premises, grants towards fares for those unable to use public transport, and aids and other equipment necessary to the job. Below we list some other organisations which aim to help disabled people find employment.

Opportunities for the Disabled
Central Electricity Generating Board
Bankside House
Room 129
Sumner Street
Bankside   SE1
Tel 261 2393
Runs an employment service for disabled people, taking care to match job-seeker with employer.

Pathway
336 Brixton Road
Brixton   SW9
Tel 737 7900
A scheme run by the Royal Society for Mentally Handicapped Children and Adults (MENCAP) which arranges for mentally handicapped people to work with companies for a trial period usually of three months.

It is hoped that after this time the employer will offer a permanent job. This office will assist people who live in the borough of Lambeth only.

Pathway
Care House
Biglands Street
E1
(See previous Pathway entry above). This office will assist people who live in part of the borough of Southwark only.

Pathway
Hill House
Church Lane
Tooting   SW17
Tel 767 5131
(See Pathway entry for Brixton above). This office will assist people

who live in the borough of Wandsworth only.

Societies & Clubs

Greenwich

Abbey Wood Club for the Disabled
Grovebury Hall
Grovebury Road
Abbey Wood   SE2
Tel 310 4432
Wheelchair access to centre via ramp, assistance given.
A club for elderly disabled people which meets every second Tuesday afternoon for tea, cakes, a chat and bingo. There are two outings a year and a Christmas party. Transport is available. Contact Mrs Thornby at 56 Godstow Road Abbey Wood SE2 or phone her at the above number.

Andy Capp Club
Shrewsbury House
Bushmore Crescent
Shooters Hill   SE18
Tel 858 7603
Wheelchair access throughout
Social club with outings and talks for disabled people aged 16-30. Transport is sometimes available. Contact Mr Wardale at 1 MacArthur Terrace Charlton Park Road Charlton Village SE7 or on the above number.

Arthritis Care Association
Central Baptist Church Hall
Sandy Hill Road
Woolwich   SE18
Tel 854 1752
Wheelchair access to centre
Social group for mostly elderly arthritis sufferers with trips to the seaside and entertainment.
Transport is available for Greenwich residents, others are asked to make a donation. Contact Mrs Paybody at 173 Villas Road SE18 or phone her on the above number.

Blind Bowling Club
Plumstead Indoor Bowling Green
Speranza Road
Plumstead   SE18
Tel 303 8325
Wheelchair access with special toilets.
Bowling for blind and visually
handicapped people of all ages.
Transport is available. Contact Mr
Huggett at 17 Birch Grove Welling
Kent or phone him on the above
number.

British Diabetic Association
Charlton House Community Centre
Charlton Village   SE7
Tel 855 5721
Wheelchair access with ramp and lift
available
All diabetics and their families are
welcome to come along for talks,
films and demonstrations, not
necessarily always on medical
subjects but also on topics of general
interest. At present there is no
transport available. Contact Mr
Bishop at Basement Flat 58
Woodland Terrace SE7 or on the
above telephone number.

Charlton Park Youth Club
Charlton Park School
Charlton Road
Charlton   SE7
Tel 856 1481
Wheelchair access throughout with
adapted toilets.
Games, music and social events for
young people aged 12 and over.
Transport is available. Contact Mr
Randall at 7 Allanswood Road SE9 or
phone him on the above number.

Charlton Swimming club
Charlton Park School
Charlton Road
Charlton   SE7
Tel 858 7501
Wheelchair access thoughout with
adapted toilets
Swimming for people with and
without disabilities aged 16 and over.
Transport may be available. Contact

Mrs Dibdin at 13 Priolo Road SE7 or
phone her on the above number.

Club 21
Greenwich & District Hospital
Vanbrugh Hill
Greenwich   SE10
Tel 852 8650
Wheelchair access to hospital
A social club with bingo and the
occasional evening out for physically
disabled people of any age. Transport
is available. Contact Mr Sexstone at
Flat C 2 Kidbrooke Park Road SE3 or
phone above number.

Disabled Drivers' Motor Club
c/o Mr Kemp
229 Minard Road
SE6
Tel 698 2210

Focus Gateway Club
Eltham Park Methodist Church
Westmount Road
Eltham   SE9
Tel 857 3183
Wheelchair access with assistance.
Social activities, rambling, sports,
crafts and holidays for mentally
handicapped people aged 16 and over.
Transport facilities may be available.
Contact Mr Simms at 150
Brownspring Drive SE9 or phone
him on the above number.

Gateway Compass Club
Glyndon Community Centre
Raglan Road
Plumstead   SE18
Tel 854 1572
Wheelchair access with assistance by
prior arangement.
Games, bingo, theatre and disco for
mentally handicapped people aged 16-
60. Transport is limited. Contact Mr
Hearnden at 42e Walmer Terrace
SE18.

**Good Companions Physically
Handicapped Club**
Pendrell Street Hall
The Slade Hall
Plumstead Common SE18
Tel 855 3261
Wheelchair access yes
Entertainment, outings, bingo and a
book exchange for physically
handicapped people of all ages.
Transport is available. Contact Ms
Britten at 24 Plum Lane SE18 or
phone her on the above number.

Greenwich Crack MS
Sandpit Centre
Charlton SE7
Tel 857 3524
Wheelchair access yes
Social and fundraising events for
people with multiple sclerosis.
Transport is available for members.
contact Mrs Culley 15 Beanshaw
Coldharbour Estate SE9 or phone her
on the above number.

**Greenwich Toy Library
Association**
17 Dowanhill Road
Catford SE6
Tel 697 1147
Supplies special toys and equipment
to disabled children.

Jewish Blind Society
Cavendish House
25-27 Dulwich Road
Herne Hill SE24
Tel 274 0563(Mon Thur)
Wheelchair access yes
Music, debate, bingo and lectures for
blind, partially sighted and
physically handicapped Jewish
people aged 50 and over. Transport is
available.

Lion Swimming club
Eltham Baths
Eltham Hill
Eltham SE9
Wheelchair access with ramp to pool
Swimming for disabled people of all
ages, occasional outings and a party

each year. No transport available at
the moment. Contact Mrs Wright at
10 Barry Avenue Bexley Heath Kent.

Mepsted Club for the Deaf
Sandpit Place
Erwood Road
Charlton SE7
Tel none
Wheelchair access check beforehand
Social events including regular
outings and bingo for deaf people
who use sign language. No transport
available. Contact Mr Smedley at 8
Eynsham Drive SE2.

MIND
(Greenwich Branch)
Ormiston Road Centre
54 Ormiston Road
Greenwich SE10
Tel 853 1735
Wheelchair access yes
Regular meetings for people who are
concerned with mental health.
Members include those who are
coming off tranquillisers and alcohol,
and people who suffer phobias.
Transport is not available.

Monday Club
Deptford Methodist Mission Hall
1 Creek Road
Deptford SE8
Tel 692 5599
Wheelchair access with assistance
Games, entertainment and outings
for mentally handicapped people aged
18-40. Transport is available. Contact
Rev Newell at the above address or
phone number.

The Multiple Sclerosis Society
(Greenwich Branch)
Day Centre
Greenwich District Hospital
Vanbrugh Hill
Greenwich SE10
Tel 852 2696
Wheelchair access to hospital
Social evenings and outings for
people with multiple sclerosis aged 20
years or more. Contact Mrs Martin

at 9 Parkgate SE3 or phone her on the above number.

National Eczema Society
(South East London Branch)
1 Dene Close
Hayes
Tel 462 4852
Wheelchair access check beforehand
The group meets at the homes of different members for help and advice sometimes from guest speakers. For people of all ages who have eczema. Transport is not available. Contact Mrs Brand 114 Inchberry Rd SE6.

Parkinson's Disease Society
(South East London Branch)
Shrewsbury House Community Centre
Bushmoor Crescent
Shooters Hill   SE18
Tel 854 3895
Wheelchair access via ramp with assistance available by prior arrangement
Social evenings and talks on medical and welfare issues of interest to people with Parkinson's disease. Limited transport is available. Contact Mrs French at 21 Cadwallon Road SE9 or phone her on 850 3305.

Plumstead Sports Club
Plumstead Sports Centre
Speranza Street
Plumstead   SE18
Tel 300 5242
Wheelchair access with ramps and special toilets
Table tennis, badminton, darts, cards and snooker (small table) for people with disabilities, mainly mental handicap. Transport is not available. Contact Mrs Oliver at 24 Willersley Avenue Sidcup Kent or phone her on the above number.

St James' Toc H Fellowship
St James' Church Hall
Kidbrooke Park Road
Kidbroke   SE3
Tel 852 8674
Wheelchair access throughout
Social evenings with entertainment, raffles, summer outings and the occasional bring and buy sale for people who are disabled and aged 60 or over. Transport is available. Contact Mrs Webb 35 Lyme Farm Road SE12 or phone her on the above number.

Sunshine Club for Disabled People
All Saints' Hall
Bercta Road
New Eltham   SE9
Tel 850 1347
Wheelchair access throughout with special toilets
Entertainment, games, fundraising and outings for disabled people of 16 and over. Transport is available. Contact Mrs Green at 50 Green Lane New Eltham SE9 or phone her on the above number.

Tideway Sculling Club for the Disabled
Tideway Sailing Centre
Riversway
Greenwich   SE10
Tel 858 3304
Wheelchair access throughout
Sailing instruction, leisure sailing and dinghy racing for all disabled people over 16 who are able to participate. Transport is not available. Contact Mr Valentine at 34 Dornberg Close SE3 or phone him on the above number.

Tuesday Club
Deptford Methodist Mission Hall
1 Creek Road
Deptford   SE3
Tel 692 5599
Wheelchair access with assistance
Entertainment and outings for

elderly people many of whom are disabled. Transport is available. Contact Rev Newell at the above address and telephone number.

Lambeth

The Association to Combat Huntington's Chorea
108 Battersea High Street
Battersea   SW11
Tel 223 7000
Fundraising and campaigning to further research and understanding of Huntington's Chorea.

Dickinson Dart Club
Clarence Avenue Day Centre
Clapham   SW4
Tel 674 1801
Wheelchair access with assistance and prior notice
Darts for people with disabilities aged 16 and over. Transport is not available. Contact Mrs Blewett at the above address or telephone number.

Disabled People Club
Havil Hall
Havil Street
Camberwell   SE5
Tel 771 2559
Wheelchair access throughout
Social events including outings, bingo, cards and fundraising for people with disabilities no matter what age. Transport is available. Contact Mrs Seaton at 2 Summit Way SE19 or phone her on the above number.

Down's Children's Association
(South London Group)
Tel 764 2698
Support group for parents of Down's syndrome children with talks on related topics held at members' houses. Parents provide transport. Contact Mrs Phillips on the above number.

Lambeth Sickle Cell Information Centre
Sickle Cell Centre
Swan Mews
2 Stockwell Road
Stockwell   SW9
Tel 737 3588
Counselling, advice and information, including lectures, video and slides. Transport is not available. Contact Mrs McTair at the above address and phone number.

Multiple Sclerosis Society
(Lambeth Branch)
Clapham Rehabilitation Centre
Clapham Road
Stockwell   SW9
Tel 671 8283
Wheelchair access throughout
Social events including outings for people with multiple sclerosis. Transport is available. Contact Mrs Davies at 43 Wavertree Road Streatham Hill SW2

Norwood Rehabilitation Centre Sports Club
(For sports activities held in Lambeth see under Southwark below)

Owls Junior Gateway Club
Santley Junior Mixed School
Santley Road
Brixton   SW2
Tel 733 8468
Wheelchair access yes
Trampolining, table tennis and other

indoor sports, painting and music for mentally handicapped children and young people aged 5-18. Transport is available. Contact Mr Lester at 37 Rupert Gardens Loughborough Road SW9 or phone him on the above number.

Phoenix Air Rifle Club
Goodrich Road School
Goodrich Road
East Dulwich SE22
Tel 701 1391
Wheelchair access throughout
Contact Mrs Marshall
Rifle and pistol shooting (weapons are supplied) for people with physical handicap. There is no transport available.

Somerleyton Gateway Club
Brixton Social Education Centre
2 Somerleyton Road
Brixton SW9
Tel 733 3248
Wheelchair access yes
Keep fit, sports and social activities for mentally handicapped people over the age of 16. Transport may be available. Contact Mrs Demmery at the above address and phone number.

St Bede's Social & Sports Club for Deaf People
St Bede's Centre
412 Clapham Road
Clapham North SW9
Tel 622 4969
Sports and social activities for profoundly deaf people aged over 16. Transport is not available. Contact Mrs Mothersole at the above address and phone number.

St Mary's (Handicapped) Club
Friendship House
200 Wandsworth Road
Stockwell SW8
Tel 674 6817
Wheelchair access to ground floor
Football, music and indoor sports including snooker, table tennis and skittles. Transport is available.

Contact Mr Fitzgerald at Holy Trinity Church of England School Upper Tulse Hill SW2 or phone him on the above number.

Windmill Gateway Club
Windmill School
Mandrell Road
Brixton SW2
Tel 767 3617
Wheelchair access throughout, some special toilets
Sports and social activities for mentally handicapped young people aged 14-21. Transport may be possible. Contact Miss Innes on 735 9081

Lewisham

Albion Club
Naborhood Centre
44a Sydenham Road
Sydenham SE26
Tel 692 3338 (after 4)
Wheelchair access yes
Talks, demonstrations, drinks in a pub and meals out for women with disabilities aged 30-55. Transport is available. Contact Mrs Steven at 44 Geoffrey Road Brockley SE4 or phone her on the above number.

Arthritis Care
c/o Mrs Flack
121b Grierson Road
SE23
Tel 690 4343 ext 50

Charlton Park Youth Club
Charlton Park School
Cemetery Lane
Charlton SE7
Tel 856 1481
Wheelchair access throughout with adapted toilets
Games, music and social events for disabled and able bodied young people aged over 13. Transport is not available. Contact Mr Randall at 7 Allenswood Road SE9 or phone him on the above number.

Companions Darby & Joan Club for the Deaf
Kane Hall
Carholme Road
Catford   SE6
Tel 699 0803
Wheelchair access by prior
arrangement, assistance needed.
Outings, bingo, parties and general
communication for profoundly deaf
elderly people. Transport is available.
Contact Mrs Viner 108 Standon Park
SE23 or phone her on the above
number.

Crescent Club
Naborhood Centre
44a Sydenham Road
Sydenham   SE26
Tel 778 3810
Wheelchair access with ramp and
assistance and special toilets
Outings to the coast, entertainment,
bingo, theatre and shopping trips for
disabled people aged 30 and over.
Transport is available. Contact Mrs
Crouch at 6 Madeline Road Anerley
SE20 or phone her on the above
number.

Deaf & Hard of Hearing Team
Eros House (Room 415)
Brownhill Rd
Catford   SE6
Tel 698 6121 ext 179
Advice and information for deaf and
hard of hearing people. Part of the
Social Services department.

Disabled Drivers' Association
(South London Group)
Ladywell Centre
148 Dressington Avenue
Lewisham   SE13
Tel 291 4061
Wheelchair access throughout with
special toilets
Disabled motorists aim to improve
conditions for drivers like
themselves. Transport is available
only in extreme circumstances.

Disabled Drivers' Motor Club
229 Minard Road
Catford   SE6
Tel 698 2210
Discussion over lunch by disabled
motorists of ways to improve driving
conditions for disabled people.
Transport is not available. Contact
Mr Kemp at the above address and
phone number.

Leegrove Gateway Club
St Augustine's Church Hall
Baring Road
Grove Park   SE12
Tel 854 5491(after 5)
Wheelchair access yes
Social activities for mentally
handicapped people aged over 16.
Transport is available for Lewisham
residents. Contact Mrs Gibbons at 6
Wickham Street Welling Kent or
phone her on the above number.

The Lewisham Group Haemophilia Society
c/o Mr Week
147 Wellmeadow Rd
Catford   SE6
Tel 698 4500

Lewisham Seals' Disabled Swimming Club
Downham Baths
Moorside Road
Downham
Bromley
Tel 639 3654
Wheelchair access throughout with
special toilets
Swimming for all disabled people.
Transport is available. Contact Mr
Richardson of 34 Wellington Close
SE14 or phone him on the above
number.

The Multiple Sclerosis Society
(Lewisham Branch)
Saville Centre
Lewisham High Street
Lewisham   SE13
Tel 857 1793
Wheelchair access via ramp

Social activities including outings
and fundraising events by people who
have multiple sclerosis. Transport is
available. Contact Mrs Maclean of 30
Le May Avenue Grove Park SE12 or
phone her on the above number.

National Eczema Society
(South East London Branch)
c/o 2 Wellmer Down Road
Catford   SE6
Tel none
Support meetings for Eczema
sufferers, including guest speakers.
Members meet at each other's houses.
Transport is not available. Contact
Mr Terry at the above address and
phone number.

Penny Farthing Club
c/o 29 Chalcroft Road
Hither Green   SE13
Tel 318 2922
Wheelchair access yes
Social evenings for physically
handicapped people aged 16 and over.
Transport is available for Lewisham
residents. Contact Mr Dyer at the
above address or telephone number.

Yates Phab Club
Ladywell Centre for the Handicapped
148 Dressington Avenue
Brockley   SE4
Tel 690 0528(day)
Wheelchair access throughout with
special toilets
Social activities including outings
for disabled people aged 18-30.
Transport is available. Contact Mr
Osborne at Towerview 17 Rushey
Mead Brockley SE4.

The Visual Handicap Team
Eros House (Room 310)
Brownhill Rd
Catford   SE6
Tel 698 6121
Provides help and information to
blind and partially sighted people.
Part of the Social Services
department.

Merton

Amandus Club
Atkinson Morley's Hospital
Copse Hill
Wimbledon   SW20
Tel 946 7711 ext 133
Wheelchair access throughout with
special toilets
Re-cycling Christmas cards, social
evenings, outings for disabled people
of all ages and their families and
friends. Transport can be arranged.
Contact Mrs Drayson at the above
address and phone umber.

**British Limbless Ex-Servicemen's
Association**
(Sutton, Merton & District Branch)
Eastway Day Centre
Eastway
Lower Morden
Tel 648 5169
Wheelchair access throughout with
special toilets
General welfare of ex-servicemen
who have lost limbs or eyes and ex-
servicemen's widows. Transport is
not available. Contact Mr Davies at
14 Rhodes Moorhouse Court Morden
Surrey or phone him on the above
number.

Community Club for the Blind
Kenneth Black Memorial Hall
Worple Road
Wimbledon   SW19
Tel 540 7077/641 3199
Wheelchair access yes
Social afternoons for mostly elderly
blind people. Transport can be
arranged in some cases. Contact Mrs
Clark at 24 Braeside SW19 or phone
her at the above numbers.

**Happy Family Social Club for the
Disabled**
St John's Ambulance Hall
122-124 Kingston Road
Merton   SW19
Tel 07373 55211
Wheelchair access yes

Entertainment and outings for mentally and physically disabled people and their families. Transport is available. Contact Mrs Sullivan at 1 Merland Rise Epsom Downs Epsom Surrey or phone her on the above number.

Merton Action for Epilepsy Group
Wimbledon Community Centre
St George's Road
Wimbledon SW19
Tel 654 4459(after 7)
Wheelchair access none
Social activities, talks and fundraising by people who have epilepsy. Transport is not available at present. Contact Mrs Evans-Patel, 30 Ashburton Road Croydon or phone her on the above number.

Merton Sports & Social Club for the Blind
c/o 13 Marlborough Rd
SW19
Tel none
Social activities and sports including tandem riding, bowls, darts and canoeing for blind and partially sighted people. The club meets at various places. Transport is available for Merton residents. Contact Mrs Cushing at the above address.

Mostyn Club
Small Hall
St Mary's Merton Church Hall
Church Path
Merton Park SW19
Tel 542 3041
Games, raffles, talks and social activities for physically handicapped people, though not people who are blind. Transport is available. Contact Mrs Blake at 24 Mostyn Road, Merton Park, SW19 or phone her on the above number.

Multiple Sclerosis
(Wandsworth Branch)
Atheldene Day Centre
Garratt Lane
Wandsworth SW18
Tel 946 9898
Wheelchair access throughout with special toilets
Social evenings with occasional outings for people with multiple sclerosis. Transport is available. Contact Mrs Swinstead at 1 Rutland Lodge, Clifton Road, SW19 or phone her on the above number.

Parkinson's Disease Society
(South West London Branch)
St Marks Church Hall
Compton Road
Wimbledon SW19
Tel 946 1072
Wheelchair access none
Social events including outings, talks and fundraising for people with Parkinson's disease. Transport is available for Mitcham residents. Contact Miss Hardy, 4 Cambridge Court, Cambridge Road, SW20 or phone her on the above number.

PHAB Club
All Saints' Centre
All Saints' Road
Wimbledon SW19
Tel 648 8237
Wheelchair access throughout with special toilets
Youth club for physically handicapped and able bodied people.

Thursday Gateway Club
Sidney Black Hall
Durnsford Road
Wimbledon SW19
Tel 540 6506(after 5)
Wheelchair access via side gate
Disco, craft, table tennis and snooker
for mentally handicapped people aged
14 and over. Transport can be
arranged. Contact Mrs Martin at 5
Cherry Close, Morden, Surrey or
phone her on the above number.

Vamp Club
All Saints' Centre
All Saints' Road
Colliers Wood SW19
Tel 648 0361
Wheelchair access throughout with
special toilets
Outings to pubs, theatres,
restaurants and the coast for disabled
people aged 16-40. Limited transport
is available. Contact Miss Osborn at
92 Wandle Road, Morden, Surrey or
phone her on the above number.

Southwark

The Association for Stammerers
c/o 86 Blackfriars Road
SE1
Tel none
Support group for people who
stammer.

**The Handicapped Fellowship
(Catholic)**
(Southwark Branch)
c/o 5 Woolstone Road
SE23
Tel 699 6924
Campaigns for a better deal for
handicapped children and adults.
Also runs a home for handicapped
children.

Havil Hall Club
Havil Street
Peckham SE15
Tel 701 4537
Wheelchair access yes

Social evenings and games for
mentally ill people most of whom are
aged over 25.

Lary's Club
Munro Clinic
Guy's Hospital
London Bridge SE1
Tel 407 7600 ext 3323
Wheelchair access none to clinic
Contact Miss Hale
Social events including outings for
laryngectomees. There is limited
transport available.

LAB
14 Verney Road
Rotherhythe SE16
Tel 851 1840
Wheelchair access with assistance
Social and sporting activities
including cricket and darts for blind
and other disabled people. Transport
is not available. Contact Mr Simmons
at 248 Mottingham Road, SE9 or
phone him on the above number.

**Norwood Rehabilitation Centre
Sports Club**
1 Parkhall Road
West Dulwich SE21
Tel 761 1235
Wheelchair access yes
Contact Mr Melville
Keep fit, table tennis, football,
swimming, shooting, indoor and
outdoor bowls and weight training
for disabled people aged 16 and over.
These sports are also held at Flaxham
Sports Centre and Clapham
Rehabilitation Centre. Outdoor
bowls are held at Clapham Common
bowls green. Limited transport is
available.

Parkinson's Disease Society
(Southwark Branch)
Baptist Church Hall
Half Moon Lane
Herne Hill SE21
Tel 761 5610
Wheelchair access yes
Social activities, advice and support

for people with Parkinson's disease.
Transport is available. Contact Mrs
Durrent at 24 Kennolds, Croxted
Road Estate, Croxted Road, SE21 or
phone her on the above number.

Rainbow Club
(National Deaf/Blind Helpers
League)
Centre for the Blind
Tooley Street
Southwark   SE1
Tel 698 0105
Wheelchair access via ramp and
special toilets
Afternoon tea, parties and an annual
outing for deaf and blind people and
those who have difficulties in
communication. Transport is not
available. Contact Mrs Pilcher at 12
Dagonet Gardens, Downham, Kent
or phone her on the above number.

**Saturday Club for Mentally &
Physically Handicapped People**
Grove Hall
Dulwich United Reformed Church
East Dulwich Grove (entrance in Tell
Grove)
East Dulwich   SE22
Tel 693 6020
Wheelchair access to ground floor
only
Social afternoon for disabled people
of all ages. Transport is limited.
Contact Mrs Perle at 175 Friern
Road, SE22 or phone her on the
above number.

Southwark London Spastic Group
Aylesbury Day Centre
Boyson Road
Walworth   SE17
Tel 237 5133
Wheelchair access throughout with
special toilets
Games, crafts, films and other
entertainments for spastic children
and young people over 11. Transport
is available. Contact Mrs Eyles at 1
William Evans House, Bush Road,
SE8.

**Southwark Penguins'
Swimming Club**
Rotherhithe Swimming Baths
Lower Road
Rotherhithe   SE16
Tel 701 7616
Wheelchair access yes
Swimming for disabled people of all
ages. Transport is available for
Southwark residents. Contact Mr
Thoms at Southwark Disablement
Association, Room 48, Aylesbury Day
Centre, Boyson Road, SE17 or phone
him on the above number.

Southwark Phoenix
Southwark Institute
Goodrich Road
East Dulwich   SE22
Tel 701 1391(day) 639 8029(eve)
Wheelchair access throughout
Badminton, darts, snooker, table
tennis, rifle and pistol shooting and
unihoc (indoor hockey) and basketry
for disabled people aged over 18.
Transport available. Contact Mrs
Marshall at 1 Rosenthorpe Road,
SE15.

**Southwark Sports & Leisure
Activities for the Disabled**
Flaxman Sports Centre
Carew Street
Camberwell   SE5
Tel 701 7616
Wheelchair access via ramp with
special toilets
Indoor archery (with outdoor
archery at Dulwich Hamlet School
July-Sept) for disabled people aged 18
and over. Transport available.
Contact Mr Thoms at Southwark
Disablement Association, Aylesbury
Day Centre, Boyson Road,
Bradenham, SE17 or phone him on
the above number.

**Southwark Sports & Leisure
Activities for the Disabled**
Peckham Rye Park
Peckham   SE15
Tel 701 7616
Wheelchair access throughout

Bowls for disabled people aged 18 and over. Contact Mr Thoms at Southwark Disablement Association, Aylesbury Day Centre, Boyson Road, Bradenham, SE17 or phone him on the above number.

Southwark Wheelchair Dancing Group
Aylesbury Day Centre
Boyson Road
Walworth   **SE17**
Tel 904 6451
Wheelchair access throughout with special toilets
Dancing for people in wheelchairs (pushers are provided). Transport is available. Contact Mrs Hough at 12 Alverstone Road, Wembley Park, Middlesex or phone her on the above number.

Wandsworth

Arndale Junior Phab Club
Courthouse Community Centre
11 Garratt Lane
Wandsworth   **SW18**
Tel 874 1095
Wheelchair access to ground floor
Youth club with pool, table tennis, art and outings for physically disabled people aged 4-16. Transport is not available. Contact Ms Buchanan at 272 Rye Hill Park, SE15 or phone her on the above number.

Arthritis Care
211 High Rd
Balham   **SW12**
Tel 648 7407
Contact Bella Spears
Wheelchair access with assistance
Transport available. For the over-35s.

Balham Gateway Club
St Mary's School Hall
Balham Park Road
Balham   **SW12**
Tel 08832 2791(eve)
Wheelchair access with assistance
Social activities, games and occasional Saturday outings for

mentally handicapped people aged 17 and over. Transport is not available. Contact Ms George at 153 Westhall Road, Warlingham, Surrey or phone her on the above number.

Battersea Gateway Club
Battersea Central Mission
14 York Road
Clapham Junction   **SW11**
Tel 228 6756
Wheelchair access yes
Open 7.30-9.30 Fri
Table tennis, snooker, disco, art and crafts for mentally handicapped people aged 18 and over. Transport is available. Contact Mr Hunt at 83 Cricklade Avenue, SW2 or phone him on the above number.

Breakthrough Trust
(Wandsworth Branch)
Rockall Centre
Eland Road
Battersea   **SW11**
Tel 223 5738
Wheelchair access and special toilets
Advice and social activities for deaf and hearing impaired people aged 18 or over. Transport is not available. contact Mr Robinson, 113 Taybridge Road, SW11 or phone him on the above number.

British Epilepsy Association
Southfields Day Centre
Gwynn Road
Battersea   **SW11**
Tel 677 2920
Wheelchair access with assistance
Contact Mrs Matthews
Transport available, meets 2nd & 4th Friday of the month.

British Polio Fellowship
(South West London Branch)
Rockall Day Centre
Eland Road
Battersea   **SW11**
Tel 876 4141
Wheelchair access yes
Social evenings including outings and advice and support for people

disabled by polio. Home and hospital visits are arranged for members who are sick.

Cancerlink
South East London Branch
Tel 659 4101
Contact Valerie Hinds
Information centre with traind nurses. Also sets up local support groups.

Centre for Cued Speech
68 Upper Richmond Road
Putney SW15
Tel 870 5335
Advises schools, clinics and other organisations on language tools for deaf people.

Cheyne Holiday Club for Handicapped Children
Tel 352 8434
Outings, shopping, barbecues, sports and indoor activities including games and discos for physically handicapped people aged 7-16, and sometimes older. Limited transport is available. Contact Miss Singleton at 61 Cheyne Walk, Chelsea, SW3 or phone her on the above number.

Coach Inn Club
Atheldene Centre
Garratt Lane
Merton SW19
Tel 622 1771
Wheelchair access yes
Social activities including discos and theatre trips for disabled people' aged 16-50.'Transport is available but fully booked. Contact Ms Jones at 101 Edgeley Road, SW4 or phone her on the above number.

Contact a Family
170 Garratt Lane
Wandsworth SW18
Tel 870 9282
Wheelchair access yes
Family outings, playschemes, parents' coffee mornings and SIBS

(group for brothers and sisters) for disabled people aged 0-19 and their families. Meetings are held at various venues. Transport is available. Also promotes the formation of other self-help groups for families with children with disabilities. Contact Mr Szlenkier at the above address and phone number.

Dragon Laryngectomee Club
The Board Room
Grosvenor Wing
St George's Hospital
Blackshaw Road
Tooting SW17
Tel 0932 240364
Wheelchair access yes
Self-help group of laryngectomees including social activities and support. Transport is available. Write to Mr Jones at 6 Trafalgar Drive, Walton on Thames, Surrey or phone him on the above number.

Friends of Imperial Cancer Research
9 Sutherland Grove
Wandsworth SW18
Tel 788 6239

Lady Allen Adventure Playground
Chivalry Road
Wandsworth Common SW11
Tel 228 0278
Wheelchair access yes
Adventure play, cooking, arts and crafts for disabled children aged 3 and over. Transport may be provided in exceptional circumstances. Contact the playleaders at the above address and phone number.

Multiple Sclerosis Society
(South West London Branch)
Atheldene Day Centre
Garratt Lane
Wandsworth SW18
Tel 946 9898
Wheelchair access yes
Social evenings which include food and entertainment and also occasional outings for people with

MS. Transport is available. Contact Mrs Swinstead at 1 Rutland Lodge, Clifton Road, SW19 or phone her on the above number.

Muscular Dystrophy Group
(Streatham & Norbury Branch)
84 Kilmartin Avenue
Streatham SW16
Tel 388 7331 ext 201
Various fundraising events by people with muscular dystrophy to further research into the illness. Transport is not available. Contact Mrs See at 11 Grieve Close, Tongham, Farnham, Surrey or phone her on the above number.

Roehampton Leisure club
Minstead Gardens Club
Danebury Avenue
Roehampton SW15
Tel 894 5088
Social occasion with games, refreshments, entertainment and slide shows for people with physical disabilities. Transport is available. Contact Mrs Crook at 8 First Cross Road Twickenham Green Twickenham or phone her on the above number.

South West London Psoriasis Group
23 Bexhill Road
East Sheen SW14
Tel 876 2634
Wheelchair access check beforehand
Support and social activities, and fundraising by psoriasis sufferers for further research into the illness. Transport is available in special circumstances. Contact Mr Burman at the above address and telephone number.

Voluntary Organisations Communication & Language (VOCAL)
South Western Hospital
Landor Road
Stockwell SW9
Tel 274 4029

An alliance of over 20 organisations concerned in improving public awareness of the problems of people who have to learn to speak again after illness or injury.

Wandsworth Epilepsy Club
Southlands Day Centre
Gwynne Road
Battersea SW11
Tel 677 2920
Wheelchair access with assistance
Social club with refreshments available and also welfare advice for epilepsy sufferers. Transport is available for Wandsworth residents. Contact Mrs Matthews at 2 Shenstone House, Aldrington Road, SW16 or phone her on the above number.

Wandsworth Leisure Club for the Physically Disabled
Club Room
Henry Prices Estate
Garratt Lane
Wandsworth SW18
Tel 878 3172
Social club for people with disabilities.

Sport

The British Sports Association for the Disabled
(South East London Branch)
2 Rutherglen Road
Abbey Wood SE2
Tel 311 5545
Organises and gives information on sports activities for disabled people in Greenwich, Lambeth, Lewisham and Southwark.

The British Sports Association for the Disabled
(South West London Branch)
11 Byegrove Road
Colliers Wood SW19
Tel 540 9238

Organises and gives information on sports activities for disabled people in Wandsworth and Merton.

Arts & Entertainment

Artsline
5 Crowndale Road
NW1
Tel 388 2227/8
Line open 10-4(Mon-Fri) 10-2 Sat
Advice and information for disabled people on arts and entertainment in London. They will tell you which theatres, cinemas and museums have wheelchair access, hearing aid systems and so on. They provide useful information leaflets if you send a large stamped addressed envelope.

Shape
9 Fitzroy Square
W1
Tel 388 9622
Creates arts activities and events for people who are mentally or physically disabled. Much of the work takes place in the form of weekly sessions in hospitals, day centres and other institutions. Activities involve drama, music, art, writing and dance.

Holidays

Your local council and voluntary organisations run holidays for disabled people. In some cases financial assistance may be available. To find out more contact your disability association (see Advice Centres above) or for council-run holiday schemes only contact your Social Services department (see Local Services). RADAR (see Other Advice Centres above) produces a directory called Holidays for Disabled People

1986 which costs £2 and is available from them or W H Smith. RADAR also publishes Holidays and Travel Abroad 1986 which you can also send for, price £1. GLAD (see Other Advice Centres above) have a free information leaflet on holidays for disabled people. Holiday Care Service, 2 Old Bank Chambers,Station Road, Horley, Surrey (Tel 02934 74535) also gives advice and information about holidays for disabled people.

Sexual Counselling

The Association to Aid the Sexual & Personal Relationships of the Disabled (SPOD)
286 Camden Road
N7
Tel 607 8851/2
Provides information and advice on all matters of sex and personal relationships. The service is for disabled people and professionals such as therapists and counsellors. Also aims to increase public awareness of the sexual needs and difficulties of disabled people. They run workshops on sexuality and disability for disabled people and those in the caring professions. You can get a list of their publications and fact sheets (many of which are free to people with disabilities).

National Organisations

Active
c/o Play Matters
68 Church Way
NW1
Tel 387 9592
Publishes worksheets for children's play, leisure and communication aid.

Alzheimer's Disease Society
Third Floor
Bank Buildings
SW6
Tel 381 3177

Arthritis Care
6 Grosvenor Crescent
SW1
Tel 235 0902

The Association for all Speech Impaired Children (AFASIC)
347 Central Markets
EC1
Tel 236 3632/6487

The Association for Research into Restricted Growth
24 Pinchfield
Maple Cross
Rickmansworth
Hertfordshire
Tel none

The Association for Spina Bifida & Hydrocephalus (ASBAH)
2 Upper Woburn Place
WC1
Tel 388 1382

The Association of Parents of Vaccine Damaged Children
2 Church Street
Shipton on Stour
Warwick
Tel 0608 61595

The Association to Combat Huntington's Chorea
34a Station Road
Hinckley
Leicestershire
Tel 0455 615558

Back Pain Association
31-33 Park Road
Teddington
Middlesex
Tel 977 5474

Break
20 Hooks Hill Road
Sherringham
Norfolk
Tel 0263 823170
Runs short stay and emergency holiday centres for children.

The British Diabetic Association
10 Queen Anne Street
W1
Tel 323 1531

The British Dyslexia Association
Church Lane
Peppard
Oxfordshire

The British Association for the Hard of Hearing
7-11 Armstrong Road
W3

The British Limbless Ex-Servicemen's Association
Frankland Moore House
185-187 High Road
Chadwell Heath
Romford
Essex
Tel 590 1124

The British Polio Fellowship
Bell Close
West End Road
Ruislip
Middlesex
Tel 71 75515

The British Tinnitus Association
c/o Royal National Institute for the Deaf
105 Gower Street
WC1
Tel 387 8033

The Brittle Bone Society
112 City Road
Dundee
Scotland
Tel 0382 67603

Buckets & Spades Charitable Trust
Lancaster Road
Hollington street
St Leonard's on Sea
Sussex
Tel 0424 52119
Short term care for mentally
handicapped children.

Cancerlink
46a Pentonville Road
N1
Tel 833 2451

Chest Heart & Stroke Association
Tavistock House North
Tavistock Square
WC1
Tel 387 3012

**Cheyne Society for Spastic
Children**
63 Cheyne Walk
SW3
Tel 352 8434

Cystic Fibrosis Research Trust
Alexander House
5 Blythe Road
Bromley
Kent
Tel 464 7211

Down's Children's Association
4 Oxford Street
W1
Tel 580 0511/2

Headway
National Head Injuries Association
200 Hansfield Road
Nottingham
Tel 0602 622382

**The Hyperactive Children's
Support Group**
59 Meadowside
Angmering
West Sussex
Tel 0243 551313/0903 725182

**The Masectomy Association of
Great Britain**
26 Harrison Street
WC1
Tel 837 0908

**The Multiple Sclerosis Society of
Great Britain**
286 Munster Road
SW6
Tel 381 4022

**The National Association for the
Deaf, Blind & Rubella
Handicapped**
311 Gray's Inn Road
WC1
Tel 278 1000

**The National Association for the
Relief of Paget's Disease**
413 Middleton Road
Middleton
Manchester
Tel 061 643 1998

**The National Association for the
Welfare of Children in Hospital**
Argyle house
29-31 Euston Road
NW1
Tel 833 2041

**The National Deaf Children's
Association**
45 Hereford Road
W2
Tel 229 9272/4

**The National Fund for Research
into Crippling Diseases**
Vincent House
North Parade
Horsham
West Sussex
Tel 0403 64101

The Parkinson's Disease Society
36 Portland Place
W1
Tel 323 1174

The Partially Sighted Society
Queen's Road
Doncaster
South Yorkshire
Tel 0302 68998

The Phobic Trust
The Grove
Coulsden
Surrey
Tel 660 0332

The Psoriasis Association
7 Milton Street
Northampton
Tel 0604 711129

Reach
The Association for Children with
Artificial Arms
85 Newlands Road
Billericay
Essex
Tel none

The Renal Society
64 South Hill Park
NW3
Tel 793 9479

**The Royal Society for Mentally
Handicapped Children & Adults
(MENCAP)**
123 Golden Lane
EC1
Tel 253 9433

The Spastics Society
2 Park Crescent
W1
Tel 636 5020

The Spinal Injuries Association
76 St James' Hill
N10
Tel none

St Dunstan's
(For men & women blinded in war
service)
PO Box 4XB
12-14 Harcourt Street
W1
Tel 723 5021

**The Voluntary Council for
Handicapped Children**
8 Wakely Street
EC1
Tel 278 9441

National Library for the Blind
Cromwell Road
Bredbury
Stockport
Cheshire
Tel 061 494 0217

**The National Society for Cancer
Relief**
Michael Sobell House
30 Dorset Square
NW1
Tel 402 8125

**The Royal Association in Aid of
the Deaf & Dumb**
27 Old Oak Road
W3
Tel 743 6187

**The Royal National Institute for
the Blind**
224 Great Portland Street
W1
Tel 388 1266

**The Royal National Institute for
the Deaf**
105 Gower Street
NW1
Tel 387 8033

6

ELDERLY

We have concentrated a lot on the financial side of life in this chapter. Many elderly people have to live on a basic pension which means that every penny counts. If you find after reading the chapter that you are entitled to benefits, however small, that you did not know you were entitled to, then we feel this chapter has served a useful purpose. It is divided into the following sections: Advice Centres, Pensioners' Organisations and Social Services departments and area offices under the borough they are in. Then comes the longest section on finance called Benefits in which you will find your Social Security office and then information on retirement pensions, supplementary pensions, housing benefit and various other allowances, grants, pensions and benefits you may be able to claim including financial help to meet heating bills. Information on help in the home, housing, transport, social life and health round off the chapter. You may find the Disability chapter also has information of interest to you.

Advice Centres

There are so many advice centres you could go to in South London that we have decided to confine the list below to centres which specialise in giving free advice and information to pensioners. Even if you want information on a specific legal point, for instance, the organisations below can help you by referring you to specialists if necessary. Age Concern, which has branches throughout South London, offers advice and information on a wide variety of subjects of particular concern to pensioners – welfare rights, heating, housing, help in the home, health – in fact all of the subjects covered in this chapter. They also publish information pamphlets on several topics. Ask them for a list of their titles to see which ones interest you. Some are free, others you will have to pay for. But often they will have a copy which you can read at their offices. They are in touch with other pensioners' organisations and they will refer you to them if necessary. They usually have lists of lunch clubs, social clubs and community centres which have facilities for elderly people. Many Age Concern offices will arrange for volunteers to visit your home, perhaps to do a job around the house, or just for company. Some run foster-a-grandparent schemes. They also run what are called 'pop-in parlours', which are clubs for pensioners.

Greenwich

Age Concern
1-3 Love Lane
Woolwich   SE18
Tel 854 6079
Open 10-1 2-4(Mon-Tue Thur-Fri)
Line open 9-5(Mon-Tue Thur-Fri)

Pensioners' Link
(formerly Task Force)
Old Town Hall
Polytechnic Street
Woolwich   SE18
Tel 854 2835
Open 10-1.30(Mon-Tue Thur-Fri)
Offer information and advice to pensioners, will put you in touch with pensioners' action groups in your area. (These are groups which campaign on issues that affect pensioners). Also arrange social events, especially at Christmas.

Lambeth

Age Concern
1-5 Acre Lane
Brixton   SW2
Tel 274 7722 ext 2009
Open 10-12 1-3(Mon-Tue Thur-Fri)
Line open 9-4.30(Mon-Fri)

Age Concern
Streatham Consumer Advice Centre
85-87 Streatham High Road
Streatham   SW16
Tel 737 3311 ext 36/37
Open 10-12.30(Tue Thur)

Asian Community Action Group
322 Brixton Road
Brixton   SW9
Tel 733 7494
Information and advice for Asian pensioners. The place is also a drop-in and runs a video club.

Caribbean-Hindu Society
16 Ostade Road
Brixton   SW2
Tel 674 0755
Advice and information service for West Indian and Hindu pensioners.

West Indian Senior Citizens' Association
105-109 Railton Road
Brixton   SE24
Tel 737 3505
Advice and information for West Indian pensioners.

Lewisham

Age Concern
20 Brownhill Road
Catford   SE6
Tel 690 4343
Open 9-5(Mon-Fri)

Pensioners' Link
74 Deptford High Street
Deptford   SE8
Tel 691 0938

Merton

Age Concern
326 London Road
Mitcham
Tel 648 5792

Asian Elderly Group of Merton
c/o Mr Ahmed
1A Bookham Court
Phipps Bridge Road
Mitcham
Tel 640 1914
Social activities for Asian pensioners.

Wimbledon Guild of Social Welfare
Guild House
30-32 Worple Road
Wimbledon   SW19
Tel 946 0735/2261
Offers practical help to pensioners.

Southwark

Age Concern
Head Office
33 Peckham Road
Peckham   SE5
Tel 703 6105
Open 10-4(Mon Wed Fri) 10-1(Tue Thur) Line open 9.30-5(Mon-Fri)

Age Concern
Bermondsey Health Centre
108 Grange Road
Bermondsey   SE1
Tel 231 2286/7
Open 9.30-12.30(Mon-Fri)

Age Concern
3 The Parade
Felbridge House
Dog Kennel Hill
East Dulwich   SE22
Tel 274 8097
Open 10.30-2.30(Mon-Fri)

Age Concern Bus
Contact Age Concern head office (see above) for times and areas the bus will service.

Age in Mind
3 The Parade
Felbridge House
Dog Kennel Hill
East Dulwich   SE22
Tel 274 8097
Practical and emotional support for pensioners.

Bermondsey Elderly Support Team
188 Jamaica Road
Bermondsey   SE16
Tel 231 2286/7
Offers advice and home visits to

pensioners in the Bermondsey area.

Wandsworth

Age Concern
229 Garratt Lane
Wandsworth   SW18
Tel 870 0325
Open 10-1 2-4(Mon-Fri)

Pensioner's Link
(formerly Task Force)
170 Garratt Lane
Wandsworth   SW18
Tel 870 7171
Provides support and advice for pensioners, including legal information. A team of volunteers does tasks for pensioners which the state doesn't provide, such as gardening and decorating.

Tooting Action for Pensioners
101 Tooting High Street
Tooting   SW17
Tel 947 0858
Open 1.30-3.30 Fri
Advice service. They also campaign for pensioners' rights.

Pensioners' Organisations

Greenwich

The Cultural Centre
Bath Way
Woolwich   SE18
Tel 855 7191 (for information only)
Keep fit, craft and other activities for ethnic minority pensioners. Also advice and counselling.

Pensioners' Centre
23 Wellington Street
Woolwich   SE18
Tel 854 0212

A pop-in parlour with various activities for pensioners.

Pensioners' Employment Bureau
(above Pensioners' Centre)
23 Wellington Street
Woolwich   SE18
Tel 854 0212
Seeks to provide employment for pensioners. They also run advice sessions on Monday and Thursday mornings.

Lambeth

Abeng Centre
7 Gresham Road
Brixton   SW9
Tel 737 1628
A drop-in centre for Afro-Caribbean pensioners. Social activities include guest speakers, keep-fit and outings.

Al-Hilal Organisation
25 Brailsford Road
Brixton   SW2
Tel not known
Asian pensioners can drop in for advice and a chat. There's also a video club.

Asian Community Action Group
322a Brixton Road
Brixton   SW9
Tel 733 7494
Drop in for Asian pensioners. The Group promotes projects according to the needs of Asian pensioners. (See also Advice Centres above).

Caine Hall Family Centre
Tyers Street
Vauxhall   SE11
Tel 582 2618
Leisure activities for pensioners such as craft and leatherwork, outings and holidays. Meals are served.

Caribbean-Hindu Society
16 Ostade Road
Brixton   SW2
Tel 674 0755

Drop-in centre with video club and library. (See also Advice Centres above).

Centre 70 Community Association
138 Christchurch Road
Tulse Hill   SW2
Tel 674 6671
Social activities for pensioners.

Clapham Community Project
St Anne's Hall
Venn Street
Clapham   SW4
Tel 720 8731
Bingo, keep-fit and a drop-in. Guest speakers, video and a choir.

Day Centre for Asian Senior Citizens
87 Streatham High Road
Streatham   SW16
A drop-in during the afternoons for Asian pensioners.

Help 71
95 Acre Lane
Brixton   SW2
Tel 274 3339
Drop-in for pensioners.

West Indian Senior Citizens' Association
105-109 Railton Road
Brixton   SE24
Tel 737 3505
A drop-in for West Indian pensioners. Activities include craft, cookery, guest speakers, outings and keep-fit. (See also Advice Centres above).

Lewisham

Pensioners' Link Heating Project
The Albany Centre
Douglas Way
Deptford   SE8
Tel 691 6099
Aims to improve heating facilities for elderly people in Lewisham. They will advise on how to budget, and will negotiate with fuel boards and act at tribunals on behalf of pensioners.

Merton

Merton & Morden Guild of Social Service
Guild House
30-32 Worple Road
Wimbledon   SW19
Tel 946 0735
Arranges coffee mornings, outings,
weekend breaks and monthly film
shows. Can also provide transport,
hairdressing at home and help for
housebound people.

Southwark

Camberwell Pensioners' Action Group
33 Sunbourne Court
Denmark Hill
Camberwell   SE5
Tel None
Campaigns for pensioners' rights.

The Civil Service Retirement Fellowship
(South London Branch)
109a Woodvale
Forest Hill   SE23
Tel 693 6347
Publishes a newsletter twice a year
and arranges coffee mornings, outings
and other activities for retired civil
servants. Contact Mr Heming at the
above address and phone number for
information on the meetings held
near you.

Dulwich Pensioners' Action Group
7 Lyall Avenue
Dulwich   SE21
Tel none
Group of pensioners campaigning for
pensioners' rights.

North Southwark Pensioners' Action Group
Borough Community Centre
56 Southwark Bridge Road
Borough   SE1
Tel 928 6476
Campaigning group for pensioners'
rights.

Southwark Pensioners' Action Group
Walworth Project Offices
186 Crampton Street
Walworth   SE17
Tel 701 8955
Campaigns for pensioners' rights.

Wandsworth

Balham Senior Citizens' Association
Russell Hall
Byrne Road
Balham   SW17
Tel none
Keep-fit, bingo and other activities for
elderly people.

Battersea Action Group
Garfield Community Centre
Garfield Road
Battersea   SW11
Tel 223 8220
A campaigning group concerned with
quality of life of pensioners.

Furzedown Project
93 Moyser Road
Streatham   SW16
Tel 677 4283
Offers company, support and welfare

advice to pensioners. You can just drop in for a chat, or you can join one of the courses they run. If you are housebound and want someone to visit you, they can arrange for that too. Outings are organised using the Project's own minibus.

Social Services Departments

Greenwich

Nelson House
50 Wellington Street
Woolwich   SE18
Tel 855 9711

Lambeth

Mary Seacole House
91 Clapham High Street
Clapham   SW4
Tel 720 0220

Lewisham

Eros House
Brownhill Road
Catford   SE6
Tel 698 6121

Merton

Crown House
London Road
Morden
Tel 543 2222

Southwark

Castle House
2 Walworth Road
Elephant & Castle   SE1
Tel 703 6363

Wandsworth

Welbeck House
Wandsworth High Street
Wandsworth   SW18
Tel 871 6060

Social Services Area Offices

Greenwich

If you're not sure which office deals with your area, then contact your borough social services department (see just above). In the case of an emergency outside normal office hours ring 854 0396.

Area Office 1
Greenwich Mini Town Hall
17-23 Woolwich Road
Woolwich   SE10
Tel 858 3210

Area Office 2
Nelson House
50 Wellington Street
Woolwich   SE18
Tel 855 9711

Area Office 3
Plumstead Mini Town Hall
256 Plumstead High Street
Plumstead   SE18
Tel 855 9651

Area Office 4
Kidbrooke Mini Town Hall
1A Birdbrook Road
Kidbrooke   SE3
Tel 856 0011

Area Office 5
Eltham Mini Town Hall
Eltham High Street
Eltham   SE9
Tel 859 0031

Lambeth

During normal office hours phone the appropriate area office (see below). If you're not sure which area you come under contact your borough social services department (see just above). Out of office hours, in case of an emergency, phone 274 7722.

Area Office 1
188-198 Kennington Lane
Kennington   SE11
Tel 735 7255

Area Office 2
44-46 Offley Road
Stockwell   SW9
Tel 735 7307/735 8277

Area Office 3
2 Herne Hill Road
Loughborough Junction   SE24
Tel 737 1441

Area Office 4
35 Clapham Park Road
Clapham   SW4
Tel 720 5051

Area Office 5
86-88 Acre Lane
Brixton   SW2
Tel 737 1331

Area Office 6
240-250 Ferndale Road
Brixton   SW9
Tel 274 0671

Area Office 7
Bentley House
225 Streatham High Road
Streatham   SW16
Tel 677 2631

Area Office 8
38 Knights Hill
Norwood   SE27
Tel 761 1911

Lewisham

To find out which area office you should deal with contact your borough social services department (see just above). In an emergency out of office hours phone 690 4343.

Northern District
St Paul's House
125 Deptford High Street
Deptford   SE8
Tel 692 1288

Southern District
Ballantyne
Lushington Road
Bellingham   SE6
Tel 698 9112

Eastern District
8-12 Eltham Road
Lee Green   SE12
Tel 852 4391

Western District
1-3 Ashby Road
Brockley   SE4
Tel 692 1288

Central District
1 Eros House
Brownhill Road
Catford   SE6
Tel 698 6121

South West District
Kingswear House
Dartmouth Road
Forest Hill   SE23
Tel 699 0111

Merton

If you're not sure which area office you come under contact your borough social services department (see above). In an emergency outside office hours phone 661 5000.

Mitcham Area Office
Worsefold House
Chapel Orchard
Church Road
Mitcham
Tel 640 1171

Morden Area Office
Gifford House
67c St Helier Avenue
Morden
Tel 640 3431

Wimbledon Area Office
42-44 Russell Road
Wimbledon   SW19
Tel 540 8791

Southwark

To find out which office deals with
your area contact your borough social
services department (see above). In an
emergency outside office hours phone
703 6311.

Area Office 1
Municipal Offices
151 Walworth Road
Walworth   · SE17
Tel 703 5464

Area Office 2
283 Tooley Street
Bermondsey   SE1
Tel 407 5344

Area Office 3
Lady Gomm House
58 Hawkstone Road
Rotherhithe   SE16
Tel 237 6644

Area Office 4
Kingsbury House
777 Old Kent Road
Peckham   SE15
Tel 732 8881

Area Office 5
4 Heaton Road
Peckham   SE15
Tel 639 7861

Area Office 6
47B East Dulwich Road
East Dulwich   SE22
Tel 693 3399

Area Office 7
Georgian House
64 Camberwell Church Street
Camberwell   SE5
Tel 701 4281

Area Office 8
27 Camberwell Road
Camberwell   SE5
Tel 703 0941

Wandsworth

If you're not sure which office deals
with your area, then contact your
borough social services department
(see above). In an emergency outside
office hours phone 871 6000.

Balham Area Office
114 Balham High Road
Balham   SW12
Tel 871 7201

Battersea North Area Office
207 Lavender Hill
Battersea   SW11
Tel 871 6060

Battersea South Area Office
207 Lavender Hill
Battersea   SW11
Tel 871 7372/7373

Putney Area Office
125 Upper Richmond Road
Putney   SW15
Tel 871 6060

Tooting Area Office
234 Upper Tooting Road
Tooting   SW17
Tel 871 6060

Wandsworth Central
Welbeck House
Wandsworth High Street
Wandsworth   SW18
Tel 871 6060

Benefits

If you have problems with claiming benefits your local Age Concern (see Advice Centres above) will be able to advise you. The GLC runs a free welfare rights telephone line: dial 100 and ask for Freephone 2838.

Social Security Offices

Social Security offices are where your pensions and allowances are worked out. Finding out which Social Security office covers your area can be a complicated procedure because a few areas cross over borough and postcode boundaries. Despite this the most reliable way is to look for your borough below and then find out which office deals with your postcode. If you're still unsure contact the one that's nearest to you, tell them exactly where you live and you might find you've struck lucky and this is the office you want. If not, they will be able to tell you. Most offices deal with retirement and supplementary benefit. Where offices deal only with retirement or supplementary pensions, we explain below which are the two offices dealing with pensions for your area.

Greenwich

SE2 SE3 SE7 SE18 SE28
Crown Buildings
Woolwich New Road
Woolwich   SE18
Tel 854 2276

SE10 SE12
110 Norman Road
Greenwich   SE10
Tel 858 8070

SE9
40 Welling High Street
Welling
Tel 301 3322

Deals with supplementary pensions only. For retirement pensions contact Well Hall Road (see below)

SE9 SE12
62 Well Hall Road
Eltham   SE9
Tel 850 2102
Deals with retirement pensions. For supplementary pensions contact Welling High Street (see above) if you live in SE9 and Norman Road (see above) if you live in SE12.

Lambeth

SW2 SW9 SE24
246 Stockwell Road
Brixton   SW9
Tel 274 7777

SE5 SW4 SW9
6 Camberwell New Road
Kennington   SE5
Tel 582 4511
Deals with supplementary pensions only. For retirement pensions go to the Stockwell Road office (see above) if you live in SW9, to Blenheim Grove (see below) if you live in SE5, to Irene House (see under Wandsworth below) if you live in SW4.

SE27 SW16
Crown House
Station Approach
Streatham   SW16
Tel 677 8122

Lewisham

SE19 SE20 SE25 SE26
9 Cargreen Road
Norwood   SE25
Tel 653 8822

SE10 SE12
110-114 Norman Road
Greenwich   SE10
Tel 858 8070

SE6 SE13 SE23
9-19 Rushey Green
Rushey Green
Catford   SE6
Tel 698 6144

SE9 SE12
62 Well Hall Road
Eltham   SE9
Tel 850 2102
Deals with retirement pensions only.
For supplementary pensions go to
Welling High Street (see below) if you
live in SE9 and Norman Road (see
above) if you live in SE12.

SE9
40 Welling High Street
Welling
Tel 301 3322
Deals with supplementary pensions
only. For retirement pensions contact
Well Hall Road (see above).

SE3 SE7 SE18
Woolwich Crown Building
48 Woolwich New Road
Woolwich   SE18
Tel 854 2274

Merton

SW19 SW20
Ravensbury House
3 Palmerston Road
Wimbledon   SW19
Tel 543 6211
For retirement pensions only. For
supplementary pensions contact St
George's Road (see below).

SW19 SW20
30-32 St George's Road
Wimbledon   SW19
Tel 947 6531
For supplementary pensions only. For
retirement pensions contact
Ravensbury House (see above).

Southwark

SE1 SE16

Wedge House
32 Blackfriars Road
Blackfriars   SE1
Tel 928 4949

SE11 SE17
206-210 Kennington Park Road
Kennington   SE11
Tel 735 8747

SE5 SE15 SE21 SE22
1-15 Bournemouth Road
Peckham   SE15
Tel 639 2040

SE5 SE15
3 Blenheim Grove
Peckham   SE15
Tel 732 1091
For supplementary pension only. For
retirement pension contact
Bournemouth Road.

Wandsworth

SW4 SW12 SW16 SW17
Irene House
218 Balham High Road
Balham   SW12
Tel 673 7722

SW8 SW11
40 Parkgate Road
Battersea   SW11
Tel 228 6454

SW15 SW18
Arndale House
Arndale Walk
Wandsworth   SW18
Tel 870 1451/8

SW13 SW14
Parkshot House
Parkshot
Richmond
Tel 940 6011
For retirement pension only. For
supplementary pension contact Brook
Street (see below).

SW13 SW14
3 Brook Street
Kingston-on-Thames
Tel 549 1400
For supplementary pension only. For retirement pension contact Parkshot House (see above).

Retirement Pension

Who Qualifies?
Women of 60 and men of 65 who are retired and have paid enough national insurance contributions.

How Much?
£38.30 (single person)
£23 (wife on husband's contributions)
£61.30 (married couple)
●If you have not paid enough national insurance contributions, you will receive less than the basic pension, in which case you probably qualify for supplementary pension (see Supplementary Pension below).
●If you are over 80 you will receive an extra 25p a week on your basic pension.
●If you chose to carry on working and claim your retirement pension, you can earn up to £75 per week (after deducting fares and other expenses) without affecting your pension.
●If you earn £75-£79 per week you will lose 5p from your pension for every 10p that you earn over £75.
●If you earn more than £79 per week, everything you earn above that figure will be taken out of your pension.
●If you are a married woman under 60 and earning more than £45 per week, your husband could lose some of his pension.

How Do I Claim?
You should receive a form from the Department of Health and Social Security (DHSS) four months before your 60th (for a woman) 65th (for a man) birthday. If you don't, then write to your local Social Security office (see above under your borough).

Supplementary Pension

Who Qualifies?
Women over 60 and men over 65 who have savings of less than £3000 and a low income. Men between 60 and 65 if you have stopped signing on as unemployed.

How Much?
£37.50 (single person)
£60 (married couple)
This pension is intended to 'supplement' your income and the amount you get will bring your total income to the basic rate shown above.
Certain amounts can be added to this depending on your age, health and other circumstances:
●If you or your spouse are over 80 you will get 25p a week added to your supplementary pension (50p if you are both over 80).
●If you or your spouse are blind you will get an extra £1.25 a week added to your supplementary pension (£2.50 if you are both blind).
●If you have a serious illness such as tuberculosis, ulcer or diabetes which is being treated by drugs and means you require a special diet, then you

can claim an allowance of £3.70 a week.

●If you have some other major illness which requires a special diet, then you can claim an allowance of £1.60 a week.

How Do I Claim?

Ask for form SB1 from your P O or local Social Security office (see above under your borough). Fill it in and send it back to the Social Security office. You will then be given an appointment or someone will visit you at home to consider your claim.

It is a good idea to find out whether you are receiving retirement pension or supplementary pension or a combination of the two. (To check how your supplementary pension has been worked out, write to your local Social Security office for form A124 which will give you a break down). If your pension includes supplementary pension, even the smallest amount, then you are entitled to claim extra benefits which are listed below.

●Free dental treatment
●Free prescriptions
●Help with National Health glasses
●Travelling expenses to and from hospital for treatment
●Single payments for certain necessities (see Single Payments below).

Housing Benefit

Who Qualifies?

If you have less than £3000 in savings and a low income and you are entitled to supplementary pension, then you should get the full amount from your borough council to cover your rent and rates. If you own your home the Social Security office should include water rates and mortgage interest payments in your pension.

●If you are not entitled to supplementary pension but are on the borderline, you may be able to get housing benefit supplement to top up your housing benefit.

●If you have savings of more than £3000 or your income is higher, you may still be able to get housing benefit for part of your rent and rates.

Housing benefit, like supplementary benefit, (see above) entitles you to claim for single payments for certain necessities (see Single Payments below and Heating – Single Payments). If you live in a residential home and your savings are less than £3000 and you have a low income, you should apply to your local Social Security office (see above). If you live in a residential home and your saving are more than £3000 or your income is high, you can still claim housing benefit from the borough council. The owners of the home will tell you how much your rent and rates come to. Council tenants get housing benefit by a reduction in the amount of rent and rates they have to pay. Private and housing association tenants get housing benefit in the form of an actual payment from the council. Home owners get housing benefit in the form of a reduction in the rates to be paid. A home owner will get mortgage interest paid from supplementary pension, not housing benefit.

How Much?

This depends on your individual circumstances.

How Do I Claim?

●If you receive supplementary pension or you are a borderline case your Social Security office will give you a form to fill in which you should send to your housing benefit office (see below).

●If your savings come to more than £3000 or your income is higher, you should apply direct to your borough council (see below).

Housing Benefit Offices

Greenwich

Housing Benefit Section
Directorate of Housing
Peggy Middleton House
Woolwich New Road
Woolwich SE18
Tel 854 8888
For council tenants only.

Housing Benefit Section
Borough Treasurer's
29-31 Wellington Street
Woolwich SE18
Tel 854 8888
For private tenants only.

Lambeth

Housing Benefit Section
Directorate of Housing & Property
Services
Hambrook House
Porden Road
Brixton Hill
Brixton SW2
Tel 274 7722
For council tenants only.

Housing Benefit Section
Directorate of Finance
18 Brixton Hill
Brixton SW2
Tel 274 7722
For private tenants only.

Lewisham

Housing Benefit Office
Cantilever House
Burnt Ash Road
Lee Green SE12
Tel 852 4391
For council tenants only.

Town Hall
Catford Road
Catford SE6
Tel 690 4343
For private tenants only.

Merton

Housing Department
Crown House
London Road
Morden
Tel 543 2222
For council and private tenants.

Southwark

Housing Department
38 Rye Lane
Peckham SE15
Tel 693 4353
For council and private tenants.

Wandsworth

Wandsworth Town Hll
Wandsworth High Street
Wandsworth SW18
Tel 871 6000
For council and private housing.

Single Payments

Who Qualifies?
If you have savings of less than £500
you can claim one-off payments for
expenses such as funeral costs,
bedding, furniture, removal costs,
re-connecting and disconnecting gas
and electricity, and materials for
decorating your house if you own it.
(See also Heating – Single Payments
below).

How Much?
This depends on the individual
circumstances.

How Do I Claim?
Write to your local Social Security
office (see above). Do not buy the
item or have work carried out until
you get the go-ahead from the Social
Security office, or you may end up
having to pay for it all yourself.

Attendance Allowance

Who Qualifies?
You can get an attendance allowance if you are severely disabled or sick and have needed someone to look after you by day and/or by night for the last six months at least.

How Much?
£20.45 if you need attention either by day or by night.
£30.60 if you need attention both day and night.

How Do I Claim?
Get form DS2 from your local Social Security office (see above). When you have filled it in send it back to them and a doctor will then come to your home to examine you. You will be told by letter whether you qualify.

Invalid Care Allowance

Who Qualifies?
If you receive an attendance allowance (see above) and live with someone who cannot work because they are looking after you for at least 35 hours a week, then they may be eligible for invalid care allowance.

But if you are already receiving at least that amount from other benefits (not counting attendance allowance or mobility allowance – see below), then your carer will not be eligible. A married woman cannot usually get the allowance, but she can claim national insurance contributions to protect her retirement pension (see How Do I Claim? below).

How Much?
£23 a week.

How Do I Claim?
Your carer should get form DS700 from the local Social Security office, fill it in and send it back to them. A married woman carer wishing to have her national insurance contributions paid should ask for the relevant form to fill in from her local Social Security office.

Mobility Allowance

Who Qualifies?
If you are unable to walk or almost unable to walk and you became so before your 65th birthday (for men and woman), then you should qualify for this allowance which is intended to help you get around out of doors.

How Much?
£21.40 a week.

How Do I Claim?
Fill in form NI211 which you can get from your local Social Security office (see above). You must claim it before your 65th birthday, and provided you still qualify you should go on receiving it until you are 75.

Invalidity Benefit

Who Qualifies?
If you have reached 60 (for a woman) or 65 (for a man) and you have been receiving invalidity benefit and are still unfit for work, you have the choice of either staying on invalidity benefit or transferring to retirement pension if you are entitled to one (see Retirement Pension above).

How Much?
Retirement pension comes to more than invalidity benefit, but it is taxable. So if you do not pay tax you will be better off transferring to retirement pension. But if the tax you would pay on a retirement pension is greater than the increased income a retirement pension would give you, then you would be better off staying on invalidity benefit.

How Do I Claim?
If you decide that you wish to transfer to retirement pension, and you have not heard from your local Social Security office within four months of your 60th (for a woman) 65th (for a man) birthday, then write to them explaining your situation. (See also Retirement Pension above).

Over 80s Pension

Who Qualifies?
A person over 80 who does not qualify for a retirement pension or who has a pension less than £23 (single person and married man) or £13.75 (married woman).

How Much?
£23 (single person and married man) £13.75 (married woman)
You will receive the above amounts if you have no retirement pension at all. If you already get a retirement pension of less than this amount, the over 80s pension will top it up to this amount.

How Do I Claim?
Contact your local Social Security office and ask for a form to fill in.

Death Grant

Who Qualifies?
A person whose spouse has died and who has enough national insurance contributions, or whose spouse paid enough contributions.

How Much?
The amount you get is based on your own or your spouse's national insurance contributions, your age and your sex. The maximum amounts are shown here.
None (men born before 5 Jul 1883)
None (women born before 5 Jul 1888)
£15 (men born after 5 Jul 1883 but before 5 Jul 1893)
£15 (women born after 5 Jul 1888 but before 5 Jul 1898)
£30 (men and women born after these dates)
If you are on supplementary pension (see Supplementary Pension above), you may get other help with the cost of the funeral.

How Do I Claim?
Call in at your local Social Security office (see above) with the death certificate (which you will get from the registrar) and a written estimate of the cost of the funeral.
Alternatively write to your local social security office, enclosing the appropriate documents. If you are on supplementary pension and want extra help with the cost, contact your local Social Security office before you arrange the funeral to see if you qualify.

Christmas Bonus

Who Qualifies?
Nearly all pensioners.

How Much?
£10

How Do I Claim?
You should receive this automatically, but if you have not by the end of December ask at your local Social Security office (see above).

Income Tax

Who Qualifies?
If you are over 65 (men and women), there are special tax rates which give you a higher level of tax free income than people under 65.

How Much?
Your annual income can reach the following levels before you are taxed: £2690 (for a single person) £4255 (for a married man).
Taxable income is based on the following: retirement pension, pension from your old job, any earning you make, interest from savings (except National Savings) and investments.

How Do I Claim?
Contact your local advice centre (see Advice Centres above).

Heating

If you are on supplementary pension, you may be able to get help with heating your home on one of more of the following grounds:

Health
● You can claim a sum of £2.20 a week for heating if you find it. difficult to move about or you have bronchitis, rheumatism or some other chronic illness.
● You can claim a heating allowance of £5.45 if you are completely housebound, or cannot leave home without someone there to help you, or if you get mobility allowance (see Benefits above), or both day and night attendance allowance (see Benefits above).

Accommodation
● If you are a householder and your home is expensive to keep warm, then you can claim an allowance of £2.20 a week.

● If you are a householder and your home is exceptionally expensive to keep warm, then you can claim an allowance of £5.45 a week.
(If you qualify on grounds of both health and your accommodation, you will get £5.45 a week).

Age
● If you are a householder aged 65 or more with a dependant aged over 65, you can get a heating allowance of £2.20 a week.
● If you are a householder aged 85 or over with a dependant aged over 85, you will get a heating allowance of £5.45 a week.

Central Heating
If you are a householder you can claim depending on the number of rooms you have (not counting the kitchen, bathroom and toilet):
● If you have up to four rooms you will get an allowance of £2.20 a week.
● If you have five rooms or more you will get £4.40 a week.
(If you qualify for more on grounds of both health and accommodation, then you will get the higher allowance).
If you pay a fixed amount for central heating in with your rent and it covers all the heating you need, then you cannot receive any additional allowances for heating, unless you live on a designated hard-to-heat housing estate which has no fixed heating charge. To find out whether you live on such an estate contact your housing estate office. If you find you do live on a hard-to-heat estate and have not been receiving this allowance, write to your local Social Security office (see above). They should backdate the amount owed to you.

Severe Disablement
● If you or your partner receive attendance allowance (see Benefits above), mobility allowance (see Benefits above), or you have an

invalid car or its equivalent, then you should receive £5.45 a week for heating for each person who gets one of these allowances.

Single Payments

If your savings are less than £500 and you are on supplementary pension or housing benefit, you can claim a single payment towards certain heating costs. Do not have the work carried out or buy the item until you get the go-ahead from your local Social Security office. Write to them (for address see Social Security offices above) if you think you are entitled to one or more of the following:
●Repair or replacement of a heating appliance
●Hot water cylinder jacket if you don't already have one.
●Installation of a slot meter if this will help you budget, or re-positioning it if this will make it easier for you to use it.

If you are on supplementary pension and your savings are less than £500, you can also claim single payments for heating bills in the following circumstances:

Exceptionally Cold Winter
It's a good idea to keep your fuel bills for at least eighteen months because to qualify for this single payment you have to be able to show that the amount on your latest bill is far higher than you expected to have to budget for.

Unfamiliar Heating System
If you have just moved or had central heating put in, you may not be used to the heating controls. If this means you cannot afford to pay your bill you may get a single payment to help you, provided you can show that you did budget to the amount you expected.

Unclaimed Single Payments
If you have not claimed previously for a single payment you would have been entitled to, then you may be able to get help with a subsequent fuel bill which you have difficulty in paying entirely yourself.

Discretionary Payments
A single payment can be made to prevent your electricity or gas supply being cut off, if this disconnection could mean a serious health risk to you or your spouse.

Loft Insulation

If your loft has no insulation you can apply for a grant towards the cost of having it done, and of insulating your hot water pipes and tank. If you are a woman over 60 or a man over 65 and are on supplementary pension or housing benefit, the grant will be 90% of the cost or £95, whichever is the less. If you are not claiming supplementary pension or housing benefit, then you will get a grant of 65% of the cost or £69, whichever is the less. Your local borough council (for address see Local Services) has a list of approved insulating materials for you to choose from. Before starting any work get a form from your council, fill it in and return it to them. Someone may come and inspect your home. Make sure you get the go-ahead from the council first, because if work starts before you get permission you will not get the grant. If you can't do the work yourself your local advice centre will suggest where you can get help (see Advice Centres above).

Emergency Heating

If your cooker or lighting or heating is faulty, or your fuel supply is disconnected and you could be at risk of suffering from hypothermia, contact your local Social Security office or Age Concern (see above) which may be able to lend you heating equipment.

Disconnections

If you get a fuel bill which is more than you can afford, then contact your local gas or electricity board immediately (the telephone number and address are written on the bill). Tell them your situation, and then seek advice from an advice centre (see Advice Centres above). Gas and electricity boards are under a code of practice which does not allow them to cut off your supply between 1 October and 31 March. You should not be cut off at all if you arrange to pay the bill in installments. (For help with paying heating bills see Single Payments above).

Help in the Home

It is government policy to provide for elderly people in their own homes rather than in institutions. The quality and cost of available help in the home varies according to which borough you live in, but below we give you an idea of the kind of help you may be entitled to so that you can continue to live in your own home for as long as possible. Many services are entirely free, so check when you make your enquiries.

Home Helps

If you are finding it difficult to cope with household tasks you should contact your local Social Services area office (see above) to find out if they can provide you with a home help. This person will assist you in cleaning, cooking, shopping and other household tasks that seem necessary.

Meals on Wheels

If you are having difficulty in cooking meals for yourself and you are unable to get to a luncheon club then contact your Social Services area office (see above) and you may be able to get meals brought to your home. There is a charge for this service which is reasonably low.

Aids and Adaptations

If you have difficulty getting up and down stairs, in and out of the bath and so on, you maybe able to get hand-rails, a stair-lift or other aids to make life easier. Contact your local Social Services area office (see above), your doctor or health visitor, and they will arrange for someone to come and assess your needs. Financial help may be available for adaptations to your home such as a ground floor bathroom.

Laundry

You may be able to get your laundry done if you suffer from incontinence. Tell your doctor, district nurse, health visitor or social worker.

Bathing

If you find it impossible to bath yourself, then tell your doctor, district nurse, health visitor or social worker and they can arrange for someone to assist you.

Home Nursing

Hoists, commodes, walking frames, back rests and other nursing aids can be supplied on long-term loan. Contact your doctor, district nurse, health visitor or social worker.

Chiropody

It may be possible to arrange for a chiropodist to come to your home if you find difficulty in getting out. Contact your doctor.

Hairdressing

If you cannot leave the house easily, it may be possible for a hairdresser to visit you.

Volunteers

If there is a job around the home that needs doing, for instance, a room decorated or the garden weeded, then it may be possible to get this done by volunteers. Contact your local Age Concern office (see Advice Centres above).

Welfare Food

Certain foods such as Bovril, Bournvita, tea and coffee are sold at cheap rates from some community centres. For more information contact your local Age Concern office (see Advice Centres above).

District Nurses

If you need frequent medical and nursing care, tell your doctor and it can be arranged for a district nurse to visit you at home.

Health Visitor

If you have been ill and your doctor thinks it is advisable that someone calls at your home to check that you are all right, then the services of a health visitor can be arranged.

Telephones

In certain circumstances, depending on your income, you may be able to have a telephone installed free of charge and the quarterly rental paid. Contact your Social Services area office (see above). You will not be able to get help in paying for phone calls, however.

Housing

You might be feeling that your present home is far bigger than you really need or you may find that you are no longer able to look after the place in the way you would like to. It is common for elderly people to move to a home which is more suited to their needs, though you should consider any such change very carefully. All too often we hear of elderly people who move to the seaside or countryside to the retirement home of their dreams only to find that they are terribly lonely, and miss the friends and neighbours they left behind. There are several different kinds of housing to consider when making the choice for yourself. It is essential that you get advice, both from the experts and friends or relatives. Don't rush the decision. After all, this could be the home where you spend the rest of your life. If possible it is advisable to start thinking about your move at least a year before you actually make it. This will give you more choice (which is always a good thing), especially if you have to join a waiting list for available accommodation. The various types of housing specifically for elderly people are described briefly below.

Sheltered Accommodation

These are small one-bedroomed or bedsitter flats, run by the council and voluntary organisations. They are purpose-built for elderly people to enable you to live independently, but have an alarm system installed to call a warden in case of an emergency. It is only fair to say that there are long waiting lists for this kind of accommodation, and applications are considered on medical and social grounds. Contact your housing advice centre (see below) or, if you are a council tenant, your housing estate office.

Residential Accommodation

Your borough council and private and voluntary organisations run residential care homes (or rest homes) for the elderly. Only if you find it extremely difficult coping at home or you are absolutely sure that this is the type of accommodation you want should you consider residential care. If you would rather stay in your own home and think you could manage if only you could get more help, see Help In The Home above. If you are considering residential care, contact your local Social Services area office (see above) for both council-run and private and

voluntary homes. It is possible to contact private and voluntary homes directly – your Social Services area office will give you a list of them, though they will not recommend one home as opposed to another. An organistion to contact about private and voluntary homes is Counsel and Care for the Elderly at 131 Middlesex Street, E1 (tel 621 1624).

Housing Advice Centres

Housing problems can get very complicated whether you are a council or private tenant or own your home. It is important that you go to the right place to get help. Each entry below tells you what sort of housing queries are dealt with and whether it's for council or private housing. If you are a council tenant you may prefer to take your query initially to your local estate office. As a general rule borough housing departments deal with council house accommodation queries (for instance you may want to go on the housing list), district housing offices deal with repair and housing management queries (for lists of these see Housing), and your local estate office will refer you to the right place if they cannot help you themselves. (You will find the address of your estate office in your rent book).

Greenwich

Directorate of Housing
Peggy Middleton House
50 Woolwich New Road
Woolwich   SE18
Tel 854 8888
For queries about council accommodation and if you want to be put on the housing list.

Greenwich Housing Rights
32-34 Hare Street
Woolwich   SE18
Tel 854 8848

An independent organisation offering general housing advice for all tenants as well as homeless people. They will not give advice about the right to buy scheme.

Housing Aid & Advice Centre
5 Greens End
Woolwich   SE18
Tel 854 8888
General advice for private tenants and homeowners only on most housing problems and on home improvement and loft insulation grants.

Lambeth

Directorate of Housing & Property Services
Hambrook House
Brixton Hill
Brixton   SW2
Tel 274 7722
For council accommodation queries only and if you want to be put on the housing list.

The Housing Advice Centre
2-7 Town Hall Parade
Brixton Hill
Brixton   SW2
Tel 274 7722 ext 2011/2665
Information and advice about all aspects of housing, particularly for private tenants and homeowners.

Lewisham

Housing Department
Leegate House
Lee Green   SE12
Tel 852 4391
For council accommodation queries and if you want to be put on the housing list.

Deptford Housing Aid Centre
171 Deptford High Street
Deptford   SE8
Tel 691 1300/1602

General housing advice to homeless people, to council and private tenants an to homeowners.

Lewisham Housing Advice Centre
Leegate House
Lee Green   SE12
Tel 852 4391
Housing advice for homeless people, council and private tenants and homeowners.

Staying Put Project
St Lawrence's Centre
37 Bromley Road
Catford   SE6
Tel 461 3000
Advice and help for elderly people who find it difficult to cope alone but wish to stay in their own homes. (See Help in the Home above).

Merton

Housing Advice Centre
Crown House
London Road
Morden
Tel 543 2222
Advice for homeless people, private and council tenants and homeowners.

Southwark

Housing Department
38 Rye Lane
Peckham   SE15
Tel 639 4353
Council accommodation queries and if you want to be put on the housing list. General housing advice for homeless people, council and private tenants and homeowners.

Wandsworth

Housing Aid Centre
Wandsworth Town Hall
Wandsworth High Street
Wandsworth   SW18
Tel 871 6000

Advice on all matters of housing for private tenants and homeowners only. If you are a council tenant you will be referred to your district housing office

Transport

GLC Travel Passes

Until the abolition of the GLC in March 1986, you are entitled to free bus and tube passes when you reach 60 (for a woman) and 65 (for a man). What will happen after the abolition is not known at the time of going to press. But meanwhile many pensioners' groups are compaigning to keep this facility. Until the end of March, then, this is the situation: After 9am and all day Saturday and Sunday you can travel free on buses and tubes and half fare on Green Line coaches in the Greater London area. You can get your pass from main post offices. Take some evidence to prove you are of retirement age, such as your pension book, and two passport size photographs of yourself. (The cost of these will be refunded by the post office when they issue your pass).

Rail Cards

If you are over 60 (for a woman) or 65 (for a man) you can buy a Senior Citizen Rail Card which means you can travel cheaply on British Rail trains.
For £7 you can buy a railcard valid for one year which entitles you to day return tickets at half-price.
For £12 you can buy a railcard valid for one year which means you can get ordinary single or return tickets at two-thirds price and day returns at half-price. You will also get some reduction on the price of weekend returns and inter-city savers. You can buy your railcard from most stations. You don't need to take along photographs, but you will be required to show evidence of your age. This railcard also allows you to travel half-price to Southern Ireland and Europe.

Taxis

If you receive a mobility allowance (see Benefits above) then you may be able to join a scheme which allows you to use a taxi at a greatly reduced fare. Contact your local advice centre (see Advice Centres above).

Mobility Allowance

For details of mobility allowance see Benefits above.

Dial-a-Ride

If you receive mobility allowance or attendance allowance (see Benefits above) or you have a certain degree of visual handicap, then you are entitled to use this service which are specially adapted for wheelchairs. There is a small charge.

Greenwich Dial-a-Ride
St Mary's Church
Greenlaw Street
Woolwich   SE18
Tel 854 9500

Lambeth Dial-a-Ride
245A Coldharbour Lane
Brixton   SW9
Tel 274 7700

Lewisham Dial-a-Ride
35 Brownhill Road
Catford   SE6
Tel 461 1169

Southwark Dial-a-Ride
Portakabin
42 Braganza Street
Walworth   SE17
Tel 582 6155

Wandsworth Dial-a-Ride
1b Yukon Road
Balham   SW12
Tel 675 4046

Other Transport

If you have difficulty travelling and
you want to go to a day centre, for
instance, it may be possible for your
Social Services area office to arrange
transport for you. If you need to get
to hospital for an appointment it
should be possible for an ambulance
to come and pick you up. Contact
your doctor or hospital. There may be
voluntary transport organisations in
your area that we haven't
mentioned. Contact your local advice
centre (see Advice Centres above) for
more information.

Social Life

Everyone suffers from loneliness at
some point in their lives, but it seems
that elderly people are those who
suffer most. However for many
elderly people this is not always
possible to be in the company of other
people, perhaps because of lack of
money or difficulties in getting
transport. Below we give you some of
the social activities on offer for
elderly people. Most of it comes
either free or at a reasonable price.
And if transport is the difficulty,
then take a look at Transport above.

Arts & Entertainment

Many community centres in South

London run drama and movement
workshops for elderly people. The
Albany Empire and Battersea Arts
Centre hold regular arts activities
for pensioners (see Theatre).

Artsline
Tel 388 2227/8
Line open 10-4(Mon-Fri) 10-2(Sat)
Phone in for news about arts and
entertainments in London. The
service is for people with special
needs. They will tell you which
theatres, cinemas and museums have
wheelchair access or hearing aid
systems and lots of other useful
information. You can send for
information leaflets to 5, Crowndale
Road, NW1 (enclose a large stamped
addressed envelope).

Shape
9 Fitzroy Square
London W1
Tel 388 9622
Creates arts activities and events for
elderly people. Much of their work is
in the form of weekly sessions in
hospitals, day centres and other
institutions. Activities include
drama, movement, music, art,
writing and reminiscence projects.

Lunch Clubs

Your council and some voluntary
organisations run a number of lunch
clubs where you can have a midday
meal in the company of other people
and at a reasonable price. You will
usually have to book and pay for
meals in advance. To find out the
best lunch club for you contact Age
Concern (see Advice Centres above).

Day Centres

Your council runs a number of day
centres. Some of them provide
activities such as craft, painting,
drama and cooking. But you don't

have to join in if you prefer not to. Many also provide lunch at a reasonable cost. If you think you would benefit by going to a day centre discuss this with your doctor or contact your Social Services area office (see above).

Clubs

There are many pensioners' clubs in your area offering entertainment and social activities. There is usually a small charge to cover the cost of tea and cakes. Some organise outings, and even holidays. Contact Age Concern (see Advice Centres above) if you want to know more.

Community Centres

There are a lot of centres which run sessions specially for pensioners. Ask an advice centre like Age Concern (see Advice Centres above) if you would like to know more.

Holidays

Many councils and voluntary organisations run holidays for elderly people. Holiday Care Service, 2 Old Bank Chambers, Station Road, Horley, Surrey (Tel 02934 74535) offers advice and information about holidays for elderly people. Advice centres (see Advice Centres above) will give you more information. For holidays run by the borough council, contact the Social Services department (see above). In some cases financial assistance may be available.

Health

For more information see the chapters on Health and Disability,

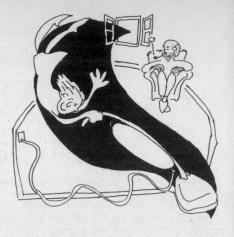

and also Help In The Home above. Age Concern publishes a booklet called Old and Healthy which you can read at your local branch.

Doctors

Your local advice centre (see Advice Centres above), post office and library can tell you where your nearest doctor is. You will not be charged for seeing your doctor, but you must register with one before you get treatment. You will not be charged for prescriptions if you are a woman over 60 or a man over 65. Just sign the declaration form at the back of the prescription before you hand it over to the chemist. You will find a list in the local paper of chemists staying open late and on Sundays.

Special Aids

You can borrow aids such as walking frames, wheelchairs and bathing aids at no cost if you are elderly or disabled and are in need. Contact your local Social Services area office (see above) and an occupational therapist will visit you at home and assess your needs.

ETHNIC MINORITIES

This chapter features Black, Asian, Irish, Vietnamese, Chinese, Latin American, Greek Cypriot, Turkish Cypriot and Polish organisations and centres in South London. We would like to have included other ethnic minority groups and hope people will contact us for our next edition. There are obviously a lot of people working hard to combat many of the negative issues facing ethnic minority communities in inner city London – racism and its consequent injustices in education, health, housing allocation, business opportunities and employment. To a greater or lesser extent, South London councils also appear to be making positive moves (see the borough sections below), though the appointment of specialist workers like Ethnic Arts Officers poses certain dilemmas in a society as multi-cultural as South London where each ethnic minority community has very different needs. Hopefully the councils will take on board much of the GLC's support of multi-cultural and multi-ethnic arts and community groups, though the situation is

unclear at the time of going to press. Some say that as a result of the insecurity over the GLC, more groups are seeking support from within their own communities. In the arts world many feel this will not alleviate the situation and have begun to form wider links for support and solidarity. The Africa Centre, the Arts Media Group, Black Cultural Archives and the London Forum of Ethnic Arts Officers are hoping with others to form an umbrella organisation for ethnic arts. More specifically, the Black Theatre Alliance is doing all it can to promote Black Theatre, which has enjoyed a healthier record over the last few years than much of Theatre's Fringe. (L'Ouverture Theatre Trust, Roots Theatre, Sass, Temba and Umoja are just a few of the Black and multi-cultural theatre companies based in South London.) There are scores of community centres and organisations in South London that offer informal classes and workshops on the history and culture of Black people and other ethnic minorities. Some schools, many adult education institutes and even mainstream colleges like Goldsmiths have incorporated aspects of this in their programmes. And, more for fun than study, there are plenty of festivals throughout South London where traditional cultures from all over the world are celebrated. (See the chapter on Festivals and Events to find out what's planned for '86.) Black history is to be the focus of a nationally important project, called Black Cultural Archives (see the South Londonwide section below).

Moving away from culture and history, when it comes to help in the community more people are turning to their local Community Relations Councils for support. Increasingly, the label of an 'establishment' organisation is being shifted.

CRCs were set up by the Commission for Racial Equality and have the same role and aims, ie 'working towards the elimination of discrimination, promoting equality of opportunity and good relations between persons of different racial groups and reviewing the work of the 1976 Race Relations Act'. They provide a wide range of services including advice and information on issues like housing, education, employment and the law. They also fund projects and workers.

In some cases they will act on an individual's behalf, if faced with discrimination. (Local CRCs are listed at the top of each borough section of below.)

This chapter is organised in two sections. Firstly, a South Londonwide section which contains organisations and venues that are of general rather than local interest. The second section is a directory of what is available locally. (Other chapters that may be of interest include Young People and Nightlife.)

South Londonwide

Black Culture

Black Cultural Archives
c/o Coldharbour Works
245a Coldharbour Lane
Brixton   SW9
Tel 274 7700
Black Cultural Archives was founded in 1982 to collect and preserve historical and contemporary artefacts to enable the rich historical traditions of Black people in British society to be understood and celebrated. From its temporary office BCA has begun to collect an invaluable source of primary material – music scores, books, maps, paintings, sculpture, photographs and oral accounts from Black people about their lives in Britain. A major cultural centre for BCA is planned on a site in Somerleyton Road where many West Indian people settled after the last war. BCA's current activities include monthly public meetings, social and cultural evenings on Black history, culture and education. They also have a touring exhibition of 12 display boards that document some of the positive contributions Black people have made to Britain over the last 200 years. The exhibition (which is available for hire), features people like Marcus Garvey, Claudia Jones (founder of the West Indian Gazette), Samuel Coleridge-Taylor, Mary Seacole and John Archer (the first Black mayor in 1913) amongst others. Videos, information packs and other material are planned for the future. Already hundreds of people have visited BCA from all over Britain and the proposed centre promises to be a unique and exciting national archive. The amount of progress and activity at BCA is quite unbelievable when you consider that it operates on a very low budget with only two full-time workers and a number of hard-

working and committed volunteers. Most worrying of all, BCA's GLC grant terminates at the end of March 1986. It would be a tragedy if all the interest and enthusiasm already invested in this important venture were to be wasted simply through lack of financial support.

Books

Balham Food & Book Co-op
92 Balham High Road
Balham SW12
Tel 673 0946
Good selection of Black and multi-ethnic books.

Black Ink
258 Coldharbour Lane
Brixton SW9
Tel 274 7858
Open 10-5(Mon-Fri)
Publishers of contemporary British Black and Asian literature dealing with political, social and ethnic issues. Also picture/reading books for children.

Bladestock Publications
Unit 1
124-8 Brixton Hill
Brixton SW2
Tel 671 7261
Bladestock Publications is a new and exciting company which imports and distributes books from the Third World and other countries including the Caribbean, America, the Indian sub-continent and African countries such as Zimbabwe, Tanzania, Kenya and Nigeria. 80% of the books are in English, some are dual language books and other are in languages like Swahili. Titles cover the history, arts, culture, politics and current affairs of the Third World and metropolitan minority groups (like the American Indian or Australian aboriginal), multi-cultural and multi-ethnic fiction and children's books, and books about Third World technology

and alternative societies. Bladestock's premises include a showroom and library and their titles can be found in most good South London bookshops. Look out for them.

Brockwell Books
64 Selsdon Road
West Norwood SE27
Tel 670 0394
Publishers of traditional stories set in a modern idiom for children from African, Chinese, Russian and many other cultures.

Peckham Bookplace
13 Peckham High Street
Peckham SE15
Tel 701 1757/0720
Open 10-6(except Thur)
Wheelchair access with assistance
A community project with a bookshop with a large stock of books by and for women, books by Black writers and multi-cultural children's books. Black studies are also taught.

Soma Books
38 Kennington Lane
Kennington SE11
Tel 735 2101
Open 10-6(Mon Wed-Fri)
Bookshop specialising in Afro-Caribbean and South Asian books. All five languages are stocked at junior and senior level.

UJAAMA Centre and Bookshop
14 Brixton Road
Oval SW9
Tel 582 5590
Ujaama is concerned with the Third World generally and there is always an interesting range of crafts and cards from Third World countries as well as books on many different cultures and issues (including a good selection for children and women).

Business Advice

The Greater London Enterprise Board
63-67 Newington Causeway
Elephant & Castle   SE1
Tel 403 0300
Set up by the GLC to help the job situation in London, GLEB offers loans and investment to approved schemes and have made some positive moves to help ethnic minority communities. GLEB ensures that each enterprise they help is shown how to provide genuine equal opportunities. They have recognised that many Black workers, although skilled, are stuck in unskilled and semi-skilled jobs and that when trying to set up in business unsympathetic bank managers and prejudiced landlords can prove a problem. GLEB has another scheme GLEBFIN which offers a consultancy service for ethnic minority enterprise including help with the preparation of business plans and other essential research. Full details of what's on offer can be found in their booklet, Black Business: Redressing the Balance, available from GLEB @ £1. (See Local Organisations for local enterprise and business advice schemes.)

Domestic Violence

ASHA Asia Women's Aid
PO Box 484
SE5
Provides advice, support and shelter to Asian women who have suffered domestic violence. The group runs a refuge for Asian women and provides assistance to them and to their families. All Asian languages spoken.
See also Emergency chapter – Domestic Violence at end of book.

Education

ACER Project
Wyvil Road
Vauxhall   SW8
Tel 627 2662
Open 9-5(Mon-Fri)
ACER was established as an independent education charity concerned with anti-racist, multi-cultural material for use in schools thereby correcting the inbalance in Black representation and enabling all children to value, respect and learn from one another. ACER's work aims not only to create a positive self image amongst children but a greater understanding and appreciation generally of the contributions of African and Caribbean people. Material is supplied at the request of teachers to schools for pupils aged 9-13 and ACER has recently expanded its development programme to included the nursery and infant stage. For the past seven years, ACER has run the Black Young Writers' Essay Competiton, which provides one of the only opportunities for Black young people to explore and express concerns. ACER has established a major collection of Afro-Caribbean material as well as some material on related issues. Their publications lists reflects their commitment to expanding the knowledge and contribution of Black people and improving the quality of educational material on offer.

African Arts in Education Project
2nd Floor
Cobourg School
Cobourg Road
Camberwell   SE5
Tel 703 1619
Contact Dr B Tsehai
This organisation breaks the mould in that it allows entertainers to become educationalists. Trained African artists spend six one-day sessions in schools using music, slides and dance

to express different cultures from African countries like Yoruba and Ashanti (Nigeria and Ghana). They also present a workshop on Islam. The sessions cover the creation of African mythology, mask-making, fabric printing, collage, breadmaking and other activities. At the end of the course there's a sharing festival when the children show their parents what they have achieved over the six sessions. The aim of the project is to break away from the traditional Eurocentric stereotyped views about different cultures and races. This is a unique and ingenious approach providing a chance for Black children to promote and understand their rich historical heritage and for White children to understand African culture. More schools should be taking advantage of it.

Caribbean Teachers Association
8 Camberwell Green
Camberwell   SE5
Tel 708 1293
This organisation aims to promote the educational interests of the Afro-Caribbean community. It has a membership of 700 teachers who deal with educational problems in schools. In their work to introduce an Afro-Caribbean perspective into teaching, they run workshops, supply information on issues of interest, produce a newsletter containing Black opinions and liaise with ILEA and the teaching unions.

UJAAMA Centre and Bookshop
14 Brixton Road
Oval   SW9
Tel 582 5590
'Ujaama' means 'co-operation' in Swahili and the project aims to provide people with the tools to understand their own situation and the position of others in society and the world as a whole. The centre is concerned most notably with those who are disadvantaged and oppressed and with enabling them to begin to

gain control of their own lives and change them for the benefit of all. They have a collection of traditional musical instruments from around the world which they lend to schools. They are able to present several workshops including one which traces the traditions and history of the Guatamalan Indians.

Zuriya
38 Brixton Road
Oval   SW9
Zuriya uses drumming, dance, poetry, storytelling and song to bring African and Afro-Caribbean cultural activity to life in schools and youth clubs.

Health

Sickle Cell
Sickle Cell anaemia is a blood disorder which mainly affects people of Afro-Caribbean origin. In people with sickle cell anaemia some of their red blood cells form a rigid 'sickle' or half moon shape and cannot flow through the blood vessels. They collect together, blocking the blood flow, which causes pain and other complications such as lowered resistance to infections and anaemia. If you have sickle cell anaemia you were born with it. You cannot catch it. You can be born with it if both your parents are 'silent carriers' of what is called sickle cell trait. This is not an illness. In fact, 1 in 10 Afro-Caribbean people have sickle cell trait and unless you have a special blood test you'd probably never know it. However, if you and your partner both have sickle cell trait there is a 1 in 4 chance that your child(ren) will be born with sickle cell anaemia. You can arrange to have a blood test through one of the organisations below.

Lambeth Sickle Cell Centre
Swan Mews
2 Stockwell Road
Stockwell   SW9

Tel 737 3588
The Centre offers genetics counselling and can arrange for blood tests and give advice to people who are carriers or actually have sickle cell anaemia.

Organisation for Sickle Cell Anaemia (OSCAR)
c/o Forest Hill Youth Project
2/4 Devonshire Road
Forest Hill   SE23
Tel 291 3976
A small group of volunteers set up this project in 1978. They give information about sickle cell anaemia and provide counselling. The group is not funded, has very limited facilities and shares the cramped premises with a youth project. It's an uphill struggle but they are determined to keep going.

Sickle Cell Clinic
King's College Hospital
Denmark Hill   SE5
Tel 274 6222
Open 9.30-12.30(Tue ages 0-15) 2-4(Tue adults)
Doctors can refer people with sickle cell trait or sickle cell anaemia to this Tuesday clinic, the only sickle cell clinic in South London. (Most hospitals see sickle cell patients in their haemotology clinics.)

The Sickle Cell Society
c/o Lewisham Way Youth and Community Centre
Lewisham Way
New Cross   SE14
Tel 692 1190/691 7633(day) 697 0941(eve)
The Sickle Cell Society is a charity which offers leaflets, information and support and can put people in touch with counsellors. This is a new branch that meets monthly at present during evening or at weekends. Anyone is welcome. A genetics counsellor has set up the group and can arrange blood tests at Lewisham Hospital's haemotology department. The Society's headquarters in Brent can be contacted any week day during

office hours (Tel 451 3293). There are plans to start a Wandsworth group in the future.

Pressure/Action Groups

Chile Committee for Human Rights
13-16 Borough Road
Borough   SE1
Tel 928 2099
The title says it all. This is a national organisation that is now based in South London.

Race Today
165 Railton Road
Brixton   SE24
Tel 737 2268
Open 10-6(Mon-Fri) by appointment
This organisaton has produced some literature explaining the action taken in the wake of the New Cross Massacre. Copies can be bought from the above address.

Solidarity With Solidarity
50 Nightingale Lane
Balham   SW12
Tel 673 4456
Contact Mr Jashamboshki
This is a national organisation which was started when martial law was imposed in Poland in December 1981. It is concerned with defending human rights in Poland generally (including freedom of expression). It is an independent organisation which has links with the TUC. It is a pressure group which works to mobilise public opinion against the excesses that are being perpetrated in Poland. It runs a campaign to protect people and families who are being persecuted in Poland, which includes a scheme whereby people from Britain can adopt families of prisoners by writing letters and giving support generally. The organisation raises funds for Solidarity and sends equipment and books to underground organisations in Poland. It also extends practical help to Polish refugees who arrive in

Britain. It arranges lectures in schools and other establishments and welcomes new members.

Solidarnosc Information Office
Park House
North Side
Wandsworth Common   SW18
Tel 874 8635
This organisation is the British branch of the Solidarity co-ordinating office in Brussels. It provides information about Solidarity and the situation in Poland and publishes a monthly bulletin which contains a number of reprints of information from the Polish underground press.

South London Cyprus Association
11 Camberwell Church Street
Camberwell   SE5
Tel 701 0788
A registered charity involved primarily in organising fund-raising events following the 1974 invasion of Cyprus. Most of the funds were used to support the needy in Cyprus though some financial help and much community support was given to refugees who arrived here after the troubles. The organisation is not so active now.

Standing Conference of Ethnic Minority Senior Citizens
5-5a Westminster Bridge Road
Lambeth North   SE1
Tel 928 8108
A campaigning organisation which brings together retired members of ethnic minority groups in the Greater London area. Through its conferences, elderly people from the West Indian, Asian, Chinese and Cypriot communities have been brought together. A recurring theme of the conferences has been that both statutory and voluntary bodies have failed to recognise that all these people have different needs. The Standing Conference would like to see a fair and flexible approach towards housing, health, social and other

services to the Black and ethnic minority elderly people of this country and also approriate funding for the different communities.

Theatre

Tara Arts Centre
356 Garratt Lane
Earlsfield   SW18
Tel 871 1458/1450
Contact Rekha Prashar
Wheelchair access to theatre & cafe
Tara Arts was founded following the murder of a young Asian, Gurdip Singh Chaggar during racist unrest in London in the summer of 1976. It is the only Asian professional theatre company that has risen solely from within the Asian community living in Britain and it aims to reflect the experiences of Asian people living in Britain today through a wide range of contemporary Asian art. As such it offers a unique contribution to contemporary theatre in Britain. Tara Arts have two professional national touring companies and are also involved in visiting local schools. Productions at the centre include a wide range of performing arts and there is an active programme of workshops, including one on Indian classical dance with an emphasis on movement and mime and an Indian vocal music workshop. Other Asian professional performers are invited from this country and the Indian sub-continent to give performances and run workshops at the centre. Live performances take place from Thursday to Saturday and workshops from Monday to Friday.

Greenwich

The Maritime Museum in Greenwich contains a macabre piece of Black history. It is one of the few places where you can see an exhibit of a ship that actually took part in the 'triangular slave trade'. The borough has a large, long established Asian as well as Black population and there is considerable number of Chinese and Vietnamese people living in the borough. A significant council development is the creation of a Race Unit as part of the Greenwich Community Affairs Section (Tel 854 8888). This is a service set up to promote the Council's policies in employment, equality of access to council services, and the creation of services that meet the needs of a multi-racial society. An Ethnic Minority Librarian has also been appointed (Tel 858 6656 Ext 35). The Council provides a wide range of services to advise and support ethnic minorities, but sadly these don't seem to be generally known about.

Community Relations Council

Greenwich CRC
Powis Street
Woolwich   SE18
Tel 855 7191

Business Advice

Greenwich Employment Development Unit
Macbean Centre
Macbean St
Woolwich   SE18
Tel 854 8888
Open 9-5.30(Mon-Thur) 9-4.30 (Fri)
This is a business advisory service for the whole community and a loan scheme for people with no other funds. Lewisham Council will be opening the Deptford Business Agency in about March '86, which will work mainly with ethnic minorities in Greenwich, Lewisham and Southwark, using city bank and council funding.

Local Organisations

Afro-Caribbean Action Group
115-131 Powis Street
Woolwich   SE18
Tel 311 0306 or 855 7191
Open 10-5.30
Advice to the Afro-Caribbean community on issues and rights. A CRC project.

Afro-Caribbean Alliance
c/o Simba Project
48-50 Artillery Place
Woolwich   SE18
Tel 317 0451
Advice to the Afro-Caribbean community on all welfare rights.

Asian Resource Centre
Macbean Centre
Macbean Street
Woolwich   SE18
Tel 854 1188
Asian advice centre with various facilities and mother-tongue classes. The women also initiate national and international Asian women's projects. They have open days and organise summer trips.

Asian Youth and Social Club
6 Tuam Road
Plumstead Common   SE18
Tel 626 3499 Ext 261
Contact Mr Ahmed
Aims to help Asian youth in the Greenwich area. Activities include excursions abroad, cultural activities, dance, drama, essay writing and painting. Advice on issues such as housing and social security. Youth club at 7-9 on Tuesday evenings at Gleyndon Hll, Raglan Road, Plumstead, SE18. Mother tongue classes at 10-1 on Saturday mornings at Plumstead Manor Youth Centre. Social activity is also organised as part of Greenwich Festival.

Black Women's Health Project
c/o St Mary's Church
Greenlaw Street
Woolwich SE18
Tel 854 3766
Health issues discussed by Black
women. Ring for times.

Cerasse Women's Health Project
39 Wellington Street
Woolwich SE18
Tel 854 3766
Open 10-5(Mon-Fri)
Wheelchair access from rear with
access provision being improved
The Project caters for women in the
Woolwich area and beyond. Although
most of the women are Afro-
Caribbean they wouldn't turn anyone
away. Advice, counselling and
support are offered on issues such as
hypertension, stress, alcoholism and
drug abuse. Several workshops are
run on health education and
pamphlets have been produced which
you can drop by and pick up. A mini
bus is available (equipped with a lift
for disabled women) and pick-ups can
be arranged. The Project is funded by
the GLC until March '86. It is a
tragedy that the future of such a
worthwhile project should be
insecure.

Cultural Centre
Bathway
Woolwich SE18
Tel 855 7191
New venue established by the CRE for
Black and Asian groups offering
facilities for the young and elderly.
Advice and information on drug
abuse, Black businesses, youth
leadership, computers, mechanics and
education. A young women's
educational discussion group, a youth
newsletter and a Black writers' group
are all planned.

**Greenwich Black Women's Health
Project**
39 Wellington Street
Woolwich SE18
Tel 854 3766
Health issues discussed by Black
women. Home visits can also be
arranged.

Greenwich Resource Centre
Macbean Street
Tel 854 9092
Woolwich SE18
A voluntary organisation which
assists Black and other ethnic
minority groups in producing
materials such as leaflets and posters
for activities and campaigns on local
issues.

Greenwich Chinese Association
c/o Greenwich House
141 Greenwich High Road
Greenwich SE10
Tel 858 2410
Umbrella group which tries to cater
for many of the needs of the Chinese
community in the Greenwich area.
Mother tongue classes to English-born
Chinese and English classes for the
Chinese elderly. Supplementary
school classes in the evenings and on
Saturday mornings. Cultural events
are celebrated and traditional Chinese
activities enjoyed such as dancing,
cooking and Martial Arts.

Greenwich Young People's Theatre
Burrage Road
Plumstead SE18
Tel 854 1316
GYPT continues to do excellent work
often about issues important to ethnic
minority groups. The organisation
includes a youth theatre (with two
youth theatre groups) and a
professional theatre-in-education
which visits ILEA schools in
Greenwich, Lewisham and
Southwark. Examples of some of the
concepts and issues tackled at schools
include justice, education, the family
and gender roles, the General Strike
and cultural conflict. It also runs a

number of arts workshops for young people (whhich are attended by a small following of Black youngsters) and for those with special needs. Theatre, dance, music and the visual arts are all offered. GYPT has two fully-equipped studio spaces, facilities for photography, video and sound, several technical workshops and a coffee bar. GYPT is there to be enjoyed by anyone over 7, with or without experience . Give them a ring to find out what's going on or just just drop by and join in the fun.

Indian Cultural Society
140 Eltham Road
Eltham   SE12
Tel 850 4143
An Asian day centre for all Asian groups. The Cultural Society also presents a television programme on Greenwich cable network at 5-6 on Sunday evenings. They have applied for a licence to broadcast on the new community radio network. Subject to approval from the Council an advice centre and social club will be opening shortly. Indian festivals are celebrated and there is Punjabi folk dancing at Glendon Community Centre, Glendon Estate in Plumstead.

Irish in Greenwich Association
c/o Greenwich CRE 115/123 Powis Street
Woolwich   SE18
Tel 855 7191 Ext 30
Contact Sarah Kelleher
Membership £1(waged) 50p(unwaged) £2 family membership
Set up two years ago, this
 rganisation aims to promote the social and cultural awareness of Irish people, to combat racial discrimination, anti Irish racism, and to create a greater awareness of the Irish community, it's culture and history. It also carries out research into areas of need in Greenwich's Irish community and campaigns for a fair share of resources for the Irish in Greenwich. It tries to promote racial

harmony and is non party political and non sectarián.

Muslim Project
115-123 Powis Street
2nd floor
Woolwich   SE18
Tel 854 6115
Contact Mr Naseer Ahmed
This project was set up to help all members of the Asian community to deal with matters relating to immigration, racial discrimination and harrassement, employment, education, unfair dismissal and how to claim supplementary benefit. Cases are taken as far as possible and project workers will accompany those concerned to tribunals.

Ramgarhia (Sikh) Community Development Project
Masons Hill
Woolwich   SE18
Tel 317 9701
Contact Mr Rayat
Open 6.30-9.30(Mon-Fri)
To help members of the Sikh community on a religious, cultural and educational basis. Their programme includes a youth club with snooker badminton and weight-lifting, an elderly club whose members meet from 11am to 5pm five days a week. There are mother tongue classes on Tuesdays and Thursdays from 5.30 to 7.30.

Simba Project
48-50 Artillery Place
Woolwich   SE18
Tel 854 0489 or 317 0451
Ring for times of classes and workshops
Facilities include free legal advice and counselling, advice on employment, housing, consumer affairs, social security benefits and education. There is also a workshop with a recording studio. Within the music workshop there's a reggae group called Ras Messengers, who often do benefits in the community. Also in the

music workshop there's a facility for training sound enginers. Within the past year six people have received training and all have found employment. Other activities include, car mechanics, photography, education classes, keep fit and weight training. There's a drop-in centre, a canteen, a creche, a summer playscheme and a housing project. The emphasis of this project is on educational training for the Black community in Greenwich. Simba works in conjunction with Turning Point (a training scheme affiliated to Goldsmiths College for Black youth workers). The bulk of funding for Simba comes from Greenwich Council with some further funding from the GLC and DOE and Urban Aid. Hopefully it won't be too adversely affected by the abolition of the GLC.

Thamesmead Multi-Cultural Funfield Association
15 Tavy Bridge
Abbey Wood　　　　　　　SE2
Tel 311 3844
Contact Frank Robertson
The Association was set up to help involve the ethnic minority community in social and recreational activities. It also advises on problems such as housing and welfare. It has organised two successful carnivals in '84 and '85. On Guy Fawkes night it organises bonfires and music for the people of Thamesmead. At the moment it's trying to organise a women's group which will bring women from different cultural backgrounds together with activities such as ethnic cuisines, keep fit and self defence.

Lambeth

Lambeth's Race Relations Unit was set up as early as 1978 and in recent years has appointed Race Relations Advisors in the Council's main Directorates. The largest council grant within the Community Affairs Section goes to the local Council for Community Relations (see CRC below). Lambeth has a Black Mayor, Councillor Lloyd Leon, and seven Black Councillors (four of whom are women). Representatives from organisations like Rasta Providential Enterprise, Melting Pot Foundation, Railton Youth Club and the Consortium of Ethnic Minorities sit on various council committees. As far as Social Services and, specifically, adoption and fostering are concerned, council policy reflects Lambeth's commitment to find foster/adoptive families of the same cultural/ethnic origin for the children in its care. Plans are currently being discussed to establish a team of exclusively Black workers to find Black families for the many Black children in care in the borough. Lambeth's Adoption and Fostering Unit would be pleased to hear from any interested Black families.

Lambeth's Sickle Cell Information Centre is a welcome development but it is understaffed, underfunded and underused.

The borough has an active community arts programme involving Black and Asian people and other ethnic minority groups. It is well-known for its striking murals and Black art and other activities often can be enjoyed at Brixton Recreation Centre. Lambeth has the fourth largest Irish population in London and the largest in South London. The Lambeth branch of the Irish in Britain Representation Group represents Irish people in social, cultural, welfare and political matters. Lambeth is also the home of over 2000 (some say many more) Latin American people from Chile and Columbia and in smaller numbers from countries such as Argentina, Bolivia and Peru as well as Belize and Guyana (which are not Spanish or Portuguese-speaking and therefore not technically part of Latin America). There are also two of

London's tiny population of indigenous people from South America living in Lambeth. South American musical evenings and fiestas sometimes take place at the Town Hall and at St Matthew's Meeting Place in Brixton and at Coronation Hall in Stockwell. In 1984 Lambeth 'twinned' with Bluefields, a town in Nicaragua (see Bluefields below). There is a sizable Chinese population in Lambeth who are represented by the Lambeth Chinese Community Association. Additionally, there is a large Vietnamese community many of whom have returned to Lambeth following the Government's failed 'dispersal' programme. Many of them are living in overcrowded accommodation doubling up with friends or in frighteningly overcrowded hotels or hostels such as the Access Hotel by Clapham Common which has been used for temporary housing by the Council. For the Greek Cypriot community in Lambeth there is a Greek Orthodox Church in Streatham and independent schools (run by the Education Ministry in Cyprus) in Brixton, Dulwich and Streatham. There is a branch of Akel, the Greek Cypriot Communist Party in Brixton. Kennington Astro Turf on a Sunday is the venue for many of the Cyprus Football Association (London League). Look out especially for 1st Division Doek, Cosmos 85 and Achilleas. There are a considerable number of Polish people living in Clapham with Saturday language schools and community centres. All Lambeth libraries have material for the Black community and many libraries contain material in Urdu, Gujarati, Hindi, Bengali, French, Spanish, Portuguese, Turkish, Greek, Polish, Chinese, Vietnamese, Italian and German.

Lambeth CRC
441 Brixton Road
Brixton SW9
Tel 274 7722/7976

Business Advice

Lambeth Business Advisory Service
Courtenay House
9-15 New Park Road
Brixton Hill SW2
Tel 674 9844
No longer a specific business incentive scheme for ethnic minorities, but assistance and grants are available.

Brixton Enterprise Centre
Bon Marche Building
444 Brixton Road
Brixton SW9
Tel 274 4000
An independent organisation that offers plots to retailers and small businesses. A reservation fee of £25 plus one month's rent (about £200) are required in advance. The project has been met with mixed success. Many Black retailers complain of continued difficulty in raising bank loans to move on to other more expansive business settings.

Local Organisations

Abeng Centre
Gresham Road
Brixton SW9
Tel 737 1628/274 5261
Open 10-6(Mon-Fri for unemployed) 4-9(Mon-Fri for young people)
Counselling and advice for Black people. Advice given on housing, which also includes a council housinig officer giving helpful hints on how to obtain accommodation. Problems in the home are also catered for. Even if you just feel like dropping in for a friendly chat, there is always someone willing to take time out to listen to what you have to say. The Unemployed are given realistic advice and help with obtaining employment With the Centre making positive moves to liaise with skill centres

throughout London and the teaching of interview techniques. Sport facilities exist as well as a healthy regard for dominoes, silk screen printing and pool. Worth a visit.

Afro-Carib Community
5-12 Mayall Road
Herne Hill   **SE24**
Tel 737 4426
Open 10-6(Mon-Fri)
Wheelchair access not as such, but special arrangement can be made Temporary base while a £2 million building is completed (probably in '86). Lively youth club with an age range of 4-25. Facilities for unwaged young people including pool, games, typing classes, drama. A music teacher will soon be joining the club. Summer playschemes are run by four other neighbouring agencies. MSchool holiday trips are sometimes arranged.

Al-Hilal Organisation
25 Brailsford Road
Brixton   **SW2**
Asian pensioners are welcome to drop in for advice and a chat. There's also a video club.

Ashby Mills School
Lyham Road
Brixton   **SW2**
Activities include an Irish language class, Irish dancing and drama, and Irish music and art classes.

Asian Community Action
322a Brixton Road
Brixton   **SW9**
Tel 733 7494
Open 9.30-5.30(Mon-Fri)
Activities for the Asian community in Lambeth including a youth club on Tuesdays and Fridays, a playgroup, women's group, elderly club, community health and general advice and casework. A computer, word processor, typewriter, photocopier,

duplicating machine, offset litho and platemaker machine and bookbinding equipment are just some of the facilities available at the centre. There is also a selection of Hindi, Bengali, Urdu, Punjabi and Gujarati video films for hire. A library contains books and newspapers in Hindi, Bengali, Urdu, Punjabi and Gujarati. There are also some records and cassettes and lots of Asian publications on relevant issues are available.

Asian Community Health
322 Brixton Road
Brixton   **SW9**
Tel 733 7494
Contact Mrs Long
Open 9.30-5.30(Mon-Fri)
Deals with problems on emigration, nationality and health issues. Members will also pay visits to hospitals and act as translators.

Asian Sheltered Residential Accommodation (ASRA)
42 Kempshott Road
Streatham Common   **SW16**
Tel 679 7758/737 0183
Contact M J Razui
This project seeks to provide sheltered housing for the most needy of the Asian elderly. ASRA in conjunction with Thames and Wandle Housing Association, has established self-contained flats for the Asian elderly who have social problems, are homeless and those who need the support of an Asian environment. It provides continuing welfare support to those who are offered accommodation within the scheme.

Bhagini Samaj
St Paul's Church
Herne Hill   **SE24**
Open 10-1(Sat)
Gujarati and harmonium classes and a women's group for moral support and exchange of information.

Black Cultural Archives
c/o Coldharbour Works
245a Coldharbour Lane
Brixton   SW9
Tel 274 7700
BCA is perhaps the most significant
current development for Black people
in Britain. It was founded in 1982 to
collect and preserve historical and
contemporary material, documenting
the rich historical traditions of Black
people in Britain. Fascinating archive
material is being collected for a
planned vast national centre and
archive to be sited in Somerleyton
Road in Brixton. (See South
Londonwide – Black Culture section
for further information.)

Black Ink
258 Coldharbour Lane
Brixton   SW9
Tel 274 7858
Open 10-5(Mon-Fri)
Wheelchair access none
Publishers of contemporary British
Black and Asian literature dealing
with political, social and ethnic
issues. Also children's picture/reading
books.

Black Women's Centre
41 Stockwell Green
Stockwell   SW9
Tel 274 9220
Open 10-6(Mon-Fri)
Wheelchair access none
Usually provides a summer project.
Information, advice and support to
Black women. One-to-one counselling,
a library, arts and crafts workshops
and creche facilities. Also provides
space for other Black women's groups
to meet in (see Women).

**Black Women's Self-Help Health
Group**
c/o Black Women's Centre
41 Stockwell Green
Stockwell   SW9
Tel 274 9220
Meets fortnightly to discuss women's

health issues including diet, self-
image, contraception, sexually
transmitted diseases and child
development.

Brixton Advice Centre
167 Railton Road
Herne Hill   SE24
Tel 733 4674
Open 1-4(Mon-Fri) 6.30-7.30(Fri for
legal advice)
General advice on immigration,
nationality and welfare for the Black
community and others.

Brixton Music Development
46 Kepler Road
Brixton   SW4
Tel 737 3237
Open 11-6(Mon-Fri)
Lively and active music project which
co-ordinates the Hip Hop Alliance,
Black Market Enterprises and the
Mobile Music Course. The Hip Hop
Alliance was started to help young
scratchers, breakers, rappers, graffiti
artists and others involved with hip
hop culture. They organise events at
the Brixton Recreation Centre. Black
Market Enterprises was set up to
promote and find work for artistes
having difficulties with mainstream
promoters and agents due to their
ethnic origin. The scheme has helped
an Australian Aboriginal group to
tour the UK and a Maori group from
New Zealand. Much of their work is
spent promoting Afro-Caribbean
music and dance forms coming out of
South London. A reggae or rap
musical is planned and they hope to
assist London-based Afro Caribbean
groups to work overseas. There are
also moves to organise
theatrical/musical promotions and
writers' workshops and to be involved
with local radio. As well as all of this
activity there's a 24 track recording
studio for hire.

**Brixton Neighbourhood
Community Association**
71 Atlantic Road
Brixton   **SW9**
Tel 274 0011
Open 9.30-6(Mon-Fri)
Legal surgery 6-7(Mon-Thur) 11-1(Sat)
MP's surgery 6-6.30(Fri)
Advice and counselling centre for the
community at large, used by many
Black people. Deals with legal matters,
housing, employment, educational,
matrimonial, police, training (ie job
training), consumer affairs, social
security, immigration and
nationality, small businesses, income
tax and insurance. Very sound advice
given by people who really do care
about your well-being and try to help
in the best way they can. If the BNCA
cannot help, they can usually refer
you to other organisations who can. It
seems a shame that MPs can only
spare half an hour a week to meet and
discuss problems with people, whom
they try to win or obtain votes from
at election times.

Caribbean-Hindu Society
16 Ostade Road
Brixton   **SW2**
Tel 674 0755
Advice and information for West
Indian and Hindu pensioners.

Dunraven School
Leigham Court Road
Streatham   **SW16**
Mother tongue Greek classes for all
ages 10-1 every Saturday – people of
all nationalities welcome. Sunday
evening youth club for Greek Cypriot
young people. Traditional dances,
games, sports and other activities.
The Achilleas Football Team
represents the local Greek Cypriot
community.

**Greek Parents Association
(Streatham)**
Tel 674 5040
Community language classes (up to O
level) are held on Saturdays and on

two nights during the week. Classes
are also held in traditional dance and
music and a youth group is planned
for the future.

IFEOMA (A Good Thing)
32 Gauden Road
Clapham North   **SW4**
Tel 627 4005
Open 9-9(Mon-Fri)
Hostel for single Afro-Caribbean and
Asian parents. Soon there will be
provision for pregnant single women.
Applicants by referral only (usually
via Social Services). General advice
and support.

Karolinka
c/o Polish Centre
6 Oliver Grove
South Norwood   **SE25**
Tel 310 4350 eve
Contact Mrs Kutereba
Karolinka is a highly regarded Polish
folk song and dance company which
celebrates the traditional village
folklore of Poland. Performers wear
the traditional costumes of each
region (about 500 exact replicas have
been handmade by members of the
company). They also have about a
dozen outstanding original costumes
(80/90 years old) which would make a
fine small exhibition. The company
has a large repertoire and performs
duets to full-scale 50-strong company
pieces. They rehearse every Thursday
night at the Polish Centre in Oliver
Grove. They perform frequently for
the Polish community, have appeared
at the Commonwealth Institute, three
times at the Albert Hall and have
toured nationally.

**Lambeth Chinese Community
Assocation**
2nd Floor
441 Brixton Road
Brixton   **SW9**
Tel 733 4377
Contact Mr Yiu Hing Cheung
Membership £1 (under 18's
free)registration fee £10 per year

Open 10.30-1 Sat
The Association aims to promote Chinese culture. Facilities include teaching English-born Chinese the language. Outings arranged. They are hoping to organize a women's group. They are looking for new premises. Classes are held at Stockwell Park School, Priory Grove, SW4.

Lambeth Community of Refugees from Vietnam
407 Wandsworth Road
Battersea   SW8
Tel 627 4798
Contact Mr Teu Vu
Community project for refugees from Vietnam.

Lambeth Irish in Britain Representation Group
Coldharbour Works
245a Coldharbour Lane
Brixton   SW9
Tel 274 7700
Contact Colin O'Flynn
Membership £2(waged) £1(unwaged)
£3 family membership
Wheelchair access to IBRG
The Irish in Britain Representation Group is a national community-based organisation with a national executive committee which operates at a branch level. IBRG aims are to promote a positive image of the Irish community in Britain, to promote Irish culture and to fight against Irish racism. The Lambeth branch has produced a charter which makes seven demands of Lambeth Council with a view to fulfilling these aims. In addition to its work as a pressure group it has an active welfare section, called Curam, which provides support to Irish elderly and disadvantaged people. There are regular language classes, video shows on topics of Irish interest every three weeks, advice on welfare benefits, a drop in club for the Irish elderly and a parent and toddler club. Regular Irish socials and traditional Irish music sessions are organised and Lambeth IBRG also

runs conferences and public meetings on topics of Irish interest. The Group meets every second Thursday at Lambeth Town Hall.

Lambeth Sickle Cell Centre
Swan Mews
2 Stockwell Road
Stockwell   SW9
Tel 737 3588
The Centre offers genetics counselling and can arrange for blood tests and give advice to people who are carriers or actually have sickle cell anaemia.

Lambeth Women and Work Project
460 Wandsworth Road
Wandsworth Road   SW8
Tel 622 9208
Campaigns for a better deal for women in Lambeth and offers advice to all women especially to those who have no qualifications or are disadvantaged in other ways. Has a training group for Black women and organises advice sessions and workshops in Brixton and on the Springfield Estate in subjects like child care, computers and manual trades. Phone for details and give them a ring first if you're planning to drop by.

Lambeth Youth Aid Project
16 Thornton Street
Stockwell   SW9
Tel 274 6760
Contact Mr Vinh Quoc Ngo or Mrs So Yu Lam
This is a special project run under the auspices of Lambeth Youth Aid. It aims to help and advise people from Vietnam who are not in full time employment and are between the ages of 16 and 25. Individual counselling includies teaching language and social skills, and how people can hold on to their own cultural identity without 'opting out' of English society. There is also group counselling.

Latin American Children's Project
c/o UJAAMA Centre
14 Brixton Road
Oval   **SW9**
Tel 582 5590
A Saturday school is held at Stockwell
Park School in Priory Grove, SW4.
The aim of the school is to teach
children their mother tongue and
culture. The classes are designed for
the age groups 0-5 and 5-15. In
addition, playschemes and outings to
the theatre are arranged. There is also
a Latin American youth club which
caters for young people up to the age
of 21.

**Latin American Community
Project**
c/o UJAAMA Centre
14 Brixton Road
Oval   **SW9**
Tel 582 5590
An advice and information resource
centre, offering help to community
groups and individuals on
immigration, health, education,
housing and interpretation. They also
offer advice on grant applications and
housing to people wishing to set up
community groups.

Latin American Football League
Clapham Common   **SW4**
Tel 671 4247
Contact Mr Avalos
Membership £1 per player
The League meets every Sunday on
Clapham Common from 9.30 to 6pm
This weekly event every Sunday
provides a meeting place for Latin
Americans and their families as well
as a good game of football.

L'Ouverture Theatre Trust
The Angell Centre
Wiltshire Road
Brixton   **SW9**
Multi-cultural theatre company
which also holds dance, drama and
singing workshops for children and
young people as well as a project for
the unemployed.

Mafalda
St Peters Hall
Prescott Place
Clapham   **SW4**
Tel 622 6285
Open 9-5(Mon-Fri)
Latin American nursery (named after
an Argentinian cartoon character)
catering for the under 5s.

Melting Pot Foundation
361 Clapham Road
Stockwell   **SW9**
Tel 274 3940
Open 9-5(Mon-Fri)
A long-established organisaation
which has shown its worth through
its longevity. A supplementary school
is provided through the Education
Welfare Service and a hostel for
adolescents. Food, clothes and other
items are all supplied. The second
phase involves self-catering. This is
for more independent young people
who will eventually live in their own
accommodation. Trips abroad as well
as around England are often
arranged.

Pakistan Service Association
120 Kings Avenue
Balham   **SW12**
Tel 674 7235
Contact M Ismail
The Association consists mostly of
retired people who keep in touch with
each other by holding religious and
cultural functions periodically. No
formal meeting place, they usually
meet in members' homes. Functions
are arranged in Upper Tooting
Methodist Church Hall.

Polish Centre
6 Oliver Grove
South Norwood   **SE25**
Tel 653 4047
Contact Mr Gudowski
A social club and community centre
which has regular Friday night social
events. Also club activities after High
Mass on Sundays from 12 until 2 and a
Saturday Polish language class for

Polish children – about 120 from 3 to 15 years of age).
This Centre is technically in Croydon.

Polish Community Centre
80 West Side
Clapham Common   SW4
Tel 228 6105/0257
A Friday evening social club, independent of any parish. Bridge is popular on Fridays and dances and other social functions take place (sometimes on a Saturday and Sunday too). To be able to join, the 200 or so members have to live in South London and have a Polish interest.

Race Today
165 Railton Road
Brixton   SE24
Tel 737 2268
Open 10-6(Mon-Fri) by appointment only
This group has produced a pamphlet explaining the action taken in the wake of the New Cross Massacre. Copies can be bought from the above address where the 10 year-old political journal Race Today is based.

Roots Theatre Company
2 Park Court
Studley Road
Stockwell   SW4
Tel 720 2707
A Black theatre company dealing with topical issues and using live music and workshops.

Sickle Cell Clinic
King's College Hospital
Denmark Hill   SE5
Tel 274 6222
Open 9.30-12.30(Tue)
Doctors can refer people with sickle cell trait or sickle cell anaemia to this Tuesday clinic, the only sickle cell clinic in South London. (Most hospitals see sickle cell patients in their haemotology clinics.)

Soma Books
38 Kennington Lane
Kennington   SE11
Tel 735 2101
Open 10-6(Mon Wed-Fri)
Bookshop with good range of Afro-Caribbean and South Asian books. All five languages at junior and senior level.

South London Irish Women's Group
South London Women's centre
55 Acre Lane
Brixton   SW2
Tel 274 7215
Contact Jean Rathbone
A meeting place for first and second generation Irish women where issues such as sexism, psychology, philosophy and religion can be discussed.

Speak Out
c/o Black Women's Centre
41A Stockwell Green
Stockwell   SW9
Tel 274 9220
Magazine produced by and for Black women.

UJAAMA Centre and Bookshop
14 Brixton Road
Oval   SW9
Tel 582 5590
'Ujaama' means 'co-operation' in Swahili and the project aims to provide people with the tools to understand their own situation and the position of others in society and the world as a whole. The Centre is concerned most notably with those who are disadvantaged and oppressed and with enabling them to begin to gain control of their own lives and change them for the benefit of all. The Centre offers space to like-minded community groups and can loan a 16mm film projector, a slide projector for no charge and, shortly, a video (for which a contribution will be requested). They also have a collection of traditional musical

instruments from around the world which they lend to schools. They are able to present several workshops including one which traces the traditions and history of the Guatamalan Indians. Ujaama is concerned with the Third World generally and there is always an interesting range of crafts and cards from Third World countries as well as books on many different cultures and issues (including a good selection for children and women). The Centre was initially funded by Oxfam and other bodies in 1976 and became a limited co-op in 1983. With the help of Lambeth Council, the members of the co-op are acquiring the lease on their property and will be increasing their activities in the future.

West Indian Ex-Servicemen's Association
10 Holmewood Gardens
Brixton Hill   SW2
Tel 627 0702
Open 10-4.30(Mon-Fri)
The Association was formed 16 years ago and has brought together Black ex-servicemen and women who served in the last war for this country, and in wars before and since. Not exclusively for Black ex-servicemen, the Association has about 325 members. They are there to help to support and help Black people generally.

West Indian Ex-Servicemen's Association
165 Clapham Manor St
Clapham   SW4
Tel 627 0702
Open 10-5(Mon-Fri)
Contact Neil Flanagan
Established 16 years ago, originally for ex-World War 2 veterans. Now a social and general counselling organisation (see above entry).

West Indian Senior Citizens' Association
105-9 Railton Road
Brixton   SE24
Tel 737 3505
A drop-in for West Indian pensioners for advice, information or a friendly chat. Activities include crafts, cookery, guest speakers, outings and keep-fit.

Lewisham

The increased community and political awareness of Black people was nowhere more dramatically expressed than in Lewisham after the tragic death of thirteen young people in 1981. It galvanised the local Black community in Lewisham and throughout London. The New Cross Fire March was a massive mobilisaton of Black people (probably the largest ever in Britain), joined by outraged White marchers.

In 1985 Lewisham elected its first Black Mayor, Councillor Les Eytle. The West Indian and African Community Association in Deptford continues its struggle for a just society. Now in its tenth year, the North Lewisham Project continues to provide support for the Association. The Steve Biko Youth Organisation has developed into a key youth organisation (see below). The church organisations in Lewisham are strong with the formation of many gospel groups and youth choirs. The Lee Gospel Choir from the New Testament Church of God in Lee High Road and the Tabernacle Young People's Choir from the Bibleway Tabernacle Church of God in Algernon Road are a few examples. In May 1985 the Calabash Centre for Black elderly people opened in George Lane, brought about chiefly by the active local CRC. They also sponsor the new hostel for homeless young Black men at 99 Burnt Ash Hill, known as '99'. The hostel is supported by the South East

London College and the Lee Centre who offer the residents (regardless of qualifications) access to further and higher education courses.

Lewisham has the smallest Irish population south of the river but it has a substantial Turkish Cypriot community. Several mother tongue classes for Turkish Cypriot children and young people are held at schools in the borough, community social functions are held at Riverside Hall in the centre of Lewisham and many local restaurants serve authentic cuisine for the Turkish Cypriot community. There are some Greek Cypriots also living in the Catford area where there is also a branch of Akel, the Greek Cypriot Communist Party.

Lewisham Council has an Ethnics Arts Officer and an artist-in-residence (Conrad Atkinson) who, amongst other activities, has been involved in judging an anti-racist greetings card competition. He is also working on a number of paving stones which will be laid around the borough, each one bearing the word for PEACE in twelve different languages.

Lewisham libraries all contain Black literature and books in Vietnamese and the Indic languages. There is a substantial stock of Indian and Afro-Caribbean material at Pepys and Deptford Libraries and Old Town Library has a good stock of Vietnamese books (see chapter on Libraries for addresses).

Business Advice

Ethnic Minority Leadership Project

1 Loampit Hill
Lewisham   SE13
Tel 469 0995
This organisation offers training for ethnic minorities in management committee skills and Black consciousness raising.

Lewisham Business Advice Service

225 Lewisham High Street
Lewisham   SE13
Tel 852 9207
This is a service for everyone but Lewisham is particularly keen to help ethnic minorities. At present only African, Afro-Caribbean and some Vietnamese and White people use this facility. Loans, grants and advice generally are offered. Lewisham Council is in the final stages of getting special money from the Greater London Enterprise Board which will go specifically towards businesses for Black and other ethnic minority communities. Another initiative in the borough is to be opened as the Deptford Business Agency in about March 1986. This will be a business development agency working mainly with ethnic minorities, using city bank and some council funding. This service will extend to Greenwich and Southwark.

Planning Department

Lewisham Council
Town Hall Chambers
Rushey Green
Catford   SE6
Tel 690 4343
Contact Joe Greenland
Joe Greenland is Lewisham's Business Advice Officer who deals specifically with any difficulties ethnic minority groups encounter. The Council is currently conducting a survey to find out how many ethnic minority businesses there are in the borough.

Community Relations Council

Lewisham CRC

48 Lewisham High Street
Lewisham   SE13
Tel 852 9808

Local Organisations

Brockley Community Project
126 Upper Brockley Road
Brockley   SE4
Tel 691 5861
Open 9.30-5(Mon-Fri)
Wheelchair access none
Deals with advice on social security
and juvenile crime.

Calabash Centre
26 George Lane
Catford   SE6
Open 9-5(Mon-Fri)
Wheelchair access and special toilets
Contact Mrs Hartnell
The Calabash Centre opened in May
1985 as Britain's first purpose-built
day centre for the Black elderly.

The Forest Hill Youth Project
2-4 Devonshire Road
Forest Hill   SE23
Tel 291 2928
Open 12-4(Mon-Tue Thur)
Drop-in for activities, information,
advice. The Black Arts Project is
based here. Phone for details.

Hearsay
Youth Aid Lewisham
17 Brownhill Road
Catford   SE6
Tel 697 2152/7435
Advice and group work which
includes a Black young people's group.

North Lewisham Project
144 Evelyn St
Deptford   SE8
Tel 692 7568
Umbrella organisation covering
The Steve Biko Youth Organisation,
the New Directions Training Project,
the Black Parents Education Project
and the West Indian & African
Community Association.

Organisation for Sickle Cell
Anaemia (OSCAR)
c/o Forest Hill Youth Project
2/4 Devonshire Road

Forest Hill   SE23
Tel 291 3976
A small group of volunteers set up this
project in 1978. They give information
about sickle cell anaemia and provide
counselling. The group is not funded,
has very limited facilities and shares
the cramped premises with a youth
project. It's an uphill struggle but
they are determined to keep going.

Pagnell Street Centre
Pagnell Street
New Cross   SE14
Tel 692 1783
Open 9.30-5(Mon-Fri) Youth Club 7-
9(Mon-Fri)
Caters for the needs of Black people
within the area. Counselling and help
to young single mothers are available.
Sport activities available, usually in
the evening. Drama group, activities.

Rushey Green Primary School
Culverly Road
Catford   SE6
Mother tongue classes for the Turkish
Cypriot community.

The Sickle Cell Society
c/o Lewisham Way Youth and
Community Centre
Lewisham Way
New Cross   SE14
Tel 692 1190/691 7633, 697 0941(eve)
The Sickle Cell Society is a charity
which offers leaflets, information and
support and can put people in touch
with counsellors. This is a new branch
that meets monthly at present during
evening or at weekends. Anyone is
welcome. A genetics counsellor has set
up the group and can arrange blood
tests at Lewisham Hospital's
haemotology department. The
Society's headquarters in Brent can
be contacted any week day during
office hours (Tel 451 3293).

Steve Biko Youth Organisation
140 Evelyn Street
Deptford   SE8
An important and established project
in the Black community. Counselling
and information sessions for
adolescents and adults as well as a
home-based educational programme.
Advice on education, law and
housing. Employment links have been
created with its community
programme. Black women's group has
two netball teams. Open events.

Stillness School
Stillness Road
Honor Oak Park   SE23
Mother tongue classes for local
Turkish Cypriots. Phone the Turkish
Association Cyprus (Tel 437 4940) for
details.

**Telegraph Hill Neighbourhood
Centre**
170 New Cross Road
New Cross Gate   SE14
Tel 639 0214
Open 9am-11pm(Mon-Sat)
Contact Rev Richard Bird
Umbrella organisation for all types of
groups, the staff at the Centre issue
support and advice to the local
community. Also West Indian
parents' group.

**West Indian and African
Community Association**
8 Walnut House
Clyde Street
Deptford   SE8
Tel 692 7568
Provides an advice service mainly for
Afro-Caribbean and African people
and struggles for a just society.

West Indian League
11 Belvoir Road
East Dulwich   SE22
Tel 693 5556
Group arranges football, swimming
and other sporting events. At present
they are looking for a new hall in
which to hold functions.

Merton

Merton has a smaller Black
population than the other South
London boroughs but the local Black
community shares the same problems
if not more acutely than the others.
There are also a number of Asians
living in Merton. The Council has a
commitment in principle to equal
opportunities, but this has still not
become policy. Recently, four new
posts to develop Merton's equal
opportunity programme have been
created and several new projects are
in the offing like an Ethnic Minorities
Centre. There is little publicity about
the local CRC which has recently
moved. The Youth Service claims that
its policy is to provide a service for
young people generally, a service
which does not discriminate between
groups. Hence Merton does not seem
to feel it is necessary to adopt policies
to meet the needs of Black people and
other ethnic minority groups. One of
their views is that boroughs like
Lambeth and Wandsworth have
particular problems which are
peculiar to them, thereby avoiding the
issues and any action. There are a
number of private companies in the
borough who have had equal
opportunities for many years.
Littlewoods, Ford and Marks and
Spencers amongst others now have
ethnic monitoring as part of their
policy.
Very few people know that there is a
sculpture of Emperor Haile Selassie,
the most potent symbol of the
Rastafarian movement in Canizzero
Park, Wimbledon. It was cast in stone
by Hilda Seligman in 1936.

Community Relations Council

Merton CRC
36 Colliers Wood High Street
Colliers Wood   SW19
Tel 540 7386

Business Advice

Merton Enterprise Agency
12th Floor
Crown House
London Rd
Morden
Tel 545 3067
Not council funded, the Merton
Enterprise Agency is an advisory
service that tries to encourage
businesses to come to Merton. They
are not able to offer any grants.

Local Organisatons

Asian Elderly group of Merton
1A Bookham Court
Phipps Bridge Road
Mitcham
Tel 640 1914
Contact Inayatullah Ahmed
The group runs a day centre for Asian
elderly persons, a refuge centre for
the neglected and deserted elderly
persons and an advice centre. It also
provides community services such as
advice on immigration, nationality,
social security, racial harassment,
education and interpretation.

Bengali Association of Merton
c/o 43 Quicks Road
Wimbledon   SW19
Tel 540 8610
The Association has a women's group
and a men's group but no fixed
premises at present. All services are
offered in members' homes and the
organisation is self-funded at the
moment which is an indication of the
dedication of the group. Facilities
include a supplementary school with
mother tongue classes. Occasionally
sports facilities are provided. Ring for
details.

South London Irish Association
138 Hartfield Rd
Wimbledon   SW19
Tel 543 0608

Wheelchair accees to club
Aims to promote the welfare, social
and cultural activities of the local
Irish community. Irish dancing
classes for children, Irish language
courses, family evenings and get-
togthers. Concerts also held when
notable artists and celebrities
perform. Darts, pool, golf and the
Emeralds soccer team. Ceilidh and old-
time sessions, a senior citizens' club
on Thursday afternoons, and live
music on Saturday and Sunday
nights. Outings and holidays are also
arranged.

Southwark

The most pressing issue for the local
Community Relations Council is the
implementation by the borough of its
equal opportunities policy.
Unemployment in the Black
community is high as in other South
London boroughs. Black people form
the largest ethnic minority group in
the borough and many feel that the
system of housing allocation is racist.
The current system is under review as
pressure from local groups and the
CRC mounts. Education is another
major concern where there are far too
many Black children in special units.
The suspension and expulsion figures
are high in Southwark. The
supplementary school has moved from
Clubland to Crawford School in
Crawford Road, where it's getting
good support from the headmaster and
the community.
Southwark has the third largest Irish
population south of the river which is
represented by an Irish in Britain
Representation Group. There is a
large Greek Cypriot community in
Southwark, especially around
Camberwell as one of London's four
Greek Orthodox Cathedrals is St
Mary's in Camberwell Church Street.
Also based in Camberwell is the South
London Cyprus Association which

was actively involved in helping those in need after the 1974 Turkish invasion of Cyprus. There are also some Turkish Cypriot Southwark residents, particularly around Peckham.

Southwark has an active community arts programme. Its libraries contain a good selection of books for ethnic minority groups, with a collection of books in Scandinavian languages at Rotherhithe Library. Harper Road Library has a good selection of books in Urdu, Bengali, Gujarati and Hindi and North Peckham Library has its main collection of books in Greek, Turkish, Vietnamese, Chinese, Hindi, Gujarati, Urdu, Bengali, Punjabi and Arabic.

Community Relations Council

Southwark CRC
352-4 Camberwell New Road
Camberwell   SE5
Tel 274 8793

Business Advice

Employment and Training Division
Southwark Council
30-32 Peckham Road
Peckham   SE5
Tel 703 6311 Ext 2219
Contact Patrick Sampson
This is a business advice service which has access to money specifically for ethnic minorities. It is a start-up scheme (£1000 to start up a project). The scheme was set up nine months ago and so far 60% of its loans have gone to the Afro-Caribbean community but it is established for all ethnic minority groups. Patrick Sampson who runs the scheme has knowledge of all schemes on offer even those not linked to the Council. He can advise on any special training schemes and other issues. The new Deptford Business Agency (see

Greenwich) will be opening around March '85 and Southwark residents will be able to make use of it.

Local Organisations

African Arts in Education Project
2nd Floor
Cobourg School
Cobourg Road
Camberwell   SE5
Tel 703 1619
Contact Dr B Tsehai (Education Officer)
Trained African artists spend six one-day sessions bringing the culture of the African peoples alive in schools. (See South Londonwide Organisations – Education at the beginning of this chapter.)

African People's Movement
226 Camberwell Road
Camberwell   SE5
Tel 701 7121
Open 10-5.30(Mon-Fri)
This organisation exists to campaign and raise awareness of African affairs and culture, to fight racism and to improve the quality of life for Africans and ethnic minorities in general. It also offers help, advice and information on such matters as housing and supplementary benefits and will give practical help to the most needy in the community and to families who are undergoing strain. Home visits are made if people cannot manage to get out. It champions the problems of children who have been sexually abused by adult members of their families. Legal representation is available for people who have been taken to court by the police.

African Women's Association
34 Colegrove Road
Peckham   SE15
Tel 237 4214 & 733 6291/2 or c/o
Women's Centre 701 2564
Contact Tania Maqhubria
Wheelchair access to Centre
Aims to bring African women

together to support each other. Offers advice on immigration and social security. Open to all African and Black women living in Southwark. Several West African languages and Zulu spoken.

Meets once a month at Southwark Women's Centre, 2-6 Peckham High Street, SE15.

Afro Asian Advisory Service
Cambridge House
137 Camberwell Road
Walworth SE5
Tel 701 0141
Open 9-5(Mon-Fri)
Advice on issues like immigration, nationality, welfare benefits and filling in forms. Staffed mostly by voluntary workers. Special emphasis on social work in Southwark.

Bengali Mahila Samity (Bengali Women's Group)
6 Rochester House
Manciple Street
Borough SE1
Centre for Bengali women.
Caribb Club
26 Elsie Road
East Dulwich SE22
Tel 693 2632
The Club organises social, sports, cultural and educational activities for young people in Peckham and Lewisham.

Cobourg Junior School
Cobourg Road
Camberwell SE5
Turkish Cypriot mother tongue classes are held either in the evening or on Saturday mornings. Ring the Turkish Cyprus Association (Tel 437 4940).

Dachwyng Parents Association
104 Kirkwood Rd
Peckham SE15
Tel 701 5110
Open Centre 9-10(Mon-Fri) Youth Club 4-10(Mon-Fri)
Wheelchair access to premises

A family centre in the North Peckham Estate. The Association aims to advance the education and social welfare of Afro-Caribbean families. Provides counselling sessions and activities such as art, keep fit, Afro-Caribbean dance, sewing and cooking. There is a Saturday school for children aged 3-16.

Gurudwara Baba Bhudda Sahib Ji
59 Sylvester Road
East Dulwich SE22
Tel 693 0559
Cultural and recreational activities for the Sikh and Hindu communities and English and Punjabi lessons for children. Also a women's group.

Karib Project
22 Linden Grove
Peckham SE15
Tel 732 3298
Open 24 hrs
Accommodation and counselling for homeless youths aged 14-18, mainly of Caribbean origin. An electronics training workshop is being established. A mini bus is used for outings.

Mama Yeabu
Black Women's Action (SE London)
Latimer House
Latimer Road
Walworth SE17
Tel 708 0117
Most members are Black single parents. The group runs an advice service, a parent and toddler group and general social and educational activities. They hope soon to have their own centre in the Walworth area. Language spoken are Temne, Yoruba, Swahili, Hausa, Fullah and Fanti.

Midas United Service Trust
45 Benhill Road
Camberwell SE5
Tel 703 5867 (due to change)
Information service about issues affecting the West Indian community.

New World Business Services
20a Camberwell Green
Camberwell SE5
Tel 703 9272
Provides advice and help to Black
people wanting to start up a new
enterprise.

Open Access Project
5-5a Westminster Bridge Road
Lambeth North SE1
Tel 928 9941
Open 9-5.30(Mon-Fri)
Wheelchair access by prior
arrangement
This organisations helps
disadvantaged groups including many
Black people and other ethnic
minorities. Their work involves
finding suitable training and
education and liaising with
organisations that have equal
opportunities' policies. They act as a
pressure group to improve current
employment recruitment. To
individuals they offer advice on
employment problems like racism,
training and education, careers, job
opportunities, skills and support for
those who are unwaged.

**Pan African Organisation (South
East)**
7 Taplow Block
Merrow Walk
Aylesbury Estate
Walworth SE17
Tel 701 2072(day) 582 7540(eve)
Open 10-1 3-5(Mon-Tue) 6-9(Thur for
legal advice) 10-1 3-5.30(Fri) 6-12(Fri
youth service)
The Pan African Organisation aims to
disseminate knowledge and awareness
of African affairs and culture and to
promote Africans and other ethnic
minorities in general. It campaigns
against racism and is actively
involved in the relief of poverty and
distress with the object of improving
the living conditions of the hardest
hit in the community. Advice and
information is offered to the
underprivileged and to families

undergoing strain. Home visits are
arranged if people are unable to get
out for whatever reason. Although
specifically an African organisation,
no-one in need is turned away. An
extremely worthwhile organisation.

Peckham Black Women's Group
10 Bedeney House
Peckham Road
Camberwell SE5
Tel 701 2651
Helps women with problems with
social security, housing and health
services. Holds conferences and has a
drop-in meeting twice a week.

Peckham Bookplace
13 Peckham High Street
Peckham SE15
Tel 701 1757/0720
Open 10-6(except Thur)
Wheelchair access with assistance
A community project with a bookshop
containing multi-cultural children's
books and Black literature.
Community classes include numeracy,
English, English as a second
Language and Black Studies.

Sass Theatre Company
9 Churchmead
234 Camberwell Grove
Camberwell SE5
Tel 703 3135
A Black women's theatre company
committed to expressing the
experience of Black women on the
stage.

St Veronica's School
Flint Street
Walworth SE17
Traditional Irish dancing two nights
a week.

South East Islamic Cultural Centre
24 Newington Causeway
Elephant & Castle SE1
Tel 407 1602
Provides religious education for
Muslim children and families and

assists the Asian community, particularly Bengalis, living near the Centre.

South East Muslim Association
51 Elm Grove
Peckham   SE15
Tel 732 4690
Caters for the social and cultural needs of Muslims and provides counselling and support.

South London Cyprus Association
11 Camberwell Church Street
Camberwell   SE5
Tel 701 0788
A registered charity involved primarily in organising fund-raising events following the 1974 invasion of Cyprus. (See South Londonwide section – Pressure/Action Groups at the beginning of this chapter for further information.)

Southwark Asian Community Association
55 Surrey Road
Peckham   SE15
Tel 639 9840
Aims to promote the welfare of Asians in Southwark and to foster racial harmony. Open to all Asian people.

Southwark Bhaghini Samaj Asian Women's Group
15 Frankfurt Road
Herne Hill   SE24
Tel 274 2653
Provides advice and support to Asian women and organises classes and activities for children. Gujarati language and Asian dance and music classes are held on Saturday mornings.

Southwark Black Workers' Group
8 Camberwell Green
Camberwell   SE5
Tel 703 1906
Contact Patricia Oakley
Provides a forum for matters of concern to the Black community. Also gives support to individuals in cases

of racial harassment, in dealings with the courts and police, and organises racism awareness training.

Southwark Campaign to oppose Racism Now
135 Rye Lane
Peckham   SE15
Tel 732 3731
Contact Joel O'Laoughlin
Set up specifically to challenge racism and to raise consciousness about issues affecting lives of those from the ethnic minorities.

Southwark Irish in Britain Representation Group
221 Rye Lane
Peckham   SE15
Tel 639 6718
Contact Sean Carty
A campaigning group whose principle aim is to fight racial discrimination in the context of the Irish community. The Group is represented on the Ethnic Minorities Sub-Committee at Southwark Council and attends police committees. It also provides welfare support and arranges some socials.

Southwark Muslim Council
26 Upland Road
Dulwich   SE22
Tel 639 9840
Aims to promote unity among Muslims. Organises social, cultural and educational activities. Meets once a month.

Southwark Muslim Women's Association
c/o Copleston Centre
Copleston Road
Peckham   SE15
Tel 732 3435(day) 732 9689(eve)
Provides social and cultural activities for Muslim women and children. Members are mostly from Pakistan and India. The Copleston Centre office is open for advice and counselling 9-2 on Mondays and Fridays and 1-5 on Wednesday. There are Urdu and Arabic classes on

Saturday and Sunday afternoons at Thomas Calton School, Choumert Road in Peckham, where women's meetings are also held on Sunday afternoons. Play schemes are organised in the Easter and summer holidays.

Temba Theatre Company
Rooom 208
Dominion House
101 Southwark Street
Waterloo SE1
A Black theatre group formed in 1972, which runs workshops and performs in schools and community centres.

Thomas Calton Youth Centre
Adys Road
Peckham SE15
Some Turkish Cypriot mother tongue classes are held either on Saturday mornings or in the evening during the week. Phone the Turkish Association Cyprus (Tel 437 4040) for information.

Umoja Theatre Company
St Michael's Vicarage Annexe
Thompsons Avenue
Bethwin Road
Camberwell SE5
Tel 701 6396
Contact Gloria Hamilton/Alex Simon
This young South London Black theatre group is developing a fine reputation. Their aims are to write, develop and perform works of theatre which are relevant to the traditional needs and culture of the community and to promote racial harmony.

Unity Social and Cultural Arts Association
c/o Race Equality Unit
Town Hall
Peckham Road
Camberwell SE5
This Association aims to promote cultural, social and educational activities for the Black community.

Wandsworth

Over seventy years ago Battersea became the first London borough council to elect a Black Mayor – John Richard Archer. Local Black people are trying to get a plaque placed on the house where he lived in Brynmaer Road, SW11. Apart from today's Black community there are many Asians from the Indian Sub-continent and East Africa living in the borough. The second largest Irish community in South London lives there too as do many Chinese people. Over 200 children enjoy a Chinese mother tongue class (the £1000 grant for which took several years to be awarded) and there is a Chinese Church in Earlsfield. There is a Greek Cypriot community in Battersea and a local Greek Orthodox Church (converted from a Protestant one) in Battersea Old Town. A large number of Polish people live in parts of Wandsworth (some say as many as 5000 Polish people live in the whole of South London). There is a fair-sized Vietnamese community living round the Wandsworth Road area. Wandsworth adoption and fostering workers work hard to find Black families for Black children and families of the same ethnic origin for other children in Wandworth's care. The Council is recruiting specialist ethnic minority workers such as an Arts Development Officer for Ethnic Minorities (Tel 871 7037) and an Ethnic Minority Employment Liaison Officer (Tel 871 6207). The borough has an Ethnic Minorities Library, a mobile library service for ethnic minorities which travels around the borough and a special service that delivers books and music to people who are housebound. There is a Black history loan collection available from the Local History Library and books for the Afro-Caribbean community can be found at Balham District Library as can a good selection of

Polish books. The Ethnic Minorities Library is based at Tooting Library and caters for Afro-Caribbean and Asian people. Books are available in five Indian languages – Punjabi, Bengali, Urdu, Hindi and Gujarati and a few books in Tamil. There are also Afro-Caribbean books written by Black authors from Africa, the Caribbean and the USA and an extensive Afro-Caribbean and Asian children's library. The selection of English books covers ethnic issues in Politics, education, literature. There is an audio section which comprises records and cassettes from Asia. The library also serves as an information and reference centre for Asian literature.(See chapter on Libraries for opening times and further details.)

Community Relations Council

Wandsworth CRC
57 Trinity Road
Tooting SW17
Tel 767 3631

Business Advice/Enterprise Schemes

Wandsworth Business Resource Service
3rd Floor
140 Battersea Park Rd
Battersea SW11
Tel 720 7053
A service available to everyone, but well used by ethnic minority communities. Business counsellors help and advise both new and existing businesses. Individual advice and half-day workshops on specific aspects of business. They offer a start-up grant scheme to complement the Government's enterprise allowance scheme (you have to have been unemployed for at least 13 weeks) and they give grants of up to £2000.

Ethnic Minority Employment Liaison Officer
Wandsworth Town Hall
Wandsworth High St
Wandsworth SW18
Tel 871 6207
This Officer advises individuals and ethnic minority groups about schemes and grants and puts them in touch with Wandsworth's Business Resource Service.

Local Organisations

ACER Project
Wyvil Road
Vauxhall SW8
Tel 627 2662
Open 9-5(Mon-Fri)
Charity that ensures that the Black perspective is included in the school curriculum by providing multi-cultural material to schools. (See Education in South Londonwide section at the beginning of the chapter.)

Anglo-Chinese Families Association
206 Beechcroft Road
Upper Tooting SW17
Tel 672 9889
Contact Tom Brown
An Association of people of Anglo-Chinese marriages and of others interested in Anglo-Chinese relations. Members are given help to improve their English, Cantonese and Mandarin. There is also a resource library for school projects on the culture of the Chinese and Vietnamese peoples, stocked with books, slides, photos and other material, some bilingual and some in English. Social and cultural activities twice monthly at the Labour Hall in Wimbledon (opposite the Polka Children's Theatre). A regular newsletter is produced for exchange of information.

Asian Parents Group
12 Ascot Road
Upper Tooting   SW17
Tel 767 0617
Contact Santha or Eddy Williams
A group of Asian parents formed this
group to address themselves to
educational matters of relevance to
Asian children. Some of its areas of
concern are the use and teaching of
Asian languages in schools, religious
and cultural matters in schools, the
involvement of Asian parents in the
running of schools, racism in schools,
the provision of nursery places for
Asian children and liasion with local
headteachers.

**Association of Jamaican Trusts
(UK)**
62 Sistova Road
Balham   SW12
Tel 675 3950
Has close links with the Jamaican
High Commission. General advice for
the West Indian community.
Information for Jamaicans wishing to
return home. Immigration and
nationality details are also given.

**Balham & Tooting Sports & Social
Club**
94 Balham High Road
Balham   SW12
Tel 874 7233(day) 673 2999(eve)
Contact N Williams Ext 246
Open 12-11(Mon-Thur) 12-2(Sat-Sun)
A non political, multi-racial Sports
and Social Club which aims to meet
the needs of the multi-cultural
community in Balham. Guest speakers
are occasionally invited to discuss
problems relating to housing,
education, employment, immigration,
social security and legal matters.
There are also interpeters and
translators available in French and
German. Team dominoes, darts and
cricket.

Balham Food and Book Co-op
92 Balham High Road
Balham   SW12

Tel 673 0946
Good selection of Black and multi-
ethnic books.

**Balham & Tooting Youth
Outreach Centre**
1-3 Hildreth Street
Balham   SW12
Tel 673 3415/8
Open 9-6(Mon-Fri)
Wheelchair access to Centre
The Centre was opened in 1970 in the
home of a Mrs Beryl Brown, who
through her work with the church,
saw the need for somewhere where
young Black people and others could
go for help. In 1983 she obtained the
above building from Wandsworth
Concil and moved in to begin her
work. The project offers young people
advice on obtaining accommodation
and on general issues. There is
counselling for ex-offenders and
guidance on police and court matters.
Classes are available in office skills,
reception duties, photography,
tailoring and dressmaking and
catering.

Battersea Black Women's Group
248 Lavender Hill
Battersea   SW11
Tel none
Womens' issues discussed from 4pm to
6pm on Sundays.

**Battersea and Wandsworth Irish
Association**
Tempo House
15 Falcon Road
Battersea   SW11
Tel 350 0661
Contact June O'Sullivan
Membership £1(waged) 50p(unwaged)
Aims to raise the profile of the Irish
and to give a voice to the Irish in
Battersea and Wandsworth, to fight
to have the Irish recognised as a
separate ethnic group and to have
Irish books and culture reflected in
local schools and libraries. This group
was formed in 1983 and meets the first
Wednesday of every month. Activities

include regular Irish nights, an Irish language class and an Irish dancing class. Newsletter produced every other month.

Black Elderly Group
Wilditch Community Centre
Culvert Road
Battersea SW11
Tel 223 9509
Open 11-3.30(Mon Wed)
Wheelchair access to Centre and special toilets
Drop-in centre for the Black elderly within the Battersea area. They do welcome clients from other areas but unfortunately have no pick-up facilities.

Black Elderly Group
4 Livingstone House
Wyndham Road
Camberwell SE5
Contact Verma Lindsay
Tel 701 8354
Open 12-3(Mon-Tue) 10-3(Wed)
Wheelchair access to centre
A day centre for Black pensioners. The Centre provides Caribbean food, craft activities and regular outings. On Mondays there are keep-fit classes, as well as a light snack. On Tuesdays discussions on any topic are usually held. Wednesday is a day for crafts and chat as well as a full cooked meal. The Group is in the process of trying to acquire a permananet building. Two permanent staff have recently been employed.

Black Elderly Project
946 Garratt Lane
Upper Tooting SW17
Tel 767 8426
Open 10-5(Mon-Wed Fri)
Wheelchair access to part of building
This centre opened in March 1985 and boasts a membership of 140. Activities include board games and a piano which is immensely popular. A luncheon club is also offered. The main function of the centre is to provide a place where the Black

elderly can meet and discuss things amongst themselves in a warm, friendly and relaxed atmosphere.

Bluefields Twinning Committee
c/o David Mazzetti
74 Cathles Road
Balham SW12
Tel 673 7901
In 1984 Lambeth 'twinned' with a town called Bluefields on the Nicaraguan Atlantic coast (facing the Caribbean Basin). Bluefields had been under British colonial rule so most of the inhabitants speak English. There is a large Black population and a minority White Spanish-speaking community. Before the 1979 Revolution the Atlantic coast was sorely neglected but there is now much greater integration with the Spanish-speaking people of the Pacific coast and Bluefields has made tremendous progress in education, agriculture and standards of health. The Twinning Committee offers moral support and sends medicines and bi-lingual (Spanish/English) books to Bluefields. A trust fund is being set up and the ACTT (the union for the film and television industry here) is hoping to improve radio and television communications in the Bluefields area so that a wider population can be reached. Contact the above address if you want to be actively involved in the Committee's work.

Chinese Church in London
4 Earlsfield Road
Earlsfield SW18
Tel 870 2251
Non conformist church which offers a range of extra activities such as Saturday mother tongue classes.

Greek Parents Association (Tooting)
86 Bramfield Road
Battersea SW11
Tel 223 7373 (day) 223 5616(eve)
Contact Tonia Kastelanides

The Association holds Greek language classes for children 9.30-1.30 on Saturdays at the Junior School, Broadwater Road, SW17. History and religious instruction are also taught and integrated into the language lessons. Children are taught to understand the Greek culture and customs. Fund raising activities and meetings with parents. Also dancing, music, singing, drama (groups available for performance). Interpreting, translating facilities available in Greek. Cookery, craftwork, needlework. 86 pupils at present.

Hindu Society
49 Fishponds Road
Upper Tooting SW17
Tel 228 9013(day) 672 9455(eve)
Contact TN Thapen (day) Miss R Sood(eve)
The Society offers cultural and religious instruction. The programme includes a women's group, drama group and keep fit. Interpreters and translators are available for Hindi, Gujarati and Swahili. Cookery, craftwork and needlework is also taught. Hindi language classes held at 11-1 on Sundays at the Millan Centre. Membership of over 100.

Idara-I-Jaaferiya
18 Church Lane
Upper Tooting SW17
Tel 672 5373
Contact Asad Baig
Open 8pm-9.30pm(Mon-Thur Sat) 1-2(Fri)
The centre acts as both an Islamic and religious centre and as a community centre. Religious and cultural education classes are held in Arabic and religious instruction (Sundays 11am-1pm). Maths O level is on Friday evenings 6.30-8.30. Other activities include games, table tennis and football. Translators on request in Parsee, Urdu and Arabic.

Islamic Cultural and Education Centre
75 Falcon Road
Clapham Junction SW11
Tel 228 4267(day) 223 1867(eve)
Contact Hafix Nisaruddin Ahmed
Classes held 10-1.30 on Saturday and Sunday mornings. This Islamic organisation runs classes in Arabic, Urdu, Bengali, English and Maths for young Muslim people of all ages as well as classes in religious and moral education. There is also a youth and women's group.

The London Mosque
16 Gressenhall Road
East Putney SW18
Contact The Imam (Maulana Sheikh Mubarak Ahmed)
Open 9-5(Mon-Sun)
The mosque offers religious instruction to its members and for anyone who is interested in the teachings of Islam. It's programme offers sports activities, informal advice on education, employment, immigration and personal matters. Group activities include a youth club, a women's group and a playgroup (throughout the year). Interpreters and translators are available for Urdu.

Memon Associates UK
231a Lavender Hill
Clapham Junction SW11
Tel 223 7787 or 785 7899
Contact Farida Osman/Haroon Omar
The association offers advice on religious and cultural issues to do with Islam, for example burials and mosques. Its programme includes a youth club at Spencer Park school (Saturday mornings 8-11), sporting activities, table tennis, badminton and keep fit. A women's group meets at Furzedown Secondary school (Friday mornings 8.30-10.30). Interpreters and translators available for Kachi, Gujarati and Urdu. Membership of over 100.

Millan Centre
59 Trinity Road
Upper Tooting   SW17
Tel 767 3631
Open 9-5(Mon-Fri)
Provides advice on immigration,
nationality and other issues for the
Asian community in Wandsworth.
Parent and toddler clubs, latchkey
scheme, luncheon club and mother-
tongue classes in Hindi, Punjabi,
Gujarati, Urdu and Arabic.

Pakistan Welfare Association
95 Fernlea Road
Balham   SW12
Tel 995 7755 Ext 221(day) 675 0909(eve)
Contact GA Butt
The organisation is concerned with
the welfare of Asians and works to
improve race relations. It also advises
the Asian community on cultural and
religious instruction. It gives
informal advice on matters relating to
the law, housing, mugging,
immigration. It works with statutory
and voluntary bodies but is not grant
aided. Interpreters and translators
are available in Urdu, Punjabi,
Gujarati, Marhati and Tamil and
English classes are provided for Asian
women. Social and musical evenings
are organised where both the host and
immigrant communities are invited.
The group takes elderly people to the
seaside once a year and arranges
outings to many locations.

Patmore Youth Project
The Tenants Hall
Thessaly Road
Battersea   SW8
Contact Vinh Quoghgo or Robin
Nailer at Lambeth Youth Aid 274 6760
This is a special project for North and
South Vietnamese people, based at
The Patmore Youth Project. English
language classes are provided for
Vietnamese and Chinese people and
Arabic classes are also held. There is a
youth club on Saturdays from 4pm to
6pm and pool and Table Tennis on
Wednesday evenings.

Probashi
76 Hydethorpe Road
Balham   SW12
A Bengali organisation which offers
support and advice to Bengalis in
Wandsworth and runs classes in the
Bengali language.

Sikh Gurbwara
142 Merton Road
Wandsworth   SW18
Tel 874 1723(day) 393 0139(eve)
Contact J Plaha
Open 7am-11.30 5.30-7.30(Mon-Fri) 10-
9(Sat) 10-12 5-7.30(Sun)
The Gurbwara is a place of worship
for people of the Sikh faith. Punjabi
classes are held every Saturday at
6pm and music classes on Saturday
afternoons 4-6pm. There is also a
youth and women's group.

**Society of Friends of Polish
Children**
50 Nightingale Lane
Balham   SW12
Tel 673 4177
Eleven classes are offered (including
O and A level) in Polish language,
literature, history and culture. There
is also a playgroup during the week
for working parents.

The South London Brahmin Samaj
294 Franciscan Road
Upper Tooting   SW17
Tel 672 1918
Contact JK Thaker
The Samaj aims to promote the social
and cultural activities of the Brahmin
community in South London.
Members meet 15/20 times per year.
Activities range from Puja (prayer
sessions) to sports festivals. The group
is affiliated to the other 15 Brahmin
Associations in the UK which meet
annually to participate in a
nationwide sports festival.

**The South London Cultural
Society**
17 Auckland Road
Clapham Junction   SW11

Tel 228 0620
Contact Mr Ganguly
The Society is active on a cultural front and organizes social and musical events for the benefit of the Asian community. It also has been active in establishing a new musical academy (the Indian Musical Academy and Resource Centre) for those interested in learning Indian music. Classes held 3-8pm on Sundays at the Courthouse Community Centre, 11 Garrett Lane, SW18.

South London Irish Association
168 Hartfield Road
Wimbledon SW19
Tel 543 0608
Open 11-11
Daily activities, with a bar, and resident welfare workers.

South West London Asian Women's Association
49 Hillbrook Road
Upper Tooting SW17
Tel 767 3631(day) 672 0668(eve)
Membership £7 per year
This organisation runs classes in Urdu, Arabic, cookery, sewing, knitting and craftwork. Advice on personal problems is offered on Thursday afternoons 2.30-3.30 at 79 Eswyn Road, SW17. Women's group meets at 10 on Tuesday mornings at Hillbrook School. Interpreters and translators are available for Urdu and Bengali. Artists can be booked for public performances. Cultural and religious activities are organized occasionally as are musical evenings and festive functions.

Tara Arts Centre
356 Garratt Lane
Earlsfield SW18
Tel 871 1458/1450
Contact Rekha Prashar
Wheelchair access to theatre & cafe
Professional Asian theatre with two touring companies and an active workshop programme at the Centre and at local schools. (For fuller description see Theatre section of South Londonwide Organisations.)

The Tooting Youth Project
St Peter's Church Hall
7a Beechcroft Road
Tooting Bec SW17
Tel 672 9643 or 674 9562
Five full-time workers give advice on education, the social welfare system, employment, the law and a range of personal problems. They help community groups and the Project sponsors a foundation training programme for 15 trainee community workers. Their are loads of interesting activities, a skills exchange and workshops. To quote from their own literature 'The Tooting Youth Project caters mainly for Black youths and its aim is to serve and develop the Black community. It is not exclusively Afro-Caribbean, there are White and Asian workers involved with the Project and all the workers are willing to serve the White and Asian communities; but we feel that we can best serve these other communities by developing and preserving our own identity. Integration as a community and integraton with the wider community should go hand in hand.' A youth club with a full programme of activities is run for unemployed young people.

UK Asian Women's Conference
108 Mitcham Road
Upper Tooting SW17
Tel 942 9102
Contact Lalita Ahmed
Open 10.30-3.30(Mon-Fri)
The Women's Conference runs musical instrument classes and has a dance and garba group. Social occasions for the elderly are also held. Interpreting facilities available in Hindi, Bengali, Gugerati and Urdu.

Unity Centre
54 Ravenswood Road
Balham   SW12
Tel 673 0793(24 hrs)
Open 9-5(daily)
Wheelchair access to Centre
Through its helpline the group aims
to help the mentally ill and depressed.
The hope to open a home for the
mentally ill and for one parent
families. Trips are organised in the
summer. The majority of the clients
are Black.

Wandsworth Boys' Hostel
117 Bedford Hill
Balham   SW12
Tel 673 6430
Much more than just a refuge for boys
with problems at home and/or with
the police. The 117 Project, as it is
known, provides a service that by
rights the Government should be
doing. The housing of homeless young
men. An active approach is made to
find accommodation for single young
Black males while allowing them
somewhere to stay while this is being
done. A very strong emphasis is placed
upon providing an educational
supplement to what has been learnt at
school, wherever needed, eg
numeracy, literacy and the filling in
of forms. A club house also exists for
sporting activities as well as musical
and drama tuition. The 117 Project
was at one time being funded by
Wandsworth Council. They are now
an independent organisation and are
linked with Pathway Housing
Association.

Westside Youth Club
Ackroydan Estate
Windlesham Grove
Putney Heath   SW19
Tel 788 1338
Progressive Club with several Black
members on the staff.

White Eagle Club (Anglo-Polish Social Club)
211 Balham High Road
Upper Tooting   SW17
Tel 672 1723
Contact Mr Pok
Open 12-3 6-11(Mon-Fri) 12-2 7-
10.30(Sat-Sun)
The White Eagle Club is a members'
Club (of about 500) which has social
amenities such as a bar and a
restaurant. The Polish Benevolent
Fund, a scheme for elderly people,
operates under the auspices of the
Club, and provides housing in
Foxbourne Road. The elderly use the
facilities of the Club on a regular basis
and are treated to a Christmas dinner.
A women's group meets on Monday
evenings and a dance group meets on
Tuesday and Wednesday evenings.
Interpreting facilities are available in
polish on request.

York Gardens Community Centre
Lavender Road
Battersea   SW11
Tel 223 7961
A Centre for the whole community
with an active Black pensioners'
group.

FESTIVALS AND EVENTS

In this chapter we have included all known 1986 events and festivals that were scheduled to take place in South London at the time of going to press. The activities in the listing are examples of what has gone on in previous years. The events range from major national fixtures to local neighbourhood fairs. For some, we have been able to give definite dates, but for any event that is unconfirmed we have mentioned the month in which it is most likely to take place and a contact number so that you can check the actual date nearer the time. Of course, nothing is certain in the world of festivities so don't be surprised if the occasional (apparently definite) event doesn't take place after all. For information about happenings that haven't been planned this far in advance, check your council's events guide and other leaflets, which should be freely available in your local library or at the Town Hall. Some of the fun is bound to be lost from our city with the departure of the GLC, previously responsible for a vast programme of community festivities in nineteen South London parks. The GLC has also hosted several major South Bank festivals, including the Spring Festival at Whit Weekend, the South Bank Festival in July, the Children's Festival in August and Thamesday in September. At the time of going to press, the future of all these events is being considered by the Department of the Environment.

Date(s)	Month	Event
1-4	January	**World Invitation Club Basketball Championships**, Crystal Palace. The largest club basketball championships in the world.
10-11	January	**Home Countries Senior Indoor Hockey**, Crystal Palace.

Date(s)	Month	Event
24 29	January- March	**Live Arts Festival**, North Peckham Civic Centre. An event each week (see Theatre – Arts Festivals).
14-16	February	**Women's National Indoor Hockey Championships**, Crystal Palace.
22-23	February	**British Canoe Union International Canoeing Exhibition**, Crystal Palace.
8-9	March	**National Dinghy Exhibition**, Crystal Palace.
14-16	March	**European Women's Judo Championships**, Crystal Palace.
22-23	March	**National Sub-Aqua Club Exhibition**, Crystal Palace. Festival of underwater sport.
29	March	**Oxford and Cambridge Boat Race**. Putney to Mortlake.
30	March	**Easter Parade**, Battersea Park. Ex-GLC event, almost certain, but ring to check. Tel 871 6354.
30-31	March	**Blackheath Kite Festival**, Blackheath. The only organised kite festival we know of in the whole of London. Demonstrations of all types of kite from all over the world as well as teddy bear parachuting!
7 17	April- May	**Lewisham Festival**. Performing arts, gymnastics, workshops, break dance, body popping, some professional events at Lewisham Theatre and countless other activities.
12	April	**National Men's Judo Championships**, Crystal Palace.
20	April	**London Marathon**. Through Greenwich, Lewisham and Southwark.
27	April	**Plants and Gardens Spring Fair**, Museum of Garden History, St Mary-at-Lambeth, Lambeth Palace, SE1. Lots of stalls and many unusual plants for sale.
10	May	**Karate Union of Great Britain National Championships**, Crystal Palace.

Date(s)	Month	Event
17	May	**Mitcham Carnival,** Three King's Place, Mitcham Common. Arena events, local charity stalls, fancy dress parade and procession with jazz band.
25-26	May	**Kennington Races,** Kennington Park. Arena events, egg and spoon races, funfair, street theatre, body popping. Donkey and Soap Box Derby on the Monday.
26	May	**Telegraph Hill Festival.** Community festival with charity stalls, side shows, children's activities, music and theatre events.
unconfirmed	May	**Battersea Arts Centre May Fair.** Home-made crafts – jewellery, pottery, knitwear, soft toys and West Indian jams and chutneys – all at good prices. Usually May Day weekend. Tel 223 8413.
unconfirmed	May	**Historic Commercial Vehicle Club Rally,** Battersea Park. Start (approx 7am) of London to Brighton commercial vehicle run. Usually first Sunday in May. Tel 871 6354.
unconfirmed	May	**Woolwich Week.** Fun and events in Woolwich Town Centre plus lots of shopping bargains and special promotions. Tel 854 8888 Ext 2309.
unconfirmed	May-July	**Brixton Festival.** Eight weeks of events and activities in Lambeth – music, dance and poetry workshops, cultural awareness programmes and lots of other events, culminating in Brixton Carnival Weekend (previously in Angell Park but possible change of venue in 1986). Tel 582 3513/3607 Bob Adam.
30 15	May- June	**Greenwich Festival.** Arts, music, theatre, dance, community fairs and countless other events (see Theatre – Arts Festivals).
31 1	May- June	**Peckham Rye Gala Weekend.** Sports events, rides, show jumping championships, local charity stalls, Southwark Mayor's carnival.
7	June	**Blackheath Village Fayre.** Large charity fair with arena events and fireworks in the evening.
14-15	June	**Belair Gala Weekend,** Belair Gardens, Gallery Road, SE21. Sports events, rides, local charity stalls.

Date(s)	Month	Event
14-15	June	**Clapham Festival**, Clapham Common. Afternoons only. Local charity stalls and arena events with attractions such as parachute jumping, motorcycle team displays and bands.
14-15	June	**Roehampton Festival**, on the green, Danebury Avenue. Bands, majorettes, small funfair, karate demonstrations and market stalls. Sports day on the Sunday.
20-29	June	**Deptford Festival.** Multi-cultural community festival and knees-up for the people of Deptford. Children's activities, a historic pub crawl, an old age pensioners' outing, a community fair and the Deptford Ball.
21	June	**Roehampton Garden Society Village Flower Show**, Parish Hall (corner of Roehampton Lane and Alton Road) at 3.15.
21	June	**Southfields Festival**, Coronation Gardens, Merton Road, Lower Wandsworth, SW18. Community festival with local charity stalls, children's activities and general entertainments.
21-22	June	**Putney Show**, Putney Common, Lower Richmond Road. Large country show with arena events.
28-29	June	**Lambeth Sports Festival**, Brockwell Park. Every sport you can imagine represented in arena events, displays and activities you can take part in.
28-29	June	**Southwark Sport and Fun Weekend**, Southwark Park. Sports activities, mini motor cycles, horse and dog show.
28-29	June	**Tooting and Balham Carnival.** Procession from Atkins Road, Balham, through Tooting to Tooting Bec Common. Charity stalls and tombola, funfair and Carnival Queen. Donkey Derby and car boot sale on the Sunday.
unconfirmed	June	**Blackheath Kite Festival.** Demonstrations and other activities. Tel 808 1280 Tony Cartwright.
unconfirmed	June	**Kodak AAA Championships (Men's National Athletics Championships)**, Crystal Palace. Tel 778 0131 Bryan Stoddart.

Date(s)	Month	Event
unconfirmed	June	**London to Brighton Bike Event.** Probably end of June. Send sae for details and application form to Mr B Popay, P O Box 75, Bath.
unconfirmed	June	**Plumstead Make Merry,** Plumstead Common. Stalls, arena with acts, fringe events, clowns, street theatre, bands and dancing. Usually in the afternoon of the third Saturday in the month. Tel 854 3895 Alan Hosegood.
unconfirmed	June	**Riverside Fair,** Clockhouse Community Centre, Defiance Walk, Woolwich Dockyard Estate, Woolwich, SE18. Community festival (part of Greenwich Festival). Stalls, puppet shows, fire-eaters, street entertainment and lots of other activities for children and adults. Tel 855 7188.
unconfirmed	June/July	**Greek Cypriot Community Festival,** Burgess Park. Song, dance, theatre and stalls at this four year-old event. Probably last Sunday in June or first Sunday in July. Tel 703 3911 Dave Sadler.
23 6	June-July	**Wimbledon Lawn Tennis Championships.**
11	July	**Peugeot Talbot Games,** Crystal Palace. Major athletics meeting, part of the Grand Prix series.
12-13	July	**London Youth Games,** Crystal Palace. Largest festival of youth sport held in Britain.
12-13	July	**Wandsworth Weekend,** King George's Park. Country show with arena events, funfair, puppet and craft workshops, sub-aqua, dry ski slope and lots of other activities.
19-20	July	**Lambeth Country Show,** Brockwell Park. Huge country show – arena events, steam engines, horse show with shire horses, crafts, horticultural tent, stalls and village green entertainment.
20	July	**Woolwich Horse Show,** Woolwich Stadium and Woolwich Common.
unconfirmed	July	**Dance Days '86,** Battersea Arts Centre. Concentrates on youth dance and develops a different theme each year (see Dance – Special Events). Usually first two weeks of July. Tel 223 8413.

Date(s)	Month	Event

unconfirmed July — **European Deaf Swimming Championships**, Crystal Palace. Tel 778 0131 Bryan Stoddart.

unconfirmed July — **Kings Acre Neighbourhood Council Fete**, Windmill Gardens. Lots of children's activities – steel bands, theatre, choir groups, community stalls, and disco 2-5pm. Possibly first Sunday of the month. Tel 274 9408/9 Angela Hay.

unconfirmed July — **Lewisham People's Day**. Outdoor event and fun day with stalls representing the council and local voluntary organisations, fund-raising events, children's entertainments and music. No venue fixed as yet. Possibly last Saturday in July. Tel 690 6368 Mary Mann.

unconfirmed July — **Spring Gardens Festival.** Children's competitions, theatre performances, bands and other events and activities. Possibly 6 July. Tel 582 4480 Ms Barker.

unconfirmed July/August — **South Bank Splash Arts festival**, organised by the National Theatre. Children's lunchtime stage shows, workshops, clowning and storytelling. Multi-cultural music events in the evening. (See Theatre – Arts Festivals.) Usually last two weeks of July and first two weeks of August. Leaflets available from beginning of June. Tel 633 0880.

unconfirmed July/August — **West Indian Festival of Art and Culture**, Brockwell Park. Bands on stage, arts and crafts stalls, West Indian food, amusements for children. Tel 671 8975 (daytime) Junior Smith.

8 August — **International Athletics Club Floodlit Meeting**, Crystal Palace.

12-14 August — **Mitcham Fair**, Mitcham Common.

unconfirmed August — **Clipper Week.** Ten days of fun and festivities around the river in Greenwich. Possibly 16-25 August. Tel 854 9217.

unconfirmed August — **Greater London Horse Show.** Previously GLC-run on Clapham Common, neither the dates nor the venue for this event were fixed at the time of going to press. Possibly 23-25 August. Tel 0753-860633.

Date(s)	Month	Event

unconfirmed August — **South London Carnival**, Battersea Park. This event didn't happen in 1985 but it has previously been held in Battersea Park since the Festival of Britain. Arena events, charity and exhibition stalls. Antique market and procession of floats on the Sunday. Usually second weekend in August. Tel 764 8491 Mr Griffiths.

unconfirmed August — **Thamesmead Carnival.** Multi-cultural carnvial celebrating West Indian, Asian, Vietnamese and other cultures. Possibly August Bank Holiday. Tel 311 3844 Peter Dyal or Frank Robson.

6 September — **Wandsworth Horticultural Show**, Civic Suite, Wandsworth Town Hall.

13 September — **Roehampton Garden Society September Show**, St Margaret's Parish Hall, Putney Park Lane, at 3.15.

unconfirmed September — **Great Britain Athletics International**, Crystal Palace. Tel 778 0131 Bryan Stoddart.

unconfirmed September — **Walworth Festival**, Walworth and Burgess Park. Lasts for a week, starting on a Friday with a local church service, the crowning of Miss Walworth and opening events. On the Saturday, a community fair with floats and procession and events (usually in Burgess Park). On Sunday, Five a Side Football and, through the coming week, events and competitions involving local schools and organisations. Tel 703 3911 Dave Sadler.

10-12 October — **Tradescant Trust Crafts Fair**, Museum of Garden History, St Mary-at-Lambeth, Lambeth Palace, SE1. Crafts and a plant stall.

unconfirmed October — **Lewisham Jazz Festival**, Lewisham Theatre. Month not absolutely certain so be sure to check. Tel 690 2317 Chris Hare.

unconfirmed October — **South London Music Festival**, Nettlefold Hall, Norwood High Street, West Norwood. A programme of new music featuring internationally known musicians, which usually takes place over 3/4 weekends on Fridays and Saturdays. Tel 656 1758 Simon Desorgher.

Date(s)	Month	Event
unconfirmed	October	**Women's National Judo Championships**, Crystal Palace. Tel 778 0131 Bryan Stoddart.
5	November	**Lambeth Fireworks** at Brockwell and Kennington Parks and on Clapham and Streatham Commons.
5	November	**Southwark Fireworks Night** at Peckham Rye.
unconfirmed	November	**Wandsworth Fireworks** at Battersea Park, King George's Park and Tooting Common. Tel 871 6354.
17-29	November	**Southwark Community Arts Festival** (see Theatre – Arts Festivals).
21-23	November	**Christmas Bazaar**, Museum of Garden History, St Mary-at-Lambeth, Lambeth Palace, SE1. Lots of stalls and some plants for sale.
unconfirmed	November	**National Judo Championships for Boys and Girls**, Crystal Palace. Tel 778 0131 Bryan Stoddart.
unconfirmed	November	**World Cup for Trampolining**, Crystal Palace. Tel 778 0131 Bryan Stoddart.
unconfirmed	November	**London Film Festival**, NFT and other venues. Usually mid-November for about two weeks. Tel 437 4355.
unconfirmed	November-December	**Dancy Brolly**. Lambeth's exciting and ambitious dance festival (see Dance – Special Events). Tel 622 6655 Ext 355.
unconfirmed	December	**Christmas Craft Fair**, Battersea Arts Centre. Home made crafts – jewellery, pottery, knitwear, soft toys, West Indian jams and chutneys at good prices. Usually first weekend in December. Tel 223 8413.

FILM
AND VIDEO

The Ritzy is one of South London's two most important assets when it comes to watching movies so we thought it only right and proper that it should be featured accordingly in this chapter. It was created by five people who moved in (as tenants of Lambeth Council) to start work on the old Classic Cinema building at the beginning of November 1977. The building had been closed for two years and gutted by the previous tenants so there was a derelict building and a lot of work to be done. Amazingly, the 480-seat Little Bit Ritzy (soon to drop its 'Little Bit') opened the following spring. Over the years the original group has changed (only one founder member remains) and the programming has become slighly more mainstream, partly because of commercial pressures but mainly due to changes in the film industry. These days there is a dearth of European art house movies. When the Ritzy began its life it could rely on at least one Bunuel, Chabrol, Wenders, Truffaut or Fassbinder a year. Sadly, this is no longer the case, though during this period some quality Hollywood movies and stylish European productions have emerged, many of which have acquired quite a cult following. The Ritzy's audience is a young one. 50% come from Brixton and surrounding areas, 45% from other parts of South London (going deep into the south) and 5% make the journey over the river. The Ritzy isn't affiliated to a distributor or to other exhibitors which means that it's placed very much at the bottom of the pile by distribution companies. If anyone gets mucked about it's small independent outfits like the Ritzy. Despite the cinema's success, some distributors disapprove of its double bill policy either because they feel more money could be made by running continuous single film programmes or because they believe 'their' film is demoted by the presence of another. 10,000 copies of the Ritzy's forthcoming programme are circulated each month to other cinemas, arts venues, colleges, bookshops and restaurants. The weekly programme doesn't stick rigidly to a set pattern though for the last four years Wednesday has been a special day either for good repertory, a season, or films that examine a topical theme. Sometimes there is no film at all and audiences are treated to a cabaret spot or live music. Sunday afternoon is the slot for benefits or films of minority interest which the cinema can't afford to put on during the week. During the summer, in conjunction with Lambeth Council and local play schemes, the Ritzy presents three children's films a week at 25p a time. All in all, between 1600 and 1700 people visit the cinema each week. Nevertheless at best it only breaks even. Pat Foster (the one founder member of the Ritzy) feels that this situation won't change unless certain major and unaffordable improvements are made to the building. There is hope that they may receive a grant for a new roof and a ventilation system but other long-term improvements (a larger screen, improved sound, seating, foyer space and toilets) are totally out of reach. At one time not so long ago there was an Inner City Partnership plan to link the Ritzy with the Tate Library, providing better toilet facilities, disabled access, a cafe, exhibition space and smaller auditorium, but when it came to it the DOE backed out. Meanwhile, despite its physical needs, the Ritzy continues to deliver quality (from its choice of movies to its locally baked carrot cake) and is much enjoyed by South Londoners far and wide.

The second major South London film venue is, of course, the NFT, which has designated 1986 Spanish Year. The first part of this season started in November '85 with a celebration of the producer Elias Querejeta. In March '86 there will be a programme of pre-Civil War Spanish Cinema and Films Under Franco. The Spanish theme continues in June '86 with films made during Franco's last years (1964-1975) and, also in June, there will be a tribute to director Carlos Saura, who will hopefully be involved in a Guardian Lecture or some other appearance during the season. December will complete the Spanish Year with a programme of Films After Franco, featuring the work of Pedro Almodovar and others. There is much else happening at the NFT in '86. January will include a tribute to John Gilbert (leading American actor of the 20s) and the films and television work of John Mortimer, who will be delivering a Guardian Lecture on 28th January. Also in January there is to be an Ingrid Bergman retrospective, and programmes entitled A Woman's Place, Film and Struggle, and Avant-Garde Cinema (including cubist cinema and the works of Epstein, Dulac and Markopoulos). January also includes the first part of two workshops – the first one, Introduction to Film, has screenings on four consecutive evenings with a discussion after each one, and the second one will look at the differences between cinema and stage acting. These themes will be taken further in February. Other planned programmes for February include the film music of Hollywood composer Dmitri Tiomkin, New Films from Taiwan, the films of Alan J Pakula and some examples of American PBS TV productions. At the time of going to press the NFT hadn't planned the rest of 1986 except for the London Film Festival which is scheduled for 13-30th November.

Much of the year will be spent continuing to work on the massive new Museum of the Moving Image next to the NFT. The opening date is expected to be some time in the winter of 1987. (See the introduction to the Museums chapter for further information about the project). There are also a number of wonderful film clubs in South London offering entire film seasons at ridiculously low prices, and the Wandsworth Cinema Club and Battersea Arts Centre have regular shows for children as does the NFT.

Cinemas and Clubs

Battersea Arts Centre
Old Town Hall
Lavender Hill
Battersea   SW11
Tel 223 8413
Wheelchair access throughout with special toilets
Induction loop system for people with impaired hearing
Membership £1(cinema only)
£7.50(includes discounts to some BAC facilities) Tickets £1.80(adults)
£1.50(unwaged) £1(children)
Sat afternoon children's films
75p(children) £1.50(adults)
Prices under review
Two main programmes a week, one on Wednesday and Thursday and the other on Friday, Saturday and Sunday. Children's films every Saturday afternoon at 3.30 and special programmes for children at half-term and in the school hols.
No smoking cinema

Catford ABC
1 Bromley Road
Catford   SE6
Tel 698 3306(answerphone with programme details)
697 6579(other enquiries)
Wheelchair access to Cinema 1 with special toilet
Tickets £2.10(adults) £1.10(children)
£1(OAPs till 6pm) £1.10(adults

accompanying children till 6pm)
Smoking and no smoking areas

Elephant & Castle ABC
26 New Kent Road
Elephant & Castle   SE1
Tel 703 4968(answerphone with programme details)
708 0066(other enquiries)
Wheelchair access to ABC 2 & 3 but no special toilets
Tickets £1.10 & £2.10(adults) £1(OAPs till 6pm)
Smoking and no smoking areas

Elephant & Castle Coronet
New Kent Road
Elephant & Castle   SE1
Tel 407 1991
Wheelchair access to cinema but no special toilets
Tickets £2.20(adults) £1.10(children)
£1(OAPs)
Smoking and no smoking areas

Greenwich Film Society
Greenwich Theatre
Crooms Hill
Greenwich   SE10
Tel see below
Wheelchair access none but lift is planned
Membership £14.50(joint) £8(single)
8 international feature films are shown on a Sunday evening roughly once a month from October to May. Members may take up to two guests. Membership details from J Hembrough (Tel 692 9689).
No smoking throughout

Imperial War Museum
Lambeth Road
Lambeth North   SE1
Tel 735 8922
Wheelchair access to cinema with special toilets
Tickets no charge
Free feature films, documentaries, newsreels and shorts about the two World Wars, usually at 3pm every Saturday and Sunday and at 12 noon

and 3pm every day during the school hols. Ring for details.
No smoking throughout

Lambeth Film Society
Nettlefold Hall
West Norwood Library
1 Norwood High Street
West Norwood SE27
Tel see below
Wheelchair access with assistance
Membership £10 £6(half-season)
£5(students & unwaged) £2.50(OAPs)
Guests £1.50
About 20 international feature films from September to June at 7.45 on alternate Tuesdays. Members may take up to two guests. Information and membership forms available from Mrs J Abbott, Hon Sec, Lambeth Film Society, 34 St Julian's Farm Road, SE27 (Tel 761 4729).
No smoking throughout

Lewisham Film Society
Lecture Hall
Bromley Road Library
170 Bromley Road
Catford SE6
Tel see below
Wheelchair access to hall but no special toilets
Membership £4.50(for 5 films) £8(for 10) £9(for 15) £10(for 15) £12(for 20 or more)
Guests £1
Over 30 feature films from October to February usually at 7.30 on Tuesdays and Thursdays. Members may take up to two guests. Information and membership details from Mr Herbert, Lewisham Council, Riverdale Offices, 68 Molesworth Street, SE13 (Tel 852 9121 Ext 285).
No smoking throughout

Lewisham Studios 6 & 7
Lewisham Road
Lewisham SE13
Tel 852 6111
Wheelchair access via steps but staff happy to help, no special toilets

Tickets £2(adults) £1(children & OAPs)
Smoking and no smoking areas

National Film Theatre
South Bank
Waterloo SE1
Tel 928 3232/3 or 633 0274(for daily ticket availability)
Wheelchair access to NFT 1 with special toilet
NFT1 has induction loop for people with impaired hearing NFT1 & 2 have some special earphones
Membership Full £13.50(monthly programme, Sight & Sound, BFI Yearbook, Three Sixty, use of BFI Library & priority booking for London Film Festival)
Full + MFB £22.50(as above plus Monthly Film Bulletin)
Associate £8.70(monthly programme, Three Sixty and priority booking at LFF)
Student £6.50(as Associate + use of BFI Library)
Senior Citizen £6(as Associate)
Tickets £2.50 £1.25(OAPs, unwaged, disabled people & accompanied children for Junior NFT shows)
£2(standby on the day)
The National Film Theatre shows repertory and world cinema in the 466-seat NFT1 and the smaller NFT2 (162 seats). NFT3 is used mainly for NFT guests, private screenings and occasional seminars. There's an excellent bookshop, bar and self-service restaurant. Because of licensing laws members are not allowed to bring guests under the age of 16 except to Junior NFT shows or films designated by a 'J' in the programme. For some of the NFT's 1986 activities see the chapter introduction above.
No smoking in NFT 1 and 2

Putney ABC
Putney High Street
Putney SW15
Tel 788 3003(answerphone with programme details)

788 2263(other enquiries)
Wheelchair access to ABC 2 with
special toilet
Tickets £2.20(adults) £1.20(children)
£1(OAPs till 6pm)
Smoking and no smoking areas

Ritzy, Brixton

Ritzy Cinema
Brixton Oval
Coldharbour Lane
Brixton   SW2
Tel 737 2121
Wheelchair access steps but staff
happy to help but no special toilets
Membership 30p pa
Tickets £2.70 70p(OAPs & children
under 14) £1.70(unwaged & students
for many shows)
The Ritzy shows double bills with
programme changes usually on
Thursday or Friday. Wednesdays are
reserved for good repertory, theme
shows, or films that are part of a
season, and one-off screenings and
benefits generally take place on
Sunday afternoons. Some music and
cabaret shows happen occasionally
and there's always a children's season
in the summer. (See intro for more
informaton.)
No smoking area

Streatham ABC
5 Streatham High Road
Streatham   SW16
Tel 769 1928(answerphone with
programme details)
769 6262(other enquiries)

Wheelchair access to ABC 2 & 3
Tickets £2.20(adults) £1.20(children)
£1(OAPs till 6pm)
No smoking

Streatham Odeon
Streatham High Road
Streatham   SW16
Tel 769 3346
Wheelchair access to Odeons 2 & 3 and
Odeon 3 has access to special toilet
Tickets £2.50(adults) £1.50(children
OAPs & unwaged)
No smoking areas in all 3 cinemas

Thames Polytechnic Film Society
Main Hall
Student Union Building
Thomas Street
Woolwich   SE18
Tel 856 9196
Wheelchair access Phone David
Lenton 855 0618 who will open side
doors in Wellington Street. No special
toilets Membership £8 for season
Tickets £1(non members)
Double bill or long feature every
Thursday evening from October till
the end of May. Bar. The Thames Poly
used to be the force behind the
Thames Film Festival screened at the
Poly and at the old Odeon in
Wellington Street.
No smoking

Wandsworth Cinema Club
York Gardens Community Centre
Lavender Road
(corner of York & Plough Roads)
Battersea   SW11
Tel 223 7961
Wheelchair access to Centre with
special toilets
Membership 30p pa
Tickets 50p(children)
80p(accompanying adults) £1(adults
unaccompanied)
A short and feature for children every
Friday at 5pm during term time.
Wednesday afternoon shows in the
school hols. Ring for details.
No smoking

Well Hall Coronet
Well Hall Road
Eltham   SE9
Tel 850 3351
Wheelchair access to Screen 2 but no
special toilets
Tickets £2.40(adults) £1.50(children)
£1.50(OAPs till 6pm Mon-Fri)
£1.50(adults accompanying children
to special children's shows)
No smoking area in Screen 1
Smoking throughout Screen 2

Wimbledon Odeon
The Broadway
Wimbledon   SW19
Tel 542 2277
Wheelchair access to Odeons 2 & 3 but
no special toilets
Tickets £2.50(adults) £1.50(children &
OAPs) Odeon 3 pullman seats £3.10 &
£2.70(adults) £1.70(children & OAPs)
*No smoking area in Odeon 1 and no
smoking throughout 2 & 3*

Woolwich Coronet
John Wilson Street
Woolwich   SE18
Tel 854 2255
Wheelchair access none
Tickets Before 6pm £1.50(everyone)
After 6pm £2.40(adults) £1.50(children
& OAPs)
Small no smoking area

Woolwich Coronet

Film and Video Makers

There appears to be plenty of film and
video activity in South London and
we list below a few of the
organisations involved.
There are also individuals who are
based in South London though not
strictly attached to a production
company. One such is camera person,
•Ross Keith, who is based in Battersea,
has done a lot of work for the BBC,
CBC and CBS and works a great deal
with Iain Bruce. While he was a
student at RCA he made a number of
videos for the Labour Movement. He
also worked with Chris Reeves (of
Platform Films) on The Cause of
Ireland, a 110 minute documentary
funded by Channel 4 from which
several bits of dialogue and a whole
sequence was censored. Platform
Films covered the whole period of the
miners' strike, making a total of eight
videos. Ross Keith and Iain Bruce are
currently discussing a project with
Channel 4 which will look at various
aspects of British society in the
aftermath of the miners' strike.
For those who would like to try their
hand at making their own videos
courses are becoming more accessible
and are being offered at adult
education institutes and colleges in
South London like Clapham-
Battersea, Morley College, Goldsmiths
and the London College of Printing.
There are courses both for beginners
and those who have had some
experience. Many youth projects have
started to buy equipment for local
groups to use, and some that already
have equipment are Teenage
Information Network, Hearsay, and
Wandsworth Unemployed Youth
Project (see Young People). Art
centres like the Albany and Battersea
Arts Centre have equipped themselves
with video facilities too. For
individuals who already have some
video experience and wish to be
involved in further projects there are
organisations like Lambeth Video and

London Video Arts (see Not Strictly South London) that will hire equipment and editing facilities. Hire prices vary enormously depending on the nature of the project and whether you are a group or an individual. There are few opportunities to see art and community videos. Art videos get an occasional airing at Brixton Art Gallery and Cafe Gallery. Music videos are shown at nightclubs like Kisses in Peckham and Boxers in South Norwood. The Fridge in Brixton really does video proud by having one hundred TV screens around the dance floor. As such, it is the definitive showcase for art and music videos in South London.

Quite a different kettle of fish altogether, there are some vast commercial set-ups in South London such as Clearwater (see below) and Ewart & Co Studio in Wandsworth Plain, which has two studios with cameras, VTR and full sound equipment. The studios are hired for promos and commercials and by companies like Channel 4.

Cable television is on the cards for Wandsworth and may be in actual operation by December '86. ITD Cable (Tel 930 7523) has the franchise for Wandsworth and is currently trying to raise finance from international banks and commerce. A lot of the investors are coming from North America where cable televison is well established. The Government is committed to cable but has stipulated that it should be laid underground and that certain standards of high technology should be met. There are three ways of producing cable programmes. A cable operator can concentrate on making local programmes, or buy-in lots of different material and assemble it for a new channel, or be supplied with a complete programme service. Thirty channels are anticipated for Wandsworth. The reason Wandsworth was chosen as a suitable area was because of the closeness of the houses, the stuff the pavements are made of and the demographics of the area. Croydon already has a cable network and apparently several other London boroughs fit the bill.

After Image
Studio 7
52 Acre Lane
SW2
Tel 735 6642

After Image is a video company that has been around for about nine years. They specialise in television programmes on the performing arts and entertainment, and work mainly for Channel 4. When Channel 4 first started they created a new-style arts magazine programme called Alter Image which won many awards. Also, more recently for Channel 4, they made a series of five musicals with Pookie Snackenburger which went out in April '85. They are currently working on four 15-minute programmes loosely based on magic, using the music of Bill Nelson (lyricist, singer, guitarist and leader of the 70s' band BeBop DeLuxe).

Albany Video
The Albany Empire
Douglas Way
Deptford   SE8
Tel 692 0231
Wheelchair access throughout with special toilets
Open 9.30-6(Mon-Fri)

Albany Video provides a useful library of video tapes made for and by community groups (as well as those made by their own production team). Ask to see their lists and go along to preview any you might want to hire. The hire charge is £10 for 48 hours and tapes can be collected or posted. Amongst others in stock there are a good variety of tapes for young people, women and ethnic minority groups. They also have equipment and an editing suite for hire to local groups. The demand is high. If you live in Deptford you can also approach their production team if you have an idea for a video. They will also give advice to anyone wanting to purchase equipment for a scheme or project. If a group wants to go on a video course they will try and organise one.

Battersea Arts Centre
Old Town Hall
Lavender Hill
Battersea   SW11
Tel 223 6557
Contact Monty Whitebloom
A new mobile film and video project at Battersea Arts Centre which offers a series of projects to groups or individuals working with film and video. People with no experience can learn the basics of both media, and advanced groups can work on projects of their own making. There is no editing suite but there are Super 8 and 16mm facilities and a range of video equipment. The plan is to participate in a wide spectrum of community and arts projects. Contact Monty Whitebloom to put your name down on a course and/or discuss projects with him.

Clearwater Film Company
185 Battersea High Street
SW11
Tel 228 8886
Clearwater is a commercial organisation, which owns three companies. Clearwater Films produces commercials, Clearwater Features concentrates on feature films and, amongst others, made the 25-part animated Thomas the Tank Engine series seen on Central TV in '85. The third company is based in New York, and is involved in American series, features and commercials made here. Clearwater also its own studio round the corner in Yelverton Road with camera and lighting facilities, which are available for hire.

Frontroom Productions
79 Wardour Street
W1
Tel 734 4603
Don't be misled, this is an (almost) genuine South London feature film company in that it used to be based here and three of its four members live South of the river (the fourth let us down by moving northward). Much of the company's work is set in South London. Intimate Strangers was made in Chaucer Road in Dulwich and Ursula and Glenys starts in Clapham. Both of these films are being shown at the '85 London Film Festival and both were directed by Robert Smith and John Davies, who are acclaimed as 'two of Britain's most distinctive and talented film-makers' in the Festival programme. Angela Topping and Gordon Hann are the other two members of Frontroom, a production co-operative which has been going for about four years and which for a long time had its cutting room in Railton Road. The company makes one major feature about every two years. Previous films have included the highly acclaimed Maeve (a BFI Production Board feature set in Belfast and later shown on Channel 4) and Acceptable Levels (also screened on Channel 4). At present the company is working on a drama called Soho, also for Channel 4, and several other projects are in the pipeline.

ILEA Learning Resources Branch
TV & Publications Cente
Thackeray Road
Battersea   SW8
Tel 622 9966
Wheelchair access by lift
Open 9-6(Mon-Fri)
The ILEA Learning Resources Branch was set up in 1967 and used to supply schools with visual material on a cable network. This was abandoned in 1978 in favour of video cassettes and most of today's material goes out on VHS. It is distributed to schools and colleges in the the ILEA area and

marketed nationally and internationally through the Central Film Library and the Christian Education Movement. The programmes consist mainly of children's programmes, drama and documentaries. Facilities include a 3-camera studio, a mobile unit, a film unit, a battery portable unit, scenic and graphics departments. There is also a training studio which schools use to help young people (over 11) learn television techniques. Some attend courses that last several weeks. Plans are afoot to make the training studio available to local community groups during the evenings and at weekends.

Lambeth Video
245a Coldhabour Lane
Brixton SW9
Tel 737 5903
Wheelchair access none
Open 10-6(Mon-Wed)
This is a community video project which has equipment as well as an editing suite for hire. Prices are worked out on a sliding scale depending on the group and project. Lambeth Video also runs training courses – ask to have your name put down on the waiting list. There are special schemes within the project for women and people from ethnic minority groups. If you wish to hire equipment you will be asked to demonstrate that you know how to use it. The Lambeth Video production team has worked on a tape about young people and homelessness and is at present making a video about sports provision in South Lambeth. Individuals as well as groups who live in Lambeth are welcome.

Pictures of Women
10a The Pavement
SW4
Tel c/o 720 5976
Contact Christina Pearle
Pictures of Women was set up as a multi-media women's co-op in October

1982. There are currently three members in the group and a trainee and they all do everything. They don't have any public funding, don't pay each other much and earn their money by doing other jobs like teaching. They aim to use a range of visuals to project women's issues. They have made a series of six films on female sexuality for Channel 4 (shot on video and using lots of animation) and more recently Words In Action which was a series of interviews with women writers from the Third World about the link between women's writing and direct political action. In late 1984 they made a film called Co-ops at Work (shot on 16mm and available on video cassette). This was a training film produced for the Lambeth Co-op Development Agency and funded by the London Enterprise Board. It looked at five very different co-ops in Lambeth and demonstrated the ideology behind co-ops, how decisions are made, how you get the right information and how you make them work. For visuals they do not restrict themselves to film and video. In 1982 they designed a poster for a national radical nurses' group which depicted a typical 'hospital romance' scene. They have a group of people who regularly join them on a freelance basis and they themselves often work on other people's projects.

Smith Bundy Video
10a The Pavement
SW4
Tel 720 5976
Smith Bundy Video is a company of five full-time workers who are joined by freelancers when the need arises. They use film (16mm) but mainly video as it's a lot cheaper. They do a lot of work for trades unions, local authorities, charities and voluntary agencies. They are currently making four programmes about the rights of private tenants for SHAC with Alexei Sayle playing the landlord. About six

months ago they made three documentaries on an equal opportunities programme for the business world, explaining the scheme to employers and authorities. They have also worked for the GLC's Welfare Benefits Office, explaining how a new micro computer can help the elderly claim their benefits. In conjunction with this, they made a couple of TV commercials encouraging people to claim benefits. Another project (made at the request of a number of associations for deaf people) involved a subtitled programme on what it's like to be deaf or to have impaired hearing. This was distributed to high street stores as part of a staff training scheme. Other subject material has included pay and grades for manual workers, a video for the TUC on the political fund vote, a visual diary of a summer holiday for mentally and physicaly handicapped children, made as a fund-raising tool for a children's charity, and a programme about the Portage learning scheme for the under 5s.

The South London Film Society
98 Lordship Lane
SE22
Tel 693 7061
Contact Peter Shinkfield
Peter Shinkfield is a documentary film-maker who uses 16mm and will work for any worthwhile organisation. He also runs the South London Film Society with a colleague, which began in Cambridge House, Camberwell Road in 1947 and then moved to a library in Lordship Lane. Its main aim was to bring film to the non cinema-going public. It seemed, however, that it was functioning much like any other film society and that those who came were already 'converted'. Thus, Peter Shinkfield and his colleage (who works in North London) changed the whole concept of the Society. Now any volutary or charitable organisation, club or local society can ring up and request a film

on a particular subject of interest. Peter Shinkfield will wade through his distributors' catalogues, book a suitable film and take it along to the organisation and project it free of charge. The films tend to be documentaries but some features are shown, in which case you are asked.to pay the booking fee.

South London Video
36 Sansom Street
SE5
Tel 701 6565
A production company which has been going for the last ten years. They make videos on commission and have mainly worked on industrial promotion tapes. Fashion, sales promotion and launching a product are some of the subjects they have covered. In 1983 they co-produced The Switch with a company called Silent Partners. This was a series of 24 music programmes which replaced The Tube's slot on Friday evenings and ran from April to November. The company is run by two partners who are joined by freelancers when the need arises. They are willing to train people and when we talked to them they were taking on a young person who was interested in television lighting.

Not Strictly South London

London Video Arts (Tel 734 7410) is

an important co-ordinating body in the network of independent video making. Many video projects and individuals become members (many of whom are South Londoners) and have access to a range of equipment as well as editing suites. You may hire equipment if you can show them that you know how to use it and there are courses in production. LVA distribute a collection of art videos called A Thousand Titles to colleges, galleries and festivals. They also exchange tapes with other countries and tapes can be submitted for inclusion in their library. They are friendly and helpful.

The Media Centre in Bracknell (Tel 0344-427272) runs the only National Independent Video Makers Festival in Britain. It is held yearly usually in November. It is particularly important because the opportunity to see and show art videos is rare. It is a 3-day weekend festival and, apart from the shows, there are seminars, a book stall, a video box where you can air your views and a video disco. The whole event is filmed. The Media Centre also produces a magazine called Independent Video and if you send in your tape it may be mentioned or reviewed. The selection shown at the Festival is made from those that have been submitted over the year, and if your tape hasn't been accepted you can show it at the cafe during the festival. The closing date for Festival tapes is at the start of October.

HEALTH

Finding a Practitioner

This chapter is about finding a practitioner - whether you choose alternative or Western medicine. It also tells you about your rights and about how the health network operates.

The Health Service

A Few Facts

● If you require emergency treatment, you may go to any NHS medical practice and be seen by a doctor.
● If you are not satisfied with your regular GP, you may change to another practice (see Family Practitioner Committees).
● You may not make a formal complaint about your GP's attitude or personality. You may only protest about what you believe to be bad medical treatment. You should look to your Community Health Council for support and advice and should lodge your complaint through your local Family Practitioner Committee.
● If you want to find a local NHS doctor who is interested in, and maybe even practices, holistic medicine (by treating the whole person and life-style rather than the disease), the place to contact is The British Holistic Medical Association (see listings under Alternative Medicine).
● You will have to pay for most of the alternative therapies, though it is sometimes possible to be treated homeopathically through the Health Service.

Family Practitioner Committees

Your local Family Practitioner Committee is concerned solely with general practice rather than the health service in general. It has a statutory obligation to find you a GP and will provide you with a list of doctors, dentists, pharmacists and opticians in your area. (This list is also available from your local Community Health Council, libraries, post offices and the council). If you are not happy with your GP, you are perfectly within your rights to try another one. It is advisable to find out in advance if there is room at your new practice. You simply have to ask your doctor to sign your medical card, releasing you from the practice you have been attending. You are not obliged to explain why you wish to leave. You should present the signed card to your new doctor. If you are moving house (even if you are remaining in the area), you don't have to ask your old doctor to sign your medical card. You simply make an appointment with a new doctor of your choice who will go through the registration process. Your Family Practitioner Committee is the body through which you can make a complaint about the medical treatment you have received from your GP and a leaflet is available from your FPC spelling out the procedure. You should discuss your position first with your local Community Health Council who will advise you how best to go about the matter.

Greenwich Family Practitioner Committee
St Nicholas Hospital
Tewson Road
Plumstead
SE18
Tel 854 2080

Lambeth Southwark & Lewisham Family Practitioner Committee
Addison House
35 Chart Street
near Old Street
N1
Tel 253 3020

Merton & Wandsworth Family Practitioner Committee
Zeeta House
200 Upper Richmond Road
Putney
SW15
Tel 788 7255

Community Health Councils

Your local Community Health Council is 'the patient's voice' – the consumer's protector against Big Brother, The District Health Authority, and watchdog of the service provided by the Family

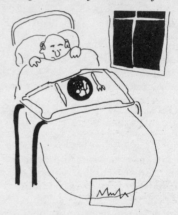

Practioner Committees. It keeps the DHA abreast of public opinion and lobbies for the development and improvement of the Health Service while campaigning against unwanted cuts. It's the place to go if you have any views or concerns about the Health Service in general and, although it doesn't investigate individual complaints, it gives advice on the complaints procedure through the Family Practitioner Committee. It provides information about local hospitals and will send out the Family Practitioner Committee's list of local GPs, health centres, dentists, pharmacists and opticians, arranged by post codes. It can also tell you where local clinics are that offer specialist care in child health, cervical cytology, ovarian scanning, family planning, the menopause, HTLV3 infections, sickle cell anaemia, drug dependency, phychiatric illness, audiology, chiropody and many other medical areas. It will have details too of the local abortion service, Wel-women clinics, Wel-patient clinics for the over 60s and STD (previously known as VD) clinics. The CHC offers a fairly personal service and can advise people on such matters as doctors who speak a certain language or practices that will undertake home births. South London is covered by six different CHCs. Ring the one that

sounds closest and you will be redirected if necessary:

Camberwell Community Health Council
75 Denmark Hill
SE5
Tel 703 9498

Greenwich Community Health Council
23 Anglesea Road
Woolwich
SE18
Tel 317 9994

Lewisham & North Southwark Community Health Council
13 Catford Broadway
Catford
SE6
Tel 690 8777

Merton & Sutton Community Health Council
29 West Street
Sutton
Surrey
Tel 642 6405

Wandsworth Community Health Council
1 Balham Station Road
Balham
SW12
Tel 673 8820/8829

West Lambeth Community Health Council
2 Cleaver Street
Kennington
SE11
Tel 582 3288/3238

Alternative Medicine

A Few Facts

● The training offered by different colleges within each profession can vary considerably in approach and emphasis and it is important that you understand these differences. The Council for Complementary & Alternative Medicine and The Institute for Complementary Medicine (see below) should be able to help with queries of this kind.
● By far the best way to find a good practitioner is by word of mouth. However obscure the connection, try and find someone who is personally

recommended. If you are not successful, contact the most appropriate organisation from the following list for the name of a local practitioner with a recognized and respected qualification in one of the main alternative therapies. The Institute for Complementary Medicine and The Koestler Foundation (see Council for Complementary & Alternative Medicine) can also put you in touch with organisations specialising in fringe therapies although they can make no recommendations or assurances about standards of practice. Only answer ads in magazines if you recognize the initials after the practitioner's name. (Many of the main professional organisations do not permit advertising.)

● Ask your new practitioner if you may pay for a short introductory session before you embark on a full course of treatment. Alternative medicine is about working together so a short meeting to get to know each other a little isn't a bad idea.

The British Holistic Medical Association
179 Gloucester Place
NW1
Tel 262 5299
The BHMA was set up for NHS and private doctors who have a holistic approach to medicine and want to develop this approach and bring their influence to bear on the training of doctors and research. It also aims to help people become less dependent on doctors and drugs, to take greater responsibility for their own health and to understand the influences of mind, body and spirit on their well-being. It offers support and advice about changes of diet, life-style and attitude, publishes leaflets explaining the different alternative therapies and refers people to local doctors who practice holistically and to

professional organisations. For £10pa (or £5 for OAPs, students & unemployed people), you can become an Associate Member of the BHMA, which entitles you to a lively quarterly newsletter, a list of doctors and the therapies they practice (arranged by area) and concessionary rates for all BHMA activities and tapes.

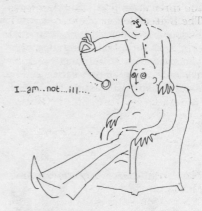

I...am...not...ill....

The Council for Complementary & Alternative Medicine
10 Belgrave Square
SW1
Tel 235 9512
A professional and respected body which was formed in 1985 to provide for stricter standards of training and competence and professional ethics. It has registers of acupuncturists, chiropractics, medical herbalists, homeopaths and naturopaths from all the main professional organisations and a register of one small school of osteopaths. The staff of the Council offer an advisory and information service and are able to explain how the various organisations differ in approach and theory (particularly relevant to acupuncture). Questions about some of the more fringe therapies can be directed to the staff of **The Koestler Foundation**, who work in conjunction with the CCAM and operate from the same address and telephone number.

The General Council & Register of Osteopaths
1-4 Suffolk Street
SW1
Tel 839 2060
The GCRO has been around since 1936 and is the place to contact if you have any questions about osteopathy. Ring or write (enclosing an sae) for the name of a local osteopath from one of the three main professional colleges - The British School of Osteopathy, The European School of Osteopathy and the London College of Osteopathic Medicine (the latter offers a post-graduate training to doctors). Alternatively, a directory of osteopaths can be seen at your local citizens' advice bureau or bought from the GCRO (1985 price was £1.50 inc pp).

The Institute for Complementary Medicine
21 Portland Place
W1
Tel 636 9543
The Institute for Complementary Medicine is a lay organisation founded by concerned members of the public. It seeks to raise standards of practice and initiate research into complementary therapies. It provides an information service, specifically about acupuncture, chiropractic, medical herbalism, homeopathy and osteopathy and will direct you to a local practitioner who belongs to a professional association of a recognised standard. It can also put you in touch with organisations for many of the fringe therapies though it can offer no assurances as to standards of practice. For written information please send sae.

Society of Teachers of the Alexander Technique
10 London House
266 Fulham Road
SW10
Tel 351 0828
A phone call or sae to the above organisation will provide you with general information about The Alexander Technique and the name of a practitioner in your area.

Note: There are also sections on Health in the following chapters – Lesbian and Gay, Women, and Ethnic Minorities.

HOUSING

- 20% of housing in South London is unfit to live in
- There are 30,000 empty houses in South London
- The GLC predicts a shortage of 60,000 dwellings by 1986.

These statistics show that South London's housing problem is a serious one, and it's getting worse.

It is difficult, if not impossible, for most South Londoners to get a council home now. Private accomodation is usually more expensive and the search can be demoralising and time-consuming. As for home-ownership, many people will never achieve it because of the soaring prices.

Councils are finding it increasingly difficult to meet the needs of applicants on their housing lists. Government financial constraints mean that new council building is confined mainly to people whose needs are greatest – the elderly and the disabled. Meanwhile, council housing lists are getting longer and longer.

The scheme introduced nearly five years ago by which council tenants could buy their own homes has brought with it problems as well as desirable aspects. The Right To Buy scheme means that until the sale proceeds are reinvested in new stock councils now have fewer properties for those on the waiting lists. Many support the Government in its policy of creating a Britain of home-owners, but others see it as a policy which will increase the gap between the rich and the poor.

'Gentrification', as is happening in Clapham, Battersea and Brixton changes the face of a neighbourhood, and once the previously cheap houses have been done up they are then out of the price range of the locals.

This chapter is arranged in the following sections:
Homelessness
Council Housing
Housing Associations
Housing Co-operatives
Short Life Housing
Squatting
Renting
Home Ownership

Homelessness

Under The Homeless Person's Act, councils (through their Homeless Persons Units) are only obliged to find temporary accommodation for people over 55 years of age, single-parent families, people with disabilities, battered wives, people under medication (suffering from diabetes etc), victims of racial harrassment and violence in the home. Fit childless people may be given advice but are unlikely to be given practical help. The Council Emergency Homeless Person Units in South london are as follows:

Greenwich
Tel 858 7178
Ring this number during office hours. Contact a police station at other times.

Lambeth
Tel 274 7722
Ask for extensions 2873 or 2762 during office hours or for the emergency desk between 5.30pm & 9am.

Lewisham
Tel 690 8211
The above number is always answered personally.

Merton
Tel 543 2222
Ask for the Homeless Persons Unit during office hours. Outside office hours, go to a police station and you will be referred to an emergency social worker.

Southwark
Tel 703 6311 (outside office hours)
Go to a local district housing office (see Council Housing section) during office hours. Outside office hours ring the above number. Emergency staff will take your number and details and get a senior housing officer to call you back even if you are in a phone box.

Wandsworth
Tel 871 6000
Ask for The Homeless Unit which has a 24 hour service.

Another useful organisation is:

The Housing Advice Switchboard
Tel 434 2522
They give general advice and information about where to go and can advise single homeless people who are not eligible for emergency help from the council. When closed, the Switchboard's number has a recorded message with hostel addresses.

The following are independent advice centres.

North Lambeth Day Centre
St John's Crypt
73 Waterloo Road
Waterloo   SE1
Tel 261 9622
Open 1-4(Mon-Fri)
Drop in day centre for the homeless, which helps people look for accommodation.

St Giles Centre
81 Camberwell Church Street
Camberwell   SE5
Tel 703 5841
Four projects are run at St Giles Centre, a day centre which offers

advice on housing, provides classes, a house magazine and tea and soup; the Eddie Brindley Project for institutionalized people who are given interim care in a house, each with their own room and kitchen, to help them cope on their own; four shared houses, each for four young women who have usually had to leave home for family reasons and who can stay for one year with visits from a social worker; and Sojourner House, a place for twelve young women with family problems, who can stay for one year.

Stopover House
48 Dakers Road
Forest Hill   SE23
Tel 699 1574
Emergency short-stay hostel for nine residents aged 16-21. Maximum stay is four weeks. Practical help in finding permanent accommodation.

Turning Point
31-32 Grove Park
Camberwell   SE5
Tel 274 4883

A South London branch of the national organisation for homeless people with mainly drug and alcohol problems, who are housed for a maximum of eighteen months, after which they are referred to housing associations.

Ujima Housing Association
Tel 733 7939
This is not an emergency centre. It provides temporary, short-life, supportive, shared housing for single Black people aged 17-31. Long waiting list. Once your housing needs have been assessed, you usually have to wait 3-4 months.

Council Housing

When you apply for council housing, you will go on a housing list along with many other households. Councils are able to house only a small proportion of the people on their housing lists, and they have to make a decision whose need is the greatest. This is usually assessed on a points or grouping system based on the information you put on your application. It is important that you put your case across well. If you think that you should be given priority, perhaps because of ill-health, poor housing or family situation, get actual documentation to support your claim – from your doctor, social services, etc. Councils tend to have slightly different systems of selection, but at present unless you have severe housing problems, you have little chance of getting a council home. If you are a single person or childless couple you may be able to get a council home under either the Hard To Let or the Mobility schemes. Hard to let properties are flats or houses deemed unsuitable for families, for instance the upper floors of a tower block. They are usually let to groups of two or three young childless people. A mobility scheme may increase your chances of a place. This involves a number of flats in ex-GLC estates being made available to people in other boroughs, entailing a move possibly to a totally different area of London. You are most likely to find a home through the mobility scheme if you will accept somewhere in the worst large estates.

In the following section, we have tried to give details about the different procedures and how the priority system works in each borough. We have also described the types of housing in each borough, average net rents excluding rates, (in some estates, room heating and/or hot water heating will be added). and we have indicated which boroughs operate special schemes.

Greenwich

Greenwich Housing Department
Peggy Middleton House
50 Woolwich New Road
Woolwich   SE18
Tel 854 8888
●Apply at the above address or at
one of the five area or five sub offices
in Greenwich. The Housing
Department will tell you which is the
nearest.
●Greenwich has 8,444 applicants on
its housing list.
●Those on the list are divided into
categories which indicate such
matters as whether the applicant's
home is for clearance or repair
and/or whether the applicant scores
points. Applicants are awarded
points because of overcrowding,
shared or lacking amenities, medical
matters, children in high-rise blocks,
family separation and the length of
time they have experienced any of
these hardships. There are
comprehensive leaflets available from
the above address which enable you
to work out the points you will score,
what kind of accommodation you are
eligible for and in which area.
●Greenwich has 58% flats, 29%
houses and 13% maisonettes.
●Housing benefit is currently dealt
with at Peggy Middleton House, but
is soon to be decentralised to the five
sub-offices.
●Greenwich has 901 sheltered and
101 other properties for the elderly.
For the disabled there are 67
properties with wheelchair access
and 106 other specially adapted
homes.
●The Council is responsible for
external and major internal repairs.
●Approximate net weekly rents
(excluding rates):
1 bedroom: flat £13, bungalow £13.50
2 bedroom: house £14.50, flat £14,
bungalow £16.60
3 bedroom: house £15.50, flat £15,
bungalow £17.50
●The points programme eliminates

the need for hard to let schemes, as
applicants can choose to go for less
desirable properties if they have few
housing points.
●The Council will nominate people
considered eligible for a housing
association if this option has been
expressed on the application form.

Lambeth

Lambeth Housing Advice Centre
2-7 Town Hall Parade
Brixton   SW2
Tel 274 7722
●Application forms are available
from the above address.
●Lambeth's waiting list is currently
14,489. In 1984/5, 73 households with
children were rehoused from the
waiting list. If the present situation
remains, households without high
housing need points could wait
indefinitely.
●There is no priority housing for
particular groups. However, because
black households are under-
represented in the more desirable
properties, the council is aiming to
allocate 35% of these more desirable
properties to black applicants.
●Lambeth's housing stock consists of
about 37,000 properties. Only about
3.5% of these are houses, the rest are
flats.
●Housing benefit for council tenants
is dealt with at:

The Housing Benefit Section
Hambrook House
Porden Road
Brixton Hill
SW2
Tel 274 7822
Housing benefit for other tenants
and owner/occupiers is dealt with at:

The Housing Benefit Section
18 Brixton Hill
SW2
Tel 274 7722
●Lambeth Council has 953 sheltered
properties for the elderly. Housing
associations in Lambeth have 444

sheltered properties and 16 other properties for the elderly. The Council has 172 dwellings with wheelchair access and 341 other homes for the disabled. At the time of going to press, there were 766 pensioners on the waiting list, and 52 people waiting for wheelchair accommodation.

● For repairs and major internal repairs, contact The Housing Advice Centre and you wil be referred to your neighbourhood management office or district housing office. Lambeth has a priority repairs system with a 24 hour service for specific emergencies.

●The overall average net rent is £16.32 per property.

●If you wish to be considered for hard to let properties, answer 'yes' in the appropriate section of the application form. You can also apply to be considered for the mobility scheme or you can ask to be nominated to a housing association.

flats Vassall Road

Lewisham

Lewisham Housing Advice Centre
Leegate House
Lee Green   SE12
Tel 852 4391
●Application form available from the above address. You have to have lived in the borough for one year before being considered for placement.

●There are 16,000 applicants on the waiting list, only 802 of whom were rehoused in 1984/5. In addition to this there were 154 households in bed and breakfast and reception centres. There were also 5,000 tenants on council transfer lists.

●Applicants are housed according to need. A system of five priority groups operates taking into account such things as homeless persons, council tenants who require a transfer due to racial harassment, applicants living in properties due for demolition, redevelopment or improvement works, medical transfer cases and so on. Homeless gay people will be interviewed by other gay people (see Lesbian & Gay).

●Housing need is also assessed under a points scheme, taking into account such factors as shortage of rooms or facilities, family separation, condition of property, medical factors and waiting time. The details of this procedure can be found in a leaflet 'Information on Housing Allocations, The Housing Act 1980 (Section 44)', obtainable from the Housing Advice Centre.

●Lewisham's housing stock consists of 42,207 properties: 29.6% houses, 69.8% flats and 0.6% bungalows.

●Housing benefit is dealt with at the above address.

●Lewisham has 628 sheltered flatlets which have a residential warden and 1,000 with a non-residential warden for the elderly. For the disabled there are 88 specially adapted homes. All new building by the council is up to 'mobility standard', which means that they are accessible by people with minor disabilities.

●The council is responsible for external repairs and major internal work. They will also undertake interior decoration and minor repairs for single parents, the elderly and disabled.

●Average net rents (excluding rates) are as follows:
1 bedroom: house £14.63, flat £12.39,

bungalow £13.10
2 bedroom: house £15.67, flat £15.30, bungalow £8.37
3 bedroom: house £16.89, flat £16.84, bungalow £18.16
●Lewisham operates a short-let scheme through housing associations. Ask at the Housing Advice Centre.
●Applicants may also be nominated to housing associations. 113 applicants were housed from the waiting list in 1984 by housing associations.

Merton

Merton Council Housing Department
Crown House
London Road
Morden
Tel 543 2222
●Application forms are available from the above address. All persons with a permanent address in the borough are eligible to be put on the list, but are not considered for rehousing if they haven't been resident in the borough for one year prior to application. The qualification period is reduced to six months for applicants who have lived in the borough for five out of the last twenty. Single persons have their applications deferred until they are thirty years old.
●There are 3,552 people on the waiting list.
●Housing need is assessed on a points system taking into account such factors as overcrowding, underoccupation, medical issues, shared accommodation, lacking, shared or badly situated facilities, discretionary points and waiting time. Full details of the system are available from the housing department.
●The council housing stock of 13,110 premises is roughly half flats and half bungalows and houses.
●Housing benefit is dealt with at the

above address.
●Merton has 233 sheltered flatlets with residential wardens and 1782 other flats for the elderly. There are 143 dwellings for people in wheelchairs, and 37 others units for people with disabilties. Merton has a policy that at least 2% of new dwellings should be for disabled people. Medical referrals are required for these dwellings.
●Merton is responsible for external and major internal repairs to properties.
●Rents are assessed on a points system, taking into account factors such as room size, garden, the location of the property in the borough and so on.
●Average net rents are as follows (rates and, in some cases, hot water and heating are added to these figures):
1 bedroom: house £20.73, flat £17.71, bungalow £19.84
2 bedroom: house £22.81, flat 20.51, bungalow £23.20
3 bedroom: house £26, flat £23.55
●A mobility scheme is operated with the GLC (not after March 1986). Some high-rise dwellings are deemed unsuitable for families with young children so are let as flatshares to three single young people.
●If there are vacancies, Merton will nominate prospective tenants to housing associations. Housing associations which have council funding give 50% of their vacancies to the council.

Southwark Housing Department
38 Rye Lane
Peckham
SE15
Tel 639 4353
●To make an application, contact the department – they may refer you to district office. You can get a series of informative leaflets that will tell you just what your position is.
●Southwark has 13,238 applicants on its housing list and 12,125 on its

transfer list.

●Southwark sorts people into groups according to housing need. The four highest priority groups are homeless people, those with very serious health problems where rehousing may help, people whose dwellings are needed by the council for repair or replacement and people referred by other councils so they can be near relatives or a job. There are also several lower priority groups. Once applicants have been put into categories, they are given points depending on such factors as facilities and room in their present home, health and disablement. More details about housing need assessment and your chances of a council home once you are on the housing list are available at your local district office.

●Two-thirds of Southwark's housing stock is council-owned and Southwark has the largest housing stock of all the inner London boroughs with 62,459 properties. 55% of these are flats, 26% maisonettes, 9% houses, 7% conversions and 3% are bungalows, prefabs, and housing for disabled and elderly people.

●Housing benefit is dealt with at the district housing offices.

●Southwark has 727 sheltered properties, 564 old people's dwellings and 243 properties for people with disabilities.

●The council is responsible for external repairs and major internal work.

●The average net weekly rent in Southwark (before rates) is £16.29.

●You should apply to your local district housing office for details of Southwark's short-life scheme which is run through housing co-operatives and housing associations.

●Ask at the district housing offices about nominations to housing associations.

Wandsworth

Wandsworth Housing Aid Centre
Town Hall
Wandsworth High Street
Wandsworth　　　　　　SW18
Tel 871 6000

●Contact or visit the Housing Aid Centre for an application form. To qualify to go on the housing list, you have to have lived in the borough for 12 months before your application is considered.

●At the time of going to press, the waiting list was 7,531 with 5,627 people on the transfer list.

●Wandsworth has a points priority scheme. Applicants are awarded points for lack of rooms, lack, sharing or bad situation of facilities, family separation, ill-health or physical disability and small rooms in the present home. Applicants have little chance of being housed unless they have a high degree of housing need and/or medical priority.

●Wandsworth's housing stock consists of 34,970 properties, about 15% of which are houses and 85% flats and maisonettes.

●Housing benefit is dealt with at the Housing Aid Centre.

●Wandsworth has 1277 sheltered dwellings for the elderly, 292 homes for the elderly without wardens and 15 purpose-built units for wheelchair users.

●The council has responsibility for

external and major internal repairs.
●Net weekly rents (excluding rates)
are:
1 bedroom: house/maisonette £22.66,
flat £21.94
2 bedroom: house/maisonete £23.73,
flat £22.66
3 bedroom: house/maisonette £24.81,
flat £23.73
●Wandsworth does not have any
short-life or hard to let schemes.
They do run a different scheme for
eleven of their estates where only
relatives of present tenants are
eligible.
●You should apply at the Housing
Aid Centre for nomination to a
housing association.

Housing Associations

Housing associations are non-profit
making organisations concerned
with providing housing as an
alternative to private or council
accommodation. They too are
experiencing financial constraints
which makes it increasingly difficult
for them to satisfy the demand.
Housing associations were started in
the middle of the last century in new
urban areas where speculative
developers had built homes which
quickly declined into slums. The 1957
Housing Act included the first legal
definition of a housing association
and gave local authorities powers to
lend housing associations money.
The 1964 Housing Act established
The Housing Corporation as a
government loan-making body for
housing associations.
Most housing association properties
are generally inner city houses,
bought in a state of disrepair, made
habitable and usually divided into
two or more self-contained flats.
These are then let at a fair rent
(assessed by a rent officer) to people
with a high housing need. They
account for about 5% of South
London's dwellings and 30% of its
sheltered housing.

The usual way of obtaining a housing
association home is through the
council. You may apply if you are
already a council tenant or, if you
are not, when you register to go on
the housing list. The council will
nominate those with reasonable
housing priority.
There are other organisations,
termed referral agencies, that may
also nominate you, often subject to
their own vetting procedures. These
referral agencies include homeless
persons units, citizens' advice
bureaux and social services
departments.
Some housing associations will
accept direct applications and decide
your housing need themselves. There
are too many housing associations in
South London to list in the
Handbook but you may find out
addresses by contacting your local
council housing department, or
housing aid or advice centre (see
Council Housing section above).
Another way is to look in the Yellow
Pages or at The Directory of
Registered Housing Associations,
which is in the reference sections of
most major libraries.
Housing associatons are often able to
help people who cannot be helped by
councils – people, for instance, who
don't have enough council housing
points, or who are classed
'intentionally homeless', or people
who have a special need (such as
sheltered housing) which the council
cannot offer.
There are also many specialist
housing associations dealing with
the needs of particular groups, like
Threshold Single Persons Housing
Association and BCAR Housing
Society Ltd, which caters for
refugees. Two examples of the larger
housing associations are The
Peabody Trust and London &
Quadrant. The Peabody Trust was
founded in 1862 by a banker, George
Peabody. Peabody's 12,000 dwellings
(40% in South London) are usually

Housing Co-op, Guildford Road

pre-war flats which have mostly been or are being rehabilitated. Rents are low (£12-£20 per week excluding rates for a two-room flat). Peabody accept direct applications. If an applicant is in a category considered suitable for rehousing, a home is usually found within 3-6 months. The London & Quadrant Housing Trust was formed in 1973 when The London Housing Trust and The Quadrant Housing Association (both founded in the sixties) became one organisation. About half their 8000 dwellings are in South London. The majority are rehabilitated properties and about 8% are newly built homes. The rents are assessed by a rent officer at about £20 per week (exclusive of rates) for a two-bedroom flat. Applicants may approach London & Quadrant direct or be nominated by councils or other referral agencies.

Housing Co-Operatives

Getting yourself housed in a co-op is hard work and takes a long time. It is sometimes possible to join an existing co-op or to start one yourself.

A housing co-op is a group of at least seven people who have an equal say in the management of their housing. They have to draw up rules for their co-op (guidelines are available from The Housing Corporation) and must also register with The Housing Corporation (this is subject to their approval of the plans submitted)

If you are one of a group of people who wish to start a co-op, get some advice from one of the organisations listed at the end of this section as it's a complicated and lengthy procedure. Once you have started a co-op it is likely to take at least two years before you actually move.

Joining an existing co-op is quite difficult at present as cuts in the Housing Corporation's grants are making it hard for many co-ops to house their own members. However, some co-ops do have their lists open. They tend to work in different ways. Some have waiting lists and you simply wait to be housed. Others house people depending on their need and/or how much energy and commitment they are prepared to put into the co-op.

The Co-op Services Unit of The Housing Corporation has a free directory of housing co-ops, which will help you find local co-ops. You could also try The Housing Advice Switchboard (Tel 434 2522) or try some of the following organisations:

The Housing Corporation
149 Tottenham Court Road
W1
Tel 387 9466

The Lambeth Federation of Housing
260 Coldharbour Lane
SW9
Tel 733 7370

The Society for Co-op Dwellings (SCD)
209 Clapham Road
SW9
Tel 737 2077

Short Life Housing

Short life housing means short-term occupation of council or housing association property that would otherwise remain empty until it can be rehabilitated or demolished. The properties are generally in working order but are often quite tatty. Some money is usually allowed for decoration.

The rents for short-term housing are generally the cheapest around. The properties are usually let by licence and renewed at intervals (often every six months). The licence means that you have to leave when asked though whoever you are dealing with will probably make an effort to rehouse you. You might have to move quite often.

Approach councils and ask to be put on their housing lists, requesting short life housing. Short life co-ops and groups (minimum seven people) tend to get quite run down properties (often listed buildings). With self-help and funding from The Inner City Partnership they turn places that are in pretty bad shape into good homes. With the aid of organisations such as The Lambeth Federation of Housing Co-ops (see end of last section), short life housing means that as much use as possible is made of housing stock, whether it involves a six-month let of a flat before demolition or the virtual rebuilding of a listed building by a short life co-op.

Below is a brief indication of each South London borough's approach to short life housing and how you might apply.

Greenwich

Greenwich runs a points scheme on all properties (see Council Housing section). They feel that this eliminates the need for hard to let properties as applicants can choose to go for the less desirable properties if they have few housing points themselves.

Lambeth

When you are filling in your housing application form, there is a section for short life and hard to let properties. Remember to answer 'yes' if you are interested in either of these two categories. Ask again when you have been allocated a waiting list number.

Lewisham

Lewisham operates short-let schemes through housing associations. Ask at The Housing Advice Centre.

Merton

Some of Merton's high rise properties are deemed unsuitable for families with young children, so they are let as flatshares for three single young people.

Southwark

Apply to the district housing offices for details of Southwark's short life scheme which is run through housing co-ops and housing associations.

Wandsworth

Wandsworth has no short life schemes.

Squatting

There are officially about 5000 homeless households in the area covered by the Handbook. This includes only the persons defined by the Homeless Persons Act. This means it excludes, for example, single people without children. So in reality there are probably a lot more. When compared to the 30,000 empty dwellings in the area the 'housing shortage' would seem to be artificial. One answer is to squat.

Squatting is not illegal though there are numerous problems to be encountered.

The best way to find a place to live is to walk the streets and look. You are likely to be able to stay for a longer time in a council property than in a private one. Be careful getting into a place. You could be prosecuted for criminal damage. Make sure gas, electricity and water are working or can be made to work. The relevant boards are obliged to supply you but they may ask for a deposit or a large connection charge.

When you have moved in, change the locks and try and keep one person in at all times. You are not required to leave until a High or County Court serves a Possession Order.

It's a good idea to get in touch with other squatters in the area. You will have a lot more strength as a group and may be able to pool resources. You will need to find out more about your rights and the practicalities of squatting. Either talk to individuals or approach the organisations below.

Squatting is quite a hassle but it's cheap, it can provide a good home and it makes a sound political point with regard to homelessness and the number of empty properties in our city.

Advisory Service for Squatters
2 St Paul's Road
N1
Tel 359 8814
Open 2-6(Mon-Fri)
Their Squatters Handbook can put you in touch with local groups. Legal advice.

Brixton Squatters Aid
121 Railton Road
SE24
Tel none
Open 3-5(Sun & at other times in emergency) 4-6(Mon-Fri bookshop only)
General advice, leaflets, Crowbar Squatters News, lists of empty places.

Renting

Private rented accommodation tends to be more expensive than other properties to let. You are also more likely to have problems with the owner.

You are, however, well protected by the rent acts. Housing advice centres, citizens' advice bureaux and law centres will be able to give you advice and there's a series of housing booklets published by the DOE, obtainable from housing advice centres, which will explain what your rights are.

Most tenancies are 'regulated tenancies' which give you many rights, the most significant being that you cannot be evicted without a Possession Order from the courts. This is obtainable by the landlord/landlady only in certain circumstances, such as the family's own need of the property or because of a tenant's misconduct.

If you and your landlord/landlady live in the same flat or house you are not a regulated tenant.

Harrassment, threats, violence, the withdrawal of services or interference of any kind to get you out of your home constitutes a criminal offence. The landlord/landlady is normally responsible for major repairs and for keeping installations such as toilets, washing facilities and heating in working order.

You will often be asked for a deposit (up to two months' rent) and references from your bank. It is not customary to be charged for key money. Seek advice on this point. The accommodation can be 'fair rent assessed' if either party requests this.

Finding a flat, particularly if you have set ideas of what you want and where you want it, is not easy. Word of mouth is the best way, so ask around. The Standard and local papers advertise flats, and Time Out, City Limits and Capital Radio have details of flatshares available. With these you have to be quick off the mark. Keep looking at the cards in local newsagents' windows too.

The alternative is accommodation agencies. They tend to be oversubscribed around September due to students looking for flats before the new academic year, so if you can look at another time, you will have more choice.

Agencies usually charge 1-2 weeks'

rent if they find you a place. Be careful of letting arrangements. At some agencies you may lose some of your rights.

Accommodation agencies in South London are listed below:

HLT Accommodation Agency
367 Wandsworth Road
Stockwell SW8
Tel 627 0171
HLT deals with the SE/SW area. Fee is 2 weeks' rent. Some holiday lets.

Homefinding Service
110A Blackheath Road
Greenwich SE10
Tel 692 7276
SE London is this agency's patch. Fee £32 (more if there are more people sharing), UB40s free. No holiday lets.

Master Accommodation Service
17 Clapham Common Southside
Clapham SW4
Tel 622 3322
Deals mainly with SW area and some SE neighbourhoods. Fee two weeks rent. Permanent lets, no families.

Metro Accommodation Agency
338 Balham High Road
Tooting Bec SW17
Tel 672 7633/9700
Metro deals with any area. Fee one and a quarter weeks rent. Holiday and permanent lets.

Southern Accommodation Bureau
7/9 Belmont Hill
Lewisham SE13
Tel 852 0244
This agency deals with SE postcodes. Fee according to flat size (bedsit £32, one bedroom flat £76, two bedroom flat £92). Permanent and holiday lets.

South London Accommodation
428 Southcroft Road
Streatham SW16
Tel 769 2117
Area covered lies within three to

four miles of Streatham High Road. Fee one and a half week's rent. Permanent and holiday lets.

Southside Accommodation Agency
15 Clapham Common Southside
Clapham SW4
Tel 622 8383
Deals with Clapham and surrounding area. Fee one and a half weeks' rent. Mostly permanent lets.

Streatham Accommodation Bureau
159 Streatham High Road
Streatham SW16
Tel 677 9089
Streatham, Norbury and Brixton are covered by this agency. Fee two weeks' rent. Permanent lets.

Home Ownership

About 50% of properties in Greater London are owner-occupied. It is Government policy that this percentage should increase.

Buying a property is probably the biggest financial commitment people make in their lives and, as such, is not to be rushed into. Most people cannot afford to buy without borrowing, and a building society is the most common place to go (although you can also borrow from the bank). In the case of a building society, you will be told how much the society would be willing to lend you on the basis of your income. A general rule is that a building society will lend two and a half times your gross annual income. Building societies may give preference to people who already have an account so, if you don't have one, start one. The branch manager of your building society will give you advice on how best to go about it. So with the help of your building society, work out your budget, not forgetting additional costs like solicitors, surveyors, stamp duty (a government tax on the purchase of houses over £30,000) and land registry fees (a charge for registering your property with The Land Registry). With a reasonable idea of how much you can afford, what kind of place you want and in which area, you can look for a property in the local papers or by contacting local estate agents through Yellow Pages or the Thomson Local Directory.

It's a good idea to go and talk to estate agents to get an idea of what kinds of properties are available and to ask them to let you know of anything suitable that becomes available. Having found a place, an offer should be made 'subject to survey and contract'. This is not legally binding. A returnable holding deposit may be payable to the estate agent, sometimes as much as 1% of the purchase price. A formal loan application may then be made. The lender, whether a building society or bank, will require information about the property and about you, the applicant. It will instruct its surveyors to inspect the property and you would be well advised to get a structural examination done by your own surveyor so that any potential major or minor repairs to the property are revealed before you commit yourself. Structural repairs can be extremely expensive.

A solicitor may have to be employed at this stage as the legal side of house buying is complicated. It is possible to

do it yourself but you risk overlooking something vital. Exchanging contracts finalises the sale and a deposit (normally 10%) is paid. A month or so after this, the property changes ownership, the balance of the purchase price is paid and you get to collect the keys. The mortgage repayments will probably account for a large percentage of your monthly outgoings. At first much of this will go in interest payments, so beware changes in interest rates. If you become unemployed or encounter some other financial difficulties, talk to the organisation that is lending you the money and you may be allowed to pay the interest only for a while. The DHSS will pay your interest payments in full if they consider them to be reasonable and assess you as being in genuine need. The 'Home Loan' scheme may be taken advantage of by first-time buyers. It gives a tax free bonus and an interest-free loan of £600 if you have been saving for two years under the scheme. So if you are contemplating home-buying, register a savings account under the scheme. You are under no obligation to buy. Improvement grants are under threat at present due to lack of funding. Home insulation and standard amenities such as bath, inside wc, hot and cold water are probably the only grants for which you will be eligible.

Ask about this at your local housing advice centre.

Organisations that may be of help include local citizens' advice bureaux (see Community Services), your local council housing department (see Council Housing section of this chapter), local building societies (see Yellow Pages or the Thomson Local Directory), and the following organisation:

The Building Society's Association
3 Savile Row
W1
Tel 437 0655
The Association produce a series of leaflets on building society loans and home-buying.

'In the area covered by the guide, 5000 officially homeless, 30 000 vacant apartments/dwellings'

5000

30 000

LESBIAN AND GAY

In this chapter we have included facilities specially provided for the lesbian and gay sub-culture. More than for any other group, it is difficult to isolate South London from the rest of London. The most exciting clubs and the most effective helplines are in the centre or north of London and are used by lesbians and gay men south of the river. However, the number of facilities for gay people locally is increasing - especially alternative facilities, funded by local authorities. There is a growing gay community in Brixton (both black and white), and in areas like Deptford there is certainly more gay activity than a few years ago.

If you need helplines see the Emergency section at the end of the book. The best guides to gay life in London are Capital Gay (free, published weekly, available at pubs and Gay's The Word), Gay Times (which has comprehensive listings), City Limits and Time Out.

Public Sector Attitudes & Funding

Until recently, gay people have been given very low priority by the public sector, both in providing for their specific needs, and in countering discrimination against gay men and women in employment and housing. One of the reasons may be the 'invisibility' of gay people; they can be treated as straight people and their needs can be ignored. Also, because many gay people do not have children (although quite a few do), we get put to the bottom of housing lists and have to take hard-to-let flats that no-one else wants. Some boroughs, however, treat gay couples and heterosexual couples as equal, with the right for both partners to be rehoused if the relationship finishes. In the area of employment not all councils have an equal opportunities clause or policy which extends to sexual orientation. Thus, in certain South London boroughs you can be denied a job simply on the grounds of being gay.

Greenwich is the only borough in South London to fund full-time gay workers. The activities of the Greenwich Lesbian and Gay Rights Group are in the listings under Advice Groups; it is extraordinary how much has been achieved in such a short space of time.

In the other South London Labour-controlled boroughs (Lambeth, Lewisham and Southwark), there are no full-time gay workers. The boroughs do not discriminate on the grounds of sexual orientation in any job appointments. Lewisham has a scheme for housing gay people in need (see Lewisham under Advice Groups). Lambeth has taken a strong line against the police using public conveniences to trap gay men for soliciting, and has a lesbian and gay working party and its first gay festival in October 1985. However, without full-time workers and a venue, progress is slow.

In stark contrast, the two South London Conservative-controlled boroughs do not have any positive policy in this area. Wandsworth is 'not aware of it being a policy matter', Merton's 'Equal Opportunities Policy' does not extend to sexual orientation. The GLC is an equal opportunities employer and has pioneered the way for the local authorities both in provision for gay people and in countering discrimination. By the time you read this, the GLC may well be no more, but hopefully the GLC-funded London Lesbian & Gay Centre, the only publicly funded gay centre in London (see below) will still be in existence.

London Lesbian & Gay Centre
67-69 Cowcross Street
EC1
Tel 608 1471

Open 6pm-12pm(Tue-Wed) 12am-12pm(Thur) 12am-2am(Fri-Sat) 12am-12pm(Sun)
Admission 30p (15p unwaged)
Free to members
Some free discos others 50p-£1.50
Membership £15pa £7.50 Concessions
Funded by the GLC, The London Lesbian & Gay Centre is the only publicly funded gay centre in London. Despite early problems, it has an open policy for most groups. It provides both a meeting place for different gay groups and a 'non scene' social meeting place, bar and restaurant, with discos on several evenings. There is a lesbian lounge on the first floor with creche facilities, a technical resources centre on the second floor (with a dark room and print workshop), a meeting room on the third floor and a theatre and disco in the basement.

Advice Groups

For advice and support, there are several local groups in South London, and there are all-London helplines (see below). Also, many women's groups are very supportive to gay women. For housing help, ring Gay Switchboard. They have full lists of flat-shares. Also, see City Limits, Time Out and Capital Gay.

All-London Helplines

Gay Switchboard
Tel 837 7324
Open & answered personally 24hrs

Lesbian Line
Tel 251 6911
Open 2-10pm(Mon Fri) 7-10pm(Tue-Thur)

Local Groups

Some groups are listed by phone number only. Please ring for addresses of venues and for information about wheelchair access.

Deptford Dykes
Deptford Women's Centre
74c Deptford High Street
Deptford
SE8
Tel none
Open 8-10pm(Mon only)
Support and social group for lesbians.
Particularly good for lesbians 'coming
out'. Discussions and outings.

Greenwich Lesbian & Gay Line
c/o Volunteer Bureau
McBean Street
Woolwich   SE18
Tel 853 4199
Line open 7-10pm(Tue mixed)
7-10pm(Thur women only)
Funded by The Lesbian & Gay Rights
Group, the Greenwich Lesbian & Gay
Line is a collective of twenty
volunteers who offer a chat or
counselling for anyone who needs
help. They have set up a gay men's
counselling group and a support group
for men with HTLV3. Ring the above
number and ask Alex for details.

**Greenwich Lesbian & Gay Rights
Group**
Tel 853 5206
Funded by Greenwich Council to the
tune of £37,000 in 1985, the Lesbian &
Gay Rights Group consists of two gay
men and two lesbians campaigning on
relevant issues with the eventual
intention of developing a social centre
in the borough of Greenwich, in the
Plumstead/Woolwich area, and
countering discrimination in the
borough. The groups holds open
meetings on the first Monday of every
month in a wheelchair accessible
venue (ring above number for details).
The group has set up a whole series of
events and campaigns. These include
mixed self-defence courses, signing for
the deaf, racism awareness workshops
and an evening class course on gay
issues. The lesbian workers have
established a social network of gay
women and have liaised with women's

groups in the borough. The group has
also mounted an exhibition which has
toured Greenwich libraries.
However, everything has not been
plain sailing. Greenwich Council is
working on the adoption of the GLC
charter for gay and lesbian rights, but
with only one gay person out of seven
on the committee. Also, the union
ACTSS has opposed the adoption of
the GLC charter and has even called
for the cessation of grants to the
workers. They claim that
'heterosexism is the social norm' and
that they are 'following the wishes of
their members'.

**Greenwich Lesbian & Gay Youth
Group**
Tel 317 9690
Line open 6-9pm(Mon Wed Fri)
3-6pm(Sat-Sun)
This is the main contact number for
the lesbian and gay youth movement
and they will give you details of your
local group. The LGYM is a self-run
group for lesbians and gay men up to
the age of twenty-six. There is no
lower age limit. The group provides
support for gay young people. It is self-
funded through discos and events and
organises holidays and penfriend
contacts.

LAGER (Lesbian & Gay Employment Rights)
Room 203
South Bank House
Black Prince Road
Vauxhall   SE1
Tel 587 1643(mixed)
587 1636(lesbian only)
Funded by the GLC, with four full-time workers, LAGER is an organisation which helps any gay people who have been sacked or discriminated against by their employer or badly treated by their union. It is also a research organisation and works for local authorities like Lambeth on equal opportunities legislation. LAGER has discovered considerable discrimination from both public and private employers. There is a Lesbian Employment Rights Group, operating from the above number.

Lewisham Friend
Tel 690 6195
Line open 8-10pm(Thur)
Telephone counselling and befriending line for men and women. Available for anyone who is concerned about being gay.

Lewisham Non Priority Homeless Scheme
Tel Geoff 692 1562(day) 853 5206(eve)
In order to lead a gay life-style, gay young people often leave home with nowhere to live, and thus end up homeless. The scheme in Lewisham is run by gay people through the Housing Needs group of the council. You would be eligible for an empty flat (usually in the New Cross/Deptford area of the borough) if you are homeless or have been harrassed where you live, but only if you work or have relatives in the borough or have lived in Lewisham for six of the last twelve months or three of the last five years. You will be seen for an interview (by gay people) and, if you fit the criteria, a flat could be yours within three months. The

scheme has provided forty flats in the last ten months. It has meant many more gay people living in the Deptford/New Cross areas of the borough, who can provide mutual support if anyone is harrassed. There are moves on the Pepys Estate to set up a lesbian and gay group.

Parents' Enquiry
(*contact Gay Switchboard 837 7324 for new address & phone number*)
Parents' Enquiry provides a counselling service for families where a child or children are gay. The service is used by parents, children and young people. Parents are seen for counselling and young people are referred to the South London Lesbian & Gay Young People's Group.

South London Lesbian & Gay Young People's Group
Tel 461 4112
Line open 7-10pm(Mon)
The South London Lesbian & Gay Young People's Group meets as a mixed group from 7-10pm on Mondays and as a women-only group from 7-10pm on Tuesdays. It provides a place for gay young people to meet as an alternative to the 'scene'. Youth workers are present but members are involved in decision-making. There is a library, video facilities and other activities.

Southwark Lesbian Group
Tel 701 2564
Support and discussion group. Ring above number for details.

Southwark Lesbian Line
P O Box 702
SE15
Tel 703 3849
Line open 2-4pm(Tue) 7.30-10pm(Thur)
Telephone line providing information, advice, support and a chat for lesbians. Lesbian Line also organises socials.

South West London Gay Youth Group
Tel Michael 232 2511(eves)
Social group of gay young men, who meet every Wednesday night in Battersea. Activities discussed among the group. A lesbian group is planned in Battersea - Tel 228 7136 and speak to Helen for details.

Streatham Area Gay Group
P O Box BM/SAGG
WC1
Tel Ian 672 0316(eve)
A social group which meets fortnightly on Wednesdays at The Manor Hall, Station Approach, SW16. Various speakers, ranging from Kenneth Williams to Ken Livingstone. Some campaigning but mostly get-togethers. About one-third women and two-thirds men.

Wimbledon Area Gay Society
Tel 733 1488
Line open 7-10pm(Mon-Fri)
Social and discussion group which meets in the upstairs room at the Prince of Wales, Hertford Road, Wimbledon, SW19 every Thursday. Members (mostly male) are from a wide area and of all ages.

Pubs and Clubs

There are constantly new gay pubs and clubs opening and closing, so check up on a venue if you are unsure about it. There are many different kinds of pubs and clubs, from leather clubs to drag pubs, and gay venues are being established in many areas for the first time. One of the 'peculiarities' of South London gay pubs is the predominance of drag. Whatever you feel about the politics of cross-dressing, some drag acts can be both entertaining and subversive, like David Dale, while others can be right-off and embarrassing.
Another feature of South London gay pubs is the predominance of men's places over women's. This may be because pubs are more important to men for cruising and socialising, but more important is The Sex Discrimination Act which prevents a single bar pub from being open to women only. All gay men's places are open to women, but few of them are, not surprisingly, frequented by gay women. We have mentioned any pub where gay women go in significant numbers.

Many of the following pubs and clubs do have wheelchair access. Ring to check first to find out what assistance, if any, is required.

Brandy's
The Crypt
St Paul's Church
Deptford High Street
Deptford SE8
Tel none
Open 8pm-12.30am(Mon only)
Nightclub
Disco dancing club for women only. Free pool, darts and snacks. The Crypt can be hard to find and, if you don't want to go in alone, visit Deptford Dykes first (see Advice Groups).

Brownies
14 Gleneagle Road
Streatham SW16
Tel 769 6998
Open Men only 1pm-12.30am(Sun)
1pm-2.30am(Mon-Thur) 6pm-2.30am(Fri-Sat)

Women only 11.30am-6pm(Fri-Sat)
Admission £5(sauna) £3-3.90(sunbed
for half an hr) Reduced prices to
members
Membership £30 pa
Sauna
Two sunbeds, a sauna, jacuzzi, snack
bar, rest room and TV and video
room.

The Cricketers
312 Battersea Park Road
Battersea SW11
Tel 622 9060
Open 11am-3pm 8pm-12am(Mon-Sat)
11am-2pm 8pm-10.30(Sun)
Only gay people after 11pm
Admission free
Drag pub
Friendly, local gay pub with drag
Wednesdays to Sundays. Popular
with gay women. A wide range of
ages and types of people.

The Crypt
St Paul's Church
Deptford High Street
Deptford SE8
Tel none
Open 9pm-2am(Sun only)
Admission £1 members £1.50 guests
(before 10pm)
£1.50 members £2 guests (after 10pm)
Membership £3
Nightclub
In the crypt of a 'working' church,
and near Deptford BR station, the
Crypt has a friendly, local feel with
mixed pop and disco music and all ages
and styles. It's a good place to dance.
Drinks at pub prices.

The Dog and Fox
24 High Street
Wimbledon SW19
Tel 946 6565
Open 9pm-1am (Tue mixed but mainly
men – doors close 11.30pm. 8pm-12pm
(Sun men only – doors close 11pm
Wheelchair access assisted at
entrance no disabled toilets

Admission Tue £1.50 Sun £1
Membership 50p pa obligatory
Pub disco
Gay disco in pub ballroom on the
above nights only. Previously the
Wags Disco, which is now run by the
pub.

The Cricketers

The Elephant & Castle
South Lambeth Place
Vauxhall SW8
Tel 735 1001
Open 7pm-2am(Mon-Sat)
12pm-2pm 7pm-10.30pm(Sun)
Admission free but £1 after 11pm
Drag pub
Drag or entertainment every night.
The Elephant & Castle has a very
mixed clientele including one-third
women, who are mostly straight.

The Goldsmith's Tavern
New Cross Road
New Cross SE14
Tel 692 3648
Open 5.30pm-12am(Mon-Thur)
7pm-2am(Fri-Sat)
12pm-2pm 7pm-11.30pm(Sun)
Admission free
Drag pub
The Goldsmith's Tavern is a new gay
pub with the emphasis on cabaret and
drag from Fridays to Sundays,
followed by a disco. On Mondays to
Thursdays there's a disco only.

The Market Tavern
Market Towers
1 Nine Elms Lane

Vauxhall SW8
Tel 622 5655
Open 9pm-2am(Mon-Sat) 12pm-2pm
9pm-12am(Sun)
Admission 50p-£1
Disco pub
The Market Tavern is an increasingly
popular gay pub with two bars. On
Mondays, there is varied
entertainment. On Tuesdays, there's a
Body Positive disco for those who are
'body positive' and their friends. On
Wednesdays, the back bar is leather
only and the front bar is the 'Low-life
Disco'. On Thursdays, the pub hosts
the South London Area Gay Society,
and on Fridays and Saturdays there's
a disco, which is free before 11pm and
£1 after. Good music and disco and
rather 'butch' clientele.

The Palm Beach Disco
Palm Beach Suite
Streatham High Road
Streatham SW16
Tel not known
Open 10pm-2am(Fri only)
Admission £2.50 £2 members
Nightclub
This Colin Peters disco is situated in
The Palm Beach Suite next to the
skating rink, opposite Streatham
Common. Membership to Benjie's and
Burlington's honoured here.

The Prince of Wales
467 Brixton Road
Brixton SW9
Tel 274 6155
Open 9pm-2am(Mon-Fri)
12pm-3pm 9pm-2am(Sat)
12pm-2pm 8pm-10.30pm(Sun)
Admission £1 after 10.30pm
Drag & disco pub
Situated right in the heart of Brixton,
the Prince of Wales has
entertainment every night and drag
most nights. It has provided a meeting
place for Brixton's growing gay
community. It is genuinely mixed,
both men and women, black and white

and some straights. 'Sleazy' to some,
the pub reflects all kinds of gay people
from drag queens to butch clones.

The Royal Vauxhall Tavern
372 Kennington Lane
Vauxhall SE11
Tel 582 0833
Open 9pm-12am(Mon-Wed)
9pm-2am(Thur-Fri)
12pm-3pm 9pm-2am(Sat)
12pm-2pm 9pm-12pm(Sun)
Admission free
£1 after 11(Thur-Sat)

Drag pub
Drag which is centrally situated near
Vauxhall tube and attracts gay men
from all areas. The Vauxhall is famous
for its drag which sometimes ends in a
spirited rendition of 'Land of Hope
and Glory', which is not to everyone's
taste. Cruisy.

The Ship and Whale
2 Gulliver Street
Surrey Docks SE16
Tel 237 3305
Open 9pm-12am(Mon-Wed)
9pm-2am(Thur-Sat)
9pm-11pm(Sun)
Admission £1 after 11pm
Disco pub
Rather off the beaten track, The Ship
and Whale is a clean and comfortable,
mainly gay pub with a young, well-
scrubbed crowd. It has an attractive
large garden for summer drinking.

Rather bland disco music with a dancing area, but a pleasant evening out.

The Two Brewers
114 Clapham High Street
Clapham   SW4
Tel 622 3621
Open Someplace (cabaret bar)
7.30pm-1am(Mon-Fri) 12pm-3pm
7.30pm-1am(Sat)
12pm-2pm 7pm-10.30pm(Sun)
Dune (disco bar)
7.30pm-1am(Mon-Sat) *Admission*
Someplace free
Dune 50p(Mon-Thur after 10.30pm)
£1(Fri-Sat after 10.30pm)
Free to members
Membership £10pa
Drag & disco pub
The re-vamped Two Brewers is plushly decorated in a bland, post modernist style. Someplace is the entertainment bar with loudish music and drag. Dune is the disco bar and is cruisy and clony with a rather cold atmosphere.

The Union Tavern
146 Camberwell New Road
Camberwell   SE5
Tel 735 3605
Open 7pm-12am(Mon-Sat)
12pm-2pm 7pm-10.30pm(Sun)
Admission free
Drag & disco pub
The Union Tavern is a long-established gay pub which has recently been modernised. The Gaiety Bar has cabaret and drag seven nights a week. The Vice Bar is leather and denim. It's a popular venue.

Straight Places

Some straight places can be very good for gay people, but have you ever been in a straight place with your affair and felt a ripple of hostility spread when you touch each other?

Here is a (very selective) list of places where gay people can go and feel at ease without encountering too many straight men to make their lives uncomfortable. The Oval House and The Albany have been fantastic in showing interesting new lesbian and gay plays and The Ritzy, especially in Gay Pride Week, present some imaginative all-night gay programmes.

The Albany Empire
Douglas Way
Deptford   SE8
Tel 691 3333
Open phone for details
Wheelchair access to theatre toilets
Admission £1.50-£3.50 Concessions
Membership £2.50pa(individual)
£4pa(family) £5pa(group)
Theatre
The Albany has played host to some of the best-known gay theatre groups including Gay Sweatshop and Bloolips. It features gay cabarets with artists such as Simon Fanshawe, Janice Perry and Faye Presto. These are often benefit nights. There are women-only nights too which are popular with lesbians.

Brixton Art Gallery
21 Atlantic Road
Brixton   SW9
Tel 735 7757
Open 11-6(Mon-Sat)

Closed for one week between shows
Wheelchair access to gallery
Disabled toilets close by
Admission free
Art gallery
In 1984, Brixton Gallery staged the show 'Art for Poofs and Dykes'. Since then a group of lesbian and gay artists have been planning a lesbian and gay art show for 1986 and have booked exhibition space for Gay Pride Week. For further details of the group, which is committed to an anti-sexist, anti-racist stance, ring the above number.

The Fridge
Town Hall Parade
Brixton Hill
Brixton   SW2
Tel 326 5100
Open 9pm-2am
Wheelchair access none at present
Admission £3.50
Nightclub
The Fridge has always had a warm attitude towards gay men and women and the management has promised to eject any straight people who cause problems for gays. Thursday night is 'macho' gay night with the emphasis on uniform. Called 'The Cooling Tower', women will only be admitted accompanied by gay men.

Oval House
52 Kennington Oval
Oval   SE11
Tel 735 2786
Open phone for details
Admission varies Concessions
Wheelchair access to theatre downstairs cafe & toilets
Theatre Workshops
The Oval House is a theatre and a venue for workshops. As a theatre, it has hosted many gay groups, including Gay Sweatshop and Hard Corps. Recently 'Patience and Sarah' has played here. It is the best theatre for new gay productions in the whole of London. The workshops provide a variety of activities from juggling to self-defence. At 7.15-9.15 on Tuesday evenings there's also a gay youth theatre workshop which began in autumn 1985 and continues through summer 1986. Membership fees are very low with concessions for the unemployed.

The Ritzy Cinema
Brixton Oval
Brixton   SW2
Tel 737 2121 or 274 0070
Open phone for details
Wheelchair access difficult but assistance given on request
Admission varies
Cinema
Repertory cinema that shows a wide range of films, many of which are relevant to lesbians and gay men. Their all-night programmes during Gay Pride Week should not be missed.

Tea Time
21 The Pavement
Clapham   SW4
Tel 622 4944
Open 9.30am-7pm(Mon-Fri)
10am-7pm(Sat-Sun)
Wheelchair access none
Tea Shop
Tea shop painted in pastel colours with 1930s genteel atmosphere. Choice of teas, sandwiches and home-baked cakes. Set teas on Saturday and Sunday afternoons when drinks alone are not served. One room is non-smoking. The cafe is frequented by anyone from old ladies to gay couples of both sexes.

Health

AIDS has been blown out of all proportion by the media. It is a rare disease. We have included a Health section in this chapter because we feel it is important that anyone who is concerned about AIDS should know who and where to turn to for responsible, informed support.

Terrence Higgins Trust
BM AIDS
WC1
Tel 833 2971
Line open 7pm-10pm daily
The Terrence Higgins Trust provides
help and information on all aspects of
AIDS and related infections. Their
evening helpline (above) tends to be
pretty busy but they're putting in
extra lines which should ease the
situation. They do check their answer
phone regularly during the day and
will contact anyone who requires
urgent attention. They publish a
range of leaflets (send a large self-
addressed envelope) and new ones are
being produced all the time. They can
also arrange one-to-one counselling.
They run a formal support group in
London for people·who have AIDS
and try and encourage them to meet
together on an informal basis. They
organise four counselling and
educational sessions a month in
London for people who have been told
they have the AIDS virus, HTLV3.
They provide help with social
services, legal and other issues and
provide a home care service for people
with AIDS. At the request of a
patient, an experienced volunteer will
sort out any practical matters, help
around the house and give continuing
emotional support both to the patient
and to the patient's partner or family.
They organise public seminars at
various London venues, which are
advertised in the gay press. They also
have a programme of meetings when
an experienced volunteer talks about
AIDS at gay pubs and clubs. They will
send speakers at the request of any
group or organisation. They have a
medical group of doctors who provide
informed medical help to the
community at large, to social workers
and to other members of the medical
profession, and they organise training
sessions at hospitals and social
services departments. Professional
enquirers should ring the general
office number during the day (Tel 278
3047).

Body Positive
c/o Terrence Higgins Trust
BM AIDS
WC1
Tel 833 2971
Line open 7pm-10pm daily
The medical term 'antibody positive'
is used when a blood test has proved
the existence of the AIDS virus,
HTLV3. When people with HTLV3
ring the Terrence Higgins Trust for
advice they are also given a number
for Body Positive, a London-based
organisation that has been set up to
offer counselling, education and
support to people with HTLV3. All the
counsellors at Body Positive have
HTLV3. Anyone who rings Body
Positive can arrange to meet a
counsellor to discuss things in person.
Body Positive offers support in a
number of other ways and arranges
activities like discussions, seminars
and social events.

Alexanda Clinic
A Block
St Giles' Hospital
St Giles' Road
Camberwell   SE5
Tel 703 0898 Ext 6024 & 6202
Open 9-30-4.30(Mon Fri) 9.30-6.30(Tue
Thur) 9.30-12noon(Wed) Thanks to
some funding from the South East
Thames Regional Health Authority,
the medical staff at St Giles' Hospital
have developed a particular interest
in AIDS and other HTLV3 infections.
They are happy to see anyone from
anywhere in South London. They are
developing their medical and
counselling expertise all the time and
are hoping it won't be long before
they can take on an AIDS
information officer.

Gay Switchboard
Tel 837 7324
Gay Switchboard offers advice and
information and is able to refer people
to a Body Positive counsellor and to
the Terrence Higgins Trust.

LIBRARIES

Joining a library these days involves simply turning up at any branch with some means of identification to show that you either live, work or study in the area, and filling in a form or card. There appears to be no standard procedure regulating the number of books you are entitled to borrow, the loan period and the loan charge (or lack of one) for records and cassettes. It depends on where you live. (Check the introductory section to each borough in the listings below.) If you already hold a library ticket and wish to borrow material from another borough this can usually be arranged on presentation of your own library membership card, though this procedure also varies from borough to borough. You are usually expected to follow the library rules of the borough in which you are a guest rather than your own borough library system. There undoubtedly was an era when libraries were places you just passed through to pick up your reading for the week but they have much more to offer the community these days and should be providing facilities to

match. We were more than a little dismayed to find that, at a time when libraries are used constantly by the public generally, by people applying for jobs and by researchers, all of whom need constant access to a phone, only one borough (Wandsworth) has public telephones in any of its libraries. What is more, only two libraries in the whole of South London have toilets (a third library has a special toilet for disabled people). Granted, libraries are often near public toilets and installing facilities in what are often old Victorian buildings must pose some headaches, but this does seem rather remiss.

Having had our little moan, we should perhaps add how impressed we have been by the many exciting collections and services on offer in South London libraries. And it seems that, all the time, new projects are being developed to meet the needs of the community.

South London's lending and reference libraries are listed below by borough followed by other South London-based

Specialist Libraries, which are listed alphabetically.

Greenwich

General Library Stock

●All Greenwich libraries contain books for adults and children, large print books, basic reference material and an information service.
●All libraries have a range of national and local newspapers and magazines (except for the smaller part-time libraries which only have local ones).
●All Greenwich libraries contain books for adults and children, large print books, basic reference material and an information service.
●All libraries have a range of national and local newspapers and magazines (except for the smaller part-time libraries which only have local ones).

Loan Procedure
●You are entitled to borrow 3 books and 2 records or cassettes for 3 weeks at a time.
●If you want to borrow more books you can request extra tickets.
●Parents are allowed 2 extra record/cassette tickets for each child.
●There is a loan fee of 15p per record or cassette (with a maximum charge of 30p) or, if you pay an annual subscription of £5, you can borrow records and cassettes for nothing.
●Concessionaries can purchase a £1 Concessionary Access Card (at the Town Hall, Public Baths, sports and leisure centres), which entitles them to borrow records and cassettes for nothing.

Music Collection

●Greenwich's record and cassette collection covers a wide musical range and is available at seven libraries in the borough.

●There is a selection of transport and communications recordings (ie engine noises, morse code sounds etc):
●Ravel and Schumann are the borough's special composers.
●Jazz musicians with surnames MA-MD are featured, with a special interest in Wayne Marsh.

Reference Material

●Basic reference material is available at all libraries.
●The main reference library in the borough is Woolwich Library.

Local History

●The Local History Library is based at Woodlands (see Local History Library in the listing).

Special Collections

●Greenwich has a Contemporary Print Loan Collection, which is housed at Greenwich Library.
●There are loan collections of jigsaws for adults and children at Charlton and Plumstead Libraries.

Other Library Services

●The borough's mobile library service consists of two large trailers, which carry about 4500 books each (no records or cassettes) to 11 fixed sites every week. There is no wheelchair access to the trailers.
●A smaller vehicle, which carries both books and cassettes, goes to 6 smaller sites each week, stopping for shorter periods. There is wheelchair access to this vehicle.
●Ring your nearest library or the Mobile Library Service headquarters (Tel 856 9794) to find out more.
●Three vans make regular library deliveries to housebound readers in the borough. Ring Charlton Library if you want to be put on the list.

●There is also a library delivery service to sheltered housing, old people's homes, hostels and mental health establishments whereby books are deposited for 3 months at a time.
●The five main hospitals in the borough all have patients' libraries and ward library rounds.
●There are permanent medical libraries at the two main teaching hospitals in Greenwich.

Exhibition Space

●All libraries have display areas of varying sizes which are used to promote local groups and activities.
●Greenwich and Plumstead Libraries have exhibition spaces (contact Greenwich Library if you wish to make a booking at either venue).

Abbey Wood Library
Eynsham Drive
Abbey Wood SE2
Tel 310 4185
Open 2-8(Mon Thur) 10-1 2-5.30(Tue Fri) 10-1 2-5(Sat)
Wheelchair access to library
General stock.

Blackheath Library
St John's Park
Blackheath SE3
Tel 858 1131
Open 9-8(Mon Thur) 9-5.30(Tue Fri) 9-5(Sat)
Wheelchair access none
General stock and records and cassettes.

Charlton Library
Charlton House
Charlton SE7
Tel 856 0264
Open 9-8(Mon Thur) 9-5.30(Tue Fri) 9-5(Sat)
Wheelchair access none General stock and records and cassettes. Loan collection of jigsaws for adults and children.

Coldharbour Library
William Barefoot Drive
Coldharbour Estate SE9
Tel 857 7346
Open 2-8(Mon Thur) 10-1 2-5.30(Tue Fri) 10-1 2-5(Sat)
Wheelchair access to library
General stock.

Eltham Library
Eltham High Street
Eltham SE9
Tel 850 2268
Open 9-8(Mon Thur) 9-5.30(Tue Fri) 9-5(Sat)
Wheelchair access ring side door bell
General stock and records and cassettes.
Photocopying

Ferrier Library
Telemann Square
Kidbrooke SE3
Tel 856 5149
Open 2-8(Mon Thur) 10-1 2-5.30(Tue Fri) 10-1 2-5(Sat)
Wheelchair access to library
General stock.

Greenwich Library
Woolwich Road
Greenwich SE10
Tel 858 6656
Open 9-8(Mon Thur) 9-5.30(Tue Fri) 9-5(Sat)
Wheelchair access none
General stock, records and cassettes and exhibition space for local groups and artists. Also, the Contemporary Print Loan Collection, which offers people who live, work or study in Greenwich the opportunity to borrow a framed print for three months at no charge. This Collection comprises mainly British prints with an emphasis on the work of local printmakers (who are quite numerous and active in Greenwich).
Photocopying

Kidbrooke Library
Brook Lane
Kidbrooke SE3

Tel 856 3473
Open 9-8(Mon Thur) 9-5.30(Tue Fri) 9-5(Sat)
Wheelchair access to library
General stock.

Local History Library
Woodlands
Mycenae Road
Blackheath   SE3
Tel 858 4631
Open 9-8(Mon Tue Thur) 9-5(Sat)
Wheelchair access none to library but will provide library material to ground floor art gallery where there is provision for wheelchairs. Special toilets next door
Local history material available for reference only. Ring first if you want to use the microfilm reader.

New Eltham Library
Southwood Road
New Eltham   SE9
Tel 850 2322
Open 9-8(Mon Thur) 9-5.30(Tue Fri) 9-5(Sat)
Wheelchair access none
General stock.
Photocopying

Plumstead Library
Plumstead High Street
Plumstead   SE18
Tel 854 1728
Open 9-8(Mon Thur) 9-5.30(Tue Fri) 9-5(Sat)
Wheelchair access none

General stock, records and cassettes and large exhibition space (contact Greenwich Library for bookings). Loan collection of jigsaws for adults and children.
Photocopying

Shrewsbury House Library
Bushmoor Crescent
Shooters Hill   SE18
Tel 854 1107
Open 2-8(Mon Thur) 10-1 2-5.30(Tue Fri) 10-1 2-5(Sat)
Wheelchair access to library
General stock.
Public toilet

Slade Library
Erindale
Plumstead Common   SE18
Tel 854 7900
Open 2-8(Mon Thur) 10-1 2-5.30(Tue Fri) 10-1 2-5(Sat)
Wheelchair access to library
General stock.

West Greenwich Library
Greenwich High Road
Greenwich   SE10
Tel 858 4289
Open 9-8(Mon Thur) 9-5.30(Tue Fri) 9-5(Sat)
Wheelchair access none
General stock and records and cassettes.

Woolwich Library
Calderwood Street
Woolwich   SE18
Tel 854 8888 (854 1939 after 5.30 & Sat)
Open 9-8(Mon Thur) 9-5.30(Tue Fri) 9-5(Sat)
Wheelchair access none
General stock of records and cassettes.
Photocopying

Lambeth

General Library Stock

●Apart from a few special collections,

all Lambeth's library stock is distributed throughout the borough so that there is something of everything at each branch.
●All libraries have a general stock of newspapers and magazines, books for adults and children, records and cassettes, large print books, literacy books for adult new readers, material for the Black community, for women, for people with disabilities and for gay men and lesbians.
●All branches also have material for people for whom English is a second language.
●At many branches there is material in Hindi, Bengali, Gujarati, Urdu, French, Spanish, Portuguese, German, Polish, Greek, Turkish, Chinese, Vietnamese and Italian.
●All branches offer basic general reference material and a local information service (which includes the regular publication of an Advice Centres Information Sheet and an information service and newsletter for small businesses in Lambeth).

Loan Procedure

●You may borrow up to 6 books and 3 records or cassettes (at no charge) for one month.

Music Collection

●Lambeth's stock of records and cassettes covers pop and rock, jazz, folk, classical, sound effects, languages and easy listening.
●There is a selection from the collection in every library in the borough.

Reference Material

●Basic reference material is available at all libraries.
●Lambeth's main reference library is on the first floor of the Tate Library in Brixton.

Local History

●Lambeth's local history material is based at Minet Library.

Special Collections

●Lambeth has a Working Materials Collection (see Tate Brixton).

Other Library Services

●All Lambeth library staff are trained in the Sympathetic Hearing Scheme to help people with hearing difficulties.
●Lambeth has two mobile libraries which make regular stops throughout the borough.
●There is also a library service for the housebound.
●Library material are delivered to local community groups.
●For details of all these special services contact your local library or ring Lambeth Amenity Services Tel 622 6655.

Exhibition Space

●There are often small book displays or shows of work by local artists in libraries in Lambeth and there is a large exhibition space at West Norwood Library which is used for shows of painting and sculpture.

Carnegie Library
188 Herne Hill Road
Herne Hill   SE24
Tel 274 3911
Open 11-8(Mon Wed) 11-6(Tue) 9-6(Fri) 9-5(Sat)
Wheelchair access none
General stock, records and cassettes.
Photocopying

Clapham Library
1 Clapham Common Northside
Clapham   SW4
Tel 622 4008
Open 11-8(Mon Wed) 9-6(Tue Thur Fri) 9-5(Sat)

Wheelchair access to library
General stock, records and cassettes.
Photocopying

Clapham Park Library
Poynders Road
Clapham Park **SW4**
Tel 674 1890
Open 11-8(Mon Thur) 11-6(Tue) 9-
6(Fri) 9-5(Sat)
Wheelchair access to library
General stock, records and cassettes.

Durning Library
167 Kennington Lane
Kennington **SE11**
Tel 735 2349
Open 9-8(Mon-Wed) 9-6(Thur Fri) 9-
5(Sat) 2-6(Sun)
Wheelchair access to library
General stock, records and cassettes.
Photocopying

Jeffreys Library
31 Jeffreys Road
Stockwell **SW4**
Tel 622 7859
Open 11-8(Mon) 11-6(Tue Thur) 9-
6(Fri) 9-5(Sat)
Wheelchair access to library
General stock, records and cassettes.

Minet Library
52 Knatchbull Road
Camberwell **SE5**
Tel 274 5325
Open 11-8(Mon Thur) 11-6(Tue Fri) 9-
5(Sat)
Wheelchair access to libraries
General stock, records and cassettes.
●Lambeth Archives Department
Tel 733 3279
Open by appointment only
Lambeth's local history material.

North Lambeth Library
114-118 Lower Marsh
North Lambeth **SE1**
Tel 928 4053
Open 11-8(Mon) 9-6(Tue Wed Fri) 9-
5(Sat)
Wheelchair access to library
General stock, records and cassettes.

St Martin's Library
220 Upper Tulse Hill
Tulse Hill **SW2**
Tel 674 5939
Open 11-8(Mon Wed) 11-6(Tue) 9-
6(Fri) 9-5(Sat)
Wheelchair access to library
General stock, records and cassettes.
Photocopying

Streatham Vale Library
162 Eardley Road
Streatham Vale **SW16**
Tel 764 2736
Open 11-8(Mon Thur) 11-6(Tue) 9-
6(Fri) 9-5(Sat)
Wheelchair access to library
General stock, records and cassettes.

Tate Library Brixton
Brixton Oval
Brixton **SW2**
Tel 274 7451
Open 9-8(Mon Wed Thur) 9-6(Tue
Fri) 9-5(Sat) 2-6(Sun)
Wheelchair access to ground floor
library

General stock, records and cassettes.
●Reference Library
Open 9-8(Mon-Thur) 9-6(Fri) 9-5(Sat)
2-6(Sun)
Wheelchair access none
Lambeth's main reference library.
Also Working Materials Collection
(viewable by appointment only) for
youth workers, play leaders and
other people whose work involves
literacy, numeracy, ESL, disability,
under 5s or advice giving.
Photocopying

Tate Library South Lambeth
180 South Lambeth Road
Stockwell **SW8**
Tel 622 3982
Open 11-6(Mon-Tue) 11-8(Thur) 9-
6(Fri) 9-5(Sat)
Wheelchair access to library
General stock, records and cassettes.

Tate Library Streatham
63 Streatham High Road
Streatham **SW16**

Tel 769 1021
Open 9-8(Mon Tue Thur) 9-6(Wed
Fri) 9-5(Sat)
Wheelchair access to library
General stock, records and cassettes.
Photocopying

West Norwood Library
Norwood High Street
West Norwood　　　　　　SE27
Tel 670 8104
Open 9-8(Mon Wed Thur) 9-6(Tue Fri
Sat)
Wheelchair access to library
General stock, records and cassettes.
Photocopying

Lewisham

General Library Stock

●There are books for adults and
children (including books in the
Indic languages, Vietnamese and
Afro-Caribbean literature), large
print books, newspapers and
magazines, an information service
and a small amount of reference
material at all libraries in Lewisham.

Loan Procedure

●You may borrow up to 6 books and 6
albums for a month at a time.
●Renewals can be made in person at
the library or by leaving a message
on a 24 hr answering machine Tel 698
7347.
●There is a loan fee of 20p per album
and 35p per double album or box set.
●Lewisham has a £25 Leisure Pass
scheme (free for OAPs, unwaged,
disabled people and students), which
entitles holders to borrow records
free of charge.

Music Collection

●There are records at several
branches (see listing) but no cassettes
as yet.

●Lewisham's special composer is
Shostakovich.
●The rest of the record collection
consists of vocal recitals, music
appreciation and jazz artists with
surnames A-BAI.

Reference Material

●There is a basic reference collection
at all libraries in the borough.
●A more extensive collection of
reference material is split according
to subject (see Deptford and
Lewisham in the listing).

Local History

●Lewisham has a Local History
Centre at Manor House Library.

Special Collections

●There is a loan collection of framed
prints, based at Deptford Library. A
full catalogue and a selection of
prints are available at every library.
●A Video Tape Collection is based at
Lewisham Library.
●There is a Resource Centre for the
Unemployed at Bromley Road
Library.
●There is a particularly
authoritative collection of Afro-
Caribbean and Indian material at
Deptford, and Pepys and Old Town
Libraries have good Vietnamese
sections.

Other Library Services

●Lewisham has a mobile library that
visits six sites in the borough.
●It also has a library service for the
housebound where home library
visits are made on a monthly rota. To
be included in this service or to find
out more, contact Lewisham Library
●Visits are also made to various
hospital wards in the borough and
there is a special medical and
patients' library at Lewisham
Hospital.

Exhibition Space

●A large exhibition space is available at Bromley Road Library which is the venue for several local groups. The Lewisham Film Society's screenings and the twice-yearly Lewisham Society of Arts exhibitions also take place there. This space is available to artists and community groups based in the borough. Ring 852 9121 Ext 285 for details.

Blackheath Village Library
Tranquil Passage
Blackheath SE3
Tel 852 5309
Open 9.30-12.30 1.30-5(Mon Fri Sat) 9.30-12.30 1.30-8(Tue Thur)
Wheelchair access none
General stock.

Brockley Library
375 Brockley Road
Brockley SE4
Tel 692 1683
Open 9.30-1 2-5(Mon Fri Sat) 9.30-1 2-8(Tue Thur)
Wheelchair access to library
General stock.
Photocopying

Bromley Road Library
170 Bromley Road

Catford SE6
Tel 698 7347
Open 9.30-5(Mon Fri Sat) 9.30-8(Tue Thur)
Wheelchair access to library
General stock and records. Special project room for unemployed people. This area is used for general activities and special workshops and contains several micro-computers, two typewriters, knitting and sewing machines, a VHS video recorder and video camera, technical drawing and photo developing equipment.
Public toilet Photocopying

Deptford Library
140 Lewisham Way
New Cross SE14
Tel 692 4535/3649
Open 9.30-5(Mon Fri Sat) 9.30-8(Tue Thur)
Wheelchair access none
General stock and records. Extensive collection of Afro-Caribbean and Indic language library material. Print room containing selection of framed classical and modern prints which can be borrowed free of charge for three months. Catalogues of the collection and a few selected prints can be seen at any Lewisham library.
●Reference Library
A large collection of commercial and technical reference material.
Photocopying

Forest Hill Library
Dartmouth Road
Forest Hill SE23
Tel 699 2065
Open 9.30-1 2-5(Mon Fri Sat) 9.30-1 2-8(Tue Thur)
Wheelchair access restricted
General stock and records.
Photocopying

Grove Park Library
Somertrees Avenue
Grove Park   SE12
Tel 857 5794
Open 9.30-1 2-5(Mon Fri Sat) 9.30-2 5-8(Tue Thur)
Wheelchair access none
General stock.

Hither Green Library
Torridon Road
Hither Green   SE6
Tel 698 1590
Open 9.30-1 2-5(Mon Fri Sat) 9.30-1 2-8(Tue Thur)
Wheelchair access to library
General stock.

Lewisham Library
Lewisham High Street
Lewisham   SE13
Tel 690 1247
Open 9.30-5(Mon Fri Sat) 9.30-8(Tue Thur)
Wheelchair access to library
General stock and records. VHS video tapes (on music, sport, hobbies and tapes for children). Base of Lewisham's Hospital and housebound services.
●Reference Library
Large collection of reference material on the arts, humanities and social sciences.
Photocopying

Manor House Library
Old Road
Lee   SE13
Tel 852 0357
Open 9.30-1 2-5(Mon Fri Sat) 9.30-1 2-8(Tue Thur)
Wheelchair access none
General stock.
●Local History Centre
Open as above
Collection of local history material.
Photocopying

New Cross Library
New Cross Road
New Cross   SE14
Tel 639 1227
Open 9.30-1 2-8(Tue Thur) 9.30-1 2-5(Sat)
Wheelchair access none
General stock.

Old Town Library
Clyde Street
Deptford   SE8
Tel 692 3623
Open 9.30-1 2-5(Mon Fri Sat) 9.30-1 2-8(Tue Thur)
Wheelchair access to library
General stock. Wide selection of Vietnamese material.

Pepys Library
Foreshore
Deptford   SE8
Tel 692 3659
Open 9.30-1 2-8(Tue Thur) 9.30-1 2-5(Sat)
Wheelchair access restricted to adult library only
General stock. Large stock of Vietnamese material.

St Catherine's Library
Kitto Road
New Cross   SE14
Tel 639 1086
Open 9.30-1 2-5(Mon Fri Sat) 9.30-1 2-8(Tue Thur)
Wheelchair access to library
General stock.

Stanstead Road Library
300 Stanstead Road
Catford   SE23
Tel 699 7439
Open 9.30-1 2-5(Mon Fri Sat) 9.30-1 2-8(Tue Thur)
Wheelchair access to library
General stock.

Sydenham Library
Sydenham Road
Sydenham   SE26
Tel 778 7563
Open 9.30-1 2-5(Mon Fri Sat) 9.30-1 2-
8(Tue Thur)
Wheelchair access none
General stock.

Woodpecker Library
140 Woodpecker Road
New Cross   SE14
Tel 692 1288
Open 2-8(Tue Thur) 9.30-1 2-5(Sat)
Wheelchair access to library
General stock.

Merton

General Library Stock

●General library stock for adults and
children (including large print books,
basic reference material, newspapers
and magazines) is distributed to all
libraries in the borough.

Loan Procedure

●In Merton, you may borrow up to 4
books (teachers and students are
allowed an extra 6) and 4 records or
cassettes (30p each) for 3 weeks at a
time.

Music Collection

●Merton has a general music
collection. Cassettes can be borrowed
from a few branch libraries (see
listings) and records from the
Gramophone Record Library.
●The borough's special music subject
is Jazz.

Reference Material

●Basic reference material can be
found at all libraries.
●The main reference stock is at
Wimbledon Library.

Local History

●There is no one local history library
in Merton but there are 3 local
history collections based at Mitcham,
Morden and Wimbledon. Specialist
librarians at these libraries will try
and help with any local history
queries.

Special Collections

●Mitcham Library has a World
History (loan) Collection and a
Cricket Collection for reference only.
●There is also a William Morris
Collection (for reference only) at
Morden Library.
●At Wimbledon Library there's a
Tennis Collection for reference only.
●There is also a collection of Talking
Books for the Blind at Donald Hope
Library.

Other Library Services

●Merton has a mobile library
scheme, details of which can be
obtained from any library (or Tel 545
3780).
●Housebound readers should ring
Mitcham Library and ask to be put
on the list for a home visit.

Exhibition Space

●There is a small space for displays
at all libraries (except for Morden
Park and Wimbledon Park). If you
are interested in booking a space,
contact the library concerned.
●There is a large exhibition room at
Wimbledon Library for local groups
(Ring 545 3780 to make a booking.)

Donald Hope Library
Cavendish House
High Street
Colliers Wood   SW19
Tel 542 1975

Open 9-7(Mon Tue Thur) 9-1(Fri) 9-5(Sat)
Wheelchair access to library
General stock and cassettes.
Photocopying

Mitcham Library
London Road
Mitcham
Tel 648 4070/6516
Open 9-7(Mon Tue Thur Fri) 9-1(Wed) 9-5(Sat)
Wheelchair access to library
General stock. Special World History Loan Collection. Also, Cricket Collection for reference only. Central office for Merton's library service for housebound readers.
●Local History Collection
Tel 648 4070
Local history material on Mitcham.
Photocopying

Morden Library
Morden Road
Morden　　　　　　　　　　**SW19**
Tel 542 2842/1701
Open 9-7(Mon-Tue Thur-Fri) 9-1(Wed) 9-5(Sat)
Wheelchair access to libraries
General stock. Also, William Morris Collection with particular focus on his connections with the borough (for reference only).
●Gramophone Record Library
Open as above but closes 10 mins earlier

Wide range of records and a special Jazz Collection. (Cassettes are not available – see Donald Hope, Pollards Hill and West Barnes.)
●Local History Collection
Tel 542 2842
Material on the history of Morden.
Photocopying

Morden Park Library
Lower Morden Lane
Morden
Tel 337 3405
Open 9-1 2-7(Mon Thur) 9-1(Fri) 9-1 2-5(Tue Sat)
Wheelchair access to library
General stock.

Pollards Hill Library
South Lodge Avenue
Mitcham
Tel 764 5877
Open 9-7(Mon Tue Thur) 9-1(Fri) 9-5(Sat)
Wheelchair access to library
General stock and cassettes.

Raynes Park Library
Approach Road
Raynes Park　　　　　　　**SW20**
Tel 542 1893
Open 9-7(Mon Tue Thur) 9-1(Fri) 9-5(Sat)
Wheelchair access to library
General stock.
Photocopying

West Barnes Library
Station Road
New Malden
Tel 942 2635
Open 9-1 2-7(Mon Tue Thur) 9-1(Fri) 9-1 2-5(Sat)
Wheelchair access to library
General stock and cassettes.

Wimbledon Library
Wimbledon Hill Road
Wimbledon　　　　　　　　**SW19**
Tel 946 7979(renewals) 946 7432(enquiries)
Open 9-7(Mon Tue Thur Fri) 9-5(Wed Sat)

Wheelchair access to library. General stock. Exhibition room available for hire by local groups (ring 545 3780 for details).
●Local History Collection
Tel 946 1136
Historical material on Wimbledon.
●Reference Library
Material includes a special Tennis Collection.
Photocopying

Wimbledon Park Library
Arthur Road
Wimbledon   **SW19**
Tel 946 3999
Open 9-1 2-7(Mon Thur) 9-1(Fri) 9-1 2-5(Tue Sat)
Wheelchair access limited access for small chairs
General stock.

Southwark

General Library Stock

●Books and general material for adults and children, large print books, newspapers and magazines, basic reference and adult literacy material and a community information service are available at all Southwark libraries.

Loan Procedure

●You are entitled to borrow 9 items at any one time for a period of 3 weeks.
●There is no loan charge for records or cassettes.

Music Collection

●Cassettes and/or records can be borrowed from many branches (see listing).
●The main music collection is housed at the Music Library in Peckham Road.

Reference Material

●Basic material can be found in all libraries.
●Newington and Dulwich Reference Libraries provide a full reference service.

Local History

●Southwark's local history material is housed at the Local Studies Library (see John Harvard).

Special Collections

●An Illustrations Collection is based at Bermondsey Library.
●A Projects Collection is also based at Bermondsey.
●There is extensive material on Sociology at Camberwell Church Street Library.
●A collection on Computers is based at Newington Library.
●There is a collection of books in Scandinavian languages at Rotherhithe.
●The South London Art Gallery has been included in the listing for its considerable Print Collection which is available for reference.

Other Library Services

●Southwark has a mobile library service. Details of its route can be obtained from any library.
●People who are housebound should phone 237 1487 to arrange for a library house call.

Exhibition Space

●In all libraries there are small display areas which local groups and artists are welcome to use.
●There are larger exhibition spaces at several branches (see listing).

Bermondsey Library
Spa Road
Bermondsey　　　　　　**SE16**
Tel 237 6677 (237 6901 after 5 and on Sat)
Open 9.30-8(Mon-Tue Thur-Fri) 9.30-5(Sat)
Wheelchair access none
General stock and records, cassettes, scores and books on music. The Illustration Collection of over 100,000 mounted illustrations (classified by subject) is available for loan for 3 weeks at a time to people living in Southwark or elsewhere. Also, for Southwark teachers wanting material in large quantities (for school projects) there is the Project Collection of over 7000 books, pamphlets, charts and other items. Large exhibition space.

Bessemer Grange Library
8 Crossthwaite Avenue
Camberwell　　　　　　**SE5**
Tel 274 8993
Open 9.30-12.30 1.30-5(Mon Sat) 9.30-12.30 1.30-8(Tue Thu)
Wheelchair access to library
General stock.

Blue Anchor Library
Market Place
Bermondsey　　　　　　**SE16**
Tel 231 0475
Open 9.30-12.30 1.30-8(Mon Thur) 9.30-12.30 1.30-5(Fri Sat)
Wheelchair access to library
General stock.
Photocopying

Borough Road Library
7-12 Borough Road
St George's Circus　　　　**SE1**
Tel 928 5562
Open 9.30-8 (Tue Thur) 9.30-5(Fri Sat)
General stock and cassettes.

Brandon Library
Maddock Way
Walworth　　　　　　**SE17**
Tel 735 3430
Open 9.30-12.30 1.30-8(Mon Fri) 9.30-12.30 1.30-5 (Tue Sat)
Wheelchair access none
General stock and cassettes. Large exhibition space.

Camberwell Church Street Library
17-19 Camberwell Church Street
Camberwell　　　　　　**SE5**
Tel 703 3763
Open 9.30-8(Mon-Tue Thur-Fri) 9.30-5(Sat)
Wheelchair access to library
General stock. Sociology Collection and main bulk of Southwark's Adult Literacy Collection. Large exhibition space in library window.
Photocopying

Dulwich Library
368 Lordship Lane
Dulwich　　　　　　**SE22**
Tel 693 5171
Open 9.30-8(Mon-Tue Thur-Fri) 9.30-1(Wed) 9.30-5(Sat)
Wheelchair access to lending library
General stock. Large exhibition space.
●Reference Library
Tel 693 8312
Open 9.30-8(Mon Tue Thur-Fri) 9.30-8(Wed)
Wheelchair access none
Extensive reference material.
Photocopying

East Street/Old Kent Road Library
168-170 Old Kent Road
Bricklayer's Arms　　　　**SE1**
Tel 703 0395
Open 9.30-12.30 1.30-8(Mon Thur) 9.30-12.30 1.30-5(Tue Sat)
Wheelchair access to library
General stock.

Grove Vale Library
25-27 Grove Vale
East Dulwich   SE22
Tel 693 5734
Open 9.30-8(Mon-Tue Thur-Fri) 9.30-
5(Sat)
Wheelchair access to library.
General stock and cassettes.

Harper Road Library
191 Harper Road
Elephant & Castle   SE1
Tel 407 3474
Open 9.30-12.30 1.30-8(Mon Fri) 9.30-
12.30 1.30-5(Thur Sat)
Wheelchair access to library
General stock, cassettes and a wide
selection of books in Urdu, Bengali,
Gujerati and Hindi.

John Harvard Library
211 Borough High Street
Borough   SE1
Tel 407 0807
Open 9.30-8(Mon-Tue Thur-Fri) 9.30-
5(Wed) 9.30-1(Sat)
Wheelchair access to library and
special toilet
General stock. Motor Manual
Collection. Large exhibition space.
●Local Studies Library
Tel 403 3507
Open 9.30-12.30 1.30-8(Mon Thur)
9.30-12.30 & 1.30-5(Tue Fri) 9.30-
1(Sat); by appointment only
Contains a copy of practically every
book about the area from the 16th
century to today. Also, local
newspapers from 1865 to date on
microfilm, thousands of press
cuttings, prints, photographs and
maps, and a small collection of
cassette recordings of Southwark's
older residents' memories.
Photocopying

Kingswood Library
Seeley Drive
Dulwich   SE21
Tel 670 4803
Open 9.30-12.30 1.30-8(Mon Fri) 9.30-
12.30 1.30-5(Thur Sat)
Wheelchair access none

General stock and records.
Kingswood Library and Community
Centre are based at Kingswood
House, once a private residence of
considerable significance. Some of
the features can still be seen in the
adult and junior libraries (see
Historic Houses in Southwark
section of Local History).

Kingswood Library

Music Library
34 Peckham Road
Camberwell   SE5
Tel 703 6311 (or 703 7384 after 5 & on
Sat)
Open 9.30-8(Mon Thur) 9.30-5(Tue
Sat)
Wheelchair access none
Large stock of records and cassettes.
Opera, classical music, jazz, soul,
reggae, rock, easy listening, folk and
ethnic. Also language courses, poetry
and plays, talking books and
shorthand dictation. Scores and
books on music and Music Minus
One recordings for musicians (of all
abilities) wishing to practice.
Southwark's special composers are
Berlioz and Messiaen and jazz artists
with surnames from JOO-LED.

Newington Library
155-157 Walworth Road
Walworth   SE17
Tel 703 3324/5529/6514
Open 9.30-8(Mon-Tue Thur-Fri) 9.30-
1(Wed) 9.30-5(Sat)
Wheelchair access none

General stock. Also, records, cassettes and scores and books on Music. A special loan collection of books and periodicals on Computers. Large exhibition space.
●Reference Library
Tel 708 0516
Open 9.30-8(Mon-Tue Thur-Fri) 9.30-8(Wed) 9.30-5(Sat)
Extensive reference stock.
Photocopying

North Camberwell Library
Wells Way
Camberwell   SE5
Tel 703 4788
Open 9.30-12.30 1.30-5(Mon Sat) 9.30-12.30 1.30-8(Tue Thur)
Wheelchair access none
General stock and cassettes.

North Peckham Library
600-608 Old Kent Road
North Peckham   SE15
Tel 639 1255
Open 9.30-8(Mon-Tue Thur-Fri) 9.30-5(Sat)
General stock, records and cassettes. Bulk of Southwark's books in Greek, Turkish, Vietnamese, Chinese, Hindi, Gujurati, Urdu, Bengali, Punjabi and Arabic, although there are some books in all of these languages in every Southwark library. Exhibition space and gallery.
Photocopying
Nunhead Library
Gordon Road
Nunhead   SE15
Tel 639 0264
Open 9.30-12.30 1.30-8(Tue Thur) 9.30-12.30 1.30-5(Fri-Sat)
Wheelchair access to library
General stock and cassettes.

Peckham Hill Street Library
167 Peckham Hill Street
Peckham   SE15
Tel 639 1624
Open 9.30-8 (Mon-Tue Thur-Fri) 9.30-5(Sat)
Wheelchair access none

General stock and cassettes.
Photocopying

Rotherhithe Library
Albion Street
Rotherhithe   SE16
Tel 237 2010
Open 9.30-12.30 1.30-8(Mon Thur) 9.30-12.30 1.30-5(Tue Sat)
Wheelchair access to library
General stock and cassettes. Collection of books in Scandinavian languages – Finnish, Swedish and Norwegian. Large exhibition space.

South London Art Gallery
65 Peckham Road
Camberwell   SE5
Tel 703 6120
Open 10-5(Tue-Fri ring to tell them you are coming) & on Sat by appt
Wheelchair access assisted by prior arrangement
Available for reference is a collection of 20th Century original prints, which was started in 1960 with the aim of including the best prints being produced each year by British artists. The Print Collection includes works by David Hockney, John Piper, Graham Sutherland, Patrick Heron and Michael Ayrton. Also available for consultation (by prior arrangement) are individual works from a number of other collections – a small collection of Contemporary British Art (formed in 1953), a collection of Topographical Paintings and Drawings of Southwark, a collection of Victorian art, some Martin ware vessels and other Victorian and Edwardian pottery (see Art).

Wandsworth

General Library Stock

●All Wandsworth libraries contain books for adults, separate children's libraries, a selection of large print books, newspapers, magazines and quick reference material.

Loan Procedure

●You are entitled to borrow 6 books and 6 gramophone records or cassettes for 3 weeks.
●There is a loan charge of 25p per cassette or record (with a maximum charge of 50p for box sets). A returnable deposit of £5 is sometimes required for Linguaphone language learning records.

Music Collection

●There are record or cassette collections at several branches (see listing).
●There are 3 main Record and Music Libraries where you can borrow records and cassettes.
●A special Music Collection of works by Prokoviev, Rachmaninov, Jazz artists with surnames LEE-LZ and film sound tracks is available at Putney District.

Reference Material

●Basic reference stock is in every library in the borough.
●The main reference material is at Battersea District and West Hill Reference Libraries.
●There are special reference collections on Building and Architecture, the Occult, William Blake and Edward Thomas.
●There is a collection of early children's books (view by appointment) and European History and Travel at West Hill.

Local History

●Wandsworth's Local History Library is based at Battersea District.
●In addition to its general local history material, it has special collections on G A Henty (writer of boys' fiction) and another loan collection for the Black Community.

Special Collections

●Polish language books, a Women's Studies section and books for the Afro-Caribbean Community can be found at Balham District Library.
●Battersea District Library contains works by playwrights with the surnames A-BAI.
●Battersea Park has collections of children's audio-visual material and illustrations (both primarily for teachers).
●Plays by writers with surnames TRE-WEB can be found at West Hill.
●York Library has a collection of fiction by authors with surnames TRE-WEB.

Other Library Services

●The Prestel information service is available at Battersea District and West Hill.
●Wandsworth operates two general mobile libraries.
●It also has a special Ethnic Minorities' mobile library, which serves the Black community.
●There is a housebound library for those who aren't well enough to be out and about. Ring your local library or 871 6350 for details.

Exhibition Space

●There are small display areas in all libraries in Wandsworth.
●There are main separate exhibition rooms at Battersea District and Earlsfield which groups and artists are welcome to book. To local artists the space is free although Wandsworth takes 12% commission on any work that is sold.

Alvering Library
Allfarthing Lane
Wandsworth   SW18
Tel 871 6398
Open 9.30-7(Mon-Tue Thur) 9.30-5(Fri) 9-5(Sat).

Wheelchair access to library
General stock.
●Wandsworth's Mobile Library Base
Tel 871 6350
Photocopying

Balham District Library
Ramsden Road
Balham   SW12
Tel 871 7195
Open 10-8(Mon-Tue Thur-Fri) 9-
5(Sat)
Wheelchair access to libraries
Basic stock. Polish language books.
Women's Studies section. Books for
the Afro-Caribbean community.
●Record and Music Library
Open 10-1 2-8(Tue Thur) 10-1 2-5(Fri)
9-5(Sat)
Records, cassettes music books and
scores. Language courses.
Photocopying

Battersea District Library
Lavender Hill
Clapham Junction   SW11
Tel 871 7466
Open 10-8(Mon-Tue Wed Fri) 9-5(Sat)
Wheelchair access to library but not
to lecture/exhibition room
General stock and plays (surnames A-
BAI). Prestel. Lecture/exhibition
room.

●Record and Music Library
Open 10-1 2-8(Mon Wed) 10-1 2-5(Fri)
9-5(Sat)
Records and cassettes. Music books
and scores. Language courses.
●Local History Library
Tel 871 7467
Open 10-1 2-8(Tue) 10-1 2-5(Wed Fri)
Other times by appointment.
Wheelchair access none
Local history material. G A Henty
collection (writer of historical
adventure stories for boys). Afro-
Caribbean material (available for
hire)
●Reference Library (entrance in
Altenburg Gardens)
Tel 871 7467
Open 9-9 (Mon-Fri) 9-5(Sat) 2-6(Sun
except July & August)
Wheelchair access to library
Reference library and information
centre. Collections on Building and
Architecture, the Occult, William
Blake and Edward Thomas.
Photocopying

Battersea Park Library
Battersea Park Road
Battersea   SW11
Tel 871 7468
Open 9.30-7(Mon-Wed) 9.30-5(Fri) 9-
5(Sat)
Wheelchair access to library not to
study room
General stock and fiction by authors
with surnames A-BAI. Cassettes.
Children's audio-visual material
(films, filmstrips, story cassettes) for
teachers. Also, illustrations
(primarily for teachers but public
enquiries welcome). Separate study
room.
Public telephone Photocopying

Earlsfield Library
Magdalen Road
Earlsfield   SW18
Tel 871 6389
Open 9.30-7.00 (Mon-Tue Thur) 9.30-
5(Fri) 9-5(Sat)
Wheelchair access to library
General stock and cassettes.

Exhibition and separate study rooms. *Photocopying*

Northcote Library
Northcote Road
Battersea   SW11
Tel 871 7469
Open 9.30-7(Mon-Tue Thur) 9.30-5(Fri) 9-5(Sat)
Wheelchair access none
General stock. Exhibition space. Separate study room.

Putney District Library
Disraeli Road
Putney   SW15
Tel 871 7090
Open 10-8(Mon-Fri) 9-5(Sat)
Wheelchair access to libraries
●Record and Music Library
Open 10-1 2-8(Mon Wed) 10-1 2-5(Fri) 9-5(Sat)
Records and cassettes. Music books and scores. Language courses. A special collection of Prokoviev and Rachmaninov, jazz artists with surnames LEE-LZ and film soundtracks.
Public telephone Photocopying

Roehampton Library
Danebury Avenue
Roehampton   SW15
Tel 871 7091
Open 9.30-7(Mon Wed) 9.30-5(Fri) 9-5(Sat)
Wheelchair access to library
General stock and music cassettes.
Public telephone Photocopying

Southfields Library
Wimbledon Park Road
Southfields   SW19
Tel 871 6388
Open 9.30-7(Mon-Wed) 9.30-5(Fri) 9-5(Sat)
Wheelchair access to library
General stock and cassettes
Public telephone Photocopying

Tooting Library
Mitcham Road
Tooting   SW17

Tel 871 7175
Open 9.30-7(Mon-Tue Thur) 9.30-5(Fri) 9-5(Sat)
Wheelchair access to main adult library only
General stock and cassettes.
●Ethnic Minorities Library
Tel 871 7174
Open as above
Wheelchair access none
Books, magazines, records and music cassettes in Bengali, Gujurati, Hindi, Punjabi and Urdu.
Public telephone Photocopying

West Hill Library
West Hill
Wandsworth   SW18
Tel 871 6386
Open 9.30-7(Mon-Wed) 9.30-5(Fri) 9-5(Sat)
Wheelchair access to libraries
General stock and cassettes. Also, plays by playwrights with surnames TRE-WEB.
●Reference Library
Tel 871 6387
Open 9-8(Mon-Wed) 9-5(Fri-Sat)
Reference library and information centre. European History and Travel Collections (includes World Wars I & 2, but excludes Great Britain). Early children's books (view by appointment Tel 871 7467).
Photocopying

The centre for Children's books

York Library
Wye Street
Battersea   SW11
Tel 871 7471
Open 9.30-7(Mon-Tue Thur) 9.30-
5(Fri) 9-5(Sat)
Wheelchair access to library
Fiction by authors with surnames
TRE-WEB. Small collection of
records and cassettes. Language
courses.
Public telephone

Specialist Libraries

The Centre for Children's Books
National Book League
Book House
45 East Hill
Wandsworth   SW18
Tel 870 9055
Open 9-1 2-5(Mon-Fri)
Wheelchair access none
Non-lending library offering
expertise and advice on all aspects of
children's books. The Current
Collection contains a copy of every
children's book published in the last
two years. The Periodical Collection
has over 50 periodicals dealing with
children's books. The Signal Poetry
Collection aims to include copies of
all poetry books for children
currently in print. The Reference
Collection contains approximately
600 books about the reading habits of
children, reviews, works of criticism
about children's literature and
material relating to running a
children's library. The Leslie Linder
Collection of Beatrix Potter originals
and first editions, The Hans
Christian Andersen Collection of
Andersen's works published in
Britain and the Collection of The St
Nicholas Magazine can be viewed on
application. Visitors to the Centre,
especially children, are welcome.

Dulwich College Library
Dulwich   SE21
Tel 299 0300

Open during term time 9-5(Mon-Fri)
by appointment only
Wheelchair access ring to check
Edward Alleyn founded Dulwich
College in 1619. The College Library
now consists of a library for the boys
at the school and the Archive, which
dates from the founder's library and
includes some of his theatrical
papers. This offers scholars
throughout the world a unique
reference resource.

**Faculty of the Built Environment
Libraries**
Polytechnic of the South Bank
Wandsworth Road
Stockwell   SW8
Tel 928 8989 Ext 7156
Open during term time 9-9(Mon-Fri)
during holidays 9-5(Mon-Fri)
Wheelchair access to building but not
to library
Books about architecture and
building. Lending library for Poly
staff and students. Reference for
everyone else.

Horniman Museum Library
London Road
Forest Hill   SE23
Tel 699 2339 Ext.31
Open 10.30-5.45(Tue-Sat) 2-5.45(Sun)
Wheelchair access ring to check
Subjects covered by the library are
natural history (especially
identification), ethnography and
anthropology (particularly material
culture) and musicology (mainly
organology, ie what instruments look
like). There are also special
collections of books on the organ,
early books on Africa and 18th
century botanical books.

ILEA Education Library
Room 453
County Hall
Waterloo   SE1
Tel 633 3111
Open during term time 9-6(Mon-
Thur) 9-4.45(Fri)
during holidays 9-4.45(Mon-Fri)

Wheelchair access to 4th floor library with special toilets on ground floor Material for teachers about education and education theory including many periodicals. Lending library for members of ILEA, reference for others.

ILEA Reference Library & Information Service

ILEA Centre for Learning Resources
275 Kennington Lane
Oval   SE1
Tel 735 8202
Open during term time 9-6(Mon-Thur) 9-4.45(Fri)
during holidays 9-4.45(Mon-Fri)
Wheelchair access assisted access from rear entrance Currently published books and audio-visual material for pupils plus an information service on education, enabling people to see what is available for pupils. Lending library for members of ILEA, reference for others.

Imperial War Museum

Dept of Printed Books
Lambeth Road
Lambeth North   SE1
Tel 735 8922
Open 10-5(Mon-Fri) by appointment only with 24hrs notice
Wheelchair access to library
Reference library containing documents, printed material, film, photographs and sound recordings relating to the two world wars and other 20th century conflicts. By appointment only. 24 hours notice required.

Labour Party Library

150 Walworth Road
Walworth   SE17
Tel 703 0833
Open 10-5(Mon-Fri) by appointment only at the discretion of the librarian.
Wheelchair access via side gate
HMSO material, printed matter and photographs relating to all political

parties, and all national Labour Party publications.

London College of Printing Library

Elephant & Castle   SE1
Tel 735 8484
Open during term time 9-7.15(Mon-Thur) 9-5.45(Fri)
during holidays 9-4.30(Mon-Fri)
Closed all of August
Wheelchair access via rear entrance
Records relating to printing, graphic arts, fine art, photography, film, television and journalism. Early printed books, illustrated books and examples of modern printing. Library open to members of the public for reference. Membership (take two passport photos and some means of indentification) is free and entitles you to borrow up to four books at any one time.

Marine Society

College of the Sea & Seafarers Libraries
202 Lambeth Road
Lambeth Palace   SE1
Tel 261 9535
Open 9-5(Mon-Fri) by appointment only
Wheelchair access to libraries
Reference library containing books and technical books on merchant shipping and the Merchant Navy.

Mark Longman Library

National Book League
Book House
45 East Hill
Wandsworth   SW18
Tel 870 9055 or 874 8526 (direct line)
Open 9-5(Mon-Fri)
Wheelchair access none
Contains specialist collection of books covering all aspects of the book trade plus the Perez Book Plate Collection. Open to the public but only members may borrow books. The Book Information Service provides bibliographical infomation on books in English.

National Maritime Museum Library
National Maritime Museum
Greenwich   SE10
Tel 858 4422
Open 10-5(Mon-Fri) 10-1 2-5(Sat)
Wheelchair access to library
Visitors must apply for a readers ticket (with proof of identification) which entitles them to free entry to the library (not the museum)
Wheelchair access
The library (reference only) contains some 60,000 maritime volumes, including rare atlases and books on navigation. Also, The Times (from 1785 to the present day) on microfilm.

Poly of The South Bank Education Library
New Kent Road
Elephant & Castle   SE1
Tel 407 8191 Ext 37
Open during term time 9-9(Mon-Fri) during holidays 9-5(Mon-Fri)
Wheelchair access ring to check
Small library specialising in teacher training and education. Multi-media packages for use in primary schools. Lending library for poly staff and students, reference only for anyone else.

Poly of The South Bank Library
London Road
Elephant & Castle   SE1
Tel 928 8989
Open during term time 9-9(Mon-Fri) during holidays 9-5(Mon-Fri)
Wheelchair access ring to check
Standard poly library. Book stock covers all the courses. Good audio-visual material with selection of video tapes and 3 micro-computers. Computerised library catalogue. Lending library for staff and students, reference only for anyone else.

Royal Artillery Library
Royal Artillery Institution
Old Royal Military Academy
Woolwich   SE18
Tel 856 5533 Ext 2524
Open 9-12.30 2-4.30 (Mon-Fri) by appointment only
Wheelchair access none
Material relating to foreign and British artillery.

Society for Cultural Relations with The USSR
320 Brixton Road
Brixton   SW9
Tel 274 2282
Open 10-1 & 2-5(Mon-Thur)
Membership £6pa £3(students Oaps and unwaged)
Admission free for members Fee payable otherwise (discuss with librarian)
Wheelchair access none
The General Library contains literature and material on the arts and history (mostly in Russian) for reference only. The Arts Library has Russian and Soviet art books covering painting, graphic design, architecture, folk art, costume and other subjects (for reference only). Also slide sets, film strips, photographs and displays for educational and commercial use.

Women Artists Slide Library
Battersea Arts Centre
Old Town Hall
Lavender Hill
Battersea   SW11
Tel 228 5771
Open 11-6(Tue-Fri) or by special arrangement
Wheelchair access to entire building with special facilities
Slides of all-women shows and of work by contemporary and past women artists. Member artists pay £6 and have a minimum of six slides of their work on file with other relevant documentation. Shows, talks and seminars are organised and a free bi-monthly newsletter is produced. The library is available for reference to students and the general public and is intended to become the largest collection of information on women's art in the country.

14
LOCAL HISTORY

This chapter consists of contributions from a number of local history experts. In the past, boroughs were arranged differently so some historical facts are featured in more than one section. For instance, both Greenwich and Wandsworth can claim the history of Blackheath. You will also notice that the various contributors have arranged their sections differently and that some have written at greater length than others. However, we were reluctant to trim such fascinating material just for the sake of uniformity. So, away with publishing conventions, we have allowed the pens to flow freely!

Greenwich

Few places can claim a richer heritage in history, noble architecture and worthy residents than the London Borough of Greenwich. Within its bounds were once two royal palaces, two royal dockyards, Wren's magnificent Greenwich Hospital for Seamen, and the Royal Military Academy. It is now the home of the Royal Arsenal, the Royal Artillery regiment in Woolwich, the Royal Naval College, the National Maritime Museum and the Royal Observatory in Greenwich. Greenwich Borough has more Thames riverside than any other London borough and this has greatly affected its development.

The Roman road from the Continent to London bisects the borough and many Roman remains have been found. Most important of these are the temple in Greenwich Park, a hill fort at Charlton and a cemetery in Woolwich. Other indications of early settlements include pre-historic mounds at Shooters Hill and Plumstead, and Saxon barrows in Greenwich Park. However, early development was concentrated near the river and this has meant the area has had close links with England's naval history.

In the Middle Ages, Greenwich, Woolwich and Plumstead were fishing villages, lying at the foot of chalk hills

which came down close to the river.
The Anglo Saxon Chronicle mentions
that the Danish fleet lay off
Greenwich in 1011. Blackheath, a
'bleak place', was the 'gateway to
London' and witnessed many scenes
of rebellion and pageantry. Wat Tyler
camped here in 1381 during the
Peasants' Revolt, as did Jack Cade's
rebels in 1450, and this was where
Henry VII fought the Cornish rebels
in 1497. Also at Blackheath,
Londoners welcomed Henry V on his
return from Agincourt, and Henry
VIII welcomed his fourth bride Anne
of Cleves, before escorting her to his
palace at Greenwich. Only Plumstead
among all the old parish churches in
the area retains appreciable remains
of its medieval church dedicated to St
Nicholas. The most important
medieval monument, however, is
Eltham Palace, which belonged to the
Crown from 1305, and was a favourite
royal residence of the 15th and early
16th centuries. Its moated site with
its splendid hall built by Edward IV
make it one of the best preserved pre-
Tudor palaces in the country.
Adjoining the Great Hall now stands
a very fine 1930s house built by the
Courtauld family.

By the time Eltham Palace was
complete, Greenwich also had a royal
establishment. The riverside home of
Humphrey, Duke of Gloucester, who
enclosed Greenwich Park in 1433, was
rebuilt and expanded by Henry VII. It
was a rambling brick building with
towers and courtyards, including the
Greenwich Armoury and a tiltyard.
Henry VIII was born at Greenwich
and christened in the early St Alfege
Church. He was the founder of the
two royal dockyards, at Deptford and
Woolwich. His flagship the Great
Harry was built at Woolwich in 1512.
Further downstream, the area called
Woolwich Warren was used for
storing arms from the 16th century,
the beginning of the career of the
Royal Arsenal, which by the early
20th century occupied the whole

Woolwich Dockyard

riverbank from Woolwich to Erith,
and was the major armaments factory
in Britain.

From the 17th century the history of
Greenwich and Woolwich becomes
different. Both grew into towns, but
while Woolwich was primarily a town
of workers, dependent on local
industry, as well as being a large
garrison, Greenwich was a more
aristocratic settlement on the fringes
of palace and park. After the Civil
War, Greenwich Palace was falling
down with neglect, but the Queen's
House, begun in 1616 for Queen Ann
of Denmark, wife of James I, was still
used. Charles II intended to build a
new palace at Greenwich, but the
King's House, (now the north west
wing of the Royal Naval College), was
the only building of this project that
was ever completed. In 1694 William
and Mary founded the Royal Hospital
for Seamen at Greenwich. Wren
designed the buildings, incorporating
the King's House, and Vanbrugh and
Hawksmoor helped with the design
and building work. James Thornhill
was responsible for the magnificent
Painted Hall, which later was the
setting for Nelson's 'lying in State' in
1805. The Hospital ceased to take
pensioners in 1869 and reopened as
the Royal Naval College in 1873. Both
the dockyards also closed in 1869,
throwing many local people out of

work. The Victorian era had seen a great increase of industry along the river, but by the 1860s it was no longer suitable for building large naval vessels.

The Royal Observatory in Greenwich Park is another Wren building. It was founded in 1675 for the purpose of discovering longitude. A method was developed dependent on accurate timekeeping, from which evolved Greenwich Mean Time, and the line from which longitude is calculated is the Greenwich or Prime Meridian. The Royal Observatory moved to Herstmonceux because of pollution around London, and the buildings in Greenwich Park are now part of the National Maritime Museum, which also includes Inigo Jones' Queen's House and the other adjoining buildings which were once the Royal Naval School.

The Royal Observatory led to the standardisation of time, made necessary by the advent of the railways, but the railways also affected the borough in other ways. The small rural villages of Charlton, Plumstead, Eltham and Kidbrooke began to grow as the railway passed through Kent. The open fields of Eltham and Kidbrooke saw housing development in the early decades of this century, both municipal and private. Plumstead and Charlton were Victorian suburbs, but have been much redeveloped in recent years. To bring history up to date, 1984 saw the opening of the Thames Barrier at Woolwich. It has been called the 'eighth wonder of the world' and is the world's largest moveable flood barrier, spanning the Thames with ten separate mobile steel gates.

Some Other People and Places of Note

The ancient parish churches in the borough are all of interest, but St Alfege's Church, Greenwich is perhaps of particular note. It was built between 1711 and 1714 by Nicholas Hawksmoor, after the early church had collapsed in a storm. The early church was the final resting place of Thomas Tallis, the father of church music. James Wolfe, the victor at the battle of Quebec is also buried in the present church. He was a resident of Greenwich, living with his parents at McCartney House, at the top of Crooms Hill. A large monument to him stands beside the Observatory in Greenwich Park, paid for by subscriptions raised in Canada. John Julius Angerstein is also buried at St Alfege's. His activities as a marine insurance underwriter led him to be known as the 'Father of Lloyds'. He was also a leading collector of old masters and thirty-eight of his pictures were bought by the nation in 1824 to form the nucleus of the National Gallery. For himself, Angerstein built Woodlands, a country villa on the edge of Blackheath (now in Mycenae Road), where his family lived for one hundred years. In 1967 Greenwich Council bought the house and after restoration it opened as an art gallery and local history library.

St Luke's Church, Charlton is a charming example of a village church next to the green and the manor house. Charlton House is a fine example of Jacobean domestic architecture, built in 1607-1612 for Sir Adam Newton, tutor to James I's son Henry who should have been king but was killed by a tennis ball hitting him on the temple. The house was purchased by Greenwich Council in 1925, and with its extensive grounds, makes a pleasant community complex. Buried in St Luke's Church is Spencer Percival, who was related to the family at Charlton House, and is the only British Prime Minister to have been assassinated.

St Nichola's Church, Deptford, has remnants of its medieval tower, but most of it is very fine 17th century church architecture. The many monuments, notably those of master shipwrights Peter Pett and John Shish, reflect Deptford's maritime history. Somewhere in the churchyard is the grave of Christopher Marlowe, murdered in a tavern brawl in Deptford in 1593. St John's Church, Eltham was rebuilt in 1875. Two unusual Eltham residents are buried in the churchyard – Thomas Doggett, actor-manager and founder of the world's oldest rowing race, and Yemmerawanyea Kebbarah, the first Australian Aborigine to visit Britain who died in 1794.

To remain with Eltham, apart from the Palace there are other places to see and visit. The Tudor Barn, Well Hall is a converted barn, part of the Elizabethan house of William Roper, Sir Thomas More's son-in-law and biographer. The house was rebuilt in the 18th century and from 1899 to 1922 was the home of Edith Nesbit and featured in some of her children's stories. The house was later demolished, but the old barn was converted by the council for use as a restaurant and art gallery. Avery Hill College of Education, which opened as such in 1906, is housed in a large Victorian mansion built in 1882 by Colonel John North who had made his fortune out of Chilian nitrates. He also constructed some marvellous Winter Gardens, now run by the Greater London Council. On the southern slopes of Shooters Hill stands Severndroog Castle. It is a triangular folly 60 feet high, built by Lady James in 1784 in memory of her husband Sir William who captured the fortress of Severndroog on the Malabar coast in 1775. From the top of this folly one can see for miles across London, Kent, Surrey and Essex. Shooters Hill was once the haunt of highwaymen, and gallows stood on the site of the present police station. The area is still covered by fine woodlands. On the northern slopes (towards Plumstead) is Shrewsbury

House, now a council community centre, built in 1923 on the site of an earlier mansion constructed for the Earl of Shrewsbury in 1789. Ten years later, Princess Charlotte, daughter of George IV lived there as a child. In the 1930s the area was developed for housing and many spectacular views of London and the Thames can be seen from this area.

To the east of Plumstead is the large new estate of Thamesmead. This area, built on marshland, is developing rapidly, and is an interesting example of many new styles in architecture. Woolwich is a town of strong military and industrial traditions, but it was also the first English town to elect a Labour MP in 1903 and it has a strong co-operative. The local co-op built a housing estate early this century at Abbey Wood. Woolwich's free ferry is another interesting feature. Opened for vehicles, passengers and goods in 1889, it was the first successful attempt to provide additional river crossings for the eastern districts of London. Paddle steamer ferries were replaced by diesel boats in 1963. There are so many people and places of interest within this borough, rich in both national and local history, that only a few have been mentioned here. Of further note are Crooms Hill, Vanbrugh Castle and the riverside taverns such as the Trafalgar in Greenwich. And, in Woolwich, the Royal Military Academy, school for General Gordon, and the Royal Arsenal, not only the major manufacturer of armaments, but also the originator of the Arsenal Football Club.

Lambeth

A map of Lambeth in 1824 shows that south of the Oval there was very little building – only houses lining Clapham Road and what is now Brixton Road, and a scattering of houses at Norwood, South Lambeth and Stockwell. The area round St Mary's Church (the old parish church beside Lambeth Palace, now the Museum of Garden History) and along the river had been developed relatively early, but it was the building of Westminster Bridge in 1750 and, especially, of Waterloo and Vauxhall Bridges in 1815 and 1816 repectively that provided a stimulus for the laying out of new roads, and attracted those anxious to escape from the grime and overcrowding of the City. Landowners realised that it was more profitable to build on land than to use it for dairy farming or market gardening. In the north of the borough this building mainly took the form of terraced housing (as in Kennington Road) but, further south, substantial detached or semi-detached houses with large gardens were the norm. One example is the house on Herne Hill in which Ruskin was brought up. However, after the coming of the railways in the 1850s there was a rapid expansion of smaller streets and terraces. By 1871, the map shows more or less solid building north of Brixton, although there was still open ground between Milkwood Road and Herne Hill and, south of St Matthew's, building was still mainly confined to large detached houses lining the main road until Norwood

was reached.

In the north of the borough, the proximity of industry and the railway lines cutting through the houses combined with the pressures of a growing population to create some of the worst slums in London. Although the building of the Albert Embankment in 1866-70 swept away the boatyards that formerly lined the shore, the riverside continued to be the main site for industry. Until 1840, Coade's artificial stone factory stood on the site of County Hall. The lion on Westminster Bridge, which once stood on the nearby Lion Brewery, was made at the factory. Other industries included brewing and shot manufacture. The firm of Doulton's, continuing a tradition of pottery-making in Lambeth going back two hundred years, had extensive premises in the High Street. John Doulton and his partner John Watts first acquired a site there in 1826, although they also kept their original pottery in Vauxhall Walk until 1829. As the business expanded the premises grew, until the factory extended from outside Lambeth Palace halfway to Vauxhall Bridge. John's son Henry was instrumental in making the firm's name world-famous as he pioneered the manufacture of glazed stoneware pipes for drainage. Under the influence of sanitary reformers and the 1848 Public Health Act the demand for such pipes grew enormously and Doulton established additional factories in Lancashire and Staffordshire to meet it. The firm also manufactured stoneware closets and sinks. However, in addition to producing sanitary ware, Doultons became famous for its art pottery – salt-glazed, decorated stoneware. A link with Lambeth School of Art brought many gifted artists and designers to work for the company. They produced not only vases and pottery figures but also terracotta panels and tiles for decorating buildings. A set of tiles depicting

Lambeth Pier

nursery rhymes was made for the children's ward of St Thomas' Hospital and the former Royal Waterloo Hospital for women and children (by the roundabout just south of Waterloo Bridge) has decorative Doulton tiles on its facade. The only factory building to survive the firm's departure from Lambeth in 1956 (at the corner of Lambeth High Street) is a splendid example of their work.

The demand for land and changing tastes in entertainment brought about the demise of one famous Lambeth institution, Vauxhall Gardens. Pepys describes them as a rural retreat famous for nightingales. The gardens reached their heyday after Jonathan Tyers became manager in 1728. He made them into a fashionable resort, visited by royalty. Concerts, fireworks, illuminations and, later, tightrope dancers and balloon ascents drew the crowds. However, in 1859, the Gardens closed and the site, bounded by Goding Street, St Oswald's Place and Vauxhall Walk was used for housing. In contrast, the Old Vic, founded in 1816 as the Royal Coburg Theatre, grew in popularity. In the 1830s, it had acquired a reputation for crude melodramas and a rough clientele, but in 1880, Emma Cons reopened it as a temperance music hall. Subsequently, under the management of her niece Lilian Baylis, it became renowned as a centre for opera, Shakespeare and classical drama. Music halls were a feature of Lambeth life, the Canterbury Theatre of Varieties in Upper Marsh being a noted example. The population continued to expand, reaching 301,895 in 1901 (compared to 160,182 in 1861). In 1900, the Metropolitan Borough of Lambeth was created. The new Town Hall opened in 1908 to replace the Vestry Hall in Kennington Road (now the Church of England Children's Society). Significantly, the choice for its location was Brixton rather than

the northern part of the borough which had declined in importance. Later, the Waterloo area was the part of Lambeth that was worst hit by bombing in World War II, after which much of the industry disappeared, to be replaced by office blocks and council housing, and, of course, the South Bank complex.

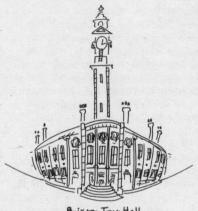

Brixton Town Hall

Brixton, on the other hand, had continued to grow rapidly as streets were laid on former fields or market gardens, or in the grounds of the large houses whose owners moved further away to escape the growth of suburbia. This process was more or less completed in Brixton by the First World War but continued further south in the borough towards Norwood and Streatham for another twenty years. The building of Bon Marche in 1876 and Electric Avenue in 1881 and the growth of the open air market confirmed Brixton as an important shopping centre. (The first covered arcade was not built until 1929.) It was also a favourite home for actors and music-hall artists and, in 1896, acquired its own theatre, which was destroyed by a bomb in 1940. Two years after this, in Carlton Grove (now Brighton Terrace), the Empress Theatre of Varieties opened, later to become a cinema in the 1950s and then a bingo hall. What is now the Ritzy

Cinema was originally the Electric Pavillion, which opened in 1910. The Academy opened as the Astoria Cinema in 1929.

After World War Two, when West Indian people came to Britain on a large scale, many settled in Brixton. This may initially have been because it was near the Clapham air-raid shelters where some of the first arrivals were temporarily accommodated and, later, because many newly arrived Black people chose to move close to friends and relatives who were already established here. In addition, the local boarding houses that had once catered for actors and the run-down Victorian houses that had been divided into flats and single rooms provided a ready supply of accommodation. The Colour Bar was still in operation at this time and many Black people made their homes in Geneva and Somerleyton Roads. (Why these two roads in particular were so significant is one of the many issues currently being researched by the Black Cultural Archives, who plan to site their national centre in Somerleyton Road.)

In 1965, the Metropolitan Borough of Lambeth was replaced by the present London Borough, which includes parts of Streatham and Clapham that had previously been in Wandsworth. However, this did not affect the decline in the population that began in the 1960s (from 341,624 in 1961 to 244,143 in 1981), or prevent the worsening employment and housing situation which were highlighted by the Brixton riots of 1981 and 1985. Lambeth is now one of the neediest boroughs in inner London, indeed in the whole country.

Whatever the changes to come, they can hardly be more drastic than those of the last 150 years, in which Lambeth has been changed from a semi-rural parish on the outskirts of London to a congested, lively, built-up inner-city borough.

Lewisham

The London Borough of Lewisham comprises three historic parishes: Lewisham, Lee and St Paul's, and Deptford. The modern borough is divided into about a dozen districts, some related to ancient settlements, others to 19th or 20th century developments.

Of the core settlements, Deptford has the more varied history. The original riverside village clustered around the ancient church of St Nicholas, patron saint of sailors, at Deptford Green (now in the London Borough of Greenwich). The present fabric, other than the late 15th century tower, dates from the 1690s, as does the little brick charnel house on the churchyard wall. The rather gruesome skulls at the churchyard gates are known locally as Adam and Eve. Christopher Marlow the dramatist is buried here, as is Captain George Shelvocke, the original of Coleridge's 'Ancient Mariner'. The area is rich in naval associations. Lord Howard of Effingham, commander of the English fleet against the Armada, had a house at Deptford Green. Queen Elizabeth I ordered Drake's 'Golden Hind' to be laid up at Deptford in 1581, as a monument to his circumnavigation of the world. In 1513 Henry founded a Royal Naval dockyard which provided the key for the growth of Deptford into a small town. The original Trinity House, founded by Henry VIII in 1514, stood just to the east of the church. The diarist, John Evelyn, whose house Sayes Court and his beloved gardens lay just beyond the dockyard wall, described Deptford around 1700 as 'neere as big as Bristol'! Samuel Pepys, as Clerk of the Acts to the Navy Board, was a frequent visitor to Deptford dockyard in the 1660s. From 1742 a Navy victualling yard (the Royal Victoria

Elizabeth I ordered Drake's
'Golden Hind' to be laid up in Deptford

Yard) flourished upstream of the
dockyard. Its gates survive in Grove
Street with, nearby, a fine terrace of
officers' houses and two ranges of
riverside storehouses built around
1790. The other visible monuments of
18th century Deptford are Thomas
Archer's grand church of St Paul
(1730) just off Deptford High Street
and, a few yards away, Albury Street
with its early 18th century small town
houses, some with intricately carved
doorcases. The High Street itself has a
fascinating collection of down-at-heel
18th and 19th century buildings
hiding behind the shopfronts.
London's first railway, the London
and Greenwich (1836) crosses it and,
beside the station, is a unique ramp,
or incline plane, built to raise road
carriages and rolling stock up to the
line.
In the 19th century, as Deptford's
urban centre became increasingly
crowded and industrialised, the
middle classes moved south to newly
developed areas along the New Cross
Road and Lewisham Way (Lewisham
High Road), in Brockley and up
Telegraph Hill. New Cross Gate is
named from the toll gate which stood
first at the top of Clifton Rise and
later where New Cross Road becomes
Queen's Road. Sir Barnes Wallis, son
of the local doctor, spent his childhood

at 241 New Cross Road, not far from
Old Deptford Town Hall (1905) with
its facade celebrating Deptford's naval
past, and the former St James's
Church where a 'ritualist'
controversy in the 1870s resulted in
the imprisonment of the vicar Rev
Arthur Tooth. Around Telegraph Hill
(from the Admiralty semaphore
telegraph station which stood on its
summit during the Napoleonic Wars)
are attractive streets of Victorian
villas carefully developed by the
Haberdashers' Company. At the top of
Lewisham Way, Goldsmiths College
was originally built as the Royal
Naval School in 1843. Travelling this
way to Lewisham we pass first, on the
left, Stone House, an unusual villa
c1770 on a circular plan, and then the
old wooden Lewisham Road Station
where no tickets have been issued
since 1917. Off Lewisham Way on the
other side are the spacious roads of
Victorian Brockley. Here, in
Tyrwhitt Road, lived the celebrated
tenor Heddle Nash, while Edgar
Wallace hid from his creditors at 6
Tressillian Crescent, earning the
house a blue plaque.
The focal point of Lewisham proper is
the High Street, now a thriving
shopping centre. Until the mid-19th
century it was lined, at intervals,
with farmhouses and the villas of city
merchants. John Wesley used one of
these villas, the Limes (near the
present Roman Catholic church), as a
country retreat. At the village's
spiritual centre stood St Mary's
Church, rebuilt in 1775-7. The old
vicarage, on the corner of Ladywell
Road, built for the Rev George
Stanhope in 1692-3, is the only house
to survive intact from the old village
of Lewisham. Ladywell itself was a
hamlet with not one but two wells.
The one near the railway station was
perhaps a medieval holy well
connected with the nearby church of
Our Lady. Its coping stones survive in
a flower bed in front of the former
Ladywell baths. To the south of St

Mary's Church is Lewisham Hospital, the oldest part of which is the block on the left, south of the entrance archway. This was the new workhouse built around 1817 to house the 'large number' of poor people in the parish. Parallel to the High Street flows the river Ravensbourne, once notable for the number of watermills it supported (eleven when the Domesday Book was compiled in 1085). Only one survives, the Riverdale mill rebuilt around 1830 and now landlocked, by the removal of the stream, between Molesworth Street and an office block. The other notable feature of the High Street is the Clock Tower built to commemorate Queen Victoria's Diamond Jubilee in 1897, but unfortunately some of its intended decoration was omitted because of the expense. Turn of the century Lewisham is carefully recorded in the semi-autobiographical Phillip Maddison novels of Henry Williamson. His family home at 21 Eastern Road looked out on to Hilly Fields (a fashionable Sunday promenade) and the old Brockley County School.

Travelling south, the High Street eventually becomes Rushey Green and, after passing Catford, the Bromley Road. The crossroads where Bromley Road and Beckenham Hill Road meet is sadly no longer recognisable as the hamlet of Southend, known as late as the 1920s as a 'lovely rural place'. All that remains is the Forster family's early 19th century chapel. The millpond which, in the 1720s and 1730s powered the Lower Mill where the How family produced noted cutlery, and which later, as Peter Pan's Pool, was filled with pleasure boats, has shrunk to an ornamental feature in front of a miniature crystal palace, now a DIY store.

Turning west at Catford along the South Circular one passes into the once wild and wooded district of Sydenham. Until its enclosure in 1819, Sydenham (or Westwood) Common covered several hundred acres. In the time of James I, the commoners, led by their vicar the Rev Abraham Colfe, marched 100-strong to petition the King against an intended encroachment upon their common rights. In the 1640s and 1650s the medicinal wells on the Common, popularised by Dr John Peter, attracted such unruly crowds that on one occasion the government felt it necessary to send a troop of horses to keep order. Sydenham Wells Park is the last open remnant of Westwood Common. Early development in Sydenham largely comprised timber houses, examples of which can still be found near the junctions of Sydenham Road with Newlands Park and Kirkdale with Dartmouth Road. With the arrival of the Crystal Palace in 1852-4, the area became very fashionable. The Palace became the focus of a thriving musical life in the area. Sir George Grove's house in Sydenham Road was visited by Arthur Sullivan and other musical figures. Other residents included the nature writer Richard Jefferies, Sir Ernest Shackleton, W G Grace, and the sad figure of Eleanor Marx who died after drinking prussic acid at her house is Jews Walk.

At its northern end, Westwood Common merged with the Forest, now Forest Hill. The earliest surviving houses here seem to be a late 18th early 19th century group at the junction of Honor Oak Road and Westwood Park. It includes the attractive Ashberry Cottage, probably linked with the Duke of Clarence (William IV) and Mrs Jordan, and perhaps originally a hunting box. With the building of the Croydon Canal after 1804, replaced in 1839 by the Croydon Railway, Forest Hill began to be opened up. Like Sydenham it became a fashionable Victorian suburb, its most notable resident being Frederick J Horniman, the tea merchant. His collection of musical and ethnographic objects so outgrew his house that he built a museum for it, and in 1901 presented the museum, grounds and contents to the people of London. Another curious object left in Forest Hill by a Victorian collector is the tip of the spire of a Wren church, St Antholin's in the City of London. After the church's demolition the spire became a feature in the garden of Round Hill House, home of the Harrild family. The house is gone but the spire remains in Round Hill. Forest Hill sheltered German refugees from the days of Bismarck to those of Hitler. The community has its own church in Dacres Road, where Dietrich Bonhoeffer ministered from 1933 until his return to Germany and eventual martyrdom in 1935.

The chief feature of the east of the borough is the common of Blackheath. As the last open space before travellers from the Continent entered London, Blackheath saw many notable meetings. The citizens welcomed Henry V here after Agincourt, in 1415. Henry VIII met Anne of Cleaves here in 1540. It was also a natural gathering ground for rebels – Wat Tyler and the Peasants in 1381, Jack Cade in 1450, and the Cornish Rebels in 1497. As the dangers from rebels and highwaymen decreased in the 18th and 19th centuries, the heath became bordered by elegant buildings, many of which survive. Outstanding are Ranger's House, home of the statesman and writer Philip 4th Earl of Chesterfield, Morden College, built in 1695 as an almshouse for 'decayed' merchants by Sir John Morden to designs allegedly by Wren, and the grand series of linked houses called The Paragon (1794-1807) by Michael Searles (all now in the London Borough of Greenwich). Equally unusual is The Pagoda, now tucked away in Pagoda Gardens but probably built around 1760 as a summer house for Montagu House which stood across the heath

Rangers House

beside the Ranger's House. Princess Caroline, the estranged wife of the Prince Regent, was lodged in Montagu House from 1799 until 1812 and is said to have taught a nursery school in the Pagoda. Blackheath Village was largely a 19th century development of shops and inns to serve the well-heeled local population. In earlier days it bore the less exalted name of Blunt's Hole, after a 17th century owner of the nearby Wricklemarsh estate.

To the south lies the ancient parish of Lee, which shows a pattern of development parallel to that of Blackheath. The original settlement seems to have been scattered, with its parish church at the top of Belmont Hill, a green at the crossroads known as Lee Green, and a cluster of farmhouses and mansions around Old Road. In 1841 the present church of St Margaret replaced the old church on a site across the road. The stump of the old church remains in the original churchyard, where can be found the tomb of the Astronomer Royal Edmund Halley, discoverer of Halley's Comet. Wealthy merchants began to move into Lee in the late 17th century. Most of their grand houses are gone, although Pentland House (c1685) and the Manor House (c1772) survive in Old Road. The Manor House, which now houses the Lewisham Local History Centre, was acquired at an auction in 1796 by Sir Francis Baring, one of the founders of

the banking firm of Baring Brothers
& Co. Other buildings from the time of
old Lee are the little brick chapel on
the Lee High Road (formerly attached
to a row of six almshouses founded by
Chistopher Boone in 1683) and behind
it the thirty additional almshouses
built in the 1820s by Boone's trustees,
the Merchant Taylors Company. The
chapel is yet another local building
popularly attributed to Sir
Christopher Wren.

The land to the north of Lee High
Road spawned Victorian villas, really
as an extension of Blackheath, but to
the south farmland survived until the
turn of the century and after. Grove
Park began in the 1870s as an area of
large detached houses (an early
resident of Baring Road was the
writer E Nesbit). Today it is
characterised by inter-war and later
suburbia. Grove Park Hospital had a
varied early history. Built in the
1890s as the new Greenwich
workhouse, it became the
headquarters of the Army Service
Corps during the First World War,
before settling down for a long period
as a sanatorium. Hither Green was
another intended upmarket suburb
which lost its initial cachet after the
Metropolitan Asylums Board built a
hospital for infectious diseases here in
1897. Its southern fringe bears the
unmistakeable stamp of the teetotal
developer Archibald Cameron Corbett
MP – a grid pattern of long, straight
roads, many with Scottish names,
with solid, turn of the century houses
and, in those days, not a public house
in sight.

This was the limit of development
until the 1920s. Beyond Catford lay
the Seven Fields and a pleasant stroll
to the hamlet of Southend. Then the
London County Council completed
the urbanisation of Lewisham by
taking the remaining fields of
Shroffold and Holloway farms for its
large cottage housing estates of
Downham and Bellingham. The latter
preserved a medieval manorial name.

Downham honours Lord Downham,
an LCC member with an interest in
housing policy. Despite the problems
of car parking, the mature estates
retain their attractive spacious
quality, and Bellingham has produced
a national celebrity, the boxer Henry
Cooper, who grew up at 120
Farmstead Road.

Merton

In 1965 the London Borough of
Merton was created by what has been
called 'the shot-gun marriage' of four
very different suburbs. In the past
their links had not been strong.
Wimbledon had been associated far
more with Putney and Mortlake, and
Mitcham with Croydon. Only Merton
and Morden were used to co-operation
as they had formed a joint urban
district council for over fifty years.
Yet, despite the inevitable suspicions,
the historical background of the four
districts have a great deal in common.
Each originated from a settlement
made by Anglo Saxons. Merton means
'farm by the pool' presumably the area
between the modern Nelson Hospital
and Raynes Park which used
regularly to flood. Mitcham signifies
'big place' or 'large village' probably
in comparison with other early
settlements like Streatham. Morden is
'the hill by the marsh', overlooking as
it does low lying ground along the
Wandle. Finally, Wimbledon is said to
mean 'Wynmann's Hill', the village
set up by a leader of an Anglo Saxon
band of settlers.

Throughout the Middle Ages, each
remained a small village, dependent
on subsistence farming and under the
control of the church. Merton was the
most important as it was the site of a
wealthy Augustinian priory, often
visited by the Court, and used for
meetings of the King's council and
even in 1437 for the coronation of

Henry VI. Mitcham was split into four manors (only Ravensbury was not owned by the Church). Morden was one of the many estates of Westminster Abbey. Wimbledon, the most isolated of the four as it was not on a main road, was owned by the Archbishops of Canterbury.

Under the Tudors, Stuarts and Hanovarians, each developed through growing contacts with the Court and the City. Here Wimbledon came off best with first the Cecils, then the Spencers as their lords of the manor, and with several other aristocrats, government ministers and many MPs living in large houses round the Common. Mitcham was also important, with residents like Sir Julius Caesar, a leading judge and councillor under James I, John Donne the poet, and Robert Cranmer, a London merchant. Merton had the leading personality Vice Admiral Lord Nelson who lived at Merton Place between 1801 and 1805. Morden had the longest surviving family as their lords of the manor, the Garths, 1553-1872.

In the 18th and 19th centuries, the four districts were strongly influenced by the River Wandle and by the coming of the railway. Along the Wandle (above all in Merton and Mitcham) water-powered mills were built to grind corn, smelt iron and copper, and, most important of all, produce snuff and calico. In 1803 these mills were linked by the first public railway, the Surrey Iron Railway, which carried goods in horse drawn trucks. Steam railways first came to Wimbledon in 1838 and to Merton and Mitcham in 1855. They led to the development of 'New Wimbledon' below the hill from the 1860s, Merton Park from the 1870s and Mitcham more slowly until the present century. Morden was unaffected and remained a village till the underground was extended in 1926. Its fields then quickly disappeared under streets and houses. All the four districts had

Wimbledon Tennis

become London suburbs.

Merton (The District)

It has two historic centres, one along the River Wandle, the other to the south of the Kingston Road round the parish church.

Near the Wandle in Station Road stand the foundations of part of the medieval priory. They were excavated in the 1970s and were due to be preserved in a public park. However, the site is threatened by developers, who at the same time want to preserve Merton's one surviving mill, Liberty and Company's print works. Part of the buildings date from the 1740s but most were rebuilt after 1910. Nearby is an 18th century wheel house with a large water wheel.

The old village of Merton developed west of the river, along and to the south of the Kingston Road. Little of historical interest survives along the Kingston Road apart from the Manor House, a timber-framed building of about 1700, and Dorset Hall, built about 70 years later. Far more significant are the buildings at the top of Church Lane and along Church Path. Chief among them is St Mary's, a Norman church with a fine roof and some interesting memorials, including one to Edward Rayne, the Victorian farmer at West Barnes, after whom Raynes Park was named. Lord Nelson came here with Lady Hamilton every Sunday while he was in residence at Merton Place. Beyond St Mary's, along Church Path, stand several cottages dating back to the 18th century, as well as the Vicarage of about 1800. By its side is a large Norman arch, the one substantial part of the Priory to survive. It was re-erected here 50 years ago.

Church Path leads into Mostyn Road and the district of Merton Park. This was laid out in the 1870s as a middle-class suburb by John Innes, a property developer who became a local landowner. He lived at the manor house, now part of Rutlish School, and employed as his architect H G Quartermain. Quartermain built substantial, half-timbered Victorian mansions along wide, tree-lined avenues, like Mostyn, Sheridan and Dorset Roads. John Innes Park off Mostyn Road was originally the garden of the Manor House. In it there can be found over forty varieties of holly. Opposite the Park, numbers 40 to 50 Mostyn Road were built by Innes to house some of his workmen. When he died in 1904, his coffin was carried on a farm wagon to his resting place in Merton churchyard and people from all around came to pay their last respects.

Mitcham

Mitcham developed around its village greens, the Upper or Fair Green, which has largely vanished, and the Lower Green with its famous cricket ground.

Linking the two greens is the London Road. Along it are two important coaching inns. They stand facing each other at the south western corner of the lower green. One, the White Hart, was also the starting point for Sampson's horse buses and has next door (numbers 346 to 348) a building which appears to be Georgian, but probably dates from Tudor times, earlier than any other in Mitcham. The other inn, the Brown Bullock, was known till recently as the King's Head. The front was put up early in the reign of George III, but a wing at the rear goes back at least to the years when Queen Elizabeth visited Mitcham and was entertained at great expense by Sir Julius Caesar (judge and councillor during the reign of James 1). Not far from these inns, on the lower green itself, stands the Vestry Hall. It was built just under 100 years ago, but it occupies the site of an earlier Hall, which had by it the stocks for criminals and a pound for straying animals. The vestry was the centre for village government and the hall was the place from which the Vestry and its successors were run till 1965. On the southern side of this green are the former Sunday and national schools building. This was put up just before the French Revolution in 1788. Four years later the widow of a Mitcham industrialist presented the clock. Further on up Church Road, is the old parish church of Saints Peter and Paul. First put up in the 13th century, it was re-built in 1819 by George Smith and some of the monuments from the earlier church were restored.

Round both greens are some of Mitcham's chief houses. The finest lies just to the north of Upper Green, Eagle House, built in 1705 for a queen's doctor. It has recently been restored and is now used for adult education. On the north side of Cricket Green are Elm Lodge, home of Dr Parrott (the leading Mitcham doctor in the early 19th century), Mitcham Court, built about 1840 and now owned by the borough, and the White House, an 18th century mansion which used to belong to Dr Parrott's successor, Alfred Bartley. Round the corner, towards the Common, is an earlier house, The Canons, which has a Tudor dovecote in its grounds. This building is now a community centre.

On the south side of the Cricket green, No 46, now a private house, was built in 1789 as a Methodist meeting place. John Wesley himself preached there. Just beyond stand the Tate almshouses, paid for by a Miss Tate, whose family had lived in a house on this site for over a hundred years.

The old ladies in the almshouses look out over one of the earliest homes of cricket. The green has seen matches played for over 250 years and famous Test cricketers, Tom Richardson, Herbert Strudwick and Andrew Sandham started their careers here. They and others are commemorated on the Ruff memorial at the south western corner.

Morden

Like Merton, Morden grew up round two centres, one along the Wandle, the other further west along London Road. By the Wandle lived the Garth family. In the late 17th century they built Morden Hall and laid out its large park. The house is now used for council offices. But the park is owned by the National Trust. In it there are 18th and 19th century snuff mills, which used to have two waterwheels of cast iron. Nearby is Morden Cottage, partly weatherboarded, which was the mill house.

A mile away to the south west is the centre of old Morden, on either side of the London Road. It is dominated by the parish church of St Lawrence, which mainly dates from 1636, the middle of the reign of Charles I, an unusual time for church building. It was made possible by the co-operation of the new rector, William Booth, and his brother-in-law, Richard Garth, the Lord of the Manor. Three years after the church reopened, Garth died and was buried in the chancel. His tomb survives, bearing the inscription 'friend of the church'. Booth

weathered all the changes of the Civil War and the Commonwealth and only died in 1671, to be succeeded by his son, Edward.

To the west of the church stands Morden Park House, a typical Georgian mansion, surrounded by pleasure grounds and a 100 acre park. It was built in 1770 for a wealthy London merchant and distiller, John Ewart. In the courtyard there is a well, 266 feet deep (over 100 feet more than the height of the borough's new headquarters, Crown House, Morden). The park has a large mound surrounded by trees. It may have been produced at the time the house was built, using the earth from the ha ha ditch which divides the ground round the mansion from the main park. However, leading historians think it is a Roman-British burial ground, especially as a major Roman road, Stane Street, runs through the park. The house is now used by the Merton Parks Department.

To the south of the church is another coaching inn, the George. Once the George and Dragon, it probably goes back to Tudor times. From 1684 the coach from Epsom to London called daily and changed horses here. Across the London Road, at the corner of Central Road, stands the Old School House. It was built in 1731 for the education of twelve poor Morden children by a widowed daughter of one of the Garths, Mrs Elizabeth Gardiner. Next door, the Parish Hall was the meeting place of the Vestry and later of the Parish Council. Just beyond is a road called Green Lane, a reminder of the days only half a century ago when Morden was a small country village.

Wimbledon

Until just over a century ago the historic centre of the village lay round the High Street and the common. With the coming of the railway it then moved down the hill as Wimbledon became a suburb of London and its fields were covered with late Victorian houses.

In the old village the chief building is Eagle House. It was built in 1613 by Robert Bell, one of the founders of the East India Company, on the site of his family house. For a long time it remained as a private house, but in 1789 it was transformed into a school. In 1860 the headmaster placed a stone eagle on the central gable. Since the last war it has been used as offices. Next door is the Rose and Crown, one of the chief inns. Its history can be traced back at least to the time of Oliver Cromwell. In the 19th century it was the starting point for one of the two coaches that travelled up every day to London.

Opposite is an interesting collection of Georgian houses and shops. A group of three Edwardian-fronted shops, numbers 32, 33 and 34 used to be a tailor's, plumber's and butcher's in the late 18th century. Ashford House, a large building with Victorian shop fronts, was the home for 70 years of a famous apothecary John Sanford, who started vaccinating the poor against smallpox in the 1790s. Beyond is Claremont House, a late 17th century building with Georgian windows.

On the other side of the road is the site of the village green. It is still partly occupied by the original houses, put up there in the 18th century. Most important are numbers 6 and 7 The Green, facing the common.

Round the common are more signs of Wimbledon's past. On Southside, among the long grass, stands the site of the old village well, covered by a commemorative stone. Nearby is Lauriston Cottage, dating from the 1720s. Then there is Rushmere (once a farm house owned by the Watney family) Southside House with two early fire insurance plates, and a Gothic Lodge with a plaque showing that it was once owned by the novelist

The Windmill, Wimbledon Common

Captain Marryat.

On the west side are more large 18th century mansions – Chester House, home of the radical parson John Horne Tooke, who wanted to be buried in his back garden ,Westside House where one of George IV's Lord Chancellors lived and Cannizaro (largely rebuilt after a disastrous fire in 1900), which gets its name from one of its owners, a Sicilian Duke.

About half a mile across the common to the north stands the windmill. Built in 1817, it has not been used for grinding corn since 1864. It has been repaired several times and now houses a museum of windmills (see Museums). Nearby is a large pond, Queensmere, dug to commemorate Queen Victoria's 1887 Jubilee. Forty seven years earlier the ground had been the site of one of the last duelsl between Captain Tuckett and the Earl of Cardigan.

At about the same time, Wimbledon's original church was being rebuilt with a new spire by the famous Victorian architect Sir George Gilbert Scott. St Mary's lies to the north east of the High Street. It contains many graves and monuments to famous inhabitants, above all Sir Edward Cecil, Viscount Wimbledon, who led a disastrous attack on Cadiz at the start of Charles I's reign. Just over the wall of the graveyard stands the Old Rectory, Wimbledon's earliest surviving house, built about 1500 and once the home of the Cecil family.

At the bottom of the hill on which the church stands is the ground which has made Wimbledon known all over the world, the All England Lawn Tennis Courts. Opened in 1922, they succeeded earlier courts which still exist just off Warple Road and were originally bought in 1868 – for croquet.

Southwark

The London borough of Southwark was formed in 1965 by the amalgamation of the former metropolitan boroughs of Bermondsey, Camberwell and Southwark. It stretches from the Thames in the north to Sydenham Hill in the south, and illustrates many aspects of old London.

Southwark was listed as a borough or burgh in the Burghal Hideage, an Anglo-Saxon document of about 911-919 AD, and the area just south of London Bridge known as The Borough (centering on Borough High Street) has the longest known history of any part of the London area apart from the City. Archeological excavations have given proof of a Roman settlement here (on the south bank of the Thames) opposite Londinium. Red Samian pottery, bone needles that stitched togas and amphorae that brought wines from Gaul and Spain are among the items found in Southwark by archeologists. Many of these can be seen in the Cuming Museum (see Museums).

In the Middle Ages, bishops and abbots lived in residences along the riverside and there were also two important monastic foundations, St Mary Overie and Bermondsey Abbey. Survivors from that period are Southwark Cathedral, formerly the priory church of St Mary Overie, and

the Rose Window and one wall of the Bishop of Winchester's Palace in Clink Street. In 1295, Southwark became the first borough in the London area, apart from the City, to send representatives to parliament. Near, or on the site of the present London Bridge there have been at least four other bridges linking Southwark with the City. There was almost certainly a bridge built by the Romans. A little way down river from today's London Bridge was the famous Old London Bridge whose story is a key to the history of Southwark. It was constructed between 1176 and 1209 and was lined

Borough High Street, Southwark

with shops and houses, with a chapel in the middle. At its southern end, it was dominated by a towered gatehouse known as Traitors' Gate. The losers in any conflict which took place here were decapitated and their heads exhibited on stakes above the gate. Until 1750 (when Westminster Bridge was built), 'Old London Bridge was the only bridge across the Thames to London. All traffic to and from the capital and the south of England, the Kentish ports and, hence, the continent of Europe passed through Southwark. The bridge before the one we know today was built by John Rennie and his son Sir John Rennie in 1831, dismantled in the late 1960s and taken to Arizona. The present bridge was designed by the City

Engineer Harold Knox King, and opened in 1973.

There were also many famous inns in Borough High Street. The Tabard was desribed by Chaucer (c1340-1400) in the Canterbury Tales as the inn where the pilgrims gathered before setting off for the shrine of St Thomas a Becket at Canterbury. Amongst the old inns still in use is the George, the last surviving galleried inn in London which was rebuilt in 1676 and now belongs to the National Trust. Plays and other annual events have been held in the yard, commemorating the anniversaries of Charles Dickens and William Shakespeare. Then there is the 18th century Anchor (on Bankside) which, with the former neighbouring brewery, is well known for its associations with Dr Samuel Johnson. The old sites of other inns are marked by alleys leading off Borough High Street, for example, King's Head Yard, White Hart Yard and Talbot (ie Tabard) Yard.

Southwark's Bankside was where the citizens of London sought their entertainment. Bear Gardens Alley once led to a bear-baiting ring. In the late 16th century, Bankside became the theatreland of Elizabethan London with Shakespeare's Globe ('The Glory of the Bank') performing many of his plays. A memorial in Southwark Cathedral and a plaque in Park Street act as reminders of those days. Other literary figures associated with Southwark include (as we have already mentioned) Dr Samuel Johnson (1709-84), compiler of the first English dictionary, and Charles Dickens (1812-70), who knew Southwark as a child and used his experiences in several novels, notably Oliver Twist, Little Dorrit and the Pickwick Papers. Robert Browning also spent his youth in Southwark and Ruskin made his home in the borough.

The river was of paramount importance to north Southwark. The riverside village of Rotherhithe was noted for its shipbuilders and seafarers, the most famous of these being Christopher Jones, master of the Mayflower. In the past, the Thames was a major highway with boats ferrying people and goods from the many river stairs, and the Southwark river front was lined with quays and wharves where ships from many parts of the world unloaded their cargoes. Hay's Wharf, dominating the Bermondsey river front, dealt with the food imported to London. Larger ships docked at the Surrey Docks at Rotherhithe which handled most of London's timber.

Further south, Southwark had remained largely rural until about 1800, many of the local inhabitants being farmers or market gardeners supplying produce to London. Walworth (sometimes known as Newington), Camberwell, Peckham and Dulwich began as self-sufficient villages and were all recorded in the 1086 Domesday Book or other mediaeval documents. The parish churches, once the centres of the old villages, still provide oases of peace and a link with the past, but today only the Dulwich neighbourhood retains something of its rural character. Here the woods and open spaces have managed to escape the developer and serve as reminders of the days when this was good hunting country and King Charles I forbade the inhabitants 'to hunt, chase, molest or hurt the king's stags with greyhounds, guns or any other means whatsoever'. Many local pubs in this area have a recorded history going back at least 200 years. Before the days of trains or motor transport, these rural parts of the borough were near enough to London for a pleasant day's outing for the residents of the City and numerous inns and other places of entertainment attracted the visitor. In Camberwell for example, there was the Rosemary Brunch in Southampton Way, in Dulwich Village there was the Greyhound, and in Rotherhithe the St Helena Tavern which gave its name to St Helena Road.

Street names indeed are always worth noting as they often serve as reminders of the past. In Spa Road, for instance, you can try to imagine the fashionable world of the 18th century coming to Bermondsey to take the waters. A number of well-to-do people in the 18th century chose to build country estates in parts of the borough (mainly in Camberwell) so that they would be near enough to make regular visits to London. One of these was the Huguenot family who gave their names to De Crespigny Park and Champion Hill. By the early part of the 19th century this whole part of the borough had developed as a fashionable suburb for wealthy merchants and professional men. During the 19th century the character of most of Southwark changed. The building of the bridges across the Thames (Westminster in 1750, Blackfriars in 1769 and Vauxhall in 1816) and the roads leading to them had linked the district south of the Thames more closely with the centre, assisting industrial expansion and rapid urban development. This brought with it a dramatic increase in the population of Southwark. You can still get a feel of this era. As you travel south through the borough, you pass some well-designed architecture surviving from the late 18th and early 19th centuries. Examples include Trinity Church Square, houses along the Walworth and Camberwell Roads, Clifton Crescent and Camberwell Grove, which were the homes of prosperous business and professional people who made the daily journey to town by carriage or coach. In other parts you will see the smaller streets and rows of terraced houses of the mid and late 19th century. These were the homes of working people who were employed locally in the docks, warehouses and factories or commuted cheaply to town by railway or tram. London Bridge Station was opened originally in 1836 as the terminus of the first passenger service in London, the London and Greenwich Railway. Firms which were to become household names were established in Bermondsey, notably Courage Brewery, Sarsons Vinegar and Peak Freans Biscuits, and this part of the borough was renowned too for its important leather industry. Southwark had become a busy, thriving area.

The next major change came with World War II, which caused terrible destruction to Southwark's crowded streets. However, much greater changes have been brought about by ambitious redevelopment schemes in recent years, when the borough introduced a vast council housing programme, and some historic neighbourhoods, notably the Elephant & Castle, have changed almost beyond recognition (many would say for the worse). Since the closure of the Surrey Commercial Docks in 1970 the whole waterfont of Southwark from Blackfriars to Rotherhithe has been undergoing redevelopment. The tall 19th century warehouses in Rotherhithe have been converted to new uses such as craft workshops and these evoke an atmosphere of the past. The proposed development of housing and industry at Surrey Docks represents one of the largest urban renewal programmes in Europe. The warehouses at Hayes Wharf are being redeveloped to provide office accommodation, a private hospital and shopping complex, and other warehouses further east have been and are being converted into luxury housing. The manufacturing and other industries, once so active in the borough, have declined dramatically and Southwark, like many other inner city areas, can offer few employment prospects to its people. However, there is one feature from Southwark's past that remains unchanged. In the centre of the river front, just south of London Bridge, we can still enjoy the oldest building in the borough, indeed, one of the oldest in the London area – the church which is today Southwark Cathedral.

Places of Interest

Cathedrals and Churches

Church of St George The Martyr
Borough High Street
Built to the designs of J Price in the 18th century, on the site of another church. In the churchyard of this previous building were buried prisoners from Marshalsea and other prisons, including Civil War leaders, as well as Nahum Tate, author of While Shepherds Watched Their Flocks By Night. This churchyard is now a public garden. The present-day church has literary connections through Charles Dickens. Little Dorrit in the novel of the name, is said to have slept here one night as a child and was later also married in this church.

Guy's Hospital Chapel
Guy's Hospital
18th century chapel where Thomas Guy, the founder of Guy's Hospital, is buried.

Southwark Cathedral
London Bridge
Legend has it that a church has been standing on this site since 606. The present church (which became a cathedral in 1905) was built by the Augustinians and indeed the choir and retrochoir date from the 13th century. Some Norman remains can still be found in the church though drastic restoration was carried out in the 1830s. It houses some interesting monuments and tombs including a plaque to Shakespeare's brother Edmund. There is also a Harvard Memorial Chapel in memory of John Harvard, the founder of the American

university who was born in the parish.

St George's Cathedral (RC)
Westminster Bridge Road
Designed by A W Pugin and consecrated by Dr Wiseman in 1848. He was made Archbishop of Westminster here in 1850. Very badly bombed in 1941, though sections of the original building have been incorporated in the new one, which was erected in 1958.

St Mary Magdalen
Bermondsey Street
Built on the site of a church first constructed in 1290 but almost totally rebuilt in 1680. Famed for its Gothic exterior and almost Wren-like interior.

St Mary Rotherhithe
St Marychurch Street
Rebuilt in 1715, this church is famous for its memorials to seafarers. Captain Christopher Jones of Mayflower fame is buried here.

Southwark Cathedral

Historic Houses

Belair House
Gallery Road
A beautiful, restored, 18th century mansion. Only the grounds are open to the public.

Kingswood House
Seeley Drive
A 19th century baronial style mansion now used as a public library and community centre. The greater part of the present building dates from the 19th century and in its heyday the house had 30 acres of land, kitchen gardens and livestock, a private laundry, its own generating plant and an illuminated private entrance to Sydenham Hill Station. Its last private owner was Lord Vestey (of M & S fame). The adult lending library with its grand oak staircase occupies what was once the great hall, and the junior library was originally a billiard and card room, the small alcove being intended as a smokers' corner.

Old College
Dulwich Village
The original Dulwich College was founded by Edward Alleyn in 1619. Some sections of this, including the chapel still remain and are to be found in the triangle of land between Gallery Road and College Road. After the 1857 Act of Parliament, the buildings became offices and new blocks in the Italian Renaissance style were constructed in the grounds of the school which is still standing. The chapel is still often open to the public.

Old Inns

Anchor
Bankside
This 18th century inn is well-known for its associations with Dr Samuel Johnson.

Angel
Rotherhithe Street
Another 17th century inn with good views of the river.

George Inn
Borough High Street
The last surviving galleried inn in London, this now belongs to the National Trust. The facade dates from

1676. Plays and other annual events are held in the yard, commemorating the anniversaries of Charles Dickens and William Shakespeare.

Mayflower
Rotherhithe Street
This riverside inn very possibly dates from the 17th century and is said to have connections with the ship Mayflower.

Other Places of Interest
Bankside Reach
Hopton Street
New riverside wall (built in the 1970s), which offers dramatic views of the Thames and St Pauls.

Engine House and Shaft of The Thames Tunnel
Rotherhithe Street
This is the original engine house used by the famous Brunel engineers (father and son) when constructing the first tunnel under the Thames which was opened in 1843. The exterior of the engine house can be seen from the street (see Museums).

Imperial War Museum
(see Museums)

Old Operating Theatre
(see Museums)

Plaques

Southwark is famous for its historic plaques in Borough High Street which were put up for the Festival of Britain. There is also one in Park Street commemorating the Globe and another to mark the site of Clink Prison.

Ruins

Winchester Palace
Clink Street
Originally built in 1109 by the Bishops of Winchester. For the next few hundred years it was an important building in London and stood in vast impressive grounds. In 1642 the building was turned into a prison and later sold to local business men. Today only fragments remain, one containing the Rose Window which used to be in the banqueting hall of the Palace.

Wandsworth

The London Borough of Wandsworth is a loose amalgamation of six ancient Surrey villages. In the main they are Saxon settlements, although recent archeological work has revealed some Roman occupation at Putney.

It seems likely that Caesar's forces crossed the Thames at Battersea

Battersea and Wandsworth are within the flood plain of the River Thames and it was not until the Saxons came along, with their heavy ploughs, that the clay could be properly cultivated. To the south, Balham is on somewhat higher ground and a Roman Road, Stane Street, connected it to its neighbour, Tooting. Roehampton, to the south-west of the borough, still has something of a village atmosphere and was the last area to be subjected to modern development.

Battersea

The original version of Battersea was Badrices Ege, meaning the island of Badric, probably the name of a Saxon chieftan. The ancient village can now only be identified as the area immediately around the junction of Battersea High Street, Westbridge Road, Battersea Church Road and Vicarage Crescent, containing the Parish Church, an old inn The Raven, Old Battersea House and Sir Walter St Johns Grammar School. This area and the streets off Battersea High Street constituted the early gravel island, and much of the land around was marshy, swamped by the Thames at each high tide. Early attempts were made to hold back the river but this was not totally successful until the present century – there was considerable flooding as late at 1928. At the time of the Domesday Survey (1086) Battersea was the most valuable Manor in Surrey, mainly due to its large number of mills (presumably driven by water power) and its consequent output of flour. Because of the value, the new King, William the Conqueror, annexed the Manor for himself. In 1067, however, he exchanged it for other lands, including Windsor, with the Abbey of Westminster who continued in ownership until the dissolution of the monasteries in 1540. In 1627 the

Manor passed into the hands of the St John family, whose presence is still recorded in such names as St Johns Hill, Falcon Road (part of the family crest) and Bolingbroke Grove, after Henry St John, Viscount Bolingbroke. They in turn sold the Manor to Earl Spencer, the ancestor of the Princess of Wales. The Earl still holds the Patronage of the parish church of Battersea.

There was probably a church in Battersea at the time of the Norman conquest, but the first documentary evidence can be found in 1157. The first recorded vicar is Robert in 1263, but we know there was one earlier than that because an unnamed vicar of Battersea was fined for non-payment of the tithe for catching salmon in the Thames. A later vicar, Owen Ridley, was also in trouble accused of consorting with witches, but he was found not guilty. The present church of St Mary, Battersea, dates from 1777. It has a notable site by the river in Battersea Church Road. The great mystic poet and painter William Blake was married there in 1782, and the American traitor of the War of Independence, General Benedict Arnold, was buried there in 1801. The painter Turner would often sketch from the vestry window of the church, and the well-known botanist William Curtis was buried in the church yard. These four men are commemorated by a series of stained glass windows created by John Hayward, and put into the church in modern times. The finest piece of stained glass in the church is the east window, a heraldic description of the St John family's antecedents. It is dated 1631 and was brought from the earlier church into the present building. At this time the Archbishop of York had a suburban house or perhaps palace in what is now York Road.

In the 18th century Battersea was developing as a fashionable residential suburb of London, and in 1766 the Earl Spencer obtained permission to build a river bridge. This original wooden construction was erected by the king's carpenter, John Phillips. It was often painted by the American artist James Whistler. The old bridge was replaced by the present structure in 1890.

Market gardening became an important industry in Battersea at this time and covered an area around the perimeter of what is now Battersea Park. Asparagus was grown there for the first time in England. The name Lavender Hill is also an indication of another notable industry of the period.

In 1838 the first railway lines crossed Battersea fields. It was the beginnig of the London and South Western, which had its terminus at Nine Elms, in the north-east corner of Battersea. By 1863 the whole network of railways in the area had been created and is called by many the 'Battersea Tangle'. Clapham Junction Station opened that year and the administrative centre of Battersea moved from the old village to the streets around the railway station. Railways brought work, and poor people were also being forced out of the wealthy developments in Chelsea and Pimlico. The conversion of Battersea from a country village to part of London was swift. In 1850 the population was 10,000. By 1870 it had topped the 100,000 mark. It became almost like a wild west frontier town. Riotous fairs were often held on the old marshes and this led the local worthies to press for a proper public space. In consequence Battersea Park was opened in 1858. The park was to gain fame in later years as the Festival Gardens of the Festival of Britain in 1951. A recent addition to the park is a Peace Pagoda built by Japanese Buddhist monks.

Few old buildings survived the holocaust of Victorian and more recent developments. Perhaps the most notable is Old Battersea House in Vicarage Crescent, dated 1699. Two housing estates are also worthy of mention. The Shaftesbury Estate was an early effort to build model houses for artisans and it is still much the same as it was when it was built over one hundred years ago. As part of the plan the estate had no public houses and no churches. On the other side of the railway is the Latchmere Estate, the first municipal estate in the country to be built by direct labour. Opened by the local MP John Burns in 1903, it has survived where many other estates have now been demolished.

Battersea is becoming a very mixed social area, and perhaps it always has been to some extent. The mansion flats in Prince of Wales Drive have always housed the more wealthy part of the population and are a notable architectural feature to the south of Battersea Park. The southern part of Battersea, beyond Battersea Rise, developed later than the areas around the old village and Clapham Junction. Many of the old family mansions survived into this century, and in fact one or two still exist. The greatest of these was a house called Battersea Rise which stood on the site now occupied by Alfriston and Muncaster roads, until 1905. It was the home of the Thornton family. Henry Thornton was a leading member of the Clapham Sect, a group of social reformers. Another member, William Wilberforce, the foremost instigator of the abolition of the slave trade, lived at Battersea Rise until Thornton built him Broomfield House just to the south. Still remaining on North Side Clapham Common is Gilmore House – one time home of John Walter, founder of the Times newspaper.

We cannot leave Battersea without mention of its two nationally known assets – the Power Station and the Dogs' Home. Battersea Power Station is noteworthy because it is probably the first industrial building where architectural design played such a large part. Sir Giles Gilbert Scott collaborated in connection with the external features of the building, which was once called the Cathedral of Industry. When it was being built in 1930 the bones of a pre-historic animal, a woolly rhinocerous, were found on the site. The Dogs' Home was opened in Battersea Park Road in 1860, having been established in Holloway a few years earlier. As an old borough guide puts it, 'many a temporarily missing canine pet has been retrieved from the Home and many an afflicted or superfluous animal mercifully destroyed'.

Other buildings of special interest

Devonshire House and Old Vicarage
42 and 44 Vicarage Crescent (early 18th century).

Grand Theatre
St Johns Hill

Wandsworth

To many people Wandsworth is no more than a tortuous knot in the South Circular road. But unlike Battersea the old village is still the centre of things, even if you fail to notice it as you pass through.

Battersea Power Station

The local Saxon leader at Wandsworth was named Wendle and the name simply means Wendle's Place. The reason for its existence is undoubtedly the tributory Thames river, the Wandle, now named after the place, but in earlier days called the Ledbourne. The little bridge over the Wandle in Wandsworth High Street is one of the earliest in the London area.

Wandsworth in its very early days was purely agricultural and park land, but it gradually developed into an area of industrial importance. It was the River Wandle, with its surrounding land, which encouraged the growth of industry. The Wandle valley was a valley of mills. In 1684 a nameless miller of Wandsworth headed 3000 Surrey men who marched on London to ask Parliament to restore the King's rights and privileges. The bleaching of calico was another early industry. The cloth was stretched out on the grass in strips, close to the river, and men would walk along the edges drenching the cloth with water. The sun did the rest. It took a month to do what modern chemicals can now do in a few hours. The manufacture of dye-stuffs and calico printing were also amongst the early industries.

Huguenots fleeing religious persecution in France in the 17th century were attracted to Wandsworth where there was already a Huguenot church. They were useful additions to Wandsworth society, being largely bankers, traders, doctors and skilled artisans of every kind.

They soon set up a number of industries, and one particularly interesting one was hat making. Hats were sent all over Europe as a result of individual orders from many well-known people. The settlers had a secret method for the preparation of rabbit and beaver skins, and this secret was kept at Wandsworth for nearly a hundred years. There is a Huguenot burial ground called Mount Nod at the top of East Hill.

In the 17th century the Dutch introduced the brass industry into England and it was carried on at Wandsworth in what were known as the Frying-pan houses in Love Lane, now called Putney Bridge Road. At this time Wandsworth appears to have had some importance as an arsenal. There was an iron mill at which shot and cannon were made. The mill is commemorated by the modern Iron Mill Place. The brewing industry was established in the very early days, and records exist showing it being carried on in 1564. Young's Brewery still occupies an important site in Wandsworth High Street – they have been brewing there for 150 years.

If you go deep into the rural countryside of England you will probably find village churches dating from the eleventh to fourteenth centuries. But in the 'London' villages the old churches were generally pulled down and replaced in the 17th and 18th centuries. Like its Battersea counterpart, Wandsworth's parish church of All Saints, in the High Street, stands on an ancient christian site. The first documentary evidence for the existence of a church is dated 1234. The oldest part of the present building is its square tower (partially destroyed in the last war and rebuilt in 1955) which was built in 1680, replacing a leaded steeple. Other parts of the church date from 1724 and 1780. There are numerous monuments and brasses in the church commemorating people from Wandsworth's past, the earliest being an officer of Henry V's army who died in 1420. The last Roman Catholic vicar of Wandsworth, John Griffiths, was hung, drawn and quartered in 1539, probably for denying the Royal supremacy. Another interesting church in the area is St Ann's on St Ann's Hill. Because of its unusual tower it is often called the pepper-pot church. Tucked away amongst a number of modern buildings in Wandsworth High Street is the plain but attractive Friends Meeting House, dating from 1778.

There is a pleasant row of Georgian terraced houses in Wandsworth Plain, adjacent to the parish church, and there are a few ancient cottages on the corner of Putney Bridge Road, some now used as shops. On the south side of West Hill is a large mansion originally called Melrose Hall, and mainly built in 1796. It has been used by the Royal Hospital and Home for Incurables since 1863.

Amongst the buildings which have now vanished is Sword House, which stood on the site of Wandsworth police station. It took its name from the fact that in the 1740s it was occupied by a military officer who decorated the front wall with Highland claymores brought from the Battle of Culloden. At that time West Hill and Putney Heath were haunted by footpads and highwaymen. It is said that some travellers took swords

from the wall of Sword House to protect themselves for the forthcoming journey.

Much of the southern part of the Wandsworth parish was agricultural land in the 18th century which gave Garrett, between Wandsworth and Tooting, a real hamlet aspect. It was here that the political burlesque called The Election of the Mayor of Garrett took place annually, often

attended by as many as 80,000 people. Candidates had names like Squire Blowmedown, Lord Twankum, and Kit Noisy.

Putney

Nationally, Putney is undoubtedly best known as the starting point of the University Boat Race, but it has a long history which makes it a significant part of the London Borough of Wandsworth. It is unique amongst the London riverside villages in that the river is approached by a steep hill meaning that it did not have a marshy approach to the Thames. It was an early crossing point and a Professor Grimes has located the pre-historic trackway Old Street as crossing the Thames at Putney. In later days travellers used to come up the river from London, disembark at Putney, and journey by road to the towns of the south-west through Kingston. Could this have led to the proliferation of boat houses in the area? Certainly the towpath with its line of boat clubs would suggest this. The old English word for harbour was Hythe, similar to the coastal town in Kent and this formed part of the original name of Putney which was Putta's Hythe or Puttenhythe. The excavations revealing Roman occupation were close to Putney Bridge, suggesting a small settlement close to the harbour.

The parish church of St Mary is also close to the bridge. The present structure dates from 1836, although the West Tower is much older. It was badly damaged by fire in 1973 and has only recently been restored. There was an earlier church, and the Bishop West Chapel, built by Nicholas West, Bishop of Ely in the reign of Henry VIII, was incorporated in the 1836 building. West was born in Putney. Luckily the Chapel escaped serious damage in the recent fire. Samuel Pepys recorded in his diary that he visited the church on several occasions. The church's greatest claim to fame is undoubtedly the fact that during the Civil War it was used by Oliver Cromwell as his headquarters, and that his Council of War frequently met there in 1647.

Putney was the home of Cromwell's army for three months

The Cromwells had a further connection with Putney because Thomas Cromwell, later Chancellor to Henry VIII and Earl of Essex was born there in 1485. Thomas's father Walter was a brewer and lived in a timber-framed, high gabled two-storey cottage close to what is now Brewhouse Lane. Another name to conjure with is Edward Gibbon, author of 'Decline and Fall of Ancient Rome'. He was born in Lime Grove, a house which stood on the east side of Putney Hill at its junction with Upper Richmond Road.

There has always been a ferry at Putney, up to the time that the first bridge, the only one between London and Kingston, was built in 1729. The ferry was owned by two people, who paid a rental of 15 shillings a year to the Lord of the Manor. The original wooden bridge built by the same man who erected Battersea Bridge, John Phillips, was a toll bridge. The charge was one half-penny which was doubled on Sundays, the extra sum making up an annuity of £62 divided among the widows and children of the Watermen of Putney and Fulham, whose income had fallen as a result of

the building of the bridge. The present stone bridge was erected in 1886 and was widened in 1933.

There was once a palace at Putney, built for John Lacey, an eminent citizen, just south of the Star and Garter in the Lower Richmond Road. Rebuilt in 1596, it was visited by both Elizabeth I and James I. George II was also a visitor at the fine Putney House which stood on the river front. This was demolished in 1857.

At the top of Putney Hill is Putney Heath. Many duels were fought there in times past. Amongst those recorded are duels between William Pitt, the Prime Minister and William Tierney MP, in 1798, and between Prince Louis Napoleon and Count Leon in 1840. It is recorded that King Charles II reviwed his army on Putney Heath in 1684.

On Putney Heath, the Telegraph Inn takes its name from a semaphore station that stood nearby, one of a chain which conveyed messages between London and Portsmouth. Another house which stood on the Heath was Bowling Green House where William Pitt died in 1806, alone and deserted by his staff.

Other buildings of special interest

Winchester House
Lower Richmond Road (18th century).

Putney Bridge Road Almshouses
(founded 1627). Victorian rebuild in Tudor style.

Park Lodge
next to Almshouses (late 17th century house with c1830 addition). Home of Lewis Carroll's uncle, Hassard Dodgson.

Chatfield House
96-98 High Street (remains of 17th century house).

The Pines
11 Putney Hill. Home of the poet Algernon Swinburne.

Green Man
Putney Hill (18th century inn)

Fire-proof house memorial obelisk
Kingston Road, just to north-west of
underpass at Tibbets's corner.

Roehampton

Beyond Putney Heath is Roehampton,
a favourite residential area which
still possesses the feeling of a village.
It has only been developed since the
last war and much of the district
retains a Georgian atmosphere,
although the parish church of Holy
Trinity dates only from 1898. The
church has a 200 foot spire and a large
stone chancel screen designed by
Prynne.
Several houses of architectural
interest survive at Roehampton.

Roehampton whirlwind, 1780

Roehampton House was built in 1710-
12 to Thomas Archer's design and was
later the home of the Earls of
Albemarle, Levin and Melville
successively. The buildings now used
by the Roehampton Colleges are also
interesting. Manressa House was built
as Parkstead in 1750 for the Second
Earl of Bessborough. Its grounds are
now covered by the Alton Housing
Estate. Upper Grove House, now the

Froebel Institute, was built in 1777
and Mount Clare, which forms part of
Garnatt College dates from 1772. Its
grounds were laid out by Capability
Brown.

Also of special interest

Fountain, junction of Roehampton
Lane and Medfield Road (19th
century based on classical tomb)

Balham

Peter Sellers has immortalised
Balham as 'Bal-Ham, gateway to the
south.' There may well have been
some truth in this quip because the
Roman Road, Stane Street, passed
along what is now Balham High Road
on its way to Chichester.
Balham did not have a separate
existence as a parish until 1865, but as
far back as the year 967 a Saxon
charter, relating to the boundaries of
Battersea, mentioned Baelgenham, a
name possibly derived from Belgae,
the Celtic tribe which was living
south of the Thames at the time of the
Roman invasion. Its early ownership
is disputed but in the reign of King
Stephen it was confirmed that a grant
of 100 acres in Balham was made to
the Norman Abbey of Bec. It was then
merged with the Abbey's Streatham
Lands, which in 1802 passed with
Tooting Bec Manor to the Duke of
Bedford. Another 200 acres of land in
Balham formed part of the Manor of
Leigham Court in the parish of
Streatham. In about 1700 this Manor
passed to Peter Du Cane whose name
is perpetuated in the large block of
flats in Balham High Road.
The parish church of St Mary, Balham
High Road, is an interesting mixture
of architectural styles. Built in 1805
as a chapel, it was much used by
members of the Clapham Sect. In 1885
it was raised to the status of a parish
church.
Among Balham's best known natives
was Percy Fender, Surrey's cricket

captain from 1921 to 1931, who scored a century in only thirty-five minutes. He was a friend of Douglas Jardine the Captain of England during the infamous 'Bodyline' tour of Australia. Fender was one of the instigators of that controversial strategy.

From 1878 to 1881 Thomas Hardy, the great novelist, lived at 172 Trinity Road, Balham. Whilst there he renewed his friendship with the elderly Alexander Macmillan (of the famous publishing house), who lived in Tooting Bec Road (then Streatham Lane) in the building which is now St Anselm's Convent School. At that time it was named Knapdale.

Balham was the scene of one of the greatest bombing tragedies of World War 11. On October 14th 1940 a bomb fell close to the tube station where hundreds were sheltering. The bomb fractured a main sewer as well as water and gas mains. The station began to fill with both water and gas as people scrambled to safety. Sixty-eight people were killed and five injured.

Of special interest

The Priory
top of Bedford Hill, (built 1822) 'Strawberry Hill' gothic.

Tooting

The origins of the name Tooting are obscure and somewhat bizarre. Many explanations have been offered. The syllable 'Tot' means a homestead and 'ing' a meadow. But one also has the choice of 'Teut' a Celtic God or 'Totingas' the tribe of the chieftain Tota. It has even suggested that 'Toot' could mean to 'peep out'.

In any event from early days the manor was actually called Tooting Graveney. The Domesday Survey shows that Tooting belonged to the Abbey of Chertsey and that there was a church and a meadow there. The Graveney part of the manor's name was added during the reign of Henry 11 when it was owned by Hamo de Gravenel.

The parish Church of Tooting is dedicated to St Nicholas. The parish is known to have been in the hands of the Abbey of Chertsey as early as AD 666. The old church which had an unusual round Saxon tower, was pulled down and replaced by the present one in 1833.

In Mitcham Road there is an octagonal shaped Congregational Church. This replaced the so-called Defoe Chapel in Tooting High Street, opposite Selkirk Road. The old building, erected in 1776, still stands and is used as a shop. In a letter dated 1892, Doctor William Anderson, minister of the Defoe Chapel, stated that the Presbyterian Congregation was founded by Daniel Defoe, author of 'Robinson Crusoe'. However, others have disputed that fact.

Local records tell much about the state of public health and the poor in the 18th and 19th centuries. In 1774 a man was granted 40 shillings for relieving the parish of a widow by marrying her, whilst in 1855 people who received parish relief had their names posted up in public. Apparently the 'Resurrection men' visited Tooting, for in 1819 a shelter box was provided for watching the graves in the Churchyard. The low standards of public health are shown by a tragedy which occurred in 1849. At a house in Tooting Broadway, 118 out of 1500 pauper children, drawn from a wide area, died of cholera.

The earliest known school in the Parish was Doctor Salvadori's Academy for Young Gentlemen, which stood on the site of the Granada Cinema. Among its later proprietors was Joseph Lancaster, the famous pioneer of popular education. Although the Granada no longer shows films, its fantastic interior decoration by Theodore

Komisavjevsky has been made the subject of a preservation order by the local authority.

One of the wealthy residents of Tooting was Ralph Thrale, owner of a brewery on the site of the Globe Theatre, Southwark. In about 1740 he acquired 100 acres of Tooting Bec Common. On this estate (known as Streatham Park), his son Henry Thrale was frequently host to Dr. Johnson. A favourite walk of the great lexicographer was The Avenue which followed the boundary between the commons.

Tooting developed as an urban area during this century. In 1891 its population was only 5,784. By the 1950s it had risen to about 38,000. The present administrative areas in London are largely loose combinations of ancient places. This tends to submerge the parts into the whole. It is our hope that at least as far as the London Borough of Wandsworth is concerned we have done something to redress that balance.

a pilgrim

LOCAL SERVICES

This is basically a chapter of useful addresses and telephone numbers. It includes advice centres, town halls, police stations, voluntary organisations and job centres.

Advice Centres

Greenwich

Asian Resource Centre
MacBean Centre
MacBean Street
Woolwich   SE18
Tel 854 1188
Advice on immigration, welfare rights and nationality for the Asian Community.

East Greenwich Community Centre
Christchurch Way
Greenwich   SE10
Tel 858 4259
General advice on housing, social security and fuel debt.

Eltham Citizens' Advice Bureau
Eltham Library
High Street
Eltham   SE9
Tel 850 6044
General and financial advice.

Greenwich Action Group on Unemployment
Building A
MacBean Centre
MacBean Street
Woolwich   SE18
Tel 854 4989
Advice on welfare and housing rights for unemployed people.

Information & Advice Centre
43 Wellington Street
Woolwich   SE18
Tel 854 8888 ext 2274/2275
Consumer and welfare rights advice.

Information & Advice Centre
17-23 Woolwich Road
Greenwich   SE10
Tel 858 3210
Consumer and welfare rights advice.

Information & Consumer Advice Centre

Kidbrooke Mini-Town Hall
1a Birdbrooke Road
Kidbrooke   SE3
Tel 856 0011
Consumer and welfare advice.

New Charlton Community Centre

217 Maryon Road
Charlton   SE7
Tel 854 7008
General and welfare rights advice.

North Charlton Community Project

38 Floyd Road
Charlton   SE7
Tel 858 1345
Legal and general advice including
welfare rights.

Plumstead Community Law Centre

105 Plumstead High Street
Plumstead   SE18
Tel 855 9817
Legal advice specialising in housing,
employment, welfare rights, race and
immigration and sex discrimination.
For residents of SE7 and SE18.

Plumstead Information Office

Plumstead Mini Town Hall
Plumstead High Street
Plumstead   SE18
Tel 855 9651 ext 221
Consumer and welfare rights advice.

West Greenwich Citizens' Advice Bureau

First Floor
Bellevue House
229-259 Greenwich High Road
Greenwich   SE10
Tel 853 5172
General advice and information.

Woolwich Citizens' Advice Bureau

Old Town Hall
Polytechnic Street
Woolwich   SE18
Tel 854 9607
Legal and general advice specialising

in financial matters.

Woolwich Common Neighbourhood Centre

57 Ritter Street
Woolwich Common Estate
Woolwich   SE18
Tel 854 7526
Advice on social services, personal
and family matters, housing and
estate problems for local residents
only.

Woolwich Simba Project

Advice Unit
48-50 Artillery Place
Woolwich   SE18
Tel 317 0451
Advice and information for ethnic
minorities particularly Afro-
Caribbean.

Lambeth

Asian Community Action Group

322a Brixton Road
Brixton   SW9
Tel 733 7494
General advice including nationality,
immigration and harassment for the
Asian community.

At Ease

St John's Church
Waterloo Road
Waterloo   SE1
Tel 633 0852

Advice and counselling on military law and personal problems for members of HM forces and their families.

Brixton Advice Centre
167 Railton Road
Brixton   **SE24**
Tel 733 4674
Legal and general advice specialising in financial, immigration and nationality matters.

Brixton Circle Project
33 Effra Road
Brixton   **SW2**
Tel 737 2888/274 2513
Advice on housing and DHSS benefits for single homeless people.

Brixton Community Law Centre
506-508 Brixton Road
Brixton   **SW9**
Tel 733 4245
Legal advice for people who live or work in Brixton.

Brixton Consumer Advice Centre
13 Electric Avenue
Brixton   **SW9**
Tel 737 3311
Advice and information particularly on consumer affairs and money for people who live or work in Lambeth.

Brixton Neighbourhood Community Association
1 Mayall Road
Brixton   **SE24**
Tel 737 3505
General and legal advice and advice from local MP.

Centre 70 Community Association
138 Christchurch Road
Tulse Hill   **SW2**
Tel 674 6671
General and legal advice.

Centre 70 Community Association
2 Norwood High Street
Norwood   **SE27**
Tel 761 1528
Legal advice.

Clapham Citizens' Advice Bureau
361 Clapham Road
Clapham   **SW9**
Tel 733 1946
Legal and general advice. Sessions with Vietnamese and Cantonese interpeter.

Clapham Town Advice Centre
Clapham Community Project
St Anne's Hall
Venn Street
Clapham   **SW4**
Tel 720 8731
Legal, housing, fuel and youth advice.

Council for Community Relations in Lambeth
441 Brixton Road
Brixton   **SW9**
Tel 274 7722 ext 2388
Advice on police, immigration, education, nationality, marital and family problems.

Family Support Service
36 Stockwell Green
Brixton   **SW9**
Tel 737 4775/2830
Advice and counselling for one parent families.

Help 71
95 Acre Lane
Brixton   **SW2**
Tel 274 3339
Advice and voluntary work.

Kings Acre Neighbourhood Council Information Centre
124a Lyham Road
Brixton   **SW2**
Tel 674 5354
Advice and information.

Lambeth Citizens' Advice Bureau Community Advice Team
323 Kennington Road
Kennington   **SE11**
Tel 582 8420
Mobile general advice centre for hospitals, day centres, homeless families units etc.

Lambeth Educational Opportunities
Strand Centre
Elm Park
Brixton   SW2
Tel 671 2961
Advice and information on further eduction for people who live or work in Lambeth.

Lambeth Planning Resource Centre
23 New Park Road
Brixton   SW2
Tel 674 9188
Advice and information on local planning problems.

Lambeth Walk Consumer Advice Centre
Unit 18
Lambeth Walk
Kennington   SE11
Tel 737 3311
Advice and information on consumers affairs for people who live and work in Lambeth.

Landor West Neighbourhood Centre
133 Landor Road
Stockwell   SW9
Tel 274 0481
General advice.

Latin American Community Group
14 Brixton Road
Oval   SW9
Tel 582 5590
Advice on social security, immigration, helath, education and housing for the Latin American community.

Loughborough Community Centre
Tenants' Hall
Angell Road
Brixton   SW9
Provides support and advice.

Melting Pot Foundation
361 Clapham Road
Stockwell   SW9
Tel 274 9566
Counselling and legal advice for young people.

Myatts Field Centre
40 Bramah Green
Brixton   SW9
Tel 582 6885
Advice on social security, housing and legal problems.

North Lambeth Citizens' Advice Bureau
323 Kennington Road
Kennington   SE11
Tel 735 9551
Legal and general advice.

Springfield Methodist Church Advice Bureau
Friendship House
200 Wandsworth Road
Stockwell   SW8
Tel 622 4897 (messages only)
Advice and information on housing, immigration, housing and legal problems.

Stockwell & Vauxhall Neighbourhood Centre
157 South Lambeth Road
Stockwell   SW8
Tel 735 5051
General and legal advice, police surgery, councillors' surgery.

Stockwell Good Neighbours
142 Landor Road
Stockwell   SW9
Tel 274 0250
General advice and counselling.

Streatham Citizens' Advice Bureau
Ilex House
Barrhill Road
Sreatham   SW2
Tel 674 8993
Legal and general advice particularly on financial matters.

**Streatham Consumer Advice
Centre**
85 -87 Streatham High Road
Streatham SW16
Tel 737 3311
Advice and information on consumer
affairs and money for people who live
or work in Lambeth.

Town Planning Advice Centre
Courtney House
9-15 New Park Road
Streatham SW2
Tel 674 9844 ext 325
Advice and information on all aspects
of planning.

Tulse Hill Advice Centre
2 Lomley House
Tulse Hill Estate
Tulse Hill SW2
Tel 674 2532
General advice.

Vassall Neighbourhood Centre
145 Brixton Road
Brixton SW9
Tel 735 1878
General advice.

Vauxhall Gardens Action Centre
c/o Vauxhall Mission
Worgan Street
Vauxhall SE11
Tel 582 4480
Advice and information.

Waterloo Action Centre
14 Baylis Road
Waterloo SE1
Tel 261 1404
Advice on welfare rights, housing,
health problems for people who live or
work in the Waterloo area. Legal
advice on employment, housing,
accidents, insurance and
compensation, matrimonial and
consumer affairs.

Lewisham

Bellingham Legal Advice Centre
New Community Centre
Sedgehill Road
Bellingham SE6
Tel 690 5360
Legal and general advice.

Borough Information Centre
Borough Mall
Lewisham Centre
Lewisham SE13
Tel 318 5421/2 (information)
318 5423 (consumer advice)
Information and consumer advice.

Catford Citizens' Advice Bureau
120 Rushey Green
Catford SE6
Tel 690 8455
Legal and general information,
particularly financial.

Evelyn 190 Centre
190 Evelyn Street
Deptford SE8
Tel 691 7180/692 7857
Advice on DHSS benefits and
housing.

Hearsay Centre
Youth Aid Lewisham
17 Brownhill Road
Catford SE6
Tel 697 2152/697 7435
Advice and information for young
people.

Hither Green Legal Advice Centre
The Crypt
St Swithin's Church
St Swithin's Road
Hither Green   SE13
Tel none
Legal Advice.

**Honor Oak Advice & Information
Centre**
Spalding House
Turnham Road
Honor Oak Estate
Brockley   SE4
Tel 692 7133
Housing and social services advice for
Honor Oak estate and surrounding
areas.

Honor Oak Legal Advice Centre
Forman House
Frendsbury Road
Brockley   SE4
Tel 693 9103
Legal advice and counselling.

**Lewisham Citizens' Advice Bureau
Community Service**
Christ Church
Bellingham Green   SE6
Tel 697 3444
Advice and information.

Lewisham Citizens' Advice Bureau
Community Service
Goldsmith Community Association
Centre
Castillon Road
Catford   SE6
Tel 698 3741
Advice and information.

**Lewisham Citizens' Advice Bureau
Community Service**
Eastern District Social Services
8-12 Eltham Road
Lee   SE12
Tel 852 4391 ext 137
Advice and information.

**Lewisham Council for Community
Relations**
48 Lewisham High Street
Lewisham   SE13
Tel 852 9808
Legal advice on employment,
immigration, housing, police, landlord
and tenant, and education.

**Lewisham Indo-Chinese/Chinese
Community School**
171a Deptford High Street
Deptford   SE8
Tel 692 2772
Advice on housing, health, education
and welfare rights. Translation and
interpretation for refugees from
Vietnam.

New Cross Citizens' Advice Bureau
2 Lewisham Way
New Cross   SE14
Tel 692 6654/5
General and legal advice.

New Cross Legal Advice Centre
170 New Cross Road
New Cross   SE14
Tel 732 9716
Legal advice.

North Lewisham Law Centre
28 Deptford High Street
Deptford   SE8
Tel 692 5355
Legal advice and representation.

Sydenham Citizens' Advice Bureau
299 Kirkdale
Sydenham   SE26
Tel 659 1764
General and legal advice.

**Telegraph Hill Neighbourhood
Council**
170 New Cross Road
New Cross   SE14
Tel 732 9716/7
Legal and general advice including
welfare rights.

Welfare Rights Unit
Albany Centre
Douglas Way
Deptford SE8
Tel 692 0231
Benefit advice and appeal tribunal
representation.

Merton

**Collier's Wood Extension Citizens'
Advice Bureau**
Collier's Wood Community Centre
High Street
Collier's Wood SW19
Tel 542 6582
Advice and information.

**Merton & Morden Citizens' Advice
Bureau**
80 Kingston Road
Merton SW19
Tel 542 9061
Legal and general advice.

Merton Resource Centre
240 Merton Road
South Wimbledon SW19
Tel 542 6223
Legal advice.

**Wimbledon Citizens' Advice
Bureau**
30 Worple Road
Wimbledon SW19
Tel 947 4946/7
Legal and general advice including on
financial matters.

**Wimbledon Town Centre Co-
ordinating Group**
4 Hartfield Road
Wimbledon SW19
Tel 879 0446
Advice on Wimbledon town centre redevelopment proposals.

Southwark

The Advice Centre in the Blue
190 Southwark Park Road

Rotherhithe SE16
Tel 231 2471
Advice and information,
representation and advocacy.

Afro-Asian Advisory Service
Cambridge House
137 Camberwell Road
Camberwell SE5
Tel 701 0141
Advice on immigration and
nationality and welfare rights,
including representation and appeals.

**Bellenden Neighbourhood Advice
Centre**
Copleston Centre
Copleston Road
Bellenden SE15
Tel 639 8447
General and legal advice including
immigration and nationality.

Blackfriars Advice Centre
Blackfriars Settlement
44 Nelson Square
Blackfriars SE1
Tel 928 9521
Advice and information on
immigration, nationality, housing,
fuel and employment.

Blackfriars Advice Centre
56 Southwark Bridge Road
Borough SE1
Tel 928 6476
Welfare rights advice.

Cambridge House Legal Centre
137 Camberwell Road
Camberwell SE5
Tel 703 3051/701 9499
Legal advice and representation.

**Campaign to Improve London's
Transport**
Third Floor
Tress House
Stanford Street
Borough SE1
Tel 928 9179
Information and advice on improving
local public transport.

Consumer Advice Centre
376 Walworth Road
Walworth   SE17
Tel 703 5049/701 2044
Consumer advice for people who live
or work in Southwark.

**Lordship Lane Information &
Advice Centre**
29-35 Lordship Lane
Peckham Rye   SE22
Tel 299 1515/6
Advice and information.

Peckham Citizens' Advice Bureau
97 Peckham High Street
Peckham   SE15
Tel 639 4471/2
Advice and information.

**Pitt Street Settlement Information
Centre**
191 East Surrey Grove
Peckham   SE15
Tel 703 4775
General advice especially for young
people.

**Pitt Street Settlement Information
Centre**
Wickway Court Community Centre
North Peckham Estate
Peckham   SE15
Tel 707 5434
General advice.

**Southwark Citizens' Advice
Bureau**
York Mansions
199 Walworth Road
Walworth   SE17
Tel 703 4198
Legal and general advice including on
financial matters. Sessions for the
Vietnamese and Bengali communities.

**Southwark Council for Community
Relations**
352-354 Camberwell New Road
Peckham   SE5
Tel 274 8793
Advice and information.

**Southwark Information & Advice
Centre**
Town Hall
Peckham Road
Peckham   SE5
Tel 703 6311 ext 2165 or 2117

Southwark Law Project
Information & Advice Centre
29-35 Lordship Lane
Peckham Rye   SE22
Tel 299 1024
Legal advice and representation for
people with low incomes, ethnic
minorities and tenants.

Southwark Law Project
Bermondsey Health Centre
108 Grange Road
Bermondsey   SE16
Tel 299 1024
Legal advice and representation for
people with low incomes, ethnic
minorities and tenants.

**Walworth Advice & Community
Work Project**
186a Crampton Street
Walworth   SE17
Tel 701 1038
General and legal advice.

Wandsworth

**Advice & Legal Representation
Project**
Springfield Hospital
Glenburnie Road
Tooting   SW17
Tel 767 6884
Legal advice and representation for
patients in   Springfield
hospital.

Balham Citizens' Advice Bureau
143-145 Balham Hill
Balham   SW12
Tel 675 2040
General and legal advice and
information.

Battersea Citizens' Advice Bureau
177 Battersea High Street
Battersea   SW11
Tel 228 0272
Legal and general advice including
financial.

**Battersea Neighbourhood Aid
Centre**
22 Battersea Park Road
Battersea   SW11
Tel 720 9409
General and legal information and
advice. Advice sessions for young
people.

Doddington & Rollo Family Centre
253 Battersea Park Road
Battersea   SW11
Tel 720 2834/627 0678
Advice and information for local
tenants particularly on benefits, rent
arrears and housing problems. An
Asian interpreter is available.

Katherine Low Settlement
Battersea Citizens' Advice Bureau
177 Battersea High Street
Battersea   SW11
Tel 228 0272/223 2845
Legal advice.

**Roehampton Citizens' Advice
Bureau**
1 Portswood Place
Danebury Avenue
Roehampton   SW15
Tel 876 6909
Advice and information.

**Roehampton & Putney Community
Law Centre**
94a Putney High Street
Putney   SW15
Tel 789 8232
Legal advice.

Threshold Centre
101a Tooting High Street
Tooting   SW17
Tel 672 2162/767 2121
Housing advice including information
on benfits for single people and
childless couples.

Tooting & Balham Law Centre
107 Trinity Road
Tooting   SW17
Tel 767 7613/672 8749
Legal advice on welfare rights,
immigration, housing, juvenile crime,
domestic violence and consumer
problems for people who live in the
Springfield, Nightingale, Balham,
Bedford, Tooting, Furzedown and
Graveney areas.

**Tooting Bec Hospital Citizens'
Advice Bureau**
Tooting Bec Hospital
Tooting Bec Road
Tooting   SW17
Tel 767 5194
Advice and information for patients,
relatives and staff of the hospital.

**Wandsworth Citizens' Advice
Bureau**
609-613 York Road
Wandsworth   SW18
Tel 870 6552
Legal and general information
including financial.

**Wandsworth Council for
Community Relations**
Neighbourhood Centre
248 Lavender Hill
Battersea   SW11
Tel 228 8532/3 223 5350
General and legal advice.

**Wandsworth Legal Resource
Project**
248 Lavender Hill
Battersea   SW11
Tel 228 2566/9462
Legal advice. 24 hour emergency
service.

Wandsworth Legal Resource Project
Balham Family Centre
91 Bedford Hill
Balham   SW12
Tel 228 9462
Legal advice.

Wandsworth Legal Resource Project
347 Garratt Lane
Earlsfield   SW18
Tel 228 9462
Legal advice.

Wandsworth Legal Resource Project
The Open Door Community Centre
Beaumont Road
Southfields   SW19
Tel 228 9462
Legal advice.

Wandsworth Legal Resource Project
Roehampton Family Centre
1 Portswood Place
Danebury Avenue
Roehampton   SW15
Tel 228 9462
Legal advice.

Wandsworth Legal Resource Project
92c St John's Hill
Battersea   SW11
Tel 228 9462
Legal advice.

Wandsworth Legal Resource Project
Threshold Centre
101a Tooting High Street
Tooting   SW17
Tel 228 9462
Legal Advice.

Wandsworth Legal Resource Project
York Library
Wye Street
Battersea   SW11
Tel 228 9462

Police Stations

If the telephone number of a police station below ends in 12 tell the operator the name of the police station you want and what your enquiry is about.

Greenwich Police Station
31 Royal Hill
Greenwich   SE10
Tel 853 8212

Eltham Police Station
20 Well Hall Road
Eltham   SE9
Tel 853 8212

Plumstead Police Station
216 Plumstead High Street
Plumstead   SE18
Tel 853 8212

Shooter's Hill Police Station
Shooter's Hill
Woolwich   SE18
Tel 853 8212

Thamesmead Estate Police Station
Titmus Avenue
Thamesmead Estate
Thamesmead   SE28
Tel 853 8651

Thamesmead Police Station
1 Tavey Bridge
Abbey Wood   SE2
Tel 310 0580

Westcombe Park Police Station
11 Combedale Road
Greenwich   SE10
Tel 853 8212

Woolwich Police Station
29 Market Street
Woolwich   SE18
Tel 853 8212

Lambeth

Brixton Police Station
367 Brixton Road
Brixton   SW9
Tel 326 1212

Clapham Police Station
51 Union Grove
Clapham   SW8
Tel 720 8011

Gypsy Hill Police Station
66 Central Hill
Gypsy Hill   SE19
Tel 761 1113

Kennington Police Station
49 Kennington Road
Kennington   SE11
Tel 928 6900

Streatham Police Station
101 Streatham High Road
Streatham   SW16
Tel 769 1113

Lewisham

Catford Police Station
333 Bromley Road
Catford   SE6
Tel 697 9212

Brockley Police Station
4 Howson Road
Brockley   SE4
Tel 853 6212

Deptford Police Station
116 Amersham Vale
Deptford   SE14
Tel 697 9212

Lee Police Station
418 Lee High Street
Lee   SE12
Tel 697 9212

Lewisham Police Station
2 Ladwell Road
Lewisham   SE13
Tel 697 9212

Merton

Wimbledon Police Station
Queens Road
Wimbledon   SW19
Tel 947 4141

Southwark

Southwark Police Station
323 Borough High Street
Borough   SE1
Tel 407 8044

Camberwell Police Station
22a Camberwell Church Street
Camberwell   SE5
Tel 703 0866/0844

Canter Street Police Station
292 Walworth Road
Walworth   SE17
Tel 703 0844

East Dulwich Police Station
173 Lordship Lane
East Dulwich   SE22
Tel 693 3366

Peckham Police Station
177 Pekcham High Street
Peckham   SE15
Tel 639 4333

Rotherhithe Police Station
99 Lower Road
Rotherhithe   SE16
Tel 237 0582

Wandsworth

Tooting Police Station
Mitcham Road
Tooting   SW17
Tel 672 9922

Earlsfield Police Station
522 Garratt Lane
Earlsfield   SW17
Tel 947 6121

Lavender Hill Police Station
Lavender Hill
Battersea   SW11
Tel 228 8565

Putney Police Station
215 Upper Richmond Road
Putney   SW15
Tel 788 1113

Wandsworth Police Station
146 High Street
Wandsworth   SW18
Tel 870 9011

Voluntary Service Councils

These are borough wide organisations
which act as umbrella groups for
voluntary organisations in their area.
They can give you information about
all kinds of voluntary and community
work which goes on in your borough,
and if you are considering setting up a
group yourself they will be able to
give you advice.

Greenwich Resource Centre
MacBean Centre
MacBean Street
Greenwich   SE18
Tel 854 9092

Lambeth Community Action
10 Bernays Grove
Brixton   SW9
Tel 737 3617

Voluntary Action Lewisham
120 Rushey Green
Catford   SE6
Tel 690 4343 ext 328

**Merton Council for Voluntary
Service**
c/o Volunteer Bureau
114 London Road
Morden
Tel 543 0099

**Southwark Council for Voluntary
Service**
135 Rye Lane
Peckham   SE15
Tel 732 3731

Wandsworth Community Forum
177 Battersea High Street
Battersea   SW11
Tel 228 0799

Volunteer·Bureaux

These are borough based
organisations which have contact
with a network of volunteers who
work in the community.

Greenwich Volunteer Bureau
Building A
MacBean Centre
MacBean Street
Greenwich   SE18
Tel 854 5499

Lambeth has no volunteer bureau.

Lewisham Volunteer Bureau
120 Rushey Green
Catford   SE6
Tel 690 4343

Merton Volunteer Bureau
114 London Road
Morden
Tel 543 0099

Southwark Volunteer Bureau
135 Rye Lane
Peckham   SE15
Tel 732 5729

Wandsworth Volunteer Bureau
170 Garratt Lane
Wandsworth   SW18
Tel 870 4319

Town Halls

Some council departments are spread
in different buildings all over the

borough. Others are concentrated in a single area. But you can find out where the department you want is by contacting your town hall.

Greenwich Town Hall
Town Hall
29-37 Wellington Street
Woolwich   SE18
Tel 854 8888

Lambeth Town Hall
Brixton Hill
Brixton   SW2
Tel 274 7722

Lewisham Town Hall
Catford Road
Catford   SE6
Tel 690 4343

Merton Town Hall
Crown House
London Road
Morden
Tel 543 2222

Southwark Town Hall
Peckham Road
Camberwell   SE5
Tel 703 6311

Wandsworth Town Hall
Wandsworth High Street
Wandsworth   SW18
Tel 871 6000

Job Centres

Greenwich

Eltham Job Centre
4-9 Pound Place
Eltham High Street
Eltham   SE9
Tel 859 5711

Woolwich Job Centre
First Floor
115-123 Powis Street
Woolwich   SE18
Tel 854 5333

Lambeth

Brixton Job Centre
422 Brixton Road
Brixton   SW9
Tel 733 5522

Stockwell Job Centre
219-221 Clapham Road
Stockwell   SW9
Tel 733 6261

Streatham Job Centre
103-105 Streatham High Road
Streatham   SW16
Tel 677 1221

West Norwood Job Centre
19-21 Knight Hill
West Norwood   SE27
Tel 761 1461

Lewisham

Catford Job Centre
62-66 Rushey Green
Catford   SE6
Tel 690 9811

Deptford Job Centre
124 Deptford High Street
Deptford   SE8
Tel 691 8723

Lewisham Job Centre
97-99 Lewisham High Street
Lewisham   SE13
Tel 318 7174

Merton

Mitcham Job Centre
246-248 London Road
Mitcham
Tel 640 7221

Morden Job Centre
41 London Road
Morden
Tel 640 2953

Wimbledon Job Centre
56 Wimbledon Hill Road
Wimbledon   SW19
Tel 947 6694

Southwark

Bermondsey Job Centre
Brunel Road
Rotherhithe   SE16
Tel 237 2864

Borough Job Centre
92-94 Borough High Street
Borough   SE1
Tel 403 2055

Peckham Job Centre
128 Rye Lane
Peckham   SE15
Tel 732 3605

Wandsworth

Balham Job Centre
122-126 Balham High Road
Balham   SW12
Tel 673 2193/9

Clapham Job Centre
Woburn House
155 Falcon Road
Clapham Jct   SW11
Tel 350 1011

Tooting Broadway
24 Mitcham Road
Tooting Broadway
Tooting   SW17
Tel 767 3414

MARKETS

Markets are curious institutions - some appear rock solid, integrated and essential to the community while others seem to be frail and dogged by instability. Certainly, since we started researching this section, some have fallen by the wayside and a few others seem to be following suit. At the same time, however, new ones have emerged and appear to be doing good business. Let's hope this will continue. Markets are not only more fun than regular shops but goods are often more attractive both in price and quality. Most large markets can usually be relied upon to offer a range of china, kitchenware, household goods, hardware and tools. Handbags, earrings, cosmetics, new and second hand clothes, bikinis, nighties, bras and shoes appear to be today's typical market merchandise for women. Wool, haberdashery and trimmings, lace curtain material, fabrics, cheap greetings cards and stationery, toys, foam rubber, vacuum cleaner spares and pet supplies are much in evidence too. Then, of course, there are the edibles - confectionery, tinned and frozen foods, fruit and veg, meat (often sold from a lorry), wet fish and shellfish.

We have selected some markets which we feel are impressive for certain items either because of quality, value or choice. In many cases these items are available at other markets (see main listings), so regard this list as our selection not as comprehensive.

Antiques
- Greenwich Antiques
- New Caledonian

Bed Linen
- Brixton
- Broadway
- Nine Elms

Books (second hand)
- Broadway (romantic novels)
- Continental
- Deptford
- Tooting

Bric a Brac
- Brixton
- Deptford

- East Street
- Greenwich Antiques
- Lewisham Bric a Brac
- Westmoreland Road

Car Seat Covers
- Deptford
- East Street

Cheese
- Brixton
- East Street

Clothes
- Brixton
- Deptford
- Greenwich Antiques

Clothes (men's new)
- Deptford (sweaters)
- Lewisham Model (leather clothing)
- Lower Marsh (T-shirts)
- Rushey Green (shirts)
- Tooting

Clothes (women's new)
- Deptford
- Lewisham Model (leather clothing)
- Lower Marsh (T-shirts)
- Nine Elms
- Southwark Park
- Wimbledon Speedway

Crafts
- Greenwich Arts & Crafts

Fruit & Veg
- Brixton
- East Street
- Lewisham Outdoor
- Northcote Road
- Wimbledon Speedway
- Woolwich

Hats
- Broadway
- Catford Broadway
- Deptford
- East Street

Jewellery
- Battersea Arts Centre

- Greenwich Antiques
- Greenwich Arts & Crafts

Meat
- Brixton
- Nine Elms

Nuts Raisins & Muesli
- Brixton
- Catford Broadway
- Grove Park
- Nine Elms

Plants
- Brixton
- East Street
- Nine Elms
- Southwark Park

Records (second hand)
- Broadway
- Brixton
- Lewisham Model
- Putney High Street
- Tooting
- Westmoreland Road

Socks
- Brixton

Sports Equipment
- Deptford (darts accessories)
- East Street (fishing tackle)
- Lower Marsh (squash & badminton etc)
- Nine Elms (martial arts accessories)
- Oval (darts accessories)
- Westmoreland Road (fishing tackle)

Tablecloths
- Grove Park

Tools (second hand)
- East Street
- Westmoreland Road

Other Items
- African & Indian objects (Brixton)
- African printed fabrics (Brixton)
- Aquarium accessories (Putney High Street)
- Babies jackets (East Street & Greenwich Arts & Crafts)

- Babies knitwear (Battersea Arts Centre)
- Cakes & savouries (Putney High Street)
- Cushions & pillows (Nine Elms)
- Cycle accessories (East Street)
- Dr Marten's boots (Plumstead)
- Fortune-telling (Broadway)
- Hair products (Brixton)
- Home-Brewing supplies (Plumstead & Broadway)

- Jamaican patties (Brixton)
- Knitwear (Greenwich Arts & Crafts)
- Pickles (East Street)
- Pizzas (Brixton)
- Prams (Rye Lane Bargain Centre)
- Rock salt (East Street)
- Sarsaparila (East Street)
- Silk flowers (East Street)
- Terracotta pots (Northcote Road)
- Trays & chopping boards (Putney High Street & Lower Marsh)
- Vacuum cleaner repairs (Broadway)
- Video tapes (East Street)
- Washing machine repairs (Broadway)
- West Indian jams etc (Battersea Arts Centre)
- Wigs (Brixton)

Although the many markets officially function most of the week, don't bank on stallholders always being there, especially if the weather is grotty. Unless otherwise stated, as a general rule, Saturday is the busiest day and the day when stallholders are most likely to turn up. The main directory does not include any of the many individual stalls that are scattered around South London. There is not the space to list everything that's available in each market but we have tried to mention the more unusual merchandise. South London has some wonderful markets. We have marked those we reckon to be the tops with a ●. In this main directory, the markets are numbered but listed by post code. The alphabetical index at the end of the chapter will give you the position of each market in the directory.

SE1

1 Lower Marsh
Open 10-2(Mon-Fri and a few stalls on Sat)
This is principally a lunch-time market whose busiest days are Tuesdays, Thursdays and Fridays. Stalls offer fruit and veg, household and general merchandise, china, handbags, clothing (several nightwear stands), vacuum cleaner parts, haberdashery, bras and babies' clothes. One stall specialises in cheap T-shirts, and some of the less common items on sale include silk flowers, squash and badminton rackets, darts and other sports' accessories, chamois leather and purses, table mats, trays and chopping boards, brass door fittings, screws and tools and some rather unusual soft toys. There's the odd bric a brac stall and, on the right near the end (going towards Westminster Bridge Road), an off-street area offers earrings, buttons and wool, and rails and rails of new, fashionable women's clothes.

2 National Theatre Market
in front of the theatre
Open 10-8(Wed Thur Sat & for extra matinees)
Arts and crafts, bric a brac, books and prints.

3 New Caledonian Market*
Bermondsey Square
Long Lane
Bermondsey Street
Open 7-4(Fri only) Dealers start
trading at 3 in the morning
Huge, busy antique market for dealers
and tourists. Glass, silver, brass, maps,
prints, furniture, antiquarian books,
bric a brac etc. Not to be missed by
antique lovers, though it's advisable
to get there early for the best stuff.
The main market is in Bermondsey
Square with indoor and outdoor areas
in Long Lane and Bermondsey Street.
Beware the traffic wardens who
populate the area in numbers. There is
talk of moving the market to a new,
larger site which seems a great shame.
All letters of protest (or support) to
Southwark Council.

4 Royal Festival Hall Craft Market
Red Level 3
Open 10-10(Sat-Sun most weekends)
Small craft market with handmade
crafts such as knitwear, printed
fabrics, quilting, jewellery, wooden
bowls and ceramics. From January
1986, there will be vacancies for
craftworkers, subject to their work
being accepted by a selection panel.

5 Tower Bridge Road
Open Mon-Sat (Thur am only)
Just a few stalls selling fruit, veg, eggs
and household merchandise.

SE5

6 Franklin's Antique Market
Camberwell Road (near Wyndham
Road)
Open 10-6(Tue-Sat) 1-6(Sun)
Despite it's name, not really a market
but a group of antique traders selling
rather over-priced furniture, brass,
mirrors, fireplace equipment, prints
and other items. Great cafe serving
food and snacks and a traditional
Sunday lunch.

SE6

7 Catford Broadway Market
Open Fri-Sat
Mixed market in pedestrian precinct
offering the usual market produce.
T-shirts, leather jackets and other
clothes, and a stall selling soft caps.
Pet foods, wool, hardware, trimmings,
eggs, flowers, fruit, veg and
wholefoods are all available.

8 Rushey Green Market
off Rushey Green opposite
McDonalds
Open Mon Thur-Sat
Modern market mainly selling high
street fashion for women. Also
earrings, some interesting designs in
men's shirts, greetings cards, linen,
pet foods, plants and other typical
market produce. There have been
rumours that this market might be
closing but at the time of going to
press it was still very much alive.

SE8

9 Deptford Covered Market
Deptford High Street (on left walking
from Deptford Broadway in old Marks
& Spencer building)
Open Mon-Sat
Rather stuffy, drab indoor market
selling a variety of goods. A sharp
contrast to the outdoor street market.

10 Deptford Market*
Open Fri-Sat (Douglas Way)
Sat only (Deptford High Street)
Huge, busy local market with great
atmosphere. Deptford High Street has
general produce and some excellent
new clothes (with an apparent
speciality in bras, bikinis and men's
sweaters). Some of the more unusual
stalls offer darts' accessories,
lampshades, wickerwork, fake fur car
seat covers, hats and garden
furniture. On the left half-way down
the High Street (coming from
Deptford Broadway) is Douglas Way
which has many busy general stalls

and a clearing off it which is packed with stalls and tables full of cheap jumble and bric a brac. Further down the High Street also on the left is a small yard with a few stalls and one, in particular, selling second-hand paperbacks.

(When you go, don't miss the tiny wholefood shop on the left hand side - a treat for anyone who's into pulses, herbs, spices and wholefoods).

SE10

11 Greenwich Antique Market*
corner of Greenwich High Road & Stockwell Street
Open 7.30-4 Sat (Sun also in summer)
For the pick of the best get there around 7.30am. Lots of old china, antiquarian books, forties' and other period clothes, jewellery (including stall of stunning modern Mexican jewellery), a few bits of furniture, clocks and watches, stamps, coins and medals and general bric a brac.

12 Greenwich Arts & Crafts Market*
off College Approach in covered wholesale veg market
Open Sat-Sun
Fairly new market of about eighty stalls which looks very much like Greenwich's version of Covent Garden. It too occupies the premises of an early morning wholesale veg market and the weekend market stalls are surrounded by trendy little shops. Shoppers and stallholders are entertained by the occasional street performer and the whole market area feels modern and alive. The quality of the crafts is exceptionally high and many of the crafts and designs are stylish and interesting. Goods tend to change every week but there are usually some fine handmade jewellery, appliqued jackets, knitwear, leather belts, silk scarves, satin cushions and many other unusual items. This is an excellent market for presents and, when you've visited the other two local markets, you can enjoy a leisurely stroll around Greenwich - an area that seems far removed from inner city London.

13 Greenwich Central Market
Stockwell Street by service station
Open Sat-Sun
New general market which will undoubtedly increase in size. At present, stalls offer clothes, fabrics, haberdashery, wool, shellfish, plants and other merchandise.

SE11

14 Lambeth Walk
Open Mon-Sat(Thur am only)
Small local market selling household goods, flowers and plants, eggs and other foods. Sometimes bric a brac also.

15 Oval Market
Oval Cricket Ground (Vauxhall Gates)
Open Sun am
Small, quiet market selling confectionery, knitwear, clothes, plants, pictures, second hand paperbacks, darts' accessories and bric a brac. Needs a lot more stalls which is sad because it's a good space and well worth developing as a market area.

SE12

16 Grove Park Market
Baring Hall Hotel Car Park (opp
Grove Park Station)
Open Fri only
Modern market which has mainly
clothing (lots of T-shirts and
nighties), earrings, handbags, bargain
shoes, toys, cards and household
goods. Also, a meat lorry, a fruit and
veg stall, another selling nuts, raisins,
muesli and sugar-free jams, and,
unexpectedly, one bedecked with
Spanish table cloths.

SE13

17 Lewisham Bric a Brac Market
Riverdale Hall Leisure Centre
Riverdale Centre (entry via High
Street or Rennell Street)
Open Mon only
General bric a brac and a few
antiques. Has the leisurely
atmosphere of a village hall event
rather than an inner city market.

18 Lewisham Covered Market
opp Lewisham Clock Tower in RACs
bldg
Open Mon-Sat
Several units selling clothes,
jewellery repairs, furniture etc.
Rather tatty, uninspiring place.

19 Lewisham Model Market
behind C & A down alley off High St
Open Mon-Sat(closed Thur)
Busy general market with good
atmosphere. Some food, clothes,
leather jackets, skirts etc), earrings,
cheap second hand records, fabrics,
pet supplies and haberdashery.

20 Lewisham Outdoor Market
Lewisham High Street (in front of
Riverdale Centre)
Open Mon-Sat
Long line of stalls selling good
quality fruit and veg, flowers, men's
clothing, fish, haberdashery and
other merchandise.

SE15

21 Bray Shopping Centre
137-141 Rye Lane
Open Mon-Sat(no early closing)
Included because it's apparently
known locally as a market although it
didn't seem like one to us. Lots of
units selling clothes (especially T-
shirts) and shoes. Freezer centre.

22 Choumert Road
off Rye Lane
Open Mon-Sat
Small popular local market, mainly
fruit, veg and flowers. Some clothes.

23 Rye Lane Bargain Centre
48 Rye Lane
Open Mon-Sat (Thur am only)
Surprisingly large, busy indoor
market. Units offer clothes, toys,
haberdashery, lace curtains, fabrics,
household goods, cookers, china, meat
and veg. There's a large pram stall,
another selling Dunlopillo and foam,
and a unit where you can spend all
your money on bingo instead.

SE16

24 Southwark Park Road Market*
Southwark Park Road.
Open Mon-Sat
Popular medium-sized local market
selling general and household goods,
fish, fruit & veg, cakes and
confectionery, excellent plants and
bulbs, vacuum cleaner spares, pet
foods, wool, cosmetics, shoes, nighties
and other clothes etc. On Saturday
there's a stall (which goes to Camden
Lock on Sundays), selling particularly
stylish high street fashion.

SE17

25 East Street*
off Walworth Road

Open Tue Thur am Fri Sat Sun am East Street's regular stallholders are there on Tuesdays, Thursdays, Saturdays and Sundays. On Fridays, the market has a slightly different flavour when casual traders replace the regular ones. There are often factory sell-offs and one-off bargains on a Friday. The liveliest time of all for East Street is Sunday morning when the local shops as well as the street are alive with bustle and excitement and when regulars and casual stallholders turn out in force. This is a wonderful market which has everything you might expect except modern china. Items on offer include lace, haberdashery, lamps, shoe polish and accessories, silk flowers, ribbons and trimmings, hats, car seat covers, garden furniture, fishing tackle, pickles, vacuum cleaner parts and coffee beans. At the Walworth Road end there's a marvellous cheese stall with masses of different kinds of cheeses, and halfway down on the right is a clearing where, on Sundays, you can buy roses, conifers, herbs and other plants at fantastically low prices. Back on East Street, near the end, is a stallholder selling beautiful reversible handmade cotton babies' jackets, another selling sarsparilla to refresh you, and a third offering rock salt cream or crystals to comfort your corns, bunions or sore feet after your long struggle through the market. At about this point, if you are there on a Sunday, you should turn left or right into Dawes Street. Turn left and you will find a street full of jumble and a yard off it full of even more, with a selection of the most extraordinary bric a brac. Slightly more upmarket items (forgive the pun) can be found in a narrow, cramped shed, through which you have to push your way with patience and resolve. Back on East Street, if you instead turn right down Dawes Street, there are a few stalls selling clothing, cycle bits and cheap blank video and audio tapes. East Street on a Sunday is not to be missed.

26 Westmoreland Road
off Walworth Road
Open Tue-Sat(Thur am only)
Small market selling fruit and veg, fresh fish and poultry, toys, household goods, haberdashery, knitwear, children's clothes etc.
Bric a Brac Market*
Open Sun am
Small, relaxed market of friendly stallholders offering an array of genuine bric a brac and jumble with tempting cries of 'nothing over 50p' and 'All LPs at 10p'. It's best to get there early (say, between 7.30 and 8.30) if you're a serious bargain hunter. It's also excellent for second hand DIY and gardening tools (a marvellous stall sells bags of nails, door hinges, heavy duty polythene etc.). Another has fishing tackle and bait and there are a few stalls offering shellfish, fruit, veg, plants and flowers.

SE18

27 Plumstead Covered Market
Plumstead Road (near Woolwich Market)
Open Mon-Sat (only a few stalls Thur am closed Thur pm)
Large covered area of units offering general merchandise, clothing, fabrics, pet supplies, meat, ham and cheese. There's also a home-brewing stand and another selling a selection of Dr Marten's boots. The hot drinks lady makes a good cuppa.

28 Woolwich Market
Beresford Square
Open Mon-Sat(Thur am only)
Large, busy market selling lots of good-looking fruit and veg. Also, wet fish, household goods, flowers and plants, electrical fittings, spectacles (you take your prescription along) and general market merchandise. Sometimes bric a brac too (usually on a Thursday).

SE19

29 Crystal Palace Collectors Market
Jasper Road
Open 9-4(Tue-Sat) 10-3(Sun)
Rather dull indoor market on two floors offering lots of bric a brac and other 'collectables'.

SE20

30 Maple Road Market
Open Tue-Sat(Wed am only)
Small local market, mainly fruit, veg and flowers. Exceptional pet stall offering fresh meat to local dogs.

SE27

31 Thurlow Arms Car Park
Junction of Norwood & Robson Roads
Open Thur only
Small, lively general market. Wet fish, fresh farm eggs, cheap cards, earrings, plants, nighties and other mixed merchandise.

SW8

32 Nine Elms*
New Covent Garden near Telecom bldg
Open 9-2 Sun (sometimes till 4)
Large, lively, spacious modern best of its kind in South London and definitely the place to go if you forgot to buy the Sunday joint or want to fill your freezer with huge quanitites of meat. Prices are keen and quality appears high. From their lorries traders sell pots and pans, china, household goods and tinned food with the aid of wit and microphone. There are earrings and some stylish clothes, market garden produce, foam cut to size, pillows and cushions ready-made or made to order, towels and bed linen, and garden furniture. Also a few good-looking fruit and veg stalls and, more unusually, a nut and raisin stall and another offering martial arts' accessories.

SW9

33 Brixton Market*
Open Mon-Sat (Wed am only)
Huge wonderful market covering many streets and arcades.
Brixton Station Road
At the High Street end of Brixton Station Road there's a good plant and cut flowers stall and, as you walk up the road, you can buy bed linen, household goods, cassettes and African and Indian objects. Half way down Brixton Station Road the stalls become laden with second hand clothes and bric a brac (best days Friday and Saturday). This is a real haven if you're looking for second hand china, pots and pans and lampshades or clothes from any period. One stall offers a good selection of fifties clothing and there's an excellent well-organised record stall.
Pope's Road
Cheap European & Afro-Caribbean fruit and veg (especially good salad stalls), wigs, jewellery, beans and pulses and some new clothing and shoes. In an adjoining arch there's a good fruit and veg stall and another selling bedding plants.
Granville Arcade
(between Atlantic Road, Coldharbour Lane & Pope's Road)
Busy covered market with skylights and stalls opening on to 'avenues'. You will find a wide range of fresh food, meat, fish, cheese and eggs of every description, mostly Afro-Caribbean in origin. Also, hair pieces and wigs in natural and bright colours, hair care products and cosmetics in abundance and record shops specialising in reggae, African, Latin and Soca. There are clothes, pet goods and some beautiful printed African fabrics too. Don't forget to stop and have a Jamaican pattie at D-Bess.
Electric Avenue
All types of fruit and veg (you'll be spoilt for choice and price) and

clothes, plants and sewing accessories at the High Street end.
Market Row
(access on Atlantic Road, Electric & Coldharbour Lanes)
Italian shoes, ornate decor for the home (of the kitsch variety), good sock stall, clothes, fresh fish, meat, cheese, eggs, veg, calculators, watches, lighters, cheap mugs and kitchenware. Also excellent pizza cafe and motorized rocking horse.
Reliance Arcade
(entrances on Electric Lane & High Street)
Bargain bed linen, religious objects, shoes, radios, calculators, lighters, fresh produce, plants, clothes and jewellery.

SW11

34 Battersea Arts Centre Craft Market
Old Town Hall Lavender Hill
Open 11-4 Sun (closed mid Aug-mid Sept)
Very small market offering home-made crafts at good prices. Some fine jewellery, soft toys, tempting West Indian jams and chutneys and unusual children's knitwear. This market expands to two larger events - over the May Day weekend and usually during the first weekend in December (see Festivals & Events).

35 Battersea High Street
Open Mon-Sat(Wed am only)
At the time of going to press, the council has just completed extensive work in Battersea High Street, widening the road and improving the area. The plan is to increase the market plots to twenty-seven. It was previously a small, rather lifeless market selling the usual fruit, veg, fish and meat, so it will be interesting to see its 'new face' once it is established.

36 Northcote Road
Open Mon-Sat(Wed am only)

Alongside the busy local shops, this market is very much part of the community. Mainly fruit and veg (excellent quality) and a few stalls selling eggs, fish, household goods, flowers and fabrics. In amongst this lot, a stall selling handsome, reasonably-priced terracotta pots comes as something of a surprise.

37 St John's Hill
Clapham Junction
Open Fri & Sat
Rather ordinary modern market selling fashion jewellery and clothing (bikinis and nighties again), cosmetics, shoes, records, sports accessories, tools, net curtain material and meat from a lorry. This site has been earmarked for development for many years, so its future isn't entirely secure.

SW12

38 Continental Market
Bedford Hill (Balham end)
Open Mon-Sat(Wed am only)
Quiet, rather unexciting indoor market which has, amazingly, been in existence for the last fifty years. Units offer shoe repairs and key cutting, West Indian grocery provisions and greengrocery. Also haberdashery and old-fashioned lingerie, second hand books (well worth looking at) and a little bric a brac. Although it has character, this market has rather an abandoned feel to it and definitely needs waking up.

39 Hildreth Street
Open Mon-Sat(Wed am only)
Small friendly local market almost exclusively selling fruit and veg (some Afro-Caribbean produce). Also fish, eggs, household goods, cards, flowers and basketry.

SW15

40 Putney High Street*
(down alley near Lacy Road)

Open Fri-Sat
Busy medium-sized market with pleasant atmosphere. Here you can buy the usual market produce - household goods, pet supplies, confectionery, clothes (yet another bikini stall), hoover parts, fresh fish and meat sold from lorries, second hand records and other merchandise. More unusually, there's a stall offering trays and chopping boards, another selling aquarium accessories, a bread stall and two stalls adorned with homemade goodies - one with mostly savoury delicacies made by a small local catering group and the other with tempting home-baked cakes and sweets, made by a French woman (who's sometimes at Wimbledon Speedway Stadium market on Sundays). This is definitely where to be if you're feeling peckish! It is sad to have to report that this market is threatened by a proposed development which would replace it with a multi-storey car park and a massive shopping precinct. There is a suggestion that there will be space in the precinct for lock-up market units but stallholders would be expected to move out for a year or two while the complex is being built. Hopefully, there will be enough local opposition to prevent the redevelopment taking place.

SW17

41 Broadway Market*
Tooting High Street
Open Mon-Sat(Wed am only)
A marvellous covered market with an old-fashioned, solid feel to it. Haberdashery, cut-price cards, general and wedding stationery, fruit, veg and grocery provisions (both European and ethnic), meat and fish, eggs, sportswear, hardware, fashion jewellery, wool, pet supplies, net curtains, bedlinen, lingerie, material, belts and purses, foam rubber, flowers, records (good reggae stock) and lots of rather out-of-date clothing with a hat stall to match. The more out-of-the-ordinary stalls offer home-brewing equipment, washing machine & vacuum cleaner repairs, second hand paperbacks (romantic novels in the main) and fortunetelling (tarot, clairvoyance, palmistry, I Ching, Rines, astrology) and Bach flower remedies are all on offer. A wonderful place.

42 Tooting Market
Tooting High Street
Open Mon-Sat(Wed am only)
Another covered market much like Broadway Market but not quite as lively. Fruit and veg, china and kitchenware, material and trimmings, toys, cards and wedding stationery, nails and screws, cosmetics, handbags, pet supplies, meat, fish and cheese. (On the days we've been here, the cheese has been cheaper than at Broadway.) There's also a wide range of second hand paperbacks and a good wool stall. More unusual goods on offer include brass and copper objects, Irish and American country music and a small selection of prams, cots and buggies.

SW19

43 Wimbledon Speedway Stadium
Plough Lane (in car park)
Open 8-2(Sun)
Crowded modern market selling many wares including meat, shellfish, frozen foods, household gadgets, kitchenware, toys, spectacles, lots of clothes at good prices and a small amount of good-looking fruit and veg. The Putney High Street stall of French patisseries sometimes comes here too.

To conclude this chapter, we asked one of our contributors to take an atmospheric look at South London's most famous market:

While Brixton Market attracts tourists from all over the world (Japanese, French, Germans, Americans and Australians, camera in hand, stalking through the market with the ever hopeful thought of catching a crazed youth throwing a brick at a passing police car), it is first and foremost a market for the local community. As you enter the main market area your senses are seduced or bombarded (depending on your mood) by smells, music, colours and the rich and colourful language and dialects of the African, Caribbean, Asian, Greek and English stallholders. On walking through, you can see that it's a bubbling, bouncing place where the range of Afro-Caribbean and African goods are second to none in London. From the bright African fabrics with patterns you cannot imagine to the latest Jamaican Dub import, luscious fruit and veg are on display everywhere — mangoes, sugar cane, guavas, pineapples, bananas, melons, yam, dashin, sweet potatoes, pumpkins, breadfruit, peppers, okra, to name just a few. Herbs and spices abound. Fish upon pungent fish, mackerel, sprat and shark(?!). Meat includes the ever-popular goat, oxtail, pig foot and, of course, chicken. Just a hint of music from all Afro-Caribbean corners of the world — reggae, soca, calypso, ju-ju, highlife, soul, jazz and blues, pumping out from one or more of the three or four record booths that occupy the market place. You can sense the atmosphere for yourself. An integral part of Brixton — visit it!

Alphabetical Market Index

Battersea Arts Centre 34
Battersea High Street 35
Bray Shopping Centre 21
Brixton 33
Broadway 41
Catford Broadway 7
Choumert Road 22
Continental 38
Crystal Palace Collectors 29
Deptford 10
Deptford Covered 9
East Street 25
Franklin's Antique 6
Greenwich Antique 11
Greenwich Arts & Crafts 12
Greenwich Central 13
Grove Park 16
Hildreth Street 39
Lambeth Walk 14
Lewisham Bric a Brac 17
Lewisham Covered 18
Lewisham Model 19

Lewisham Outdoor 20
Lower Marsh 1
Maple Road 30
National Theatre 2
New Caledonian 3
Nine Elms 32
Northcote Road 36
Oval 15
Plumstead Covered 27
Putney High Street 40
Royal Festival Hall 4
Rushey Green 8
Rye Lane Bargain Centre 23
St John's Hill 37
Southwark Park Road 24
Thurlow Arms 31
Tooting 42
Tower Bridge Road 5
Westmoreland Road 26
Wimbledon Speedway Stadium 43
Woolwich 28

MUSEUMS

This section contains details of over thirty museums, places of interest, and special collections in South London. The future promises lots of new small archives as well as some large-scale, nationally important projects such as The Black Cultural Archives whose home will one day be in Somerleyton Road in Brixton. The plan is to build a large cultural centre (containing a museum, library, bookshop, conference theatre and art galleries), which will focus on the culture of African peoples from Britain, the Caribbean, Africa and America, and document the Black contribution to world as well as British history. Although there is still a long way to go and a lot of money to raise, the idea of BCA has engendered a great deal of enthusiasm and voluntary activity to raise funds and collect archival material. Anyone interested in helping should contact The Black Cultural Archives, c/o Coldharbour Works, 245a Coldharbour Lane, SW9. Tel 274 7700 Another important future South London archive is The Museum of

The Moving Image, scheduled to open next to the NFT in the winter of 1987. There are to be over twenty sections in the permanent collection, covering pre-cinema history and the development of the film industry, film production techniques, the invention and history of television (this section will include an operational TV control room), and an animation workshop for children. There are to be live talks, evening showings of classics from the National Film Archive, and special exhibitions once or twice a year.
More of these projects in our next edition!

Bakelite Museum
12 Mundania Road
East Dulwich   SE22
Tel 691 2240
Open by appointment but 12-9(Tue) can usually be arranged
Wheelchair access none
Admission free
For lovers of vintage and contemporary plastics, this is a dream

of a museum - alive with enthusiasm, relaxed and informal, and crammed with amazing objects. Set in a handsome 1930s block, an entire flat is filled with around 7000 pieces - Bakelite radios, clocks, plastic umbrella handles, 'duck' clothes brushes, cups, plates of every colour and shape - some classic pieces, others bizarre, individualistic and amusing. Although many of the objects are Bakelite there are also plastics dating from their first invention in the 1860's until the 1960's and several present-day items. It is Patrick Cook whom we have to thank for collecting all these wonderful pieces over the past fifteen years and he and his colleagues deserve a special mention too for their spirit and welcome which make the museum an even more delightful place to visit. Enthusiasts of plastics should be sure to join The Bakelite Museum Society (at the same address), which produces an excellent magazine, called Plastiche, and arranges frequent events for members such as outings to places of interest, discussions, meetings and an annual 'Bakelite Picnic'.

Bakelite Museum

The Bear Gardens Museum of the Shakespearean Stage
1 Bear Gardens
Bankside　　　　　　　　SE1
Tel 928 6342

Open 10-5.30(Tue-Sat) 2-6(Sun)
Wheelchair access difficult
Admission £1(adults) 50p(OAPs students children unwaged)

The Bear Gardens Museum of The Shakespearean Stage (less than a hundred yards from where The Globe Theatre once stood in Bankside) charts the history of the Elizabethan and Jacobean stage and, with the aid of models and other visual material, tells the story of the playhouses, players and audiences from 1576 to 1642 and of Bankside's vibrant and colourful past. Bankside experienced its heyday as an entertainment area in the 16th and 17th centuries when thousands of Londoners and visitors flocked south across the river to enjoy the bear-baiting and brothels (or 'stewes' as they were known). Any over-indulgent revellers soon found themselves sobering up in the local Clink Prison. Bankside was the home of five great outdoor playhouses, the most famous of which was The Globe, 'The glory of the Bank', built in 1599, where many of Shakespeare's best-known plays were performed. In 1613, during a performance of Henry VIII, an over-zealous stage hand went OTT with the gunpowder when filling a cannon, and the theatre went up in smoke. A second Globe was built on the same site and flourished for thirty years until the Civil War. The area declined when the Puritans closed the playhouses in 1642 and, after the Restoration, the West End became London's theatreland. During the 18th and 19th centuries Bankside became a thriving commercial centre but life was finally sucked out of the area when the docks closed about fifteen years ago. Since this time, however, members of The Shakespeare Globe Trust (headed by actor/producer Sam Wanamaker) have been struggling to revive the cultural and community life of Bankside by planning a third Globe Theatre (see Theatre).

Brixton Windmill

Brixton Windmill
Blenheim Gardens
off Brixton Hill
Brixton SW2
Tel 673 5398 Mr Jerome
Open 9am until an hour before sunset
Wheelchair access none
Admission free but a small charge
may be introduced

Brixton Windmill was built in 1816
for the Ashby family who were
millers. It was driven entirely by wind
but, by 1862, the area had become so
built up the mill was no longer able to
function efficiently. The Ashbys
decided to transfer their business to
watermills in Mitcham. Two years
later, the sails were removed and the
windmill was used only for storage. In
1902, the Ashbys began using the mill
again and installed a steam engine
and, later, a gas one to drive the mill
stones. The mill continued to be used
until 1934 by which time the demand
for wholemeal flour had dwindled
considerably. The following year the
last member of the Ashby family (the
grandson of the original owner) died
and left the mill to his housekeeper to
be administered by a trust. In 1957 the
mill was bought by the LCC and in
1964 it was restored as close to its
original appearance as possible. The
mill was transferred to Lambeth
Council and, in 1985, was returned to
working order.

Brunel's Engine House
Tunnel Road
Rotherhithe SE16
Open 11-4(every Sun June-Sept)
11-4(1st Sunday of the month Oct-
May)
Wheelchair access not known
Admission free
Part of the works constructed in
1825/6 by Marc Isambard Brunel to
contain the steam engines which
drained the first underwater tunnel
in the world, the Thames Tunnel. The
tunnel was opened for pedestrians
but, in 1865, was sold to a railway
company. It now carries underground
trains from Rotherhithe to Wapping.
Visitors can see a large steam
pumping engine built by J & G Rennie
of Southwark and there is a display
describing the building of the Thames
Tunnel and the work of Marc Brunel.

Cuming Museum
First Floor
Newington District Library
Walworth Road
Elephant & Castle SE17
Tel 703 3324/5529/6514
Open 10-5.30(Mon-Fri till 7 on Thur)
10-5(Sat)
Wheelchair access difficult but
assistance given with prior notice
Admission free
Local boy Richard Cuming began
collecting things when he was given
three fossils and an Indian coin for his
fifth birthday in 1782. His collection
and that of his son were reputed to be
of considerable historical and
scientific significance and led to the
creation of a public museum
specialising in local archeological and
environmental history. Many items
relating to the local history of
Southwark illustrate its prehistoric
riverside beginnings, its much later
status as a small rural market town at
the foot of London Bridge, and today's
busy urban sprawl. Exhibits include

Roman sculptures (amongst which is a box for the ashes of a dead person), a hat badge from the time of Richard III, the water pump from the Marshalsea debtors' prison and some items associated with Dickens' connections with the borough. On show too is The Lovett Collection of charms and amulets which illustrate the past superstitions of Londoners. Also to be seen is a collection of plaster models by George Tinworth (1843 - 1913), who designed for Doulton, and some items relating to the scientist, Michael Faraday (1791 - 1867), who was born locally. The most significant objects from the collection are on permanent display along with temporary exhibitions, some of which are loaned by other museums.

Cutty Sark
King William Walk
Greenwich Pier
Greenwich   SE10
Tel 858 3445
Open 10-5(Mon-Sat) 12-5(Sun) Oct-April 10-6(Mon-Sat) 12-6(Sun) May-Sept
Wheelchair access to first deck
Admission £1.10(adults) 55p(children)
No unaccompanied children

The famous clipper ship, The Cutty Sark, is a magnificent sight, and enthusiasts of historical ships should certainly climb aboard to see her decks, quarters and collection of figureheads. Built in 1869 for a little

over £16,000, she sailed in both the China tea and Australian wool trades and was one of the fastest vessels of her day.

Gipsy Moth IV
King William Walk
Greenwich Pier
Greenwich   SE10
Tel 858 3445
Open 10-6(Mon-Sat) 12-6(Sun) May-Sept
Wheelchair access none
Admission 20p(adults) 10p(children)
Moored opposite the Cutty Sark on the other side of Greenwich Pier, Gipsy Moth IV looks tiny by comparison. It seems incredible that Sir Francis Chichester sailed right round the world in her. Built in 1966, she cost £35,000 - more than twice the price of her grand neighbour.

Greenwich Borough Museum
Plumstead Library
Plumstead   SE18
SE18
Tel 855 3240
Open 2-8(Mon) 10-1 2-5(Tue Thur Fri Sat)
Wheelchair access none
Admission free
Greenwich borough's local and natural history museum was formerly known as Plumstead Museum. Roman coins and a huge collection of interesting items found in, or relating to, the borough are on permanent display and there is a regular programme of temporary exhibitions.

HMS Belfast
Symons Wharf
Vine Lane   SE1
Tel 407 6434
Open 11-5.20(daily Mar-31 Oct)
11-4(daily 1 Nov-19 Mar)

Wheelchair access none
Admission £2(adults) £1(children OAPs)

London Bridge   SE1

The 11,000 ton cruiser, HMS Belfast, was launched in 1938 and badly damaged a year later by a German magnetic mine in the Firth of Forth. Following an almost complete rebuild, she rejoined the Home Fleet in November 1942. She helped to cover convoys to Russia and played a key role in the Battle of North Cape in December 1943. In June 1944, she led the cruiser bombardment which supported the Allied landings on D-Day. The rest of her war career was spent in the Far East where she returned after extensive modernisation in the fifties. Her active career ended in 1963. The Imperial War Museum fought to save her from the scrapyard and she now stands in pristine shape in Symons Wharf for the admiration of her ship-loving visitors.

Horniman Museum

100 London Road
SE23
Tel 699 1872/2339/4911
Open 10.30-6(Mon-Sat) 2-6(Sun)
Wheelchair access to ground floor by prior arrangement
Admission free

Forest Hill   **SE23**

The Horniman Museum is housed in a fine Art Nouveau building designed by C. Harrison Townsend in 1901, on the front of which is a huge mosaic panel by Robert Anning Bell, depicting the course of human life. The museum is named after its founder, Frederick Horniman, who travelled extensively for his tea company during the 1870s and acquired a fascinating ethnographic and natural history collection which forms the basis of the wealth of material to be seen today. Specialising in the natural history, religious beliefs and arts and crafts of the peoples of the world, this is an irresistible haunt for children. A working beehive, an aquarium containing tree frogs and piranha fish, stuffed birds and animals (including a walrus), lots of costumes, jewellery, charms and other magical and religous objects can all be seen at The Horniman as can Egyptian mummies, skeletons and a shrunken head from Ecuador. There is a display of tea-making equipment, one devoted to Darwin's theory of Evolution, and there are some marvellous collections of antique musical instruments. There are frequent visiting exhibitions of special interest too.

Imperial War Museum
Lambeth Road
Lambeth North   **SE1**
Tel 735 8922
Open 10-5.50(Mon-Sat) 2-5.50(Sun)
Possible changes in 1985/86 due to major reconstruction
Wheelchair access to museum
Parking for disabled drivers by prior arrangement
Admission free

Extensive building work to the Imperial War Museum in 1985/6 means that many of the exhibits are provisionally in store. During this period an interim exhibition on World Wars I and II has been arranged. Normally, the museum focuses on all aspects of war since 1914 with particular emphasis on Britain and The Commonwealth's roles in the two World Wars. There is also coverage of the Korean, Arab/Israeli and Vietnamese conflicts. Special exhibitions are held intermittently. The art gallery contains some powerful war paintings including works by J D Fergusson, Paul Nash, Dame Laura Knight, Wyndham Lewis and Stanley Spencer, although many of these, of course, are currently in store. The reference collection of documents, films, photographs, books and sound records can be viewed by appointment (see Libraries).

Livesey Museum
next to Christ Church
682 Old Kent Road
Bricklayer's Arms   SE1
Tel 01-639 5604
Open 10-5(Mon-Sat during
exhibitions) Closed usually June-Oct
Wheelchair access to ground floor &
toilets
Admission free
In 1891, Sir George Livesey, chairman
of the South Metropolitan Gas
Company, gave this imposing red
brick building to the people of
Camberwell for their first public
library. It now houses the Livesey
Museum which has changing
exhibitions of local and general
interest. Recent shows have included
The History of Crafts, The River
Thames, Evolution, and Up The
Market from Victorian times to the
present day. Free worksheets and
slide shows can be arranged when
booking groups. There are also several
interesting bits of street furniture to
be seen in the museum's courtyard.
The museum is closed for several
months in the summer while
exhibitions are being changed so be
sure to check before going.

The London Cab Company Museum
1-3 Brixton Road
Oval   SW9
Tel 735 7777
Open 9-5(Mon-Fri) 9-2(Sat)
Wheelchair access none
Admission free
On view at the London Cab Company
Museum are ten London cabs which
date from 1907 to 1985. They were all
in regular use in their time except for
two of them which were withdrawn
after a couple of years because they
were uneconomical to run.

The London Dungeon
28/34 Tooley Street
London Bridge   SE1
Tel 403 0606

Open 10-5.30(Mon-Sun)
Wheelchair access to museum
Admission £3.50(adults) £2(OAPs &
children under 14) Sept-May £3.80 &
£2.20 respectively Jun-Aug
Definitely not for the squeamish, life-
size scenes depict British medieval
torture, disease, witchcraft,
demonology and other horrors of the
Dark Ages, The Reformation and the
tortures of The Tower of London.
Sound-effects and lighting contribute
the appropriate atmosphere to each
scene. This survey of the horrors of
our murky past is doubtless
instructive for the thousands of
excited children and young people
who throng through the doors of The
London Dungeon each year.

**The Mander & Mitchenson Theatre
Collection**
5 Venner Road
Sydenham   SE26
Tel 778 6730
Open to theatre researchers by
appointment only
Wheelchair access none
Admission free
Though a considerable part of this
famous collection has been moved to
The Mansion in Beckenham Place
Park (where the entire archive will
one day be located), much of great
importance remains in Sydenham.
There are special collections devoted
to Wilde, Maugham and Coward (to
name a few), theatrical memorabilia
such as props, posters and statuettes,
and a remarkable library of books
covering all aspects of theatre
(including dance and opera). For
material on London and regional
theatre productions (programmes,
photographs, playbills, notices etc), a
trip to The Mansion is necessary
where an archivist and several part-
time helpers work at maintaining
hundreds of boxes of theatrical
history). Theatre researchers from
around the world use the Mander-
Mitchenson collection (now over forty
years old), and rarely does a

publication on theatre appear without some acknowledgement being paid to it. The collection is a charitable trust.

Museum of Garden History
St Mary-at-Lambeth
next to Lambeth Palace
Lambeth Palace Road
Lambeth Palace SE1
Tel 261 1891(between 11 & 3)
Open 11-3(Mon-Fri) 10.30-5(Sun) 1st Sun in March until 2nd Sun in Dec
Wheelchair access to church & garden
Admission free
Saved from demolition by The Tradescant Trust in 1977, St Mary-at-Lambeth church is the home of the world's first Museum of Garden History. It is a modest museum with a curiously peaceful and rural atmosphere. Display boards celebrate the Garden and the work of important plant hunters of the past. Much of the exhibition concentrates on the 17th Century plant and seed collectors and gardeners par excellence, John and (son) John Tradescant. They were gardeners to many noblemen and served by royal appointment to Charles I and Henrietta Maria. They travelled extensively in Europe, Russia and Virginia, collecting strange exotic plants which they introduced to the gardens of England. (These include the Red Trumpet Honeysuckle, Yucca and Tulip Tree.) Later, they founded the first public museum in England by opening their South Lambeth Road house and garden to the public so that people could see the plants and objects they had collected on their travels. (The collection of objects contained the first abacus to be seen in England and was to become the basis of today's Ashmolean Museum in Oxford.) St Mary's churchyard has been planted with many of the plants and flowers that the Tradescants grew and some plants are on sale. Both Tradescants are buried in the churchyard and their tomb lies alongside the tomb of

Admiral Bligh of Bounty fame. Apart from the exhibits and the garden, St Mary's functions as a centre for anyone interested in gardens, gardening and conservation. Many open meetings, demonstrations, lectures and exhibitions (see Art) are held Past topics have included 'Seventeenth Century Vegetables', 'The History of Medicinal Herbs and their use through the Ages', and 'The European Influence on the American Garden'. A yearly subscription of £5 entitles you to membership of The Tradescant Trust and four newsletters a year, detailing the year's events and activities. An annual Plants and Gardens Spring Fair takes place on the last Sunday in April and The Tradescant Trust Country Market and Craft Fair in October (see Festivals & Events). There is a well-stocked gift shop and a tea and coffee table for visitors.

Museum of the Pharmaceutical Society of Great Britain
1 Lambeth High Street
Albert Embankment SE1
Tel 735 9141
Open strictly by appointment only
Wheelchair access none
Admission free
Collection of pharmaceutical ceramics (including English Delft drug jars), dispensing apparatus, medicine chests and microscopes. Visits by appointment only.

London Cab Company

The NAAFI Historical Collection
Imperial Court
Kennington Lane
Kennington   SE11
Tel 735 1200
Open by appointment only
Wheelchair access none
Admission free
This small exhibition charts the
history of the NAAFI from 1921 to the
present day and some pre-NAAFI
material is also viewable. Historical
photographs and documents,
uniforms, ration cards, crockery and
cutlery, medals awarded to NAAFI
staff and a 1930's bicycle (the
forerunner of today's motorised
mobile canteen) are some of the
exhibits of this highly specialised
collection.

**National Maritime Museum
(including
The Old Royal Observatory)**
Greenwich Park
Greenwich   SE10
Tel 858 4422
Open 10-5(Mon-Fri) 10-5.30(Sat)
2-5(Sun) Winter
10-6(Mon-Sat) 2-5.30(Sun) Summer
Wheelchair access limited but
extra provision available by prior
arrangement
Admission £1(adults) 50p(children
over 7 OAPs & unwaged) to each
museum or £1.50 & 75p respectively
to both Prices expected to change
during 1986
Visitors will find a vast collection of
maritime paintings, prints,
photograpahs, charts, swords, medals,
navigational and astronomical
instruments and historic timekeepers
(Harrisons chronometers are in this
collection). Nelson's Trafalgar
uniform and many of his personal
possessions are on display as are
pieces of china and silver. There is
also a large collection of models and
actual craft, including magnificent

state barges such as that of Prince
Frederick and the Reliant paddle
steamer. In the courtyard of the
Observatory one can experience the
unique journey of travelling from the
eastern to the western hemisphere
with one step across the meridian
line. The tomb stone of Norice Halley
can also be seen here. (Halley's comet -
best viewed in late 1985/early 1986 for
the first time in 76 years - see
following paragraph on Spaceworks
and Festivals & Events). Sadly, The
Queen's House (designed by Inigo
Jones c1616) is closed for all of 1986
and possibly beyond. The museum also
offers two bookshops and a coffee
shop.
From November 1985 to December
31st 1986, The National Maritime
Museum celebrates the return of
Halley's comet with a major
exhibition, called Spaceworks. It
shows how satellites have
revolutionised our everyday lives
with special emphasis on Giotto, the
European Space Agency's Mission to
the comet. The exhibition will keep
abreast of the progress and there will
be live transmission of the encounter
with the comet, when the spacecraft is
expected to be destroyed.

Nature Study Centre
Wandsworth Common
near Dorlcote Road
Wandsworth Common   SW18
Tel 785 9916
Open 2-4(Wed Fri) 1-4(Sun)
Wheelchair access to centre
Admission free
This small centre is open a couple of
afternoons a week and is an ideal low-
key place to take a child who is
interested in nature. There is a 4ft
aquarium containing fresh water
invertebrates, one or two other live
exhibits and some examples of locally-
found funghi in the autumn. There
are permanent and temporary

displays and posters explaining such matters as the making of birds' nests and Dutch Elm Disease and general information concerning the nature and conservation of Wandsworth Common and other local open spaces.

Old Operating Theatre
Chapter House
St Thomas' Street
London Bridge   SE1
Tel 407 7600
Open usually 12.30-4(Mon Wed Fri) and at other times by arrangement but ring first because of building work
Wheelchair access none
Admission 70p(adults) 35p (students OAPs & children)
The only surviving example in England of a 19th century hospital operating room and apothecary herb garret. From 1225 until 1862 St Thomas' Hospital was at London Bridge and today's Southwark Cathedral Chapter House was the parish church attached to the hospital. Rebuilt in 1702 by Sir Christopher Wren, the loft of the church was used by the hospital for drying and storing medicinal plants with which most of the hospital's medicines were made. Next to the herb garret was the women's operating theatre which has been meticulously restored to convey the working atmosphere of its day. Displays illustrate the history of surgery and nursing and the work of Florence Nightingale, and there are medical specimens and examples of early surgical equipment. A fascinating exhibition offering real insight into the conditions and standards of 19th century surgical practice.

Polka Children's Theatre Museum
240 Broadway
Wimbledon   SW19
Tel 542 4258
Open 10-4.30(Tue-Fri) 12-6(Sat)
Wheelchair access to museum
Admission free
An 18th Century Country Fair is the theme of the Polka Children's Theatre exhibition room. A stunning collection of puppets of the world illustrates the history of puppets from early Indonesian shadow puppets to the puppets of today. Many of the puppets and other exhibits were given to Polka by the famous puppeteers, puppet makers and puppet collectors of the 1950's, Waldo and Muriel Lanchester. There are Punch and Judy displays, props and masks of every description and always bits and pieces that are linked to Polka's current theatre production. This is a real pleasure palace for children and many of the exhibits can be made to work by pushing buttons and turning handles, which causes great delight. Upstairs the British Toymakers Guild 'Best Toys of the Year' are on show and some of these award-winning hand-crafted toys can be made to order.
Museum sheets geared for different age groups are available to school parties.

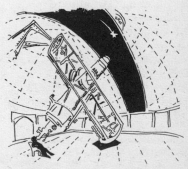

28" telescope, Greenwich

The Ronald Grant Archive
Raleigh Hall
1-3 Effra Road
(entrance in Saltoun Road)
Brixton   SW2
Tel 737 3208
Open strictly by appointment
Wheelchair access none
Admission free
Ronald Grant started his collection of
cinema memorabilia when he was a
young boy and has been committed to
the preservation of film history ever
since. His Archive of today is a
triumph - a unique place of reference
for media students, researchers and
serious enthusiasts of cinema history.
Crammed into fifteen rooms are
countless film stills, colour
transparencies and posters from past
and recent productions and a
considerable collection of books on
film and performers. In addition,
commissionaires' uniforms, cinema
furnishings, projectors and other
equipment, negs, photographs and
momentoes saved from demolished
cinemas record the golden days of the
picture palace. New material is
constantly added to the collection
(there is, occasionally, work for
volunteers), and due to lack of space,
Ronald Grant is looking for larger
premises for the Archive with a view
to opening a public Cinema Museum.
Let's hope it stays in South London.

**The Rotunda (Museum of
Artillery)**
off Repository Road
Woolwich Common
Woolwich   SE18
Tel 854 2424
Open 12-5(Mon-Fri) 1-5(Sat-Sun)
April-Nov
12-4(Mon-Fri) 1-4(Sat-Sun) Dec-
March
Wheelchair access to museum
Admission free
This regency metal tent (designed by
Nash) was orginally erected in St

James' Park when the allied
sovereigns who had been fighting
Napoleon visited London in 1814. It
was then put in the gardens of
Carlton House, the home of the Prince
Regent, who had it removed four
years later to Woolwich to house 'The
military curiosities usually preserved
in the Repository of the Royal
Artillery'. The original tent ropes can
be seen in the present permanent
structure. Among the exhibits on
view are stone-age implements, a 14th
century bombard, blunderbusses,
rockets and rocket equipment, and
guns from the Second World War.
There is also a breech loading gun
from the wreck of the Mary Rose,
which sank off Spithead in 1545.

Royal Artillery Museum
Royal Military Academy
Academy Road
Woolwich Common
Woolwich   SE18
Tel 856 5533 Ext 385
Open 10-12.30 2-4(Mon-Fri)
Wheelchair access none
Admission free
Uniforms, dioramas, pictures, models
and other historic exhibits tell the
story of the Regiment of Artillery
from 1716 to modern times.

Soseki Museum
80b The Chase
Clapham Common   SW4
Tel 720 8718
Open 10-12(Wed Sat) 2-5(Sun)
Wheelchair access none
Admission free
The Soseki Museum commemorates
the life and work of the famous
Japanese writer, Natsume Soseki
(1867 - 1916), and concentrates
particularly on his stay in London
from 1900 to 1902. His last lodging
house was in The Chase opposite the
museum. His time in London was not

a happy one but it is generally felt that the experience inspired many of his philosophies and writings, and it was during his stay that he adopted the resolution that one should 'think of oneself first' which he later developed in his major work 'Bungakuron'. Soseki is perhaps best known here for his satirical novel 'I am a Cat' which looks at the values of petty bourgeois 'civilised' society from a cat's point of view. Visitors are able to browse through an entire collection of Soseki's writings as well as critical essays about him and an impressive selection of modern Japanese literature. There are also photographs, letters and many other items recording his stay in London and the city he must have known.

Southside House
Wimbledon Common
Wimbledon   SW19
Tel 946 7643
Open for hourly guided tours 2-5 (Tue Thur Fri 31 Oct-31 March) Special visits by application in writing to The Administrator of The Pennington-Mellor Charity Trust at the above address)
Wheelchair access none
Admission free
Southside House is an old family home that is still lived in by the descendants of the man who built it in 1687. Robert Pennington had taken his wife and daughter to the safety of rural Wimbledon to escape the Plague and, some years later, built Southside House for the family, employing Dutch architects. Statues of two female figures stand, one on either side of the front door, 'Plenty' (fashioned after his wife) and 'Spring' (after his daughter). Much of the furniture Pennington brought to the house remains and there are a number of other interesting items from Southside's illustrious connections with family and visitors over the years. Among them are Anne Boleyn's vanity case, the necklace that fell

from the beheaded Marie Antoinette, and many belongings of the infamous Duke of Wharton (who hid in Southside when he was outlawed for supporting Bonnie Prince Charlie and for practising Black Magic). In 1750, The Prince of Wales came to stay and his bed can be seen as can the 'musik room' that was prepared for him, lit by 80 candles in crystal chandeliers. It is a refreshing change to see items of historical interest in the domestic setting of their time. (Southside is only open for six months of the year - see above.)

Thames Barrier Centre

Thames Barrier Centre
1 Unity Way
Woolwich   SE18
Tel 854 1373
Open 10.30-6(daily April-Sept) 10.30-5(daily Oct-March)
Wheelchair access to Centre & most of Barrier none to embankment
Admission free
Exhibitions and audio-visual displays on the background, design and building of the Barrier. Has a viewing walkway, souvenir shop, buffet, gardens and pier.

The Thomas A'Becket Boxing Museum
320 Old Kent Road
Old Kent Rd   SE1
Tel 703 2644
Open 11-3 5.30-2am(Mon-Sat) 11-3 5.30-12pm(Sun)

Wheelchair access assisted to ground floor only
Admission free

Old Kent Road SE1

The Thomas A'Becket pub/museum is a must for boxing enthusiasts. There are about 1500 exhibits, including gloves and outfits used in famous contests, souvenir programmes, books, posters, pictures and other boxing memorabilia. Round the bar are framed facts and figures about boxing and, above, large pictures of boxing heroes whom the general public have nominated to join 'The British Boxing Hall of Fame'. (Nomination forms are available from the bar at 10p a time, proceeds to charity.) About four boxers are nominated to join the Hall of Fame every year and invited to an award ceremony at The Thomas A'Beckett. Many of the British champions can be watched limbering up in the professional gym above the bar (Barry McGuigan was there before his WBA world featherweight title triumph against Eusebio Pedroza), continuous films (from 1880 to the present day) are shown on a six foot screen in the bar and bands play live music every night except Monday. The Thomas A'Becket sure is a lively place!

Thomas a Becket Boxing Museum

Wimbledon Lawn Tennis Museum
The All England Club
Church Road
Wimbledon SW19

Wheelchair access to museum & toilets
Admission £1.50(adults) 75p(OAPs & children)

Models of the great tennis heroes, sets, trophies, equipment, photographs, sound effects and other material show how tennis had its beginnings in Ancient Greece and how the game has developed from the first Wimbledon Tournament in 1877 to the game we know today.

The Wimbledon Society
26 Lingfield Road
Wimbledon SW19
Open 2.30-5(Sat only)
Wheelchair access none
Admission free

Local history museum full of books, photographs, manuscripts, maps, press cuttings and other ephemera, and a natural history collection. Also many paintings and drawings, though only a few of these can be displayed at any one time due to lack of space.

The Wimbledon Windmill Museum
Windmill Road
Wimbledon SW19
Tel 788 7655
Open 2-5(Sat & Sun Easter-end of Oct)
Wheelchair access none
Admission 25p(adults) 10p(children)

Wimbledon windmill was built in 1817 by Charles March, a carpenter rather than a millwright, which may account for the unusual structure of the mill. It is believed to be the only remaining example of a hollow post flour mill in this country (ie the shaft driving the machinery passes through the hollowed-out core of the main supporting post). The outside of the disused mill is still complete. Inside, on one floor, there are bits of original machinery, scale models illustrating the different kinds of mill, diagrams, pictures and other displays covering their history and development over the years.

NIGHTLIFE

In this chapter we list places in two sections. **To Dance** is where you get up and do it. **To Listen and Watch** is where you sit back and enjoy rock and pop, disco, cabaret or classical music. For venues that are specifically for gay people, see Lesbian and Gay. If you want to play snooker (New World Snooker Clubs are 24hr) or go ice-skating see Sport – Private Facilities. At the time of going to press all the following clubs and venues were alive and well but bear in mind that nightlife has a habit of changing with the seasons and the trends, so check before going. If you have a yearning for early morning fresh bread and cakes there is a bakery called Hilkene & Sons at 168 Borough Hall Street SE1 which is open at 6am Monday to Friday.

Opening times given are for the specific event being described. Venues are often open at other times too. Many of the following places do have wheelchair access. Ring to check first to find out what assistance, if any, is required.

To Dance

South London has a strange mix of clubs from psychedelic basements to smart funk clubs and alternative dance dives to clean cut discos with all the flashing lights. Clubs tend to turn up overnight and disappear within months. Popularity shifts, and established places are constantly updating their image, music and programmes. You will find places to dance in nightclubs, pubs, converted pubs, crypts of churches, halls and on the river. Some we haven't mentioned are irregular and happen as one-night events so look out for leaflets and check City Limits and Time Out. Others we haven't mentioned are semi-legal and happen in disused buildings (often warehouses). You get to know about these from leaflets, listings or other venues but the best way is by word of mouth. You can usually be sure of having happy feet dancing (often to soul/funk) till dawn in an unusual environment. You can take your own drink. For riverboat discos which happen once or twice a

month from April to December phone
858 6895/857 6146. They leave
Greenwich pier at 8 come back at
midnight, cost £4 per person
(reductions for parties), sell food and
drink and play popular disco. Boats
are also available for private charter
and although the hire charge goes up
after midnight you can party on board
and buy drinks legally from the bar all
night. Clubs often follow the principle
of having a different emphasis of
music, style or group on different
nights so check before going that it's
the right night for you.

Albany Empire
Douglas Way
Deptford SE8
Tel 691 8016
Open 11-2 (Fri-Sun)
Admission £2.50 Concessions
Membership 50p late night
●Cabaret Disco Live music
A series of late night clubs. Jazz,
soul/funk disco, mad cabarets and
live bands followed by disco. Good
spacious dance floor, slightly raised
movable stage and lightshow. Bar
and balcony upstairs which
overlooks the dance floor. Clubs are
often good so watch out for them and
catch them while you can.

The Bizz
The Royal Oak
Tooley Street
London Bridge SE1
Tel 407 0211
Open 9-2 (Sat)
Admission £3 £2.50 members
Membership £2 pa
●Nightclub
A 60s club run on two floors of the
pub which also houses the Special
Branch on Friday nights. The disco
upstairs is 60s danceable pop and
downstairs is 60s Rhythm and Blues.
Smart dress is absolutely essential.

Boxers
17 Station Road
South Norwood SE25

Tel 771 3760
Open 10-2 (Wed-Sun)
Admission £3
●Nightclub
Soul Club with resident and guest
DJs.
Stage with video screens, dance floor
that lights up, and light show.
Wednesday night is the laid-back,
trendy Camel Club who play rock and
soul. Thursday is electro/funk mixing
night. Friday is disco and mainly for
a younger crowd. Saturday is for the
over 20s funk/soul disco. Sunday is
more laid-back funk. Friday and
Saturday are very crowded. Boxers
serves burgers, Italian and West
Indian food, although when it's
crowded eating is difficult after 11.
The space is for hire. Dress should be
smart and no jeans or trainers.

The Crypt
St Pauls Church
High Street
Deptford SE8
Open 9-very late (Fri)
Admission £3 Concessions
●Nightclub
60s psychedelic disco set in the cellar-
like Crypt with its distinctive brick
arches. Two bands, and a 60s light
show with moving images (some wax
lamp!) projected onto walls, videos
showing love-ins, and parquet dance
floor. After the bands you can dance
to a range of psychedelic music. The
same venue on Saturday nights is
used for private functions except for
the last Saturday in every month
which is live R & B music night. Bar
serving refreshments till late and
some snacks available. (See also
Lesbian and Gay.)

The Dog and Fox
High Street
Wimbledon SW19
Tel 946 6565
Open 8.30-12 (Wed)
Admission £1.50
Membership 50p
●Dance Disco

Flim-Flam

A weekly Solo Dance is held on Wednesdays in the banqueting suite. It is grand with a good-sized dance floor and has a capacity for 250-300 people. Music played by the DJ is everything from ballroom to popular disco, mainly for the mid 20s plus. Every last Thursday of the month a disco is held for the 20s and over which has popular dance music. There are also regular gay nights (see Lesbian and Gay). The banqueting suite is available for hire and you should also look out for one-off events like a night of George Melly.

Downs
40 Wimbledon Hill Road
Wimbledon SW19
Tel 946 3246/0344
Open 8.30-2 (Mon-Sat) last food orders 12.30
●Dinner dance
The downstairs restaurant has a disco and dance floor. The food is mixed French and Italian with a jokey menu. The DJ will play your requests and other dance music. The first half of the evening has quieter music while you eat, and the party begins to swing later. Friday and Saturday are quite busy. They welcome parties.

Downtown
Odessa Street
Rotherhithe SE16

Tel 231 8838
Open 8-12.30 (Mon Tues Wed), 8-1 (Thurs), 8-1.30 (Fri Sat)
Admission £15 (Tues Wed), £18 (Thurs), £25 (Sat)
●Dinner dance
Riverside restaurant with dance floor. Set price includes dinner. Tuesday, Wednesday and Thursday disco plays middle of the road dance music. Friday and Saturday floor show as well as disco. English and Continental food – bookings taken.

Dun Cow
279 Old Kent Road
Old Kent Road SE1
Tel 237 4764
Open 8-12 (Tues Wed), 8-2 (Thurs Fri Sat)
Admission £1.50 (Thurs), Fri Sat £2.50 (Fri Sat) Free Tues Wed and before 10.00
●Disco
Two Bars and dance floor on the ground floor. Disco music all week with soul/jazz funk emphasis on Tuesday. Different DJs. Escape from the music to sit and chat in the champagne bar upstairs where light snacks (pizzas, pies, burgers) are served.

Flim Flam
Harp Dance Club
Clifton Rise
New Cross SE14
Open 10-2 (Fri)
Admission £2.50 Concessions
●Nightclub
Close to New Cross Town Hall, Flim Flam is set in a wonderful dance hall built in 1957 and virtually untouched since then. Features like the mural on the side of the stairs, the wood veneer, the original formica on the tables upstairs, and the spaciousness of the three levels makes it feel like an experience before you've even begun. The ground floor has a sprung dance floor, is large, and has a mirrorball beaming patterns down. The Flim Flam crew who started this

club are set up on the stage on one side of the room and play hard funk, go-go, electro, soul and a few 60s dance favourites. The tempo keeps up and the atmosphere is good. There are a few tables to sit at and a bar on the side of the dance floor. On the next level is the balcony with seating rather like a train buffet car and space to hang over the side and watch the dance floor below or admire the mirrorball or the columns set regularly round the balcony. There is also a small bar in this area. Yet another bar upstairs in the 'room at the top' – a place to sit at tables and drink and chat or dance on the smaller dance floor. It is intimate and relaxed, the music is jazz, Latin, Reggae and African. The 3 DJs alternate on a rota system to provide a good mix of music. Although Flim Flam is usually full, you never feel crowded because of the variety of spaces and music. All in all, not to be missed. The Flim Flam crew also organise events at other venues like the Albany and various warehouses, and they had a boat party in summer 1985 which left from Greenwich Pier. Look out for them.

The Fridge
Town Hall Parade
Brixton Hill
Brixton   SW2
Tel 326 5100
Open 9-2am
Admission £3.50-£4
●Nightclub
Popular club in an old cinema building (most recently the Ace), which was burnt out by fire. Refurbished in 1985 (retaining the charred ceiling as a feature), the Fridge is now a spacious venue with a large dance floor, long bar downstairs, stage and upstairs balcony which is to be turned into a bar. Excellent rough and ready feel. Good stage for bands. Instead of a conventional lightshow on the dance floor there are 100 TV sets featuring

a video extravaganza. Wednesday night is name band night followed by disco. Thursday is the Cooling Tower which is a gay disco for men (women allowed) playing hi-energy. The Fridge is one of the few venues which takes risks with bands and Friday often features alternative, experimental, interesting and unusual live music. After the bands a disco. Saturday is dance party night which includes a live act of some kind – cabaret, music, or fashion show. The late night license at the Fridge is now in full swing. At the time of going to press there were plans to open a restaurant selling cheap fresh food like pasta salads and fresh fruit salad as well as tea and coffee. Recommended.

The Frog and Nightgown
148 Old Kent Road
Old Kent Road   SE1
Tel 701 1689
Open 9.30-2 (Tues-Sat) 9.30-12 (Sun)
Admission £1 after 10.30
●Disco Live music
Middle of the road pop groups play till 12 after which a resident DJ spins popular dance hits.

Henry Cooper
516 Old Kent Road
Old Kent Road   SE1
Tel 237 1872
Open 8-1 (Thurs), 8-2 (Fri Sat), 8-12 (Sun)
Admission £2 free before 10
●Disco
Pub converted into one plush room for disco dancing with bar and dance floor, and smaller bar next door open all week. Mainstream disco music with different DJs through the week. Good late drinking/dancing license.

Kisses
43 Peckham High Street
Peckham   SE15
Tel 703 7142
Open 9-2.30 (Fri) 9-3 (Sat) 8-1 (Sun)
Admission £4 £2-£3 members

Membership £1

●Nightclub

Smart soul/funk club. Set on two floors. Downstairs – bar, dance floor, large video screen, lightshow, smoke effects, fish tank and mirrors. Upstairs – another bar, two pool tables and video games. Different emphasis depending on DJ. Resident DJs as well as guest spot. Friday night is party night when they play soul, funk, jazz, boogie and a touch of calypso. Saturday they play up-front soul and new hard funk including the latest imports. Sundays include various competitions like bring your favourite three tracks and be DJ, best-dressed girl and bloke, and dancing competitions. Every Bank Holiday Sunday they have an allnighter from 10-5, the bar stays open till 2 and they serve soft drinks after that. Young, lively crowd. They are particular about dress and don't allow jeans or trainers. Hot snacks (hamburgers, patties, chips) are served. Recommended.

The Fridge

La Balera

66 Streatham High Road

Streatham   SW16

Tel 769 2646/0669

Open 6 till late (Tue-Sun)

●Dinner dance Live music

Listen and dance to live music while eating Italian food.

La Gondola

78 Streatham High Road

Streatham   SW16

Tel 769 2541/2601

Open 6 till late (Tue-Sun)

●Dinner Dance

Downstairs is a restaurant disco for Italian food and dance.

La Pergola

78a/b Streatham High Road

Streatham   SW16

Tel 769 2001/2541

Open 6 till late (Tue-Sun)

●Dinner Dance

Dance floor, live music and Italian food.

Lakeside Restaurant

Belvedere Road

Thamesmead   SE2

Tel 311 3773

Open 8-2 (Sat)

●Dinner dance

This restaurant serves international (mainly French and Italian) food, has a large dance floor and live music on Saturday nights. The resident band plays popular music – a bit of everything and requests. It gets crowded and the dance gets lively.

Lilliput Hall

9 Jamaica Road

Rotherhithe   SE16

Tel 237 5903

Open 8.30-2 (Thurs Fri Sat)

Admission free £2 after 10pm

●Disco

At the back of the pub there's a dance floor where DJs play a mixture of Beatles and top of the pops music.

A Million Rubber Bands

Harp Dance Club

Clifton Rise

New Cross   SE14

Open 10-2.30 (Sat)

Admission £2.50 Concessions

●Nightclub

Co-ordinated by the Flim Flam Crew in the downstairs of the same extraordinary building as their

Friday night club, the music is punk, new wave and 60s psychedelic. Upstairs in the 'room at the top' is a country and western club which is run separately but people are welcome to go to both and apparently do quite freely. A whacky mix which works well.

Nelsons Nite Club
49 Durnsford Road
Wimbledon SW19
Tel 946 2464
Open 8.30-12.30 (Thurs),
8.30-2.30 (Fri Sat)
Admission £4.50 £3 members £2 before 10
Membership £15.00
●Disco Dinner dance Cabaret
Smart disco/cabaret dinner dancing club for anyone over 24. A la carte restaurant. Check local listings for events. Private parties can book the club on other nights.

Old Queen's Head
Stockwell Road
Stockwell SW9
Tel 737 410
Used to be Slummin, check new plans.

Rodos
10 Streatham High Road
Streatham SW16
Tel 769 2946
Open 9-2 (Fri Sat)
●Dinner Dance
Downstairs Greek restaurant with a dinner dance on Friday and Saturday. Resident band plays a mixture of Greek, Latin American and English music and almost anything on request. Lively atmosphere and as the evening progresses it often turns into a sing-along.

The Roebuck
25 Rennell Street
Lewisham SE13
Tel 852 1705
Open 8.30-12 (Tues Fri Sat)

Admission £1.50 (Tues) £1 (Fri Sat)
●Disco Live music
Large venue with stage and dance floor in pub basement (entrance at side of building). Live music on Friday and Saturday. Bands play Rock and Roll on Friday (usually with a resident band). Saturday is easy listening and bands that do cover versions. Tuesday is a singles and separated disco with a DJ playing middle of the road and popular disco.

Saxon Tavern
Southend Lane
Catford SE6
Tel 698 3293
Open 8-1 (Thurs-Sat)
Admission £1.50-£2
●Disco
A divorced and singles club on Thursday and Saturday nights in this club above a pub. Membership is £5 and drinks are pub prices. Music is mainstream disco. On Friday nights there is a heavy metal club with a resident DJ.

Scene on the Green
289 Camberwell New Road
Camberwell SE5
Tel not known
Open 10 till late
Admission £4 £2 members
●Nightclub
Reggae/funk/soul club open till late. Long plain room with bar at one end

and sound system at the other. A lot of people stand around the bar drinking and watching the dancers. A good place to go for live toasting. Reggae is interspersed with funk/soul/electro according to DJ and guests. If you're just waking up when everyone else wants to go to bed this is one of the few SL venues open till dawn. Recommended.

Sir John's
101 St Johns Hill
Clapham Junction   SW11
Open 8.30-1am (Wed Thurs), 8.30-2 (Fri Sat)

Admission £3 free before 10
●Disco Live music
Small club with dance floor and lightshow. Wednesday is live trad jazz, Thursday cabaret with a resident team of performers, Friday and Saturday disco dance music. Membership is free and drinks are almost pub prices. Restaurant downstairs serving meals and light snacks (sandwiches, burgers) till 11.

Special Branch
The Royal Oak
Tooley Street
London Bridge   SE1
Tel 407 0211
Open 9-2 (Fri)
Admission £3
●Nightclub
Club on both floors of a pub. Upstairs is large and for sitting around, drinking and talking, but you can also dance to jazz and tropical music. Downstairs is plush with a funk and soul disco, a small dance floor and comfortable seating. A DJ for each floor, joined by guests now and then. Bars on both floors and some chicken-in-a-basket type food. Smart dress essential.

Spreaders
1-2 Stockwell Street
Greenwich   SE10
Tel 853 2333
Open 8 till late (Fri Sat)

Cover charge £2 £5
●Dinner dance Jazz Live music
64-seat restaurant and dance floor with live music – 30s, 40s and 50s nostalgia which includes swing, be-bop and even ventures to flamenco guitarists. Changing bill and comfortable air conditioned surroundings. Some other programmes on Wednesday, Thursday, and Sunday nights. Classic Bistro food till midnight.

The Studio
158 Streatham Hill
Streatham   SW2
Tel 674 5868
Open 9-2am
Admission £3 cheaper before 10
●Nightclub
Newly refurbished (used to be the Cat's Whiskers) exclusive disco where personal appearance is important. Live bands, cabaret, as well as DJs. Soul/disco emphasis in this large club. Young crowd.

The Swan
215 Clapham Road
Stockwell   SW9
Tel 274 1526
Open 10.30-1.30 (Fri Sat)
Admission £2.50
●Dance Disco
Above the Swan pub, there's a Friday dance and Saturday disco for the over 25s (neat dress is required). Friday always features a band, mostly country and western, and the entrance charge varies slightly with name bands. The Saturday disco plays mostly top of the pops spun by the resident DJ. The entrance charge includes food (sausage and chips or fish and chips). The pub downstairs does nightly live music – folk, pop and rock and good value food at lunch time (especially salads).

Square One
The Harrowgate Ballroom
Eltham Road
Eltham   SE9

Tel 850 2244
Open 8-12.30 (Sun)
Admission £2
Membership £5 pa
●Singles disco
Massive hall with a capacity of 600 which has a regular singles disco every Sunday. Mixed age group. Resident DJ plays wide variety of popular disco and some oldies. Bar open till 12. Look out for other one-off events at the same venue.

Temple Bar
Walworth Road
Walworth   SE17
Tel 703 4117
Open 7.30-12 (Mon-Sat) 7.30-10.30 (Sun)
Admission free (Sun-Wed) £1 (Thurs Fri Sat)
●Disco
Converted pub with mirrored ceiling, elaborate disco lighting, long American-type bar and dance floor. Disco every night with a varied programme. Monday is 60s, Tuesday 50s 60s and 70s, Wednesday, Thursday and Sunday popular and top twenty, Friday and Saturday popular dance disco. Live jazz band Sunday lunchtime. Burgers and snacks.

Theo's Cosmopolitan
200-204 Putney Bridge Road
Putney   SW15
Tel 789 2515
Open 6-2am (nightly) lunch 12-3
●Dinner dance
International and cosmopolitan food (some Greek specialities) with live Greek music played by musicians who can play almost anything. Greek dancers and belly dancers do a cabaret spot and there is a dance floor. Lots of character to this place and lively atmosphere. Parties welcome.

The Tunnel
The Mitre
338 Tunnel Avenue
Woolwich   SE10

Tel 858 0895
Open 8-12 (Sun-Fri), 8-2 (Sat)
Admission £3.50-£3.50
●Live music Disco
This converted pub makes a large live music venue with stage PA and lights. New bands on Monday (so send in tapes, especially if you're a good local band), R & B on Tuesday (there's usually a resident band), cabaret on Wednesday (described as 'limp wristed under the table club'), and name bands and disco on Thursday, Friday and Saturday. Drinks are slightly above pub prices.

Waterside Theatre
Rotherhithe Street
Rotherhithe   SE16
Tel 231 2976
Open 8.30-2 (1st Sat of every month)
Admission £3 Concessions
●Cabaret Disco
Different cabaret each month and from midnight disco dancing in this beautiful old warehouse overlooking the river.

Winston's
7 McMillan Street
Deptford   SE8
Tel 692 0585
Open 7.30-12 (nightly)
Admission Wed £1 (includes free buffet) free (rest of week)
●Disco Cabaret Poetry
Cocktail bar selling beers from all over the world. Funk disco every night with different DJ's.
Wednesday is the Atlas Room club – a cabaret/poetry night with all kinds of acts including ballet.

Zeetas
200a Upper Richmond Road
Putney   SW15
Tel 785 2101
Open 7pm-1am (Tues-Sat)
●Supper Club
Beautiful 1930s Art Deco style supper club with live jazz to match, based on the idea of the Cotton Club.

Interesting new a la carte English cuisine, cocktails and two bars. You have to eat if you want to buy drinks. Available for special functions.

To Listen and Watch

Here we list places where you can watch or listen to cabaret and live music of many different kinds. We have included pubs with live bands and discos, function rooms attached to pubs which have different nights for live bands, folk music and cabaret, and restaurants which have cabaret spots. The listing is not exhaustive since to make it so would require an entire book rather than a chapter. There are countless pubs and wine bars, which tend to rely on locals for support and offer changing programmes of entertainment so look-out for these in your area. At the end of this section there is a brief listing (**Sometime Music Venues**) of places which occasionally have music events but usually serve another purpose.

The Academy
211 Stockwell Road
Brixton   SW9
Tel 326 1022
Admission £5-£7
●Live music
South London's biggest live music venue with a capacity of 4,300. Has a variety of international big-name acts including many Reggae Superstars and hosted the Alternative Miss World event in '85. There are plans to run smaller clubs and The Academy has the potential to become one of London's main music venues.

The Archduke Wine Bar
Under the Arches
South Bank   SE1
Tel 928 9370
Open 8.30-11 (Mon-Sat)
Admission free

●Jazz
Wine bar/restaurant with free live jazz.

The Atlantic
389 Coldharbour Lane
Brixton   SW9
Tel 274 2832
Open 8-11 (Thurs Fri Sat)
Admission free
●Disco Live music
Lively pub in the heart of Brixton with loud disco on Thurday and Friday in one of the bars. Live funk bands on Saturday.

Battersea Arts Centre
Old Town Hall
176 Lavender Hill
Clapham Junction   SW11
Tel 223 6557
Open 9-11.30 (Fri Sat Sun)
Admission £2.50 Concessions
●Cabaret Live music Disco
In the cafe of BAC or in the studio theatre a mixed cabaret usually with a main band or show and guest acts. Now and then there's a variety of bands in the main hall with accompanying DJ discos, playing jazz, funk and highlife.

Battersea Folk Club
The Plough
St Johns Hill
Clapham Junction   SW11
Tel 874 6637
Open 8.30-11 (Thurs)
Admission £1.50 £1 Members
Membership 50p
●Folk club
Round the back of the pub a Folk club (with a bar) which includes some blues and jazz. One guest act is booked weekly and then there's an open to all ad-lib section. Go along to perform or listen.

The Bull
Upper Richmond Road
East Sheen   SW14
Tel 876 2345
Open 8.30-12 (Wed Thurs Fri Sat)

Admission £2
●Live music
Mainly rock bands. A selection of local and name bands.

Bull's Head
Barnes Bridge
Barnes   SW13
Tel 876 5241
Open 8-12 (every night)
Admission £2-£6 according to band
●Live jazz
Beautiful old riverside pub with adjoining restaurant/carvery. Famous on the jazz circuits and in operation for the last 25 years, there are different live acts every night of the week and Saturday/Sunday lunch-times. International stars are brought over and often do shows all over the country too. The venue seats 80 and admission is on a highly civilised first come first served basis. Run with real enthusiasm and dedicated initiative. Recommended.

Centurion
Deptford Broadway
Deptford   SE8
Tel 692 1474
Open 8-11 (Nightly)
Admission free
●Disco Live music
All-week disco with resident DJ playing funk and soul. Pub hours, pub prices. Free live bands on Friday and Saturday, but drinks are slightly above pub price.

The Cricketers
The Oval   SE11
Tel 735 3059
Open 8 (nightly)
Admission £2-£3 Concessions
●Live music
Well-known as a rock venue on the London circuit. Every night different bands – rock, folk, R & B and jazz. Name bands as well as local bands. Live music at Sunday lunchtime too. Recommended.

The Duke
125 Creek Road

Deptford   SE8
Tel 692 1081
Open 8-11 (Fri Sat)
Admission free
●Live music
Duos and bands playing jazz, folk and rock and roll (modern and 50s).

Duke of Wellington
128 Old Woolwich Road
Woolwich   SE10
Tel 853 1918
Open 8 (Thurs Fri Sat Sun)
Admission free
●Live bands
Bands, local and all-star (musicians from name bands who get together for a night's jamming).

Father Red Cap
319 Camberwell Road
Camberwell   SE5
Tel 703 9208
Open 8.30-11 (Fri Sat Sun)
Admission free
●Live bands
Live, mostly rock bands, often all-star.

Gate at the Latchmere
503 Battersea Park Road
Battersea   SW11
Tel 228 4011
Open 11-12 (Wed Thurs) 10.30-12 (Fri Sat)
Admission £2.75
●Cabaret Live music
An after-theatre cabaret club on Friday, Saturday (and sometimes Wednesday and Thursday). A variety of shows, satirical, feminist, political et al. Free live music downstairs in the pub from 10-11 on Sunday to Thursday. Mostly R & B. A range of regular, local and new bands through the week.

George Canning
95 Effra Road
Brixton   SW2
Tel 274 6329
Open 8.30-11 (Thurs Fri Sat)
Admission free
●Live bands Disco

Live bands Thursday and Friday.
Funk, soul, rock. Often have a
resident band. Local and name bands.
Disco on Friday between and after
the band and on Saturday.

Half Moon
10 Half Moon Lane
Herne Hill   SE24
Tel 737 4580
Open 8-12 (Mon-Sat)
Admission £1.50-£2.50 no admission
after 11
●Live bands
Well known venue. Contemporary
rock and pop. Good local and name
bands. Monday is audition night so
send in tapes.

Half Moon
93 Lower Richmond Road
Putney   SW15
Tel 788 2387
Open 8.30-11 (nightly)
Admission £2-£4
●Live bands
Well-known venue (in a separate
room of the pub) offering an
interesting range of rock, jazz and
folk. Mostly name bands.
Recommended.

Jongleurs
The Cornet
Lavender Gardens
Clapham Junction   SW11
Tel 627 3266
Open 9 till late (Fri Sat)
Admission £3.50 Concessions
●Cabaret
Successful cabaret venue above a
pub. A good platform for new
performers with a changing bill of
approximately 4 acts per night and
an audition spot. The compere hosts
the show and acts include juggling,
magicians and live music. The
audience sit at tables to watch the
new variety and inexpensive meals
and drinks are available at just above
pub prices. Usually an interesting
night of entertainment.
Recommended.

Montpelier
99 Queens Road
Peckham   SE15
Tel 732 4100
Open 7-11(Thu-Sat)
Admission free
●Live Bands
Pub with bands 3 nights a week.
Country and Western on Thursday
and London circuit rock bands on
Friday and Saturday.

Newlands Tavern
40 Stuart Road
Peckham   SE15
Tel 639 0563
Open 8.30-11 (Thurs Fri Sat Sun)
Admission free
●Live Music
Free live, rock and easy listening
middle-of-the road disco.

Old Tigers Head
351 Lee High Road
Lee   SE12
Tel 852 9708
Open 7-11 (Mon-Sat) 7-10.30 (Sun)
Admission free except for name acts
£1
●Live music
Bands play in the lounge of the pub.
A resident band plays rock and roll
on Tuesday and Saturday. The rest of
the week there's a mixture of rock
bands with Sundays reserved for
rock and pop. Local and name bands.
Dance floor and stage.

The Old White Horse
261 Brixton Road
Brixton   SW9
Tel 487 3440
Open 8.30-11.30 (Fri)
Admission £2.50 Concessions
●Cabaret
Cast presents new variety at the Old
White Horse every Friday during the
autumn/winter season. It is set in a
room next to the pub which has a
stage area and rows of seats for the
audience. The feel is intimate and
you have to fight for drinks at the
crowded bar. Bands, comedians, and
novelty acts combine to make a series
of unusual and entertaining
evenings. Would-be acts should ring
for details of audition days which are
held 2-3 times per year. The Old
White Horse is planning events on
other nights so watch for new
programme. Recommended.

Plough
90 Stockwell Road
Stockwell   SW9
Tel 274 3879
Open 9.15-12 (Wed-Sun)
Admission Free
●Live bands Jazz
Music pub with stage at the back.
Wednesday night is audition night
when new bands are given a chance
(send tapes). Thursday, Friday and
Sunday are R & B nights with well-
known bands on the London/national
circuits. Saturday is a regular jazz
night featuring established bands
and musicians.

Prince of Orange
118 Lower Road
Rotherhithe   SE16
Tel 237 9181
Open 7-12.30 (Mon-Sat) 7-11 (Sun)
Admission free £1-£2 for name bands
●Jazz bands
Bands play in the pub every evening
and on Sunday at lunchtime. A
mixture of jazz, jazz funk and R & B.
Large variety of local, London
circuit and name bands.

Prince of Wales
467 Brixton Road
Brixton   SW9
Tel 274 6155
Open 9-2 (Mon-Sat) 8-10.30 (Sun)
Admission £1 after 10.30
●Gay nightclub
Entertainment every night, drag
most nights. Genuinely mixed gay
club – both men and women, black
and white (see Lesbian and Gay).
Straight people are welcome.

The Railway Tavern
Clapham High Street
Clapham   SW4
Open 8.30-11 (*Thur-Mon*)
Admission free
●Disco
Within the pub there is a disco (for
listening only) and lightshows. Music
varies each night. Thursday is
traditional, Friday and Saturday
popular, Sunday is 70s and Monday is
60s. There's a function room upstairs
for private bookings and some events.

Rub-a-dub Club
The Greyhound Pub
315 Kirkdale Road
Sydenham   SE26
Tel 778 9412
Open 8-11 (Thurs)
Admission £2.50
●Cabaret Live music
Alternative cabaret set in the
function rooms of the Greyhound
Pub.
There are tables and chairs to sit at
and vegetarian food is served at the
bar. Acts include stand-up comics,
sketches and live bands. There are
other music nights at the Greyhound
and jazz on Sunday at lunchtime.

The South Bank Concert Halls
South Bank   SE1
Tel 928 9131
●Classical & chamber music Cabaret
Dance Films Poetry
Purcell Room
Small intimate hall used for recitals
by solo artists and chamber groups.

Also used for cabaret, dance and poetry events. Classical music season from late September to early July.

The Queen Elizabeth Hall
There is a seating capacity of 1,100. Concert season from September to July followed by a summer season which usually includes dance, films and some events for the South Bank summer music festival.

The Royal Festival Hall
Seating capacity of 3,000 in this major classical music venue. The yearly programme begins in September and continues to Christmas. There is then a 3 week ballet season (see Dance – London Festival Ballet) and the second half of the concert programme begins at the end of January. It runs until July when the summer season begins. This offers a variety of ballet, jazz, classical, folk and pop music and other staged productions.
A leaflet is produced every month advertising all the events at the South Bank concert halls including foyer exhibitions (see Art – Royal Festival Hall). Free music and performances in the foyers have helped to create a new and lively atmosphere. The RFH has a daily changing lunchtime programme from 12.30-2 of live musicians and performers doing cabaret, chamber and classical music. In the riverside cafe on Friday, Saturday and Sunday there is live jazz from 8-10pm. Recommended.

Squire
350 Bromley Road
Catford SE6
Tel 698 8645
Open 8-11 (Sun Tues Fri)
Admission free
●Disco
In the pub there's a free disco with DJ and lightshow. Popular music. A function room attached to the pub houses one-off events – live bands

discos and cabaret. The entrance fee varies and they are open till 1 for these events. The function room is available for hire.

Thomas a' Becket
320 Old Kent Road
Old Kent Road SE1
Tel 703 2644
Open 7.30-12 (Wed) 7.30-1 (Thurs) 7.30-2 (Fri Sat)
Admission free except £1.50 (Fri Sat)
●Live music
Modern bands playing different kinds of music (including cover versions of rock and pop) appear in the old boxing ring of this boxing pub/museum (see Museums). A welcome late license.

Tramshed
51-53 Woolwich New Road
Woolwich SE18
Tel 855 3371
Open 7-11 (Nightly)
Admission free (Mon) varies from £1-£4 (Tues-Sun) Concessions
●Cabaret Live music Jazz
Pub in the day time and lively evening venue where you are entertained while you eat and drink. Jazz on Monday and Wednesday, rock on Tuesday and Thursday, and cabaret (consisting of new variety by Fundation) on Friday, Saturday and Sunday. Capacity of 180.

Two Brewers
147 East Hill
Wandsworth SW18
Tel 874 4128
Open 9-11 (Fri)
In a room behind the pub with its own dance floor and dining room, an Irish band plays traditional music to young people and families.

Walmer Castle
102 Peckham Road
Peckham SE15
Tel 703 4639
Open 8-11 (Thurs Fri Sat) 8-10.30 (Sun)
Admission £2

●Live Jazz

Pub with a separate room and bar for live and recorded jazz. On Thursday DJ plays old and new jazz. On Friday, Saturday and Sunday there are live bands who are well-known on the jazz circuit.

White Lion
14 Putney High Street
Putney   SW15
Tel 785 3081
Open 8-11 (Sun)
Admission £2.50 Concessions
●Cabaret

In the Astoria Suite of the White Lion there is a cabaret every Sunday. The acts consist of mainly stand-up comics with a spot of ad-libbers. If you wish to be considered as an act, go and audition in the ad-lib spot. Bar and dance floor.

Sometime Music Venues

There are regular and irregular festivals and events throughout the year which have live music (see Festivals and Events).
Look out for one-off programmes at the following:

Battersea Park (871 6354)
Rock pop and cabaret in the summer formerly organised by the GLC
Brixton Recreation Centre (733 9078).
Hip-Hop alliance Reggae PAs
Admission £1.50 Concessions
In a room behind the pub with its own dance floor and dining room, an Irish band plays traditional music to young people and families.

Clapham Common (622 6255)
Live rock pop jazz reggae in the summer
Crystal Palace Bowl (633 1707)
Summer programme of Classical music formerly run by the GLC
Forest Hill Library (699 2065)
Classical music
Greenwich Borough Hall (317 8687)
Classical and popular live music
Greenwich Park (317 8687)
Rock pop and classical concerts in the summer
Lambeth Town Hall (622 6255)
Reggae PAs Discos
Lee Centre (852 4700)
Live music Discos
Lewisham Theatre (690 3431)
Classical music Light rock and pop Variety Cabaret Jazz
Merton Libraries (946 7432)
Classical music
Morley College (928 8501)
Student recitals Operas
Nettlefold Hall (670 6212)
Reggae PAs Live bands
North Peckham Civic Centre (703 2917)
Dinner dance Cabaret Live music
Rangers House (317 8687)
Classical music programme (previously organised by the GLC)
Royal Naval College (317 8687)
Classical concerts October-April in the Wren Chapel
Southwark Cathedral (407 2939)
Classical music and lunchtime concerts
Tara Arts Centre (871 1458)
Asian music
Wandsworth Town Hall (871 6354)
Classical music
Well Hall Open Theatre (317 8687)
Live music Bavarian evenings
Wimbledon Theatre (540 0362)
Live music Cabaret
Woolwich Public Hall (317 8687)
Classical and popular live music

There are lots of local music societies and orchestras/bands to join. Find out about them at libraries and Adult Education Institutes.

PARKS

There are nine square miles of public open space in the area covered by the Handbook and some of London's most attractive parks such as Dulwich, Battersea, Crystal Palace and Cannizaro are situated south of the river. Streatham Common and Peckham Rye are another two delightful areas of green and, on a grander scale, Greenwich provides South London with its own Royal Park. Because London south of the Thames was developed much later than North London, the commons in the south have remained relatively intact compared with the corresponding area north of the river. We are fortunate in having as many as ten commons - Barnes, Wimbledon, Streatham, Clapham, Wandsworth, Peckham Rye, Blackheath, Plumstead and the two Tootings. Nowadays, the ownership of the commons comes under a public authority. In the past, they were each owned by the local Lord of the Manor who allowed his tenants to keep pigs, cattle, horses and chickens on the land. They were also permitted to dig for clay and gravel.

This was not to continue, however. History reflects the situation we continue to face today. As the capital developed land was needed for building, which caused its value to soar. Landowners saw their chance and were driven by greed to sell, which undermined the whole principle of common land. Thus the face of London's open spaces began to change over the years. A turning point came with the Metropolitan Commons Act of 1866 which was introduced to protect common land. It was only the beginning of a long struggle, however. Even after the Act bits of land continued to be sold. The railway companies were particularly keen to buy, since, to them, it made perfect sense to run railway lines through apparently useless open spaces. Barnes, Wandsworth and Tooting have, sadly, suffered accordingly. Interestingly though, Clapham Common (an obvious place for a railway line) escaped this fate because Clapham's wealthy inhabitants refused to allow their common to be spoilt in this way.

This section would be incomplete without a mention of two important South London walks:

The Green Chain Walk
Just over fifteen miles of sign-posted walks through a chain of parkland linking Thamesmead and the Thames Barrier with Cator Park in Beckenham. A series of four booklets is available from The Green Chain Working Party, John Humphries House, Greenwich, SE10.

Wandle Heritage Trail
Walk from Colliers Wood underground station to Mitcham Junction railway station along the banks of the historic River Wandle. The walk takes in many of the sites of industries once associated with the river: snuff mills, corn mills, fabric dyeing, cleaning and bleaching. The Liberty Mill and The William Morris Merton Tapestry Works are just two of the businesses that were based in the area. A leaflet on the Trail is available from Harry Galley, c/o Links School, Frinton Road, SW17. Tel 769 4587.

In the main directory the parks are numbered but listed by post code. The alphabetical index will give you the position of each park in the main directory. All the parks have sports facilities (see Sport) unless otherwise stated below.

SE1

1 Archbishop's Park
Originally part of the grounds of Lambeth Palace and still technically owned by the Archbishops of Canterbury. Lawns and flower beds surrounded by a good variety of shrubs and trees including lime, tree of heaven, catalpa, ash and London plane.

SE2

2 Bostall Heath and Woods
Along with the adjoining Lesnes Abbey Woods, this forms one of London's largest areas of woodland. The heath was part of the original common land of the Manor of Plumstead, whilst the woods were, until 1893, the private property of Sir Julian Goldsmid. (He played a significant role in the legal battle to save Plumstead Common and further demonstrated his principles by selling Bostall Woods to the public at well below their market value.)

3 Lesnes Abbey Woods
Includes the remains of the 12th century Lesnes Abbey and - a sight said to be unsurpassed in the south of England - twenty acres of wild daffodils. Cafe. Orienteering course (competitive navigation on foot!) See Park Manager for details.

SE3

4 Blackheath
Two hundred and seventy acres of grassland, Blackheath has for at least a thousand years been a strategic marshalling point for alien troops and rebellious peasant armies. The country's first golf club played here shortly after James I introduced the ancient Scottish game in the early 1600s.

SE5

5 Burgess Park
New lake with sailing and angling facilities - both with wheelchair access. Information centre. This adventurous new park was started in 1950 on an area of bomb and demolition sites. What in 1965 was fifteen acres, is now 88, and by the year 2000 will be 135 acres.

6 Myatt's Fields
Named after a market gardener who, in the nineteenth century, grew some of London's finest strawberries. Landscaped as a public park in 1887-8,

it still contains its original bandstand. Shaded walks, red chestnuts, rhododendrons and azaleas.

7 Ruskin Park
Named in honour of John Ruskin the local author, this park has an unusually rich variety of well-known trees including Indian bean, Judas and tulip trees. By the charming ornamental lake are gingko, sugar maple and corkscrew willow.

SE6

8 Forster Memorial Park
Pleasantly secluded grassland and rose garden encircled by a narrow strip of woodland. The land was a gift to the public from a local resident and one-time Governor-General of Australia, Lord Forster.

SE7

9 Maryon Park
Named after Sir Spencer Maryon Maryon-Wilson who presented the park to the public in 1891. The steep wooded banks to the south and west contribute to the park's seclusion whilst Cox's Mount to the north provides an excellent view of the new Thames Flood Barrier.

10 Maryon Wilson Park
Presented to the public in 1912 by the son of the donor of Maryon Park - Sir Spencer Pocklington Maryon-Wilson. Children's zoo. Pleasantly wild landscape.

SE9

11 Avery Hill
Magnificent, domed winter garden with such exotic specimens as bluefield bananas, Arabian coffee and Mexican breadfruit. Open every afternoon except the first Monday of the month and Christmas Day. Wheelchair access to winter garden and toilet near cafe.

12 Oxleas Wood
One of London's finest remnants of ancient woodland. Supports a great diversity of wild life including all three species of woodpecker and some lovely spreads of bluebells. Designated as a site of special scientific interest but currently under threat from plans for a four-lane highway.

13 The Tarn
Nine and a half acres of tranquil garden (a third of which is occupied by a closed bird sanctuary used for nesting). Some fine trees, a rustic bridge over a large clear lake, a small pond with a waterfall and an ice well. Seventy-three species of birds have been sighted in The Tarn, including kingfishers, and the autumn colours and 5000 daffodils in spring are magnificent.
No sports facilities

14 Well Hall Pleasaunce
Only the moat, rose garden walls and barn remain from the one-time home of Margaret Roper, the daughter of St Thomas More. Beautiful flower gardens, mature trees, art gallery and restaurant.

SE10

15 Greenwich Park
Two hundred acres enclosed from

Blackheath by Humphrey, Duke of Gloucester, in 1433. Famous for the Old Royal Observatory and National Maritime Museum, though of interest also for its old trees, including the stump of the historic 'Queen's Oak'. Lake, rhododendrons, herb garden, deer enclosure and tea house.

SE11

16 Kennington Park
Until its opening as a public park in 1854, this was the common grazing land of Kennington Manor. Today its most attractive features are undoubtedly its secluded Old English Garden and the two Park Keepers' cottages, which were built by Prince Albert as examples of ideal homes for the working man! In Bolton Crescent there is a special adventure playground for handicapped children. *No sports facilities*

SE12

17 Ladywell Fields
Almost a mile of riverside meadows along the Ravensbourne, Ladywell Fields was named after the old wells by the church of St Mary the Virgin. Nature trail. Pleasant for walking and picnicking. Refreshment kiosk. Pretty rose garden in the church grounds nearby.

18 Manor House Gardens
These gardens and the Manor House (now a public library) were originally part of the private estate of the landowning Baring family. One of the most beautiful of London's smaller parks, the grounds contain some handsome trees, an ornamental lake and remains of the original ice house. Nature trail.

SE14

19 Telegraph Hill Park
The park's name derives from the old semaphore station which once stood where the tennis courts now are. The park is in two parts either side of Kitto Road. Sunken rose garden, willow-lined pond, good views, nature trail.

Kennington Park

SE15

20 Peckham Rye Common
Common land which once extended as far west as Goose Green. What now remains was saved through a legal campaign by local inhabitants against the Lord of the Manor in the 1860s. Once well-wooded, the common is now mostly grass, providing a pleasant setting for Peckham Rye Park.

SE16

21 Lavender Pond Ecological Park
Rotherhithe Street
One of the city's new ecological parks, these two acres cover part of the former Lavender Dock. Though its primary function is for nature study, the public are welcome to come her just to relax.
No sports facilities

22 Russia Dock Woodland
Redriff Road
Part of the new Surrey Commercial Docks redevelopment, this is a narrow

strip of parkland built over the former Russia Dock. Though still rather stark, over 1000 trees have been planted and several ponds created since 1980.

SE18

23 Castle Wood
Named after the fascinating triangular folly, Severndroog Tower, which was erected here in the 18th century to commemorate William James' victory over the pirates of Severndroog in 1755. This crenellated folly still stands, with steep terracing below and beautiful rose garden.

24 Plumstead Common
Saved in the 1870s by a campaign of civil disobedience led by a local resident, John De Morgan. With its undulating grassland and deep ravine by 'The Slade', this is one of the most attractive and interesting commons in London.

25 Shrewsbury Park
Formerly part of the grounds of Shrewsbury House in Bushmoor Crescent, the park is mostly oak and silver birch woodland, fenced in parts to provide a wildlife sanctuary. Fine views out over the Thames and a good spot for picnicking.

26 Woolwich Common
Although undoubtedly once common land in the true and legal sense, it belongs to the Ministry of Defence. All attempts to prove the legal or moral survival of the common rights may have failed but the Ministry does permit public access to the greater part of it. Rough grassland.
No sports facilities open to the public

SE19

27 Beaulieu Heights
A remnant of the Great North Wood which at one time covered this part of England, giving its name to nearby Upper Norwood.
No sports facilities

28 Crystal Palace Park
Named after the enormous glass palace originally built in Hyde Park

for the Great Exhibition of 1851 and moved to this site in 1852. The palace was destroyed by fire in 1936, but many of the park's original lakes and model pre-historic monsters survive. Children's zoo, summer lakeside concerts.

29 Dulwich Upper Wood
Farquar Road
One of the city's new ecological parks. With community support, the Ecological Parks Trust has constructed paths, a tree nursery and areas of coppiced woodland.
No sports facilities

SE21

30 Belair Park
Not as well-known as it deserves to be, Belair Park has at least forty-three species of tree including such rarities as the cork oak and white mulberry. The lake forms the only part of the ancient River Effra still to run above ground. The surviving Georgian mansion after which the park is named, was built by John Adam.

31 Dulwich Park
Seventy-two acres of landscaped parkland, noted for its azaleas, rhodedendrons and unusually wide variety of mature trees. Boating lake, tree trail and aviary. The land was presented to the public by the governors of Dulwich College in 1885. Good access for disabled people.

SE22

32 Peckham Rye Park
Homestall Farm was purchased as an extension to the common and opened as Peckham Rye Park in 1894. A thoughtful blend of the wild and cultivated, with ornamental lake and charming Old English Garden.

SE23

33 Horniman Gardens
Named after Mr F J Horniman who established the gardens as a public park in 1897. Contains one of London's finest anthropological museums (see Museums), large sunken garden, secluded water garden, small children's zoo, bandstand, rose garden, three nature trails and excellent views.

34 One Tree Hill
One Tree Hill takes its name from the 'Oak of Honor' which once served as a boundary marker between Camberwell and Lewisham. The summit of this 300 foot wooded hill offers fine views, whilst below to the north is Brenchley Gardens - a section of disused railway laid out as a terraced rose garden.
No sports facilities

SE24

35 Brockwell Park
Fine views, open air theatre, attractive chain of lakes and walled-in Old English Garden with roses, golden yews, wisteria and honeysuckle.

The Bandstand, Brockwell Park

Originally the home of John Blades, a wealthy glass manufacturer, Brockwell Park was opened to the public in 1892.

SE26

36 Sydenham Hill Wood
Sydenham Hill
A relic of the ancient Great North Wood, part of which is presently under threat from Southwark Council plans for a housing estate. The most attractive access is via the tree-lined Cox's Walk, leading from the junction of the road known as Dulwich Common and Lordship Lane.
No sports facilities

37 Sydenham Wells Park
Named from the medicinal wells famous here in the 17th century. Attractive trees and shrubs amidst undulating grassland with ornamental lakes. Rich variety of water fowl including Chilean flamingoes.

SW4

38 Clapham Common
Described by some as a two hundred acre traffic island, yet the common has retained some wild, secluded

corners. Its focal point is the brightly painted bandstand brought here in 1890 from the old Royal Horticultural Society Garden in South Kensington. Open air chess club, two lakes, fishing.

SW11

39 Battersea Park
Reclaimed from the Thames around 1560 and opened by Queen Victoria as a public park in 1858. These 200 landscaped acres contain a large boating lake, Old English Garden, children's zoo and, most magnificent of all, the recently completed London Peace Pagoda. Wheelchair access to toilets.

40 Wandsworth Common
Though once stretching as far west as Wimbledon and east to Clapham, this has suffered from encroachments more than any other common in London. Primarily used for sports, but popular also as a walking route to shops and station. Nature trail and Nature Study Centre (see Museums).

SW13

41 Barnes Common
Wild but well kept. Popular in the summer with picnickers, naturalists and blackberry pickers. Gorse and broom abound amidst clumps of oak and birch. The whole common has been designated by the Nature Conservancy Council as a sight of special scientific interest.

SW15

(see entry 49 Putney Heath)

SW16

42 Biggin Wood
Another one of the few remnants of the ancient Great North Wood. As such it provides a small bird

sanctuary in an otherwise built-up area.

43 Norwood Grove
Originally enclosed from Streatham Common in 1635 to form a shooting estate for the first Earl of Portland. Near the centre is the early 19th century 'White House' (now a listed building) and below, fine views across flower gardens and fountain to the south-west.

44 Streatham Common & The Rookery
The grassy slope rises to an attractive area of woodland and two beautiful old gardens once enclosed from the common as private estates and since

The Rookery, Streatham

re-incorporated: Norwood Grove (see immediately above) and The Rookery. Fine views, terraced gardens, a historic medicinal well (once containing water with medicinal properties) and a garden laid out entirely with white flowers.

45 Tooting Commons
Technically two commons, one for each manor: Tooting Bec and Tooting Graveney. The wilder and more wooded areas are often overlooked but these, along with a small bird sanctuary by the main lake, introduce a sense of countryside. Nature trail.

SW18

46 King George's Park

Opened by King George V and Queen
Mary in 1923. The northernmost
section contains colourful flower beds,
a pets' corner, a scented rose garden
(originally designed for blind and
partially sighted people), many
mature trees and an ornamental lake
fed by the Wandle.

SW19

47 Cannizaro Park

Situated behind Cannizaro House,
this is one of London's most beautiful
and botanically interesting parks.
Visit in spring for the magnificent
rhodedendrons, azaleas and
magnolias. Fine sunken garden beside
the mansion, aviary, pond, cascades

and over two hundred species of trees
and shrubs.
No sports facilities

48 Morden Hall Park

One of the Wandle's many riverside
parks, its central features are the old
Morden Hall, Morden Cottage and
two water-powered snuff mills.
No sports facilities

49 Wimbledon Common & Putney Heath

By far London's largest common - 1100
acres - saved by a local campaign in
the late 1860s and protected now by
the Wimbledon & Putney Commons
Act (1871). Attractive mixture of
ponds, heath and woodland. The
windmill is England's only surviving
example of a hollow post mill (see
Museums).

Alphabetical Parks Index

Archbishop's Park 1
Avery Hill 11
Barnes Common 41
Battersea Park 39
Beaulieu Heights 27
Belair Park 30
Biggin Wood 42
Blackheath 4
Bostall Heath & Woods 2
Brockwell Park 35
Burgess Park 5
Cannizaro Park 47
Castle Wood 23
Clapham Common 38
Crystal Palace Park 28
Dulwich Park 31
Dulwich Upper Wood 29
Forster Memorial Park 8
Greenwich Park 15
Horniman Gardens 33
Kennington Park 16
King George's Park 46
Ladywell Fields 17
Lavender Pond 21

Lesnes Abbey Woods 3
Manor House Gardens 18
Maryon Park 9
Maryon Wilson Park 10
Morden Hall Park 48
Myatt's Fields 6
Norwood Grove 43
One Tree Hill 34
Oxleas Wood 12
Peckham Rye Common 20
Peckham Rye Park 32
Plumstead Common 24
Putney Heath 49
Ruskin Park 7
Russia Dock 22
Shrewsbury Park 25
Streatham Common & Rookery 44
Sydenham Hill Wood 36
Sydenham Wells Park 37
The Tarn 13
Telegraph Hill Park 19
Tooting Commons 45
Wandsworth Common 40
Well Hall Pleasaunce 14

POETRY AND PROSE

Our research has uncovered enough evidence to suggest that writing is a furiously popular activity. South London appears to be a healthy breeding ground for workshops, performance venues and publications, all of them initiated by people living, working, or doing whatever in the area. There is a growing amount of radical performance poetry and many groups of Black, women and community writers. Maybe this creativity is born out of necessity, maybe it's the political climate, maybe it's just good fun.

Every workshop is different but often the setting is minimal. Perhaps nine people seated round a square formica table under a fluorescent tube, in a community centre or an adult education institute. On the other hand, the venue might be a pub or somebody's living room. Wherever they are, workshops usually involve a lot of talk, cups, glasses, poems, stories and, sometimes, songs. Some workshops are run as a series, some are like courses, some are transient, some last a long time. Some groups

concentrate on performing, some on publishing and others on hosting guest writers. Clockhouse Writers in Woolwich is one example of a South London workshop, which has been going for three years. The group meets every Wednesday and is an informal meeting of ever-changing people, who read, perform and provide one another with a critical audience. Peckham Writers is another example. This group is affiliated to the Federation of Worker Writers, which consists of about thirty autonomous workshops throughout the UK, all committed to a common cause of words.

Poetry in performance, especially, seems to be occupying a lot of people's attention and can be found in pubs and clubs all over South London. Mobile poetry collectives likes Apples and Snakes (based in Forest Hill) and cabaret events like Cast (see Old White Horse) and the Tunnel Palladium at Woolwich are providing a platform for performance poetry. Many South London Borough Arts Officers have taken note of this activity and are including poetry in their diaries of events. Look out for workshops and performances at local festivals (see Festivals and Events) and listen out for the rappers emerging from the Electro funk zones of the music world for they are truly spontaneous in rhythm and rhyme. There are South London organisations involved in publishing poetry and prose. One of these is the Peckham Publishing Project, which is interested in work by children, women, Black and community writers, as well as autobiographies and local history material. Black Ink publishes work by contemporary Black writers, Brockwell Books produce books for children from different cultures, and Label is a poetry and prose magazine which presents the works of writers and artists from Clapham, Hong Kong, Europe, North America, you name it. Another magazine which regularly features poetry and prose is Lambeth Arts, produced every other month by Lambeth Arts Council. Free copies are available from Lambeth libraries and arts venues in the borough.

The following alphabetical listing contains brief details of South London poetry and prose places. Poetry performance collectives are organisations that promote poetry as a performance art, sometimes using a cabaret style. Other terms used in the listing are, we hope, self-explanatory.

Apples and Snakes
24 Worsley House
Shackleton Close
Forest Hill   SE23
Tel 699 5265
Contact Mandy Williams
●Performance poetry collective
Probably the most active organisation promoting poetry as a performance art and cabaret-style entertainment in London, England, Europe. The emphasis is on thought provoking accessible poetry, usually supported by music acts. Apples and Snakes have worked all over South London in clubs, pubs, theatres and community centres in an effort to attract and surprise audiences not normally interested in poetry. Since they started in '82, they have worked with a kaleidescope of innovative talents and they are still challenging the rigid conception of poetry as a bookish occupation. As P R Murry wrote in the introduction to Apples and Snakes' first published collection, 'Poetry is a living art form, it talks to people, it makes electrical and chemical currents fire in their brains, it awakens obscure memories and tired taste buds...'. Poetry as an oral form of expression, as song and as dance, is being demonstrably revitalized by the likes of Apples and Snakes. Phone for programme details.

Battersea Arts Centre
Old Town Hall
Lavender Hill
Battersea   SW11
Tel 223 6557
Contact Diana Warden
Wheelchair access to entire building and special facilities
●Venue
Battersea Arts Centre is becoming a well-known venue for poetry and prose performances. Apples and Snakes regularly appear, book launches are often held (such as Akira Press with Desmond Johnson, Marsha Prescod, J D Douglas) and there are Irish Poetry Evenings with poets from Anvil Press and elsewhere. International Women's Day at the beginning of March '86 is being celebrated at BAC with several days of women's events which should include some interesting work. A two week literature festival, probably to be called Write On, is also being planned for the end of September '86. This will feature local and other poets and lots of different styles of

prose and poetry, including dub, rap and traditional.

Blackheath Poetry Society
27 The Lawns
Lee Terrace
Blackheath   **SE3**
Tel 852 7271
Contact Miss Elkins
Meets 2nd Monday of the month usually in a member's home
Wheelchair access phone first
●Workshop
The Society has a membership of 20-25 people, who meet in one another's homes to read and discuss their favourite literature. On occasions guest speakers are invited to talk to the group on literary topics, such as the poetry of Ted Hughes. Also, guest poets are invited. Past guests have included the local and nationally acclaimed poet Roy Fuller.

Black Horse Workshop
The Black Horse
Rushey Green
Catford   **SE6**
Tel 527 8750(day) 732 8321(eve)
Contact Bill Parkinson
Meets alternate Tuesdays at 8
Wheelchair access to workshop but no special facilities
●Workshop
Every fortnight a few poems or a prose piece by one of the members of the workshop is photocopied and posted to other members of the group. Enough time is allowed to give them the chance to look closely at the texts and offer the writer the benefits of critical attention. It is a small group. However, it is rarely quiet.

Black Ink
258 Coldharbour Lane
Brixton   **SW9**
Tel 733 0746
●Publishers
Black Ink publishes contemporary poetry, stories, novels and plays by Black writers from South London and all over the country. They are sensitive to political and social (especially ethnic) issues. Their titles include 'Hamzad', a novel by Asian writer Allen Goodwin, poetry books by Tony Goffe and Lorraine Simeon, and anthologies of poetry and prose such as 'Wasted Women, Friends and Lovers', written mainy by women. Black Ink also publishes children's picture/reading books. Prices range from 65p to £4.50.

Black Women's Writing and Creativity Workshop
c/o The Albany
Douglas Way
Deptford   **SE8**
Tel 692 0231
Contact Zhana
Meets Mondays at 7
Wheelchair access to the workshop and special facilities
●Workshop
One of the aims of this workshop is to make writing fun, to de-mystify the whole process through creativity games and exercises, such as writing in the workshop situation and writing as a group – with chain poems, 'cut-ups' and other improvisational techniques. Feedback is considered essential as an encouragement to writing skills and responsiveness to the work of others.

Brixton Recreation Centre
27 Brixton Road
Brixton   **SW2**
Tel 274 7774
Wheelchair access to all areas (ring first) and special toilets
●Venue Workshop
Brixton Recreation Centre is a venue for groups and workshops of all descriptions, including writing and performing poetry. The Hip Hop Alliance have regular events that feature rappers (see Young People – Brixton Music Development). Two poets, Markus John and Spartacus R, held residencies at BRC in late '85 and organised a series of workshops

to develop oral and performance techniques. These included singing, drumming and story-telling and featured several special guests. There will almost certainly be some events involving local poets during '86 and at the Brixton Festival (dates unconfirmed at press date).

Brockwell Books
64 Selsdon Road
West Norwood   SE27
Tel 670 0394
●Publishers
Started three years ago, Brockwell Books publish traditional stories for children from African, Chinese, Russian and many other cultures but always in a modern idiom and setting. They are designed to be read aloud and to provoke discussion on social questions between child and parent/teacher/adult. One example is 'The Tiger in Brockwell Park', an adaptation of 'Little Black Sambo' told in a form that is relevant to a child's experience.

Clockhouse Writers
The Clockhouse Community Centre
Dockyard Estate
Defiance Walk
Woolwich   SE18
Tel 699 5265
Contact Chris Cardale
Meets Wednesdays at 8
Wheelchair access to Clockhouse and special facilities
●Performance workshop Publishers
The group has 20 members, who come and go all the time. The core of the group is involved in all aspects of writing, performance (including music and stage craft), and publishing (anthologies and magazines). Members are motivated by one another to get directly involved in community affairs. For instance, Greenwich Borough has recently 'twinned' with the North-east mining town Easington, and writers from both areas have played host to one another, organising

exchange trips, readings and a joint publication.

Goldsmiths Poetry Workshop
Goldsmiths College
32 Lewisham Way
New Cross   SE14
Tel 692 7171
Contact Adult Education Dept
Meets Wednesdays 7-9
Wheelchair access to workshop but please phone first
Admission £25.50pa £5(unwaged)
●Workshop
This poetry workshop is chaired by the well-known poet Allen Fisher. The workshop deals with all aspects of writing and the emphasis is on experimentation. Members can work with the sound and vision facilities available to the group. For instance, it is possible to make video/voice recordings for presentation or to aid performance technique. They also publish small collections of their work.

Label Poetry and Prose Magazine
57 Effingham Road
Lee Green   SE12
Tel none
Editor Paul Beasley
Subscription 90p per copy or £1.60 for 2 issues
●Publisher
Label is a biannual anthology of poetry, prose, artwork and reviews. Its aim is to present the work of new and not so new writer/artists, whose work reflects or concerns itself directly with social and political pressures. The magazines subscribes to no particular aesthetic. The surreal and the socially real can be found side by side. Concrete and performance poetry are regularly featured. Contributors include South London poets, Chris Cardale and Emile Sercombe, also Carol Burdett and Patricia Pogson. Artists include Gary Walton, John Frankland and Conrad Atkinson (Lewisham's Artist-in-residence). Label is produced twice a year with the help

of Lewisham Arts Council, local print workshops and the facilities of community and resource centres in South London. The magazine is virtually handmade, typeset and printed offset litho on variously tinted re-cycled papers. It's about fifty pages thick with a silkscreen cover and graphics. The quality of the work and production belies the fact that it costs only 90p (post included).

Morley College Writers Workshop
61 Westminster Bridge Road
Lambeth North   SE1
Tel 928 8501
Contact Colin Falck
Meets Tuesdays 10-12
Wheelchair access to building but please ring first
Membership £24pa £1(unwaged)
●Workshop
Chaired by ILEA tutor, Colin Falck, this workshop is run like a course in creative writing. The class is called 'Writing Poetry' and the college prospectus informs that the sessions aren't suitable for complete beginners. Admission is by application to the tutor at the first or subsequent meetings of the group and involves a submission of material.

Old White Horse
Brixton Road
Brixton   SW9
Tel 487 3440
Meets Fridays in autumn/winter
Wheelchair access one small step but direct access through pub by prior arrangement (Tel 274 5537)
●Cabaret venue
Cast presents a variety of cabaret acts every Friday night through autumn and winter at the Old White Horse. Jugglers, stand up comics, always live music (reggae, rock, punk) and, occasionally, a poet (always of performance calibre and usually musically inspired). Past poets have included Benjamin

Zephaniah. Cast holds a 2-3 day long audition every year for new performers and acts so phone to enquire.

Open Poetry Conventicle
Dance Attic
214 Putney Bridge Road
Putney   SW15
Tel 785 2116/2055
Contact Carol Fisher
Meets Last Sunday of the month 2-4
Wheelchair access to workshop but please phone first
Admission £2 per session
●Performance workshop
The Conventicle (which actually means 'a dissenting religious meeting') is a combination of workshop and performance. A guest writer, usually a published poet, will read and invite questions. After a break for refreshments, the members of the group (about 10-12 people) read and discuss their work amongst themselves and with the guest writer. There is a hard core of regulars and others who come and go. Lively, and not at all daunting, so go and read your work or join in the discussion. Past guests have included Carol Satyamuiti, Wendy Cope and Jeremy Reed.

Peckham Publishing Project
The Book Place
13 Peckham High Street
Peckham   SE15
Tel 708 0025
●Publishers
Peckham Publishing Project is part of a national movement in community publishing and an associate member of the Federation of Worker Writers and Community Publishers. It publishes local/oral history, autobiography, poems and short stories and is interested in work written by children, women, Black and community writers. Examples of titles are 'This is England', an anthology of short stories relating the experiences of

West Indian, African, Irish and East European people coming to England. Also, Jim Allen's collection of short stories about growing up in South London in the 30s, called 'Godfers'. The Press is committed to giving a voice to the working class culture and experience.

Peckham Writers
The Peckham Settlement Community Centre
Staffordshire Street
Peckham SE15
Tel 378 6860
Contact Dave Heary
Meets alternate Tuesdays 7-9
Wheelchair access to centre and special facilities
●Workshop
Peckham Writers is an independent group but also a member of the Federation of Worker Writers. It actively endorses the general manifesto of that organisation 'to further the cause of working class writing' in the face of cultural suppression. The meetings ae lively affairs where members' work is read out and discussed along with Federation activities, such as readings and conventions.

Poetry South East London
Kidbrooke House
90 Mycenae Road
Blackheath SE3
Tel 852 9704
Contact Martin Jenkins
Meets alternate Thursdays at 8
Wheelchair access to buiding and special facilities
Admission 25p for newcomers
Membership £2
●Workshop
Small informal meetings where the members of the workshop read out and discuss their own work. There is a general emphasis on craft and criticism. The workshop has so far produced two collections of work.

Ragged Trousers Cabaret
21 Cavendish Road
Sutton
Tel 661 8877(day) 661 7375(eve)
Contact Pat Cunnane
●Performance poetry collective
This group takes poetry to the political front-line with benefit performances in Neasden, in the Kent coalfield and in welfare clubs during the miners' strike. It is also active throughout South London, providing entertainments for the Labour and Trade Union Movements. Shows involve poetry (performance/cabaret style) and music.

Skill Centre Writers Group
The Skill Centre
Brownhill Road
Catford SE6
Tel 698 8547
Meets Thursdays 2-4
Wheelchair access throughout and special facilities
●Workshop
This writers' group is a friendly gathering of older, retired people (some write, some listen, some comment), who usually link up with a group of young people from local schools. The group has recently put together its first collection of poetry and organised a launch/reading at the Centre. Occasionally, guest writers visit.

Staunch Poets and Players
Manor House
58 Clapham Common Northside
Clapham SW4
Tel 228 2015
Contact Don Kinch
●Performance
Poets, musicians, dancers, writers, directors and actors present the Black experience, past and present.

The Tunnel Palladium
The Mitre
338 Tunnel Avenue
Woolwich   SE10
Tel 858 0895
Meets Sundays at 9
Wheelchair access ring to check
●Cabaret venue
Alternative comedy groups and
poetry acts. Past performers have
included John Cooper-Clarke.

Women Writers Workshop
Clockhouse Community Centre
Defiance Walk
Woolwich   SE18
Tel 267 4128
Contact Kate Pahl
Meets Thursdays 10-12 noon
Wheelchair access throughout and
special facilities
●Workshop
This is a small group started by an
ILEA tutor. Members read out their
own work and the work of writers
they particularly admire. Members
are encouraged to practise writing in
the workshop situation. For example,
'automatic writing' is encouraged as
a means of uninhibiting expression.

Zuriya
38 Brixton Road
Oval   SW9
Tel 582 9479
●Performance workshop
Zuriya is concerned with Afro-
Caribbean cultural expression and
uses dance, drumming, singing,
poetry, drama and storytelling. They
aim to popularise cultural activity by
making it fun and often work with
children and young people in schools
and youth clubs. They perform the
work of writers such as Leopold
Sedar Senghor from West Africa,
Aime Caesaire from Martinique
(author of 'Return To My Native
Land'), and Langston Huges and
other poets of the Harlem
Renaissance.

RESTAURANTS

This chapter does not pretend to be a comprehensive guide to restaurants in South London. We have merely described a few of the ones we happen to like most. Please tell us about some of your favourite places so that we can investigate them for our next edition. We have mentioned only briefly those restaurants that are often written about in other guides and have allowed more space for those we feel have been somewhat overlooked. Since hardly anyone we know can manage three courses at one sitting, we have quoted an average price for a 2-course meal per head excluding wine. This should be considered only as a rough guide. Depending on what you eat, you could spend a bit less or considerably more.

The Clearing House
London Bridge
(entrance off Tooley Street)
London Bridge   SE1
Tel 407 0927 or 378 6778
Open 11.45-3 5.30-9(Mon-Fri) 12-2.30(Sun)
Wheelchair access to restaurant

2 course meal £5.50-£6.50
Set meals 4-course Xmas meal £11.50
and 17 special party menus
House wine £4.45
●American
This two-storey restaurant has its home in a magnificent old clearing house just under London Bridge and close to a fine open piazza by the river. The high tech two-storey interior in yellow, black and white and the large indoor plants and trees give a fresh and spacious feel to the place. The standard menu evolved from 1600 questionnaires that were completed by visitors to the restaurant over a long period. It offers a choice of six starters, thirteen main courses plus a range of pizzas with adventurous toppings, followed by eight desserts. In addition, there are at least two chef's specials a day. Starters include deep fried brie with gooseberry and port relish, baked potato skins with a variety of dips, deep fried mushrooms in breadcrumbs with garlic mayonnaise (tasty but a little greasy), and a superb vegetable soup

(presumably made from local Borough Market produce). Examples of main dishes are turkey stuffed with asparagus and ham accompanied by a jacket potato and salad, tortilla filled with chilli in a piquant sauce and pork stuffed with stilton cheese. We are happy to report that we played a significant role in persuading the management not to abandon their excellent smoked salmon, cream cheese and bagels. The Clearing House salad is a large fresh American-style salad with ham, feta, tomato, egg, cucumber, croutons, bacon, onion and lettuce. Puddings include banana barge, Black Forest gateau, profiteroles, sorbets and ice creams. The house white is a Blanc de Blanc and the red

'The Clearing House'

is an acceptable vin de l'Herault. However, for just a little over a pound more we suggest you try the 1981 Rioja which in our opinion is positively silken. The Clearing House is in a working area of London so lunchtime is their busy period (they do a range of tempting open Danish sandwiches). All the same, unlike other restaurants in the area, they are also open for dinner. Their courage and the efficiency of their enterprise should be supported.

Diks

8 Nelson Road
Greenwich   SE10
Tel 858 8588
Open Mon Wed-Sun(lunch)
Mon Wed-Sat(dinner)
Wheelchair access to restaurant only
Set meals Lunchtime buffet £3
Sunday lunch £5.50 Dinner £8(3 courses) £10(4 courses)
House wine £4
●International

Diks is a family-run restaurant in the middle of Greenwich, which specialises in excellent set meals at reasonable prices. A carving buffet at lunchtime offers customers one or more cold roast meats with a plate of salad (you help yourself) and a baked potato, or a hot dish with the same trimmings for much the same price. The three-course Sunday lunch consists of a choice of hot roasts (usually beef, lamb, turkey and pork) and, in summer, the addition of cold salmon salad has proved very popular. A three or four-course dinner with coffee completes Dik's range of set menus. Presentation has a somewhat French style – there is a large pot of butter on the table for one and all, a bowl of crudites with a dip, and those who ask for pate and soup are given a whole pate to cut from and soup in a huge terrine with a ladle for self help. Other enjoyable starters include galia melon with lime sorbet, and quiche lorraine. To follow, we can recommend roast stuffed duckling, roast leg of lamb stuffed with mint and rosemary, and marmite dieppoise (a casserole of salmon, prawns and whitefish). All the dishes at Diks are home-made and every one delicious. Brandy cake is an unexpected but not disappointing piece of rich fruit cake and other sweets on offer include marzipanice with dark chocolate, butterscotch and almond coupe and eight different kinds of fruit sorbet. There is a choice of red, white, German and rose house wines all at the same price and the house red Rioja is unusually good.

'Diks' Greenwich

Dining Room
Winchester Walk
London Bridge　　　　SE1
Tel 407 0337
Open 12-3 7-10 (Tue-Fri)
Wheelchair access none
2 course meal £6 per head
House wine £4.50
●Vegetarian/Wholefood
Just occasionally Dining Room's food can be a little stodgy but nevertheless we have no hesitation in naming it as our favourite vegetarian cum wholefood restaurant south of the river. It is also a special space. Deep in the basement of an old warehouse, the room (with its collection of magazines and baby pink walls) has a relaxed, contemplative mood.

Erawan Thai Restaurant
161 Mitcham Road
Tooting　　　　SW17
Tel 672 3972
Open 12-2.30 6-11.30 daily
Wheelchair access to restaurant only
2 course meal £7-£8 per head
House wine £4.50
●Thai
The setting at The Erawan is

pleasing, the welcome is always warm and the service courteous and helpful. It needs to be, since the names of the Thai dishes will probably be unfamiliar and you'll have lots of questions to ask. For starters, we can thoroughly recommend the khanom cheeb dim sim (laced with lots of garlic and served with soy sauce and pickled chillis). Another one well worthy of praise is the hoy jor (described as a deep-fried crab meat sausage). Some main courses you should try are kai pud prik (a huge portion of fried chicken Thai-style), muh tod (shallow-fried pork with a garlic and pepper sauce), nua pud numnan hoi (beef, mushrooms and spring onions in oyster sauce with cashew nuts), pla tod (deep fried crispy cod served with a fish sauce) and muh pud king (slices of pork fried with ginger and jelly). Pud Pak is the Thai name for a selection of seasonal vegetables which we have always enjoyed. We have also tried some rather interesting noodles with beansprouts. The house wine is French red and Blanc de Blanc white and there　are more expensive wines (including a good Medoc) on the list.

Fanaria
180 Upper Richmond Road West
East Sheen　　　　SW14
Tel 878 8143 or 876 6559
Open 12-2.30(Mon-Sat) 6-11(Mon-Thur) 6-12(Fri-Sat)
Wheelchair access to restaurant only
2 course meal £5
Set meals Meze £6 per person
House wine £4.50
●Greek
The food at Fanaria is freshly made by a chef who cares about authentic Greek cuisine. The houmous and the taramosalata are quite different from the usual English versions and, if you like that kind of thing, the loukanika (smoked Greek sausages) will not disappoint you. The moussaka (made of pork and lamb) is excellent and

cheap and the sheftalia (minced pork with onion, parsley and cumin) is really interesting. Highly recommended also is the souvla, a piece of lean lamb on the bone, which has been marinated for several hours in wine and oregano and then cooked gently over charcoal. By the time it reaches your table, the meat is subtly flavoured and tender and positively falls off the bone. All three dishes are sensibly served with a green salad. There are plenty of other tempting dishes including meze (a selection of cold starters and charcoal grill dishes) and a sirloin steak is soon to be introduced. For wine, we recommend the Nemea (a dry red Greek wine) although there is a slightly cheaper house wine and well-known names such as Demestica. The only regret is that Fanaria has no fish dishes. Their space is limited so they have chosen to concentrate on a smallish menu, providing quality rather than quantity. The proof, as they say, is in the eating.

Gandhi's
347a Kennington Road
Oval   SE11
Tel 735 9015
Open 12-2.30 6-11.45 daily
Wheelchair access to restaurant
2 course meal £10 per head
House wine £5
●Indian
Small, rather smart Indian restaurant which has served consistently good food since it opened. The waiters could be a bit more cheerful but we have no other complaints.

Hung Foo
6 West Hill
Wandsworth   SW18
Tel 870 0177
Open 12-2.15 6-11.45(Mon-Sat)
Wheelchair access to restaurant only
2 course meal £7 per head
House wine £4.95
●Peking

We much preferred the Hung Foo when it was a scruffy, friendly little restaurant with flock wallpaper and cramped surroundings. It expanded into the next door building some years ago and it's as if the character was knocked away with the wall. However it is still rightly popular (be sure to book) and the food is as good as it always was.

Jacaranda
11-13 Brixton Station Road
Brixton   SW9
Tel 274 8383
Open 10-10(Mon-Sat)
Wheelchair access to ground floor with access to toilets which are not specially adapted
2 course meal £5.50 per head and lots of cheaper snacks from £1.25
House wine £4.25
●International
The Jacaranda has an upstairs restaurant and a more informal space on the ground floor where you can sit and chat over a cup of tea, a snack or a full meal. The food is truly international in that it comes from the West Indies, South Africa, Latin America, Europe and other continents. Almost half the dishes are vegetarian. Both upstairs and

downstairs are open during the day
and serve the same fare, but only the
restaurant tends to be open in the
evening. Stuffed tomatoes, avocado
with a cheese and cream dressing,
snails, and crab thermidor are just a
few examples of the starters often on
offer. Regular main dish favourites
include pasticcio (lasagne in a cheese
sauce with tomatoes and cheese),
bobotie (a spicy South African beef
bake), rice and peas, and there are
always several tempting specials of
the day. Sweets include some
excellent homemade cakes, a pear
and brandy tart, zuccotto (an Italian
chocolate sponge stuffed with double
cream, hazelnuts, cherries and
liqueur), and that good old nursery
food, queen of puddings. The
Jacaranda's snacks make great
lunchtime eating. Pan bagna is a
hunk of French bread stuffed with
tuna, anchovies and salad
(apparently a traditional French
farmer's meal), chicken Jenetta is
chicken with mayonnaise, gherkins
and salad, and the American club
special is a delicious multi-layered
sandwich with lettuce, chicken,
mayonnaise, bacon, tomato and
cucumber. Finally, pan dominique, a
brown bap with cottage cheese,
lettuce and avocado is a wonderful
combination. If you're a woman and
the waiter comes to clear your table,
don't pass him your dishes for he will
tell you in the friendliest of ways
that this is the job he is paid to do,
that you are suffering from
conditioning, and that all you should
be doing is relaxing and enjoying
yourself. How right he is!

The Khyber
346 South Lambeth Road
Stockwell   SW8
Tel 622 3541
Open 12-3 6-12 daily

Wheelchair access to restaurant only
2 course meal £7 per head
House wine £4.40
●Indian
We watched with baited breath as
the local veg shop was transformed
into the Khyber in the Summer of
'85. Since it opened in July and over
the last hectic months it has become
our regular, both as a take-away and
as somewhere to take a breather. The
restaurant is delightfully arranged
with perspex dividers engraved with
birds, flowers and elephants. The
staff are friendly and the food has
always been good. We suggest you
have your starter(s) with your main
course. The breadcrumbed mixed
vegetable and chicken pakoras
(technically starters) go particularly
well with creamy dishes like the
excellent lamb badam pasanda
(flavoured with almonds and other
nuts), the shahi korma (a mild meat
dish cooked with cream and nuts) or
the tandoori butter chicken (off the
bone in a creamy tomato sauce). The
prawn bhuna is also excellent and
the sag panir (homemade whey with
spinach and loads of garlic) is
positively irresistible. 10% discount

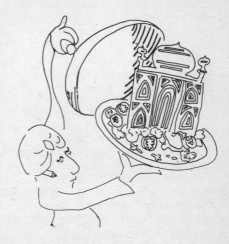

for take-aways. At last Stockwell has
a good eating place!

The Laughing Buddha
41 Montpelier Vale
Blackheath SE3
Tel 852 4l6l/2166
Open 12-2.30 6-midnight daily
Wheelchair access none
2 course meal £10 per head
Set meals Special feasts £8.50 & £12 per head
House wine £4.95

If you like Peking and Szechuan food, The Laughing Buddha is well worth a visit but book first as it's popular with the locals. It's a sophisticated rather chic place and, while it's not wildly expensive, it's certainly not your average cheap Chinese local. There are several feasts (see above), fresh sea food is a speciality, and the dishes are unusual and, for the most part, excellent. We recommend the grilled fish Peking style, the shredded chicken with garlic sauce, and the 'quick fried three kinds of seafood'. The crispy lamb comes with a plate of even crispier lettuce, in which it is wrapped and dunked in a rather delicious sweet sauce (Peking duck-style). The hot mixed special starter (for two) is a Peking fry-up with mashed prawns on toast with sesame seeds, crispy won ton, deep fried chicken pieces and a particularly delicious spring roll. There are a number of other vegetarian dishes on the menu. 10% off for take-aways before 8pm

Le Bonjour
252 Wandsworth Road
Stockwell SW8
Open 12-3(Mon-Sat) 7-11(Mon-Thur Sun) 7-1(Fri-Sat)
Wheelchair access to restaurant only
2 course meal £5-£6.50 per head
●Caribbean French and English
Le Bonjour has been open since March '85 and it too is one of our regular local eating places. The style has changed somewhat over the months. The original menu is now split into three separate ones (Caribbean, French and English). This causes a certain amount of physical stress as you jostle with the sheer volume of paperwork and mental anguish at the thought of missing something on somebody else's menu. There is no need to fear. The starters and the fish dishes are more or less the same on all the menus. The meat dishes do vary, however. The Caribbean menu might offer beef ocho rios and dumplings, braised oxtail, Caribbean lamb and Caribbean chicken. By contrast, the French menu includes dishes like coq au vin, chicken supreme, beef stroganoff, veal escalopes and (not strictly French) tournedos rossini. Traditional English diners are tempted with grilled best end of lamb, steak and kidney pudding, lambs liver and bacon and several steaks. The desserts are almost the same on all three menus. We have always stuck to the Caribbean menu and can thoroughly recommend pan fried mullet and grilled sword fish. (The fish is bought from one of London's best fishmongers across the road so is always likely to be good.) We also always enjoy the Caribbean chicken, the lamb cona and the Caribbean lamb (cassaroled or otherwise). Most of the dishes are served with European vegetables but you can also order plantain, yam and other Caribbean vegetables. There is no house wine as such, the wine list has no pretensions and the prices are

excellent. The most expensive wine is a Mateus Rose at £4.75, although we prefer the cheaper Castellino at £3.50. The manager of Le Bonjour is a treat. He really cares about his restaurant and his customers, and will stop the evening's proceedings to plead with people to book their tables in advance so that he can be well prepared and able to look after them in the best possible manner. 'Away Away!' hails the chef as each meal is ready to be presented, and off darts the manager into the kitchen to bring his gastronomic delights to the waiting diners.

The Light of India
50 Atlantic Road
Brixton   SW9
Tel 274 8600
Open 12-3 6-12(Mon-Thur) 12-12(Fri-Sat)
Wheelchair access and to toilets which are not specially adapted*
2 course meal £6 per head
House wine £4.75
●Indian

All the staff at The Light of India are welcoming and friendly and the restaurant has a really good feel. The food is excellent value and we have never been disappointed by anything we have tried from the surprisingly long menu. We particularly enjoy the tandoori butter chicken which comes with a huge piece of butter on top, the korai gosht, the niramish (green beans), the chana moslander (chick peas), and the home-made motor panir. We have also tried the reshmee kebab as a starter, which is like a spicy meatball. The house wine is a good price and there is an slighly pricier vintage Medoc and St Emilion. The restaurant is cosy and not extravagantly done up. All in all, The Light of India seems to have got its priorities right.

Maharaja Cuisine
250 The Broadway
Wimbledon   SW19
Tel 542 7697
Open 12-2.30(daily) 6-12(Mon-Thur Sun) 6.30-12.30(Fri-Sat)
Wheelchair access none
2 course meal £5-7 per head
House wine £5.30
●Indian

Thank goodness for Indian restaurants like the Maharaja Cuisine. No fancy decor here just excellent food at very reasonable prices. To begin with, we suggest a samee kebab (two small meat patties, subtly flavoured with garlic and ginger), and the wonderful prawn and puri. (The prawns are in a tomato and onion sauce with a lot of garlic, a little chilli and 'a few selected spices', served piping hot inside a puri.) The karai gosht (made with meat or chicken, red and green peppers and lots of fresh coriander) takes its name from the cast iron pot or karai in which it is cooked and brought to the table. Also highly recommended is the meat (lamb) passinda which is cooked in a rich red wine and cream sauce, flavoured with cashew nuts and almonds. The mixed vegetable korma is unusually sweet but delicious. The Maharaja has recently introduced a fish tandoori which is excellent. Be sure to order one in advance or you may be disappointed. You will need to say how big a fish you want. When it comes to wine, something we appreciate at the Maharaja is that the bottle is left on the table for you to pour at your own pace. Similarly, when you ask for water you are given a jug of iced water rather than the usual single glass. Generosity is a characteristic of the restaurant. The owner and his wife say they are committed to serving authentic Indian food to their customers. See what you think – we certainly support them.

Majestic Restaurant
4 Clapham Common Southside
Clapham SW4
Tel 622 4960
Open 12-11.30(till midnight on Sat)
Wheelchair access none
2 course meal £2.80-£5.50 per head
No licence
●Greek-Cypriot
The Majestic has been in Clapham
since 1961 and is open non-stop from
noon every day. It has no licence but
you are welcome to take your own
wine and will be charged no corkage.
In spite of its excellent prices, The
Majestic is not a cafe. When you step
inside you are in an authentic
family-run Southern European
restaurant where the decor is basic
and formal (white linen tablecloths
cover the tables) and where the
priorities are the warmth of the
welcome and the quality of the food.
You really do have to have a healthy
appetite, however. The portions are
huge and the selection is equally
plentiful. Starters include soup,
melon, and homemade houmous and
taramosalata. To follow, there is a
whole range of roast, grilled and
fried English dinners and a small
selection of Greek specialities which
are superb. We recommend the
moussaka (one of the best we've
tasted), the stifado, the afelia and
kleftico. The meat is always tender
and all four dishes are remarkably
free of grease and fat. They come
with various combinations of rice,
roast potatoes and salad so you need
stamina to venture forth into the
world of puds. Try to keep some
space, however, because here you can
get genuine sultana, sponge or rice
pudding, jelly and cream and
baklava. A great place.

Rebato's
169 South Lambeth Road
Stockwell SW8
Tel 735 6388
Open 12-2.30(Mon-Fri) 7-11.20(Mon-
Sat)

Wheelchair access to restaurant only
Set 3-course meal £9 per head
House wine £4.95
●Spanish
It comes as quite a shock when you
first step off South Lambeth Road
and venture through the bar into
this long, spacious, extremely elegant
restaurant with its own fountain.
Somehow, you feel you have to be on
your best behaviour here!
Nevertheless, despite its grandeur
the staff are welcoming and you soon
feel at ease. More importantly, the
food is marvellous. A mainly Spanish
menu with other European
influences offers you a set 3-course
meal with lots of choice. We have had
some good meat dishes and can also
highly recommend the parrillada, a
wonderful concoction of fish and
shellfish. If you feel like something
less elaborate you can relax in the
bar and feast upon a selection of
freshly made tapas (small traditonal
between-meal Spanish snacks).

RSJ
13a Coin Street
Waterloo SE1
Tel 928 4554
Open 12-2(Mon-Fri) 6-11(Mon-Sat)
Wheelchair access to restaurant only
2 course meal £14 per head
House wine £5.95
Elegant restaurant which has never
failed to please. Imaginative, stylish,
nouvelle cuisine with a fine wine list
to match. Definitely somewhere to
go for a treat.

Rupali Tandoori
266 Wandsworth Road
Stockwell   SW8
Tel 622 0455
Open 12-3(daily) 6-12(Mon Thur Sun)
6-12.30(Fri-Sat)
Wheelchair access none
2 course meal £4-5 per head
House wine £3.80
●Indian
This is an old favourite of ours and
one of the best Indian restaurants in
the area. Don't miss the Rupali
special, a chicken dish cooked in a
mild but interesting yoghurt and
cream sauce. This restaurant is often
much emptier than it ought to be so
go and help fill it up.

Something Spicy
112 St John's Hill
Clapham Junction   SW11
Tel 228 4412
Open 7-12(Mon-Thur Sat-Sun)
Wheelchair access to restaurant only
2 course meal £10-£12 per head
Set meals £8.95 per person (for 8
dishes)
House wine £5.60
●Spicy food
Something Spicy opened at the end of
April 1985 and the Sri Lankan
owner/chef and his family have taken
enormous care over their restaurant.
The decor is imaginative and the
tables are well spaced and beautifully
presented. The style of service is
efficient and formal and, above all,
extremely courteous (the first
example of this is the glass of bucks
fizz which diners are given on
arrival). The menu offers spicy food
from many parts of the world and is
full of unfamiliar names and
exciting-sounding dishes like chutu
karulla (spiced, stuffed quail with
almonds in a lemon sauce), malu
(salmon steaks in a mild curry gravy
with a hint of coconut), batelu kakul
(marinated lamb steak, chargrilled
and served with apple chutney) and
butter lemon chicken (marinated in a
lemon liqueur and cooked in butter

with cashew nuts). There are several
vegetarian dishes, including a
cashew nut curry, creamy spiced
lentils and bithara (a spiced omelette
served in a curry gravy). There are
two rather pricy special dishes for
two persons (which have to be
ordered three and a half hours in
advance) – a whole pheasant soaked
in port, cooked in butter with onions
and served with vegetables, and a
wild duck cooked in cointreau with
herbs and also served with
vegetables. The set meal for two
includes venison cooked in spiced red
wine, chicken tikka (not a bit like
the usual version), cashew curry
(cashew nuts in a spicy, creamy
sauce), spiced lentils, a fresh
coriander salad, rice and onion and
coconut sambols. The equally
interesting starters include salmon
parcels (light stuffed pancakes) and
spicy lamb-filled bites. If you happen
to still have some space, a deliciously
fluffy chocolate mousse or a cherry
and kirsch ice cream are two ways of
rounding off your meal. The French
house wine is very drinkable but the
rest of the wines are, sadly,
somewhat over-priced – the only
unattractive feature of an otherwise
pleasing restaurant.

South of the Border
8-10 Joan Street
Waterloo   SE1
Tel 928 6374
Open 12-2.45(Mon-Fri) 6-11.30(Mon-
Sat)
Wheelchair access to restaurant only
2 course meal £10 per head
Set meal Indonesian menu for two £8
each
House wine £5
●International
Thoroughly reliable and welcoming
restaurant whose Australian chef
has slowly but surely been
introducing Indonesian dishes to
complement the excellent bistro style
food. This has obviously been a hit as
he has recently added a full

340

Indonesian menu and a 7-course
Indonesian meal for two with a jug of
quattrini kooler or suleman soother
to wash it down.

Stanton's
24 Clapham Road
Oval   SW9
Tel 587 0259
Open 12-2.30 7-10.30 daily
Wheelchair access none
2 course meal £10 per head
House wine £4.50 & £5.50
●English/French
Stanton's opened in March '85 and is
a sibling of Wellies in Battersea and
the Brasserie in Bellevue Road. It
couldn't be more different, however.
The menu changes about every three
weeks and always offers a choice of
starters, lighter and main courses
(both of which include vegetarian
dishes), desserts and a selection of
cheeses. The fare is imaginative and
everything we have tried has been
interesting and successful. A fresh
soup is provided daily and the ones
we have ordered have been very
tasty. Other starters to be
recommended are fish parcels (with
salmon and halibut, encased in won
ton pastry and deep fried), and, to
remain with the packaging theme,
vegetable envelopes (vegetables and
rice in a lightly steamed cabbage
envelope, covered in a tarragon
sauce). The chilled ballontine of fresh
trout and halibut with watercress
sauce is unusual and not immediately
likeable but the strong watercress
flavour grows on you. The Lighter
Dishes include offerings like steamed
squid on a leek puree, cured duck
breast with a radish and fennel salad
topped with Thai sauce, fresh
spinach and cheese served in a
wholemeal pancake, a jambonette of
chicken with a warm rosemary cream
sauce, and a cold French salad of
frise, mignonette, endive and
radicchio (wild chicory) in a special
dressing. Main dishes to recommend
are wild goose with a brandy and

apple sauce on a bed of cabbage and
herbs, mille feuille of salmon with a
beurre blanc sauce, and noisettes of
lamb stuffed with wild mushrooms
and encased in puff pastry, served
with a madeira sauce. For puds,
there's a tempting selection of
sorbets and ice creams, all made with
natural ingredients, and lots more to
choose from including a hot winter
berry crepe with a tangerine sauce.
Both the red and the white house
wines are French and there are
several other whites and a pleasing
house claret for a pound more. In
early spring '86 Stanton's are
opening their basement as a
restaurant and using the ground
floor as a wine bar with light snacks.
Let's hope the quality stays the same.
They have a small patio for outdoor
eating.

The Vault
(under London Bridge)
1-3 Tooley Street
London Bridge   SE1
Tel 403 7312
Open 12-3(Mon-Fri)
Wheelchair access none
2 course meal £8-£10 per head
House wine £4.40
●British
The Vault, which you will find
literally under London Bridge, is
unlike any other restaurant in this
chapter in that it only opens for
lunch. (It does however have a wine
bar which stays open till 8.30 during
the week.) Although the restaurant
attracts a considerable number of
local business people the high vaulted
room (from which it takes its name)
allows space and privacy for
everyone. All the food is prepared
and made on the premises using fresh
vegetables from neighbouring
Borough Market. The list of starters
includes cornets of smoked salmon
with scrambled egg, Venetian-style
mussels, and poached egg Benedict
(served on a muffin). Home made pies
are the chef's speciality.

SCHOOL

General Advice

**Advisory Centre for Education
(ACE)**
18 Victoria Park Square
E2
Tel 980 4596
ACE publishes a useful booklet,
Choosing A School (£1.75 inc pp), and
offers advice on all aspects of
education. Send an sae for a complete
publications list.

State Schools

If you are a parent living in
**Greenwich, Lambeth, Lewisham,
Southwark** or **Wandsworth**, your
education authority is ILEA, which is
split into ten divisions. You should
ring or write to your local division
(see below) for a list of nursery and
primary schools and then contact the
school of your choice direct, making
the necessary arrangements for your
child's admission. ILEA has a system
of 'banding' whereby final year
primary school children are given an
anonymous test so that the authority
can know how many children in each
band (1=above average, 2=average
and 3=below average) need to be
placed in local secondary schools. The
aim is to arrive at a balanced intake of
children of differing abilities. The
primary school head teacher decides
which band is appropriate for each
child. If you are having to consider
your child's move to a secondary
school, you should contact your ILEA
division and ask for their booklet
about local secondary schools which
will also outline the general
procedure regarding selecting a
school, your right of appeal etc. Local
secondary schools have a programme
of open days for parents and children
(usually some time in October or
November) and you will be invited to
visit your child's primary head
teacher in November or December to
express your first choice. It is possible
to ask for a place at a school in the
area of another local education

authority but it's best beforehand to seek advice from that authority about the likelihood of your child's admission. In March you will be told whether you have been succesful in securing a place for your child at the school of your first choice. If your child has not been offered a place, you may appeal against the decision but should, nevertheless, express a second and third choice when you are invited to see your child's primary school head teacher in mid-March. At this interview you may also ask for an appeal form. Appeals are usually heard before the end of the Summer Term. If your child has particular educational needs, you should arrange an appointment with a specialist at your local ILEA divisional office so that it can be decided whether your child's needs can be met by mainstream education or whether special provision is required.

Greenwich (Division 6)
Riverside House
2nd Floor Tower Block
Beresford Street
Woolwich   SE18
Tel 855 3161

Lambeth (Division 9)
50 Acre Lane
Brixton   SW2
Tel 274 6288

Lewisham (Division 7)
Capital House
47 Rushey Green
Catford   SE6
Tel 698 4633

Southwark (Division 8)
2 Camden Square
Peckham Road
Peckham   SE15
Tel 703 0855

Kirkdale Free School

Wandsworth (Division 10)
78 Garratt Lane
Wandsworth   SW18
Tel 874 7262

If you live in **Merton**, you are outside the ILEA area but much of the procedure is similar to the above. However, Merton does not operate a 'banding' arrangement and has a primary, middle and high school system rather than the primary and secondary ILEA one. Merton's Education Department has a useful booklet covering general information and another called 'Admission to Schools' which is published each year.

Merton Education Dept
Crown House
London Road
Morden
Surrey
Tel 545 3262

Independent Schools

Montessori Nursery Schools

Montessori nursery schools aim to provide an environment in which

children can develop as independent individuals within a group. Children are encouraged to become absorbed in carefully chosen activities, to correct their own mistakes and thereby acquire practical and creative skills rather than knowledge for its own sake. There are several Montessori schools in South London:

Battersea Montessori Schools
at Bridge Lane & Cabul Road
Battersea SW11
Tel 622 7658 (eves)

Parkgate Montessori School
St Mary-le-Park Church
Parkgate Road
Battersea SW11

Right Impressions Montessori Nursery School
144 Merton Road
Southfields SW19
Tel 947 0087

The Montessori Children's Home
St John Ambulance Hall
124-6 Kingston Road
Wimbledon SW19

The Village Montessori School
All Saint's Church Hill
Tranquil Vale
Blackheath SE3
Tel 690 7525 (after 4pm)

Rudolf Steiner

Rudolf Steiner believed that being born is a process that continues long after birth and his schools aim to nurture equally the artistic, practical and intellectual faculties of children so they can live in society with confidence, purpose and direction. The teaching approach is inspired by Steiner's philosophy (Anthroposophy) which has its roots in Christianity but it is not directly taught and pupils are encouraged to formulate their own views. Steiner held that children reach a certain level of maturity in their seventh year and that this is, therefore, the best time at which to begin to teach them to read and write. The children's first six and a half years in Kindergarten contain no formal intellectual instruction but concentrate on learning through play and physical movement. In the Lower School (from 6 to 14) the emphasis shifts to the development of the imagination and emotions. In the Upper School the accent is on the education of thinking and the development of personal judgement. From the age of six and a half for the following eight years, children at Steiner have the same class teacher who holds special responsibility for their welfare, happiness and personal development. Public examinations are not compulsory. At present, there is only one Steiner school in South London:

The Waldorf School of South West London
Balham SW12
Tel 673 4881

This small Steiner school opened in September 1984 and currently has two Kindergarten groups and a Lower School. The aim is to meet the educational needs of children up to university entrance.

Free Schools

Kirkdale School
186 Kirkdale
Sydenham
SE26
Tel 778 0149
Kirkdale is a parent/teacher collective which has regular meetings and no hierarchy. The school takes a maximum of 35 children and has a staff to children ratio of 1:8. Children are welcome to join the school at any age between three and a half and thirteen though most move on at eleven. They are divided into three age groups, hold weekly group meetings among themselves to discuss issues and solve any difficulties, and can move freely from one group to another, participating in the timetable that seems most interesting. Occasionally, parents and other adults provide additional activities. Kirkdale has three class rooms, separate rooms for music, painting, and woodwork, a small yard and a large garden. Lack of money means that the facilities aren't great but there's a spirit of enjoyment and mutual affection among the children

at Kirkdale which more than compensates for the trappings of material wealth. Kirkdale's fees are low and at present children can come from anywhere, though a catchment area might be enforced by ILEA if the school's grant application is successful.

Other Independent Schools

Independent Schools Information Service (ISIS)
Murray House
3 Vandon Street
SW1
Tel 222 7274
ISIS is a useful organisation for those parents wishing to find out about other independent schools in South London.

Education Out of School

Education Otherwise
18 Eynham Road
W12
Education Otherwise offers a support and advice service for parents wishing to work with their children at home. There is quite a large network of families in South London who have chosen to educate their children out of school. Contact the above address for the name of your local co-ordinator.

SPORT

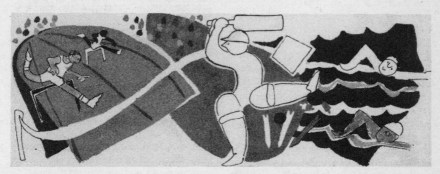

Perhaps you've never thought of taking up a sport... Nothing's interested you? Nowhere to leave the children? No proper facilities for disabled people? Equipment and entry charges too expensive? There are countless reasons why people have been excluded or have excluded themselves from sport.

Local sports facilities may not be perfect but many are changing to meet the needs of the community. Now, more than ever before, sport is on the agenda for everyone.

Over 200 sports are practised in London and there is a string of organisations providing information, advice and sometimes grants to develop sport.

Many sports centres run training sessions for women, disabled and retired people.

'Come and Try' days when people can try out any sport of their choice are becoming increasingly popular, and there's a huge network of clubs and classes covering every standard for you to join. If you need some coaching or wish to meet people of a similar standard with whom you can practise, you might enjoy attending an ILEA course. Charges vary depending on the length of the course and the number of sessions, though there's a standard fee of £1 for claimants and OAPs. See chapter on Adult Education for your nearest institute.

Community Sport covers Multi-Purpose Recreation Centres (Crystal Palace and the centres in our six boroughs) and Swimming Pools. (Don't forget many pools offer other facilities as well.)

The next section is called **Private Facilities**.

Then we have **Sports Round-Up** which contains a list of local, London-wide and national sports organisations, a few miscellaneous bibs and bobs, and some information about specatotor events in the area.

Finally we have charts showing the facilities available in South London's many Parks and Open Spaces.

Community Sport

We have tried to include membership rates and a range of fees for the various facilities at each centre. At the end of each entry you will find information about concessionary rates. Greenwich, Lewisham and Southwark all run schemes that offer certain people access cards to sports centres and swimming pools either free, or at considerably reduced fees. You have to be a resident in one of these boroughs and fulfill certain requirements. You can apply for one of these cards at a local leisure centre, many swimming pools or at the Town Hall. If you live in Greenwich and are a disabled person, unemployed, a one-parent family or an OAP, you qualify for a Concessionary Access Card (for £1). If you are a Lewisham resident, a £1 Lewisham Leisure Pass is available for unemployed, disabled people, OAPs and students. If you live in Southwark and are unemployed you can obtain a free Southwark Leisure Card or, if you are disabled, an OAP or under 16, you are entitled to Southwark's half-price card.

Multi-Purpose Recreation Centres

Crystal Palace National Sports Centre
Ledrington Road
Norwood   SE19
Tel 778 0131
Open 9-10.30(Mon-Fri) 9-930(Sat) 9-5(Sun)
Swimming times vary
Wheelchair access with ramps to all areas and special toilets
Membership £8.80(adults) £5(children) £20.40(family) or daily 45p(adults) 30p(children)
Fees 80p-£14.35(tennis court) per session
Indoor arena, 4 badminton courts, cricket school, multi-gym, weightlifting room, athletics, training track, five-a-side area, two gyms, 10 squash courts. 8-lane 50m racing pool, diving pool (two 1m and two 3m spring and 5m, 7.5m and 10m fixed diving boards). Teaching pool, training pool. Outdoor floodlit athletics stadium, two synthetic pitches, artificial ski slope and tennis courts. Courses offered include swimming for adults, under 5s, children, ante and post natal and synchronised swimming. Water aerobics, weight training, gymnastics for girls. Squash, karate, badminton, trampoline, aerobics, jazz dance and keep fit.

Crystal Palace Sports Centre was opened in July 1964. Since then it has hosted national and international events as well as providing local facilities for South Londoners. The range of activities grows yearly as new facilities are added to the complex. As well as the Athletics Stadium and fully equipped sports centre, there is an artificial ski run, built on the side of a natural wooded slope. All of the facilities are available for casual use but times vary according to the needs of national squads, competitive events, clubs and schools. Worth watching out for are the 'Come and Try' specials if you're under 16. For just 50p, you can try any sport you fancy. See the chapter on Festivals and Events for 1986 fixtures.
Some facilities at reduced rates for OAPs/unwaged/children and off-peak scheme (before 4.30)for everyone

Greenwich

Elm Terrace Fitness Centre
Elm Terrace
Eltham   SE9
Tel 850 1234
Open 8.30-10(Mon-Fri) 8.30-6(Sat) 8.30-2(Sun)
Wheelchair access to all areas and special toilets
Membership £8(adults) £12(family) £2(junior/student)

Fees approx £1 per session
Weight training, circuit training,
aerobics, keep fit, martial arts, keep fit
in retirement, wrestling, judo, karate.
Activities for disabled people. Sports
injury clinic.
*Free membership & normal fees
(unwaged). £2 membership & half-
price fees (OAPs, children, students).*

World Cup for trampolining, Crystal Palace

Greenwich Pools Sports Hall
Trafalgar Road
Greenwich   **SE10**
Tel 858 0159
Open Oct-Mar times not finalized
Wheelchair access to hall
No special toilets
Membership none
Fees not finalized
Roller skating rink, 4 badminton
courts, 1 tennis court, five-a-side,
table tennis. Multi-gym and small
pool.

Plumstead Sports Centre
Speranza Street
Plumstead   **SE18**
Tel 854 9217
Open 9-11(Mon-Fri) 9-9(Sat Sun)
Wheelchair access to all areas (except
bar) and special toilets
Membership £5
Fees £2.80-£8(football pitch) per
session
Large sports hall. Four badminton
courts, table tennis, volleyball,
rollerskating, five-a-side football,
netball, basketball, keep fit,
trampolining, gymnastics, archery
(also for disabled people). Free

membership for Concessionary Access
Card users but full fees.
*Free unemployed sessions on
Thursday mornings. £2 membership
for OAPs and Under 16s. Off-peak
(before 6) cheaper fees for everyone.*

Lambeth

Brixton Recreation Centre
27 Brixton Road
Brixton   **SW2**
Tel 274 7774
Open 9-10.30(Mon-Fri) 9-10(Sat Sun)
Wheelchair access to all areas (ring
first) and special toilets *Membership*
£1.50 + passport photo
Fees £1-£6(five-a-side pitch) One main
pool (25m), teaching pool, sauna,
sunbeds. 8 badminton courts, 2
basketball courts, 2 indoor team sport
courts (netball, volleyball etc). Bowls
hall, 8 squash courts, cricket nets,
archery, street hockey, rifle range
(small calibre), weights room. Martial
arts practice area, boxing, gymnastics.
Dance studio with women-only
activities, self-defence, cricket, weight
training. (Any classes can become
women-only if there's sufficient
demand.) Short-stay (2hrs) creche
open 9-8. Restaurant (capacity 200),
fast food catering area, vending
machines, 3 social rooms, bar.
Brixton Recreation Centre opened
amid a flurry of controversy. It cost
Lambeth Council £25 million to build,
was sold for £10.5 million to the GLC
and opened without full use of its
facilities. Dubbed The Whites'
Elephant by some, it faced an uphill
struggle to shake off a cool reception
and swing into operation. The project
had gone through many changes
during its ten-year building
programme, but by the time it opened
its main priority was, and is, to
provide a sports and recreation centre
with first-class facilities – one that
would be geared to the needs of the
community. To do this, the Centre
caters for a wide range of activities
and the staff are always open to

suggestions for new sports that might be developed on the premises. *Membership £1 for unemployed. Free activities 9-12 and 2-5 daily for everyone.*

Ferndale Sports Centre
Nursery Road
Brixton   SW9
Tel 733 5703
Open 9.30-10(Mon-Fri) 9.30-3(Sat)
Wheelchair Access none
Membership none
Fees 60p-£9(seven-a-side pitch)
Mainly outdoor centre. Floodlit pitch marked for football, hockey, tennis, netball. 200 metre four-lane running track. Cricket practice nets. Indoor gymnasium marked for badminton, volleyball, basketball, small multi-gym and 2 trampolines. Sessions in keep-fit, yoga, martial arts, gymnastics. Playscheme upstairs. Creche.
Free off-peak sessions Mon-Fri (9.30-11.30) for all.

Flaxman Sports Centre
Carew Street
Camberwell   SE5
Tel 737 3350
Open 9.30-10(Mon-Fri) 9.30-3(Sat)
Wheelchair access none
Membership none
Fees 60p-£5(five-a-side pitch) Two squash courts, badminton, multi-gym, martial arts, practice area, archery facilities, trampolining, basketball, keep-fit, yoga, gymnastics. Family keep-fit, sessions for disabled people, senior citizens fitness class.
Half-price for Under 16s and certain free sessions for unemployed people.

Loughborough Park Amenity Centre
Moorland Road
Brixton   SW9
Tel 733 2658
Open 9.30-9.30(Mon-Fri) 10-3(Sat)
Wheelchair access none
Membership none
Fees 60p-£5(five-a-side pitch)
Multi-purpose sports centre. Floodlit

pitch marked for football (five-a-side), hockey, netball, volleyball, basketball, tennis. Table tennis, weight training, circuit training, martial arts practice area, keep-fit, women's sports sessions. Adventure playground. Enclosed play area for under-5s.
Half price for Under 16s and free 9-11.30(Mon-Fri) for everyone.

Lewisham

Crofton Leisure Centre
Ewhurst Road
Crofton Park
Brockley   SE4
Tel 690 0273
Open 9-10.30(Mon-Fri) 9-5.30(Sat-Sun)
Wheelchair access to all areas˙
Membership £6 (Lewisham residents)
Fees 35p entrance (non-members) 90p-£2.50 per session (slightly more for non-members)
4 squash courts, 8 badminton courts, 6 table tennis tables, martial arts practice area, karate, judo, keep fit, aerobics. 3 outdoor tennis courts. Junior Saturday morning club.
Some free activities for Leisure Pass users. Free membership with sessions at members' rates for OAPs. Some off peak rates for everyone.

Lewisham Leisure Centre
Lewisham Centre
Lewisham   SE13
Tel 318 4421
Open 9-11(Mon-Fri) 9-10(Sat) 9-6(Sun)
Wheelchair access to all arreas with special toilets
Membership £8.50 (£6.50 Lewisham residents)
Fees approx £1 per session (adults)
Sports hall, badminton, bowls rink, archery, rifle shooting, five-a-side football, fitness training, keep fit. Martial arts practice area, judo, karate, table tennis, trampolines, aerobics, volleyball. Women's leisure morning 10-12(Fri). Creche. Under 5's gymnastic club. Junior gymnastics Sat morning.

Leisure pass users have free activities in daytime, half-price in eves. Reduced membership for Under 16s (£2.50 non residents, £1 residents) and sessions at half price.

Pagnell Street Centre
Fordham Park
Pagnell Street
New Cross　　　　　　　　SE14
Tel 691 8935
Phone for details
Small sports hall. Football, street hockey, indoor cricket, weight training, keep fit, basketball, netball, badminton, five-a-side football. Pool tables, table tennis, dance classes. Girls/women-only sports sessions. Creche.

Merton

YMCA
200 The Broadway
Wimbledon　　　　　　　　SW19
Tel 540 7255
Open 2-10(daily)
Wheelchair access to all areas
No special toilets
Membership £5.50-£32(family)
Members only in the evenings
Fees 50p-70p(members) £1.50(non members)
Badminton, basketball, circuit training, cricket, dance studio, judo, keep fit, table tennis, fitness studio, weight training, yoga.
Sliding scale of membership rates according to age.

Southwark

Colombo Street Sports and Community Centre
Colombo Street
Waterloo　　　　　　　　SE1
Tel 261 1658
Open 9-10(Mon-Fri) 10-4(Sat-Sun)
Wheelchair access to all areas and special toilets
Membership £4.50
Fees 30p admission(non members) 15p-£1.25 per session

Gymnasium, football, 3 badminton courts, weight training, boxing, karate, keep-fit, netball, rollerskating, yoga, dance table tennis, tennis, hapkido. Women-only sessions. Creche. Playschemes during holidays. *One free session a week and others at reduced rates for UB40s. £1 membership Under 16s and OAPs. Free sessions for OAPs.*

Elephant & Castle Recreation Centre
Elephant & Castle　　　　SE1
Tel 582 5505
Wheelchair access to all areas and special toilets
Open 10-10(daily) but schools use facilities 9-12.30 2-4(Mon-Fri)
Membership none
Fees admission 20p(10p children) 50p-£12(five-a-side), Aikido, 6 badminton courts, 2 basketball courts, boxing (including professional), cricket nets, 2 indoor five-a-side pitches, gymnastics, indoor hockey, judo, martial arts, 2 netball courts, sauna, solarium, 4 squash courts, table tennis, trampolining, English and East African volleyball courts, leisure lagoon and teaching pool (see swimming pools).
Free facilities for UB40 Leisure Card users. Half price for Half Price Card users (OAps, disabled, Under 16s). Off peak half price rates for all.

Wandsworth

Latchmere Leisure Centre
Burns Road
Battersea　　　　　　　　SW11
Tel 871 7470
Open 7-30-10(daily)
Wheelchair access to all areas Ramps and special toilets
Membership £10
Fees 70p-£3(£12 per pitch)
25p(non members entry fee)
Swimming 65p(adults) 35p(children)
Leisure pool and teaching pool. Also new sports hall (not yet open at press

date) for sports like badminton, cricket, gymnastics, volleyball, five-a-side and netball. Mirrored studio/activities room for aerobics, dance, martial arts and table tennis. Weight training room. Bar. Creche. Meeting rooms available for hire. *No membership or entry fee for OAPs and disabled users to Leisure Centre. Off peak swimming sessions.*

Swimming Pools

Greenwich

Eltham Pools
Eltham Hill
Eltham SE9
Tel 850 4756
Open 8-8.50(Mon-Fri) 8-6(Sat check closing time before going) 7.30-3.50(Sun main pool) 7.30-10 12.30-3.30(small pool family splash Sun) 11-12.30(small pool disabled users Sun) *Wheelchair access* to all areas and special toilets
Admission 60p(adults) 25p(children) Main 30-metre pool, small 18.3 metre-pool, 1 metre fixed diving board, 3 metre spring board. Main pool (30m), small pool (18.3m), 1m fixed diving board, 3m spring board. Hydrotheraphy pool for disabled people.
Free to holders of Greenwich Leisure Pass (see intro).

Eltham Park South Swimming Pool
Glenesk Road
Eltham SE9
Tel 850 9890
Open 7-6.15(summer May-Sept) 7-9.30am(winter Sept-March)
Wheelchair access with ramp to pool area Assistance given to sun deck No special toilets
Admission 65p (adults) 20p (children, OAPs, unwaged). Free in winter and 7-9am summer.
Outdoor pool (50x18m). Sundeck.
Admission 20p(Under 16s, OAPs and unemployed).

Greenwich Pools
Trafalgar Road
Greenwich SE10
Tel 858 0159
Open Summer 8-8.50(Mon-Fri) 8-6.50(Sat) 8-11am(Sun)
Winter (small pool only) 8-6.50(Mon-Wed Fri) 8-8.50(Thur) 8-5.50(Sat) 8-11am(Sun) *Wheelchair access* to all areas No special toilets
Admission 60p(adults) 25p(children) Main pool (30m), small pool (25m), teaching pool, multi-gym. The main pool is boarded over and a covered multi-purpose sports hall is fitted (see Multi-Purpose Recreation Centres above).
Free to holders of Greenwich Leisure Pass.

Hornfair Lido
Charlton Park Road
Charlon SE7
Tel 856 7180
Open Spring Bank Holiday – August Bank Holiday 10.30-6.30(Sun-Fri) 10.30-5.30(Sat)
Wheelchair access to all areas but ring first No special toilets
Admission 70p(adults) 35p(children) Large pool (50.29m x 20.11m) with small paddling pool.
Free to holders of Greenwich Leisure Pass.

Plumstead Pools
High Street
Plumstead SE18
Tel 854 9217
Open 8-10(Mon-Fri) 8-7(Sat) 8-4(Sun) *Wheelchair access* to pool area No special toilets
Admission 60p(adults) 25p(children) £2.20(sauna)
30m and 25m pools. Sauna.
Free to holders of Greenwich Leisure Pass.

Lambeth

Brockwell Park Lido
Dulwich Road
Herne Hill SE24

Tel 274 7991
Brockwell Park Lido is being
completely refurbished with a new
roof, lighting for late night swimmers,
a fitness training gym, meeting rooms
and full disabled access with special
facilities. Expected to open by June
1986.

Clapham Pool
10 Clapham Manor Street
Clapham   SW4
Tel 622 2786
Open 8-7(Mon Wed Fri) 8-8(Tue) 8-
9(Thur) 6.15-7.45(Thur family swim)
10-5(Sat) 8-2.15(Sun)
Multi-gym and main hall close slightly
later
Wheelchair access to all areas and
special toilet
Membership £1.20 to multi-purpose
gym.
Fees 60p-£2.80 for main hall.
Membership £1.20 to multi-gym *Fees*
£60p-£2.80 for main hall
Main pool (30m), teaching pool, multi-
gym, 2 badminton courts, table tennis,
keep-fit and aerobics.
A series of art workshops are held at
Clapham Pool. There is a well-
equipped art room, a photograhic
studio with a dark room and a pottery
room with 2 kilns.
*All facilities free to disabled users and
OAPs. Off peak free use of sports and
arts facilities.*

Kennington Lido
Kennington Park
Oval   SE11
Tel 735 3574

Open 7.30-7(daily except Fri & Sat in
winter ie Sept through June)
Wheelchair access to all areas No
special toilets
Admission 50p(adults) 20p(children)
Outdoor pool open throughout year
(see times). Also, open to all, free cold
water canoeing course 11-1 on
Thursday from first week in
September to first week in July.
*Free all winter and 7.30-10.30 in
summer*

Streatham Pool
384 Streatham High Road
Streatham   SW16
Tel 769 6971
Open Baths 8-9(Mon) 9-6(Tue Wed
Fri) 9-7(Thur) 10-5(Sat) Check times of
adult-only periods and adult/children
periods
Multi-gym 8-8(Mon) 9-8.30(Tue) 9-
8(Wed-Fri) 8-5(Sat) 8-11(Sun) Table
tennis ring for times
Wheelchair access with ramps to all
areas and special gents toilet
Admission Baths 50p(adults)
20p(children)
Multi-gym 60p *Membership* Multi-
gym £1.20 after introductory course
Fees Table tennis 60p(adults)
30p(children)
Main pool(30m), multi-gym and table
tennis.
*Free swimming sessions 9-11.40 2-
3.40(Mon-Fri). Free sessions in multi-
gym 9-11.30(Mon-Fri) with users card.*

Lewisham

Forest Hill Baths
Dartmouth Road
Forest Hill   SE23
Tel 699 3096
Open 8.30-7.15(Mon-Fri) 8-5.15(Sat)
Wheelchair access none
Admission see Ladywell for swimming
charges
Coaching some
Main pool 26 x 9m, second pool 25 x
8.2m, slipper baths. Gym being built.
*OAPs free. Free swimming before 6pm
for holders of Lewisham Leisure Pass.*

352

Ladywell Baths
Lewisham High Street
Lewisham SE13
Tel 690 2123
Open 8.30-7.15(Mon-Fri) 8-5.15(Sat) 8-11.15(Sun)
Wheelchair access none Special facilities being installed
Admission 50p(adults) 25p(children) Mon-Fri 55p(adults) 30p(children) Sun
Fees 30p-£3.50 per session
Main pool 33.3 x 12.8m, teaching pool 16.5 x 7.3m, 1m and 3m spring diving board, 5m fixed diving board. Family splash sessions, women-only swims. Turkish baths, Russian vapour baths, slipper baths. Multi-gym with facilities for fitness training and weight lifting. Martial arts, sunbeds, sauna and jacuzzi. Two activity rooms.
OAPs free. Free swimming before 6pm for holders of Lewisham Leisure Pass.

New Cross Baths
Laurie Grove
New Cross SE14
Tel 692 3378
Open as Ladywell but closed Wed & Sun
Wheelchair access none
Admission 40p(adults) 20p(children) for swimming
£1(adults) 50p(children) for gym
Main pool, multi-gym, slipper baths, gymnasium, martial arts, canoeing, keep-fit. Inflatables (during school holidays). Well used and enjoyed by children. Free parent and baby swimming classes on Saturday mornings.
OAPs free. Free swimming before 6pm for holders of Lewisham Leisure Pass.

Merton

Wimbledon Baths
Latimer road
Wimbledon SW19
Tel 542 1330
Open main pool 9-5.15(Mon) 9-7.15(Tue-Fri) 9-5.45(Sat) 8.30-9.30(Sun)
Check times for other facilities

Wheelchair access to all areas and special toilet
Admission 85p(adults) 40p(children)
Fees vary with facilities
Four badminton courts, table tennis, fitness room, multi-gym, five-a-side, aerobics, sports hall.
Off peak and special off peak rates. Half price for disabled people and OAPs for all activities. Half price for unemployed until 5pm.

Southwark

Camberwell Baths and Dry Sports Centre
Camberwell Church Street
Camberwell SE5
Tel 703 3024
Open pool 9-6(Mon-Thur) 9-5(Fri) 9-3.45(Sat) Early adult sessions 7.15-8.30(Tue Fri) 8.30-11.30(Sun)
Check times for other facilities
Wheelchair access with ramp to pool area Special facilities and toilets
Admission 50p(adults) 15p(children)
Fees vary for other facilities Main swimming pool, weight training and ball games area (netball, volleyball, badminton). Good value rollerskating on Friday evenings. Creche.
Free or half price for Leisure Card users, 22p(students).

Dulwich Baths
45 East Dulwich Road
Goose Green SE22
Tel 693 1833
Open pool 9-6.45(Mon-Fri) 9-3.45(Sat)
Wheelchair access through side entrance in Crystal Palace Road
No special toilets
Admission 50p(adults) 15p(children)
Fees vary 27m swimming pool, slipper baths, 2 badminton courts. Bowls in winter with club matches in evenings.
Free or half price for Leisure Card users.

Elephant & Castle Recreation Centre
Elephant & Castle SE1
Tel 582 5505

Open 9-9.30
Wheelchair access for spectators &
participants Notify reception on
arrival Special toilets
Admission 60p(adults) 30p(kids)
Leisure pool, and several slides.
Wave machine. No diving boards
(only 5ft deep). Warmish water.
Children's splash pool, small teaching
pool. Main leisure pool has good access
for disabled swimmers. Lunchtime
adult-only swimming sessions,
facilities for adults and children and
aquatic aerobics (some women-only
sessions). Creche.
*Unemployed 20p for holders of Leisure
Card. Half price for disabled people,
OAPs, Under 16s with Half Price
Card.*

Geraldine Mary Harmsworth Park
Lambeth North   SE11
Tel 582 5505
Open 2nd May Bank Hol-Sept 10-5.30
daily
Wheelchair access none
Admission free
Open air splash pool.

Peckham Rye Open Air Pool
Peckham Rye Park   SE22
Open June-August
Admission free
Phone for other details

Rotherhithe Baths
Lower Road
Rotherhithe   SE16

Tel 237 3296
Open 9-5.15(Mon) 9-7.30(Tue) 9-
6.30(Wed Fri) 9-6(Thur) 9.45-4(Sat)
8.30-11.30(Sun)
Check times for other facilities
Wheelchair access to pool area and
special toilet
Admission 50p(adults) 15p(children)
Fees vary
Main swimming pool and teaching
pool. Badminton court, table tennis,
public laundry and slipper baths.
*Free for OAPs, disabled people and
unemployed.*

Southwark Park Outdoor Pool
Hawkstone Road
Southwark Park   SE16
Tel 582 5505
Open June July Aug 7-6(daily)
Wheelchair access to pool
No special toilets
Admission free in 1985 but nominal
charge may be introduced.

Wandsworth

Balham Pool
Elmfield Road
Balham   SW17
Swimming pool.
Closed for refurbishment (£1&
million.) Due to open in Autumn 1986
with gym, 4 squash courts, fitness
room and weight training.

Putney Pools
Dryburgh Road
Putney   SW15
Tel 871 7092
Open 7.30-9(Mon-Fri) 8.30-5(Sat) 8.30-
2(Sun winter) 8.30-5(Sun summer)
Closing times vary so check first
Wheelchair access to pool
Special facilities and toilets
Admission max £1(adults) max
£60p(children)
Main pool, teaching pool, 1m and 3m
spring diving board, 5m fixed board.
Sessions for disabled swimmers.
50p off peak, free (OAPs, disabled
people, under 5s).

Tooting Bec Lido
Tooting Bec Road
Tooting Bec   SW16
Tel 871 7198
Open 6.30-8 (or sunset daily in
summer) 7-1(Wed Sun in winter)
Wheelchair access to pool and special
toilets *Admission* 65p(Mon-Fri)
85p(Sat-Sun)
Large unheated outdoor pool.
*Free (OAPs, disabled people, under
5s.)*

Tooting Swimming Pool
Greaves Place
Garratt Lane
Tooting   SW17
Tel 871 7176
See Putney Pools for details
Main pool, teaching pool, 1m spring
diving board. Women-only swims and
coaching for asthmatics. New sports
hall with similar facilities to
Latchmere to open end of summer
1986.
*See Putney Pools for concessionary
rates.*

Private Facilities

This section is by no means
comprehensive and is intended merely
to give you brief information about
some of the private sports facilities in
your area. When we came to list
information such as fees and
membership details we were faced
with a daunting task. Membership
can vary according your sex, the
particular sport you are wanting to
practise and the time you choose to
go. There are sometimes indoor rates,
outdoor rates, social rates (ie you
watch and drink at the bar), some
clubs have concessions and others
don't. Some of the more outrageous
rates we discovered were one club
which offers a yearly adult
membership of £70, £110 for a joint
membership and £15 every time you

turn up to use the club's facilities.
Another offered its facilities for £160
for six months or £260 for the whole
year though, to be fair, it offered some
fairly reasonable off-peak rates. In
fact, though private sports clubs are
far more expensive than council or
community sports centres, many of
them are quite reasonable, several
offer concessions and some are
amazingly cheap. Gymini, for instance
(see SE5), boasts a gymnasium that's
equipped to Olympic standard and
membership is a mere £5 a year with
sessions at £1 for children and £1.75
for adults with concessions. Gymini
also offers classes for deaf, blind and
mentally handicapped people. The
Yokohama International Judo Club
(see SE6) appears to be good value too
with membership at £5 a year and
session fees of 75p for adults and 50p
for children. The Elmwood Lawn
Tennis Club (see SW16) has a yearly
membership of £37 for adults and
that's it – no further court fees are
charged unless you require coaching.
So, there obviously are some excellent
deals around – pick a few clubs from
the listing that follows and let's hope
you're lucky. And, finally, if you feel
like an all-nighter, visit one of the
New World Snooker Clubs, open 24
hours a day with a yearly membership
of £7.50 and hourly session fees from
about about £1.60-£2.50 depending on
when you go.

To help you find facilities in your
area, the entries are listed
alphabetically by postcode.

SE2

Abbey Wood Sports Centre
Eynsham Drive
Abbey Wood
Tel 310 6889
ILEA-run sports centre, used by
schools and youth centres. Some
public use. Swimming pool, sports hall,
4 badminton courts, basketball,
volleyball..

SE3

**Blackheath Cricket, Football &
Lawn** Tennis Club
Rectory Field
Blackheath
Tel 858 3677
Cricket pitch, 2 squash courts, 2 rugby
pitches, football pitch.

Charlton Bowls Club
Harvey Sports Ground
Harvey Road
Tel 854 0314 (5-6pm)
Bowls green. Clubhouse.

North Kent Squash Club
Parkgate
Blackheath
Tel 852 4276
Gymnasium, 6 squash courts, sauna,
solarium.

SE5

Gymini
Warwick Hall
Kimpton Road
Camberwell
Tel 703 1078
Gymnastics for all ages, men and
women. Keep-fit, dance. Fully
equipped to Olympic standard. Classes
for mentally handicapped, deaf and
blind people.

New World Snooker Club
315 Camberwell New Road
Camberwell

Tel 703 0501
20 full size tables. Light refreshments.
Open 24 hours

Temple Bowling Club
Sunset Road
Herne Hill
Tel 274 2449
Indoor green, 2 bowls greens, snooker
table, shuffleboard. Clubhouse.

Tokei Martial Arts
326 Lewis Estate
Warner Road
Camberwell
Tel 403 5979
Full range of martial arts schooling.

SE6

**Bellingham Bowling & Lawn
Tennis Club**
Bellingham Road
Bellingham
Tel 698 1643
Badminton court, 2 bowls greens, 3
all-weather tennis courts, 2 en tout
cas courts. Clubhouse.

**Blackheath Hockey Club
Catford & Cyphers Cricket Club
Catford Squash Club**
Rubens Street
Bellingham
Tel 699 2423
All-weather hockey pitch, 5 other
hockey pitches, 2 squash courts, 2
cricket pitches, table tennis, billiards.
Clubhouse.

**Yokohama International Judo
Club**
171 Firhill Road
Lewisham
Tel 698 4260
Budo, judo, kendo, aikido, karate and
self defence. Classes for all ages.

SE8

Broadway Leisure Centre
9/12 Deptford Broadway

Greenwich/Deptford
Tel 692 9259
14 full-size snooker tables. 3 private
rooms, television lounge, light
refreshments.
Open 24 hours

New World Snooker Club
197/199 Deptford High Street
Deptford
Tel 692 4693
17 full-size tables. Light refreshments.
Open 24 hours

SE9

Castaways Sports Association
Southwood Road
New Eltham
Tel 850 5573
Football pitch, cricket pitch, sports
ground, pavilion.

New World Snooker Club
140 Eltham High Street
Eltham
Tel 850 1361
15 full-size tables. Light refreshments.
Open 20 hours

Shapes Health & Fitness Centre
400 Westbourne Avenue
Eltham
Tel 859 7600
Weight training, weight lifting, body
building, dance studio, aerobics,
sauna, solarium, beauticians.

Sparrows Farm Leisure Centre
Sparrows Lane
Eltham
Tel 859 2921
6 squash courts. Sauna.

SE12

**Blackheath Wanderers Sports
Club**
63 Eltham Road
Lee Green
Tel 852 5901
Hard tennis court, 4 grass courts,

cricket square, senior football pitch.

Ladbroke Squash & Athletics Club
Weighall Road
Blackheath
Tel 852 2924
3 squash courts, 2 tennis courts,
solarium, sauna, snooker. Clubhouse.

SE13

New World Snooker Club
100-104 Lewisham High Street
Lewisham
Tel 852 9762
10 full-size tables. Light refreshments.
Open 24 hours

SE18

Woolwich Ski Slope
The Barracks
Repository Road
Woolwich
Army training slope. Dry ski run to
suit beginners to advanced skiers.
Available for public use at selected
times.

SE19

**Crystal Palace Snooker & Social
Club**
Jasper Road
Crystal Palace
Tel 670 8000
17 full-size tables. Light refreshments.

SE21

Dulwich Riding School
Dulwich Common
Tel 693 2944
18 rides. School instruction only.

Dulwich Sports Club
Turney Road
Dulwich
Tel 274 3117
4 grass tennis courts, 6 hard courts, 4
squash courts, 5 cricket pitches, 6
hockey pitches, 2 bowls greens, 2

croquet lawns. Clubhouse.

Honor Oak & Tulse Hill Club
Dulwich Common
Tel 693 3222
Badminton court, 2 cricket squares, 3
hockey pitches, 4 sand tennis courts, 2
squash courts. Clubhouse.

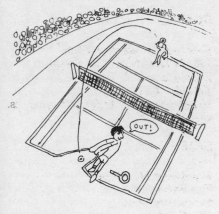

Old College Lawn Tennis & Croquet Club
Gallery Road
Lewisham
Tel 693 3511
4 grass tennis courts, 4 hard courts,
croquet lawn. Clubhouse.

SE23

Forest Hill Bowling Club
28 Wynell Road
Forest Hill
Tel 699 2096
Bowls green and clubhouse.

Forest Hill Sports & Dining Club
68 Perry Rise
Forest Hill
Tel 699 3819
4 squash courts, 2 hard tennis courts,
open air swimming pool (summer
only). Clubhouse and billiards room.

SE27

South London Riding School
117a Canterbury Grove

West Norwood
Tel 670 0775
22 rides, schooling, riding club. Hacks
at Streatham and Tooting.

Unit 4 Gym
Nettlefold Place
West Norwood
Tel 761 1114
Multi-gym, weights machines,
aerobics, dance studio, solarium,
sauna, power training.

West Norwood Lawn Tennis & Social Club
128 Knights Hill
West Norwood
Tel 670 4592
3 all-weather tennis courts, 2 squash
courts, table tennis. Clubhouse.

SW2

Telford Park Lawn Tennis Club
35a Killieser Avenue
Streatham
Tel 674 3061
4 grass tennis courts, 2 all-weather
floodlit tennis courts, 3 shale tennis
courts, netball, snooker room.
Clubhouse.

SW8

London Judo & Karate Society
89 Lansdowne Way
Stockwell
Tel 622 0529
Karate and judo. Contact for list of
London-wide approved clubs.

London South Bank Squash Centre
124 Wandsworth Road
Vauxhall
Tel 622 6866
15 squash courts (9 glass backed),
aerobics, keep-fit, multi-gym, sauna,
jacuzzi, solarium and snooker.

SW11

Battersea Hippic Riding Stables
14a Winders Road

Battersea
Tel 223 0909
19 rides, hacks, outdoor schooling and jumping. Riding for handicapped children.

Metropolitan Club
Sheepcote Lane
Battersea
Tel 228 4400
6 squash courts, nautilus gym, sauna, jacuzzi, dance studios, solarium. Restaurant, bar, creche facilities.

Rugby Netball League
26 Stormont Road
Clapham
Tel 228 0487
10-a-side sport, played with rugby ball on football pitch using a combination of rugby/netball tactics. Played in South Clapham area since 1907. Season May-July on Clapham Common.

New World Snooker Club
66 Battersea Rise
Battersea
Tel 228 0934
16 full-size tables. Light refreshments. Open 24 hours

SW12

Balham & Tooting Sports & Social Club
94 Balham High Road
Balham
Tel 673 8115
Snooker, pool, dominoes. Restaurant.

Grafton Lawn Tennis & Squash Club
79a Thornton Road
Streatham Hill
Tel 673 2891
3 squash courts, 8 shale tennis courts (1 floodlit). Clubhouse.

Grove Hall Gymnasium
Balham Grove
Balham
Tel 673 0371

Keep-fit, multi-gym, weight training/lifting, power training. Sauna, showers, solarium. Separate sessions for men and women.

New World Snooker Club
191/5 Balham High Road
Balham
Tel 673 0399
14 full-size tables. Light refreshments. Open 24 hours

SW13

Barnes Sports Club
Lonsdale Road
Barnes
Tel 748 6220
2 hockey pitches, 2 squash courts, 3 hard tennis courts, 1 cricket pitch, 1 croquet lawn, 1 bowls green. Snooker table, clubhouse.

SW15

Thames Rowing Club
The Embankment
Putney
Tel 788 0676
Mixed club. Novice to elite standard. 25 boats. Training pool, gymnasium, clubhouse.

Richmond Park Public Golf Course
Richmond Park
Tel 876 3205
18-hole golf course sited in Richmond Park. Open to the public and good value.

SW16

Belmont Bowling Club
Broadlands Avenue
Streatham
Tel 769 3175
6 bowls rinks. Clubhouse.

Elmwood Lawn Tennis club
19 Brockenhurst Way
Streatham
Tel 764 6437

3 en tout cas courts. Coaching for under 16s. Clubhouse.

Silver Blades Ice Rink
Streatham High Road
Streatham
Tel 769 7861
Ice skating, ice hockey, figure skating, speed skating. Lessons and skate hire available.

London Marathon

Streatham Squash Club
Ockley Road
Streatham
Tel 769 2903
9 squash courts, gymnasium, dance studio, aerobics class, saunas, creche.

Wigmore Lawn Tennis Club
43 Becmead Avenue
Streatham
Tel 769 3671
8 shale courts, 2 hard courts. Clubhouse.

SW18

Billiards Club
569a Garratt Lane
Wandsworth
Tel 946 5273
11 full-size tables, snooker and billiards. Light refreshments.

King George's Park Squash Club
Burr Road
Wandsworth
Tel 870 8483
10 squash courts, 2 gymnasiums, aerobics, keep-fit, cricket, sauna, solarium, jacuzzi.

Olympic Centre
115/7 Wandsworth High Street
Wandsworth
Tel 874 4146
Fitness, health and beauty. Multi-gym, fitness studio, saunas, solarium.

Wandsworth Snooker Club
63 Wandsworth High Street
Wandsworth
Tel 874 1252
12 full-size tables. Light refreshments.

Waterscene
Mapleton Road
King Georges Park
Wandsworth
Tel 870 4955
Outdoor pool only open in summer (approx April-September). Heated water, big water shutes and fun facilities. This pool used to belong to Wandsworth Council.

Wimbledon & District Bowls Association
7 Skeena Hill
Wandsworth
Tel 785 2142
Will give information on all bowls clubs in Wimbledon, Merton and Morden.

Yard Fitness Centre
121b Wandsworth High Street
Wandsworth
Tel 870 9927
Fitness studios, coffee bar.

Yawara-Tomike Aikido Centre
205 Merton Road
South Wimbledon
Tel 874 3658
Aikido, judo, karate classes.

SW19

Wimbledon Common Golf Club
Camp Road
Wimbledon
Tel 946 0294
18 hole golf course on Wimbledon Common. Open to public Mon/Fri. Clubhouse.

Wimbledon Park Golf Club
Home Park Road
Wimbledon Park
Tel 946 1002
Next to All England Tennis Club in
Wimbledon Park close to lake. 18 hole
course. Indoor driving nets.
Clubhouse. Open to public Mon-Fri.

**Wimbledon Squash & Badminton
Club**
Cranbrook Road
Wimbledon
Tel 946 6077
6 squash courts, 7 badminton courts.
Clubhouse.

Wimbledon Village Stables
24a/b High Street
Wimbledon
Tel 946 8579
20 rides. Hacks on Wimbledon
common and Richmond Park.
Schooling for every standard.
Jumping.

SW20

West Wimbledon Bowling Club
55 Durham Road
West Wimbledon
Tel 946 4676
Bowls green and clubhouse.

Sports Round-Up

If you still haven't found local
facilities to meet your needs, contact
your council's Sports Officer at the
places listed below – they may be able
to help. Some of the councils also have
sportslines, called Action Sport,
which were set up to promote sport in
the local community by the Sports
Council for a three year period
(ending in March 1986). There are
three in South London and it is likely
that the councils will continue to run
them when their time is up.

Greenwich

Plumstead Baths
High Street
Plumstead   SE16
Tel 854 9217

Lambeth

Lambeth Amenitities Department
Clapham Park Road
Clapham   SW4
Tel 622 6655

Lewisham

Leisure Services Department
68 Molesworth Street
Lewisham   SE13
Tel 852 9121

Action Sport
Tel 690 9539

Merton

Recreation & Arts Department
Crown House
London Road
Morden
Tel 545 3661

Southwark

Sports Advisory Council
28 Peckham Road
Camberwell   SE5
Tel 703 6311

Action Sport
Tel 237 4838

Wandsworth

Leisure & Amenities
Room 224b
Wandsworth Town Hall
Wandsworth High Street
Wandsworth   SW18
Tel 871 6373

Below is a list of groups, campaigns and departments working to promote sport and improve facilities both locally and nationally.

British Sports Association for the Disabled
South East London Region
2 Rutherglen Road
SE2
Tel 311 5545
Contact F Duhig

British Sports Association for the Disabled
South West London Region
11 Byegrove Road
Colliers Wood
SW19
Tel 540 9238
Contact B Stoner

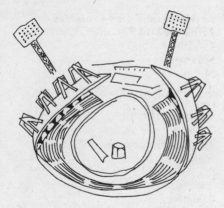

Sports Council – Greater London & South East
P O Box 480
Crystal Palace National Sports Centre
Ledrington Road
SE19
Tel 778 8600
Works to advise and promote sport and recreation for all.

GLC Sportsline
Tel 222 8000
Provides information and advice on all sports in London. Has details on concessions, disabled access, creche facilities. Open 10-6 daily.

GLC Sports Team
Tel 633 1245
Develops and promotes all types of sporting activities. Special interest in sport for disabled people, girls, women, ethnic minorities. Gives help and advice to individuals, groups and boroughs. Plans from April 1st 1986 (ie post GLC) unclear.

UK Sports Association for People with Mental Handicap
Tel 885 1177

Umbrella Organisations.

If no London-based organisation exists, we have mentioned the national head-quarters. These contacts below will put you in touch with the nearest facilities to your home.

Aikido

British Aikido Association
331 Old Farm Avenue
Sidcup
Kent
Tel 302 9307 (after 5.30)

Angling

London Anglers Association
Forest Road Hall
Hervey Park Road
E17

Archery

Mr Miller
Flat 0
6 Peabody Avenue
Sutherland Street
SW1
Tel 821 1735

Athletics

**Amateur Athletics Association &
Women's Amateur Athletics
Association**
Francis House
Francis Street
SW1
Tel 828 4731

Badminton

Badminton Association of England
National Badminton Centre
Bradwell Road
Loughton Lodge
Milton Keynes
Tel 0908 568822

Kent Badminton Association
Woodnook
15 Grange Road
Saltwood
Hythe
Kent
Tel 0303 66806

Surrey Badminton Association
14 The Maples
Sutton Lane
Banstead
Surrey
Tel 07373 54489

Ballooning

British Balloon and Airship Club
London Region
17 Irving Street
WC2
Tel 839 4819

Baseball

Southern Baseball League
26 Bunns Lane
NW7
Tel 959 3764

Basketball

British Association of Basketball
26 Ickenham Close

West Ruislip
Middlesex
Tel 08956 73955

London School Basketball
Moberly Youth Centre
Kilburn Lane
W10
Tel 960 2336

Bicycle Polo

Bicycle Polo Association
5 Puffin Gardens
Peel Common
Gosport
Hampshire
Tel 0329 285967

Billiards & Snooker

London and Home Counties
Billiards and Snooker Association
23 Tithe Farm Avenue
South Harrow
Middlesex
Tel 734 7282

Body Building

English Federation of Body
Builders
27 Ailsa Road
Twickenham
Middlesex
Tel 892 7037

Boxing

LBA
68 Central Buildings
Southwark Street
SE1
Tel 407 2194

British American Football

The American League UK
Amway House
Mitchigan Drivve
Tongwell

Milton Keynes
Tel 0908-617911

Canoeing

British Canoe Union
Flexel House
45-47 High Street
Addelstone
Weybridge
Surrey
Tel 97 41341

Caving

National Caving Association
Whernside Manor
Sedbergh
Cumbria
Tel 05875 213

Cricket

Club Cricket Conference
353 West Barnes Lane
New Malden
Surrey
Tel 949 4001

Women's Cricket Association
16 Woburn Place
W1
Tel 387 3423

Cycling

British Cycling Federation
16 Upper Woburn Place

WC1
Tel 387 9320

London Cycling Campaign
Tress House
3 Stamford Street
SE1
Tel 928 7220

Fencing

Amateur Fencing Association
The De Beaumont Centre
83 Perham Road
W14
Tel 385 7442

Football

London Football Association
Aldworth Grove
SE13
Tel 690 9626

Women's Football Association
1 Portsea Mews
W2
Tel 402 9388

Frisbee

British Ultimate (Frisbee) Federation
28 Aliwal Road
SW11
Tel 228 0759

Gliding

London Gliding Club
Tring Road
Dunstable Downs
Bedfordshire
Tel 0582 63419

Grice Ball

The Griceball League
c/o Ben Corderey
68 Zion Road
Thornton Heath

Surrey
Tel 689 1451

Gymnastics

**British Amateur Gymnastics
Association**
London Area
2 Buckingham Avenue East
Slough
Berks
Tel 75 32763

Handball

British Handball Association
90 Penrym Avenue
Fishermead
Milton Keynes
Tel 0908 678339

Hang Gliding

British Hang Gliding Association
Cranfield Airfield
Bedfordshire
Tel 0234 751688

Hockey

**All England Women's Hockey
Association**
Argyle House
29-31 Euston Road
NW1
Tel 278 6340

Men's Hockey Association
16 Upper Woburn Place
WC1
Tel 387 9315

Ice Ball

Ice Ball Players Club
Streatham Ice Rink
386 Streatham High Road
SW16
Tel 769 7771

Ice Hockey

The Ice Hockey Association

c/o Pat Marsh
48 Barmouth Road
Shirley
Croydon
Tel 654 6851

Judo

London Judo Society
89 Lansdowne Way
SW8
Tel 622 0529

Keep Fit

London Keep Fit
30 Catherine Grove
SE10
Tel 691 3081

Kendo

British Kendo Association
23 All Saints Terrace
Cheltenham
Gloucestershire
Tel 0242 510501

Korfball

British Korfball Association
2 Torrington Close
Mereworth
Maidstone
Kent
Tel 0622 813115

Lacrosse

**All England Women's Lacrosse
Association**
16 Upper Woburn Place
WC1
Tel 387 4430

Martial Arts

Martial Arts Commission
Broadway House
15 Deptford Broadway
SE8

Tel 691 3433
Sam To Dang Society of Martial Arts
689 London Road
Thornton Heath
Surrey
Tel 689 9313

Netball

All England Netball Association
2nd Floor
Francis House
Francis Street
SW1
Tel 828 2176

Rambling

Rambling Association
1-5 Wandsworth Road
SW8
Tel 582 6878

Riding

British Equestrian Society
Stonleith
Kenilworth
Warwickshire
Tel 0203 52241

Roller Hockey

The Rolley Hockey Clubs
c/o Dr Weatley
528 Loose Road
Maidstone
Kent
Tel 0622 43155

Rounders

National Rounders Association
122 Staines Road
Wraysbury
Staines
Middlesex

Rowing

Amateur Rowing Association
6 Lower Mall
W6
Tel 748 3632

Rugby

Rugby Football Union
Whitton Road
Twickenham
Middlex
Tel 892 8161

Rugby Netball

Rugby Netball League
26 Stormont Road
SW11
Tel 228 0487

Sailing

Royal Yachting Association
Victoria Way
Woking
Surrey
Tel 04862 5022

Skateboarding

English Skateboard Association
50 Park Street

Hereford
West Midlands
Tel 0432 279133

Skating

National Skating Association
15-27 Gree Street
EC1
Tel 253 3824/0910

Squash

Squash Rackets Association
Francis House
Francis Street
SW1
Tel 828 3064

Women's Squash Rackets Association
345 Upper Richmond Road West
SW14
Tel 876 6219

Sub Aqua

British Sub Aqua Club
16 Upper Woburn Place
WC1
Tel 387 9302

Surfing

British Surfing Association
G S Burrows Chambers
East Burrows Road
Swansea
Tel 0792 461476

Swimming

Amateur Swimming Association
Harold Fern House
Derby Square
Loughborough
Tel 0509 230431

Street Hockey

Street Hockey Association

5N Peabody Building
Duchy Street
SE1
Tel 261 9878

Table Tennis

English Table Tennis Association
21 Claremont
Hastings
East Sussex
Tel 0424 433121

Tai Chi Chuan

British Tai Chi Chuan Association
7 Upper Wimpole Street
W1
Tel 935 8444

Tae Kwondo

World Tae Kwondo Federation
14 Hedgeside
Potten End
Berkhamsted
Herts
Tel 04427 71108

Tennis

Lawn Tennis Association
Barons Court
W14
Tel 385 2366

Trampolining

British Trampoline Federation
152a College Road
Harrow
Middlesex
Tel 863 7278

Volleyball

Volleyball Association
13 Rectory Road
West Bridford
Nottingham
Tel 0602 816324

Water-skiing

London Ski & Windsurfing Centre
553 Battersea Park Road
SW11
Tel 228 0430

Weightlifting

Press & Jerk
c/o John Whyte
51 Dominic Drive
SE9
Tel 857 3943

Windsurfing

London Ski & Windsurfing Centre
553 Battersea Park Road
SW11
Tel 228 0430

Wrestling

English Olympic Wrestling Association
Greater London & South East Region
38 Rodney Road
Mitcham
Surrey
Tel 640 0316

Yoga

British Wheel of Yoga
London Region
59 Mayow Road
SE23
Tel 699 5988

The following South London based organisations didn't fit easily in any other section so we list them here. MASDA has been described below. The Richmond Public Golf Course sounded really good value and a shame to leave out. The four South London-based water sports centres are listed purely because there seemed to be no other place for them in the chapter and, since we had found out about them, we thought you should know about too.

MASDA
403-405 Brixton Road
Brixton   SW9
Tel 733 9145(day) 674 2168(eve)
Contact Terry Williams
In 1974, Mohammed Ali visited Lambeth at the invitation of Tulse Hill School. As a result of the visit, the Mohammed Ali Sports Development Association was set up to promote and develop sporting activities for youth in the heart of urban London. MASDA has a membership of about 10,000 amongst community groups, clubs and youth centres. It organises training courses for coaching, competitions, finds venues for activities and provides equipement as well as running its own sports clinics. Currently MASDA is looking for venues to set up more clinics along the lines of Dick Sheppard Youth Club which offers a wide range of activities from gymnastics to street hockey.

Richmond Park Public Golf Course
Richmond Park   SW15
Tel 876 3205
Open dawn till dusk daily
Wheelchair access none
Membership none
Fees £3(weekdays) £5(weekends)
Some concessions.
South East London Aquatic Centre
Europe Road
Woolwich Dockyard Estate

Woolwich Church Street
Woolwich SE18
Tel 855 0131
Open 10-8(Apr-Sept) 10-6(Oct-March)
10-5(Nov-Feb)
Membership £4(adults) £2(juniors and
OAPs) £5(family)
Angling dock, canoeing and scuba
diving. Angling for disabled people.

Surrey Docks Water Sports Centre
Greenland Cock
Surrey Docks SE16
Tel 237 4009
ILEA-run water sports centre. Open
to the public. Diving school holidays.
Sailing and canoeing.

Tideways Sailing Centre
Riverway
off Tanner Avenue
Greenwich Marshes SE10
Open all year round (club closes 6)
Membership £15
Sailing, cruisers, dinghies, sailing for
disabled people.

Trafalgar Rowing Centre
11-13 Crane Street
Greenwich SE10
Tel 858 9568

Open mainly weekends and eves Wed
is club night
Membership £40(adults) £3.20(social)
Rowing club, skulling (fours & eights)

Spectator Events

If, by the end of this chapter, you are
still reluctant to join in, you can
always be an observer, and there
certainly are some major sports
venues in South London. You can
watch football league at Charlton and
Crystal Palace, cricket at the Oval,
tennis at Wimbledon, greyhound
racing at Catford and Wimbledon
Stadiums (speedway at the latter too,
and a host of national and
international championship events at
Crystal Palace (see Festivals and
Events). There is also ice-skating at
Streatham Ice Rink, boxing at
Elephant & Castle Recreation Centre
and the big boxing champs can
sometimes be seen going through
their paces in the gym above the
Thomas A' Becket in the Old Kent
Road. Or, you can prop up the bar and
forget about sport.

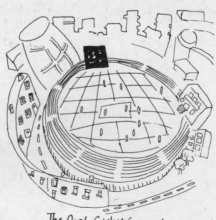

The Oval Cricket Ground

Greenwich

Parks and Open Spaces

Park		All-weather pitch events	Athletics field events	Boating/sailing/canoeing	Bowls green	Cricket nets	Cricket pitch(es)	Fishing	Five-a-side	Floodlighting	Football	Hockey	Horse-riding	Netball/korfball	Orienteering	Putting	Rugby	Running track	Tennis
Abbey Wood Park	SE2										■								
Avery Hill	SE9						■				■	■				■	■		■
Bostall Gardens	SE2				■														■
Bostall Heath	SE2				■	■	■							■					
Castlewood	SE18													■	■				
Charlton Park	SE7						■				■	■					■		■
Eltham Park	SE9						■				■					■			■
Fairy Hill	SE9															■			■
Hornfair Park	SE7																		
Jackwood Park	SE18													■					
Maryon Park	SE7															■			■
Oxleas Wood	SE18										■		■	■					
Plumstead Common	SE18										■								
Shrewsbury Park	SE18																		
Southwood Park	SE9																		
Sutcliffe Park □	SE9	■		■			■			■	■			■		■			
The Course	SE9																		■

Facilities for disabled
Avery Hill
Bostall Heath

Special Features
American Football pitch □

Lambeth

Parks and Open Spaces

Park		All-weather pitch events	Athletics field events	Boating/sailing/canoeing	Bowls green	Cricket nets	Cricket pitch(es)	Fishing	Five-a-side	Floodlighting	Football	Hockey	Horse-riding	Netball/korfball	Orienteering	Putting	Rugby	Running track	Tennis
Agnes Riley Gardens	SW4	■																	
Archbishop's Park	SE1					■								■		■			■
Brockwell Park	SE24	■				■					■			■					■
Clapham Common		■				■	■	■			■	■		■			■		■
Kennington Park	SE11	■									■	■							■
Larkhall Park	SW4	■									■								■
Mostyn Gardens	SE5 □ □																		
Myatts Fields	SE5															■			■
Norwood Park	SE19										■								
Ruskin Park	SE5				■						■			■					■
Streatham Common	SW16						■				■								■
Streatham Vale Park	SW16	■							■					■					■
Vauxhall Park	SW8				■														■
Valley Road	SW16										■								

Special Features
6 Rugby Netball pitches □
1 Gaelic Football pitch □

Skateboard area □ □

Lewisham

Parks and Open Spaces

		All-weather pitch events	Athletics field events	Boating/sailing/canoeing	Bowls green	Cricket nets	Cricket pitch(es)	Fishing	Five-a-side	Floodlighting	Football	Hockey	Horse-riding	Netball/korfball	Orienteering	Putting	Rugby	Running track	Tennis
Blackheath	SE3		■		■		■				■						■		■
Chinbrook Meadows	SE12						■				■								■
Deptford Park	SE8		■								■							■	
Fordham Park	SE14	■									■								
Forster Memorial Park	SE6										■			■		■			
Hilly Fields	SE4				■														■
Home Park	SE26	■									■								
Horniman Gardens	SE23															■			■
Ladywell Fields	SE13	■	■								■						■		■
Mayow Park	SE26				■														■
Mountsfield Park	SE6										■								■
New Deptford Green	SE14	■				■			■					■					■
Northbrook Park	SE12										■								
Pepys Park	SE8										■								
Senegal Fields ☐	SE16	■									■			■					
Sydenham Wells Park	SE26															■			■
Telegraph Hill	SE14																		■

Special Features
Rollerskating rink ☐

Merton

Parks and Open Spaces

		All-weather pitch events	Athletics field events	Boating/sailing/canoeing	Bowls green	Cricket nets	Cricket pitch(es)	Fishing	Five-a-side	Floodlighting	Football	Hockey	Horse-riding	Netball/korfball	Orienteering	Putting	Rugby	Running track	Tennis
Abbey Recreation Ground	SW19						■				■								
Beverley Meads	SW20												■			■			
Colliers Wood	SW19										■								■
Commons Extension	SW20						■				■	■							
Cottenham Park	SW19					■	■				■								■
Dundonald Road	SW19					■	■				■								■
Durnsford Road	SW19					■	■				■								
Garfield Road	SW19										■								
Haydons Road	SW19					■	■				■								■
Holland Gardens	SW20																		■
John Innes Rec Ground	SW19					■	■				■								■
Joseph Hood Rec Ground	SW20					■	■				■	■							■
Putney Heath	SW19												■						
Raynes Park Ground	SW20	■				■	■		■		■	■				■			
Wandle Park	SW19										■								
Wimbledon Park	SW19	■				■	■				■					■			■

Southwark

Parks and Open Spaces

Park	Postcode	All-weather pitch events	Athletics field events	Boating/sailing/canoeing	Bowls green	Cricket nets	Cricket pitch(es)	Fishing	Five-a-side	Floodlighting	Football	Hockey	Horse-riding	Netball/korfball	Orienteering	Putting	Rugby	Running track	Tennis
Belair Sports Ground	SE21					■					■			■			■		■
Bermondsey Playground	SE1								■					■					■
Brimmington Gardens	SE15									■	■								
Browning Street	SE17										■								
Brunswick Park	SE5								■		■								■
Burgess Park	SE5	■	■								■	■		■					
Dulwich Park	SE19			■	■		■						■			■			■
G M Harmsworth Park	SE1								■					■		■			■
Hatfield Gardens	SE1								■	■				■					
Herne Hill ☐	SE24		■														■		
Honor Oak Park	SE22		■				■												■
King George's Fields	SE16								■				■						■
Marlborough Playground	SE1										■								
Mellish Playing Field	SE16				■		■										■		
Nelson Recreation Ground	SE1																		■
Newington Gardens	SE1										■			■					
Paterson Park	SE1										■			■					
Peckham Rye Park	SE22		■		■				■			■					■		■
Rosemary Gardens	SE5	■																	
St Paul's Park	SE16									■	■						■		■
Southwark Park	SE16	■	■				■			■	■			■			■		■
Tabard Gardens	SE1								■		■	■		■					
Warwick Gardens	SE15										■								

Special Features
Cycling track ☐

Wandsworth

Parks and Open Spaces

		All-weather pitch events	Athletics field events	Boating/sailing/canoeing	Bowls green	Cricket green	Cricket nets	Cricket pitch(es)	Fishing	Five-a-side	Floodlighting	Football	Hockey	Horse-riding	Netball/korfball	Orienteering	Putting	Rugby	Running track	Tennis
Battersea Park	SW11			●	●	●	●			●	●	●						●		●
Falcon Park	SW11										●	●								
Furzedown Rec Ground	SW17				●												●			
Garratt Green	SW17											●								
Garratt Park □	SW17											●								
Heathbrook Park	SW8									●	●									
King George's Park	SW18			●		●				●		●			●					●
Leaders Gardens	SW15																			●
Openview Park	SW18			●		●						●			●					●
Putney Lower Common	SW15			●											●					●
Tooting Common	SW17	●	●			●				●		●		●				●		●
Wandsworth Common	SW11			●		●				●	●	●		●		●		●		●
York Gardens	SW11									●	●									

Special Features
Cycle track □

THEATRE

Theatre reflects the kind of society we live in, and it's significant that on the whole the theatre which has emerged in South London is of the alternative fringe type, the sort that challenges the established order both in theatre itself and in society at large. The Fringe, which began in the 1960s, changed the image of a night out at the theatre, previously an excuse to dress up, eat out and have one's prejudices confirmed. The Fringe set out to change the world. It hasn't succeeded but it's made a start. It has proved that you don't need expensive sets, costumes and props to create exciting theatre, that you don't need a conventional theatre building when the upstairs room of a pub will do. During the seventies and eighties feminist, Black and gay theatre emerged each with its own specific challenge to the established power structure. During the second half of this century Fringe has even managed to change the exclusively middle-class image of theatre, though there's still a long way to go. Some argue (it's often the funding bodies) that poverty enhances creativity, but there's a limit. It may be true that out of financial constraint came the wonderful inventiveness of some Fringe theatre companies, but today theatre practitioners all over South London are wondering whether they can afford to carry on any longer, and their uncertainty is made even worse by the abolition of the Greater London Council which at least was willing to break new boundaries in the companies it funded. In April when the hard-pressed boroughs take over the GLC's responsibilities towards theatre in London, it is almost certain that some companies will no longer be funded to the same level, if at all. Meanwhile it would be a tragedy if the creative energies of so many talented companies are sapped instead of fed by a struggle for finance that in the end proves too much for them.

Venues and Companies are catagorised according to the type of theatre they show. Most are self-explanatory, but where a venue is described as 'Producing' this means it has its own theatre company. Theatre-in-Education is a specialist theatre for schools which deliberately involves the children on an emotional and intellectual level, encourages them to make decisions on issues brought up during the performance and generally attempts to educate and develop the personalities of young people. Where venues are described as 'Council-run' this means the local borough has responsibility for the administration and artistic policy of the theatre. 'Youth Theatre' means theatre by non-professional young people, and 'Young People's Theatre' means theatre presented by professionals for young people.

Venues

For details about Fringe theatre Time Out and City Limits are best. They also give information about mainstream theatre as does the national press and the Standard. Local papers usually tell you about theatre in your immediate area. The telephone numbers given below are box offices and nearly all venues, even the smallest, operate a reliable booking system, though this often means turning up half an hour before the show starts to collect your tickets. Some of the larger theatres operate a credit card system which avoids all this.

Albany Centre
Douglas Way
Deptford   SE8
Tel 691 1367
Wheelchair access to theatre toilets
Admission £1.50-£3.50 Concessions
Membership £2.50pa(individual)
£4pa(family) £5pa(group)
●Producing Arts Centre Youth theatre
Deptford SE8
Theatre, music, dance, cabaret and workshops for and by a young multi-

cultural community. The main theatre space has an informal atmosphere with productions often staged 'cabaret style' where you can eat and drink during the performance. The Albany Empire (why do they keep this offensive name?) has its own company, The Combination, which stages mainly new plays about South London people. Both established modern writers such as Barrie Keefe and lesser known playwrights get their work put on here. Shows for children are half-price. The Basement Youth Theatre, part of a community youth arts project here, has its own studio space where it stages devised work relevant to a young multicultural community. The Second Wave Young Women's Project and the Lewisham Academy of Music, both youth schemes, are based here. The centre runs workshops and residencies by professional companies for young people wishing to learn more about all aspects of theatre: directing, playwriting, improvisation, acting technique, stage management, design and technical. Fridays and Saturdays there's the late night club with live bands, and Sunday lunchtimes family entertainment over the traditional Sunday meal - story telling for the children, workshops for young people and a live show for the parents.

Battersea Arts Centre
Old Town Hall
Lavender Hill
Battersea   SW11
Tel 223 8413
Wheelchair access to theatre toilets
bar cafe cinema darkroom
Admission £3.50 Concessions
Membership £1pa
●Arts Centre
Professional and community arts workers have replaced local councillors in this building which was formerly the town hall, though some people still occasionally turn up

saying they've come to pay their rates! There are two performance areas, or rather three, if you count the cafe which sometimes houses shows for pensioners. The main theatre is the former council chamber in all its grandeur - note the 'ayes' and 'nos' above the doors as you go into the auditorium. BAC did have its own resident theatre company for a short time during 1984-5, but this has now disbanded. Its programme is made up of shows by visiting companies, some local, with the accent on new plays with a high comedy and entertainment element. The versatile studio space is used for dance workshops as well as performances by community and professional groups. Experts based at BAC run workshops in silk screen printing, photography, pottery, art, dance, music, drama and sculpture, and there are sessions specially for children and pensioners, people who are unemployed, and mentally and physically handicapped. It seems that any excuse is good enough to have a festival here: there's the dance festival, the Summer festival, the mime festival and even the fiddle festival. BAC is also a base for the London International Festival of Theatre (see Arts Festivals below). Two independent groups are housed in the building: the Puppet Centre (see Other Theatre Organisations below) and the Women's Slide Library (see Libraries).

Bear Gardens Museum Theatre
Bear Gardens
Bankside SE1
Tel 928 6342
Wheelchair access phone in advance
Admission £2-£3.50 Concessions
Membership 25p per day £1pa
●Fringe Theatre
Visiting semi-professional theatre companies perform Jacobean and Elizabethan plays on a replica of an early seventeenth century stage. There are also occasional Sunday afternoon lecture performances on the history of theatre on Bankside which, during the middle ages, particularly the 16th and 17th centuries, was a centre of entertainment. Many of the open air theatres were built then, the most famous of all being Shakespeare's Globe in 1599. It was destroyed by fire only fourteen years later during a performance of his Henry The Eighth, and for many years now it has been the dream of film maker Sam Wanamaker to reconstruct the Globe as faithfully as possible to the original design and only a few yards away from its former position on Bankside. The 'project' as it is called has suffered several financial and local planning setbacks, not least of which is the claim by Southwark Council that they cannot find another location for their roadsweepers' depot, which currently occupies the proposed site. Let's hope that one day we will be able to see Shakespeare's plays in exactly the kind of theatre where they were originally performed (see Museums).

The Bob Hope Theatre
Wythfield Road
Eltham SE9
Tel 850 3702
Wheelchair access phone beforehand
Admission £2.50 Concessions
Membership £10pa(adults)
£5pa(OAPs students) £3pa(under 18)
●Amateur Theatre
The Eltham Little Theatre was having grave financial problems before the comedian Bob Hope, who was born in Eltham, stepped in. Not only did he lend his name to the theatre, but also helped it financially through the Bob Hope Classic Golf tournaments in Britain. The group is fairly enterprising in its choice of plays from Edward Bond to the Christmas pantomime. Auditions are held for any members wanting to take part. You can hire costumes at a comparatively low cost.

Bridge Lane Theatre
Bridge Lane
Battersea SW11
Tel 228 8828
Wheelchair access to theatre bar
Admission £3.50 Concessions
Membership 25p per day £1pa
●Producing Fringe Theatre
The resident company performs
classical and new plays in its
converted temperance hall. These are
interspersed with shows by visiting
companies. Also late night
performances. And there's a bar
despite its history of abstinence.

**The Clockhouse Community
Centre**
Defiance Walk
Woolwich SE18
Tel 855 7188
Wheelchair access throughout
Admission £1-£1.50 Concessions
●Fringe Theatre
This arts-based community centre
presents visiting theatre companies
roughly once a month in a general
purpose hall.

Copper Theatre Club
206-208 Tower Bridge Road
Bermondsey SE1
Tel 407 0968
Wheelchair access phone beforehand
Admission £1-£2.50 Concessions
Membership 25p pa
●Producing Fringe Theatre
Visiting and resident companies
stage a variety of plays many of them
premieres in this pub venue. There
are also lunchtimes shows.

**The Courthouse Community
Centre**
11 Garratt Lane
Wandsworth SW18
Tel 874 1094
Wheelchair access to ground floor
only not to theatre
Admission £1-£2.50 Concessions

●Fringe Theatre
The brief of the centre is to promote
the Arts, including theatre. Amateur
and semi-professional companies use it
as their base. It's also a place for
visiting amateur and occasionally
professional companies. The plays
vary enormously from Shakespeare to
musicals. There's a friendly
impromptu atmosphere here. Drinks
and snacks are equally impromptu,
meaning they're available sometimes!

Bear Gardens

The Elephant Theatre Club
84 Borough Road
Elephant & Castle SE1
Tel 928 0912
Wheelchair access to theatre bar
Admission £3(evening)
£2(lunchtime) £2(late-night)
Concessions
Membership 25pa
●Fringe Theatre
Mostly new plays and lots of them,
with lunchtimes and late-nights as
well as evening shows. The policy
here is to give actors a chance to be
seen and writers a chance to be
heard.

Greenwich Theatre
Crooms Hill
Greenwich SE10
Tel 858 7755
Wheelchair access to restaurant bar
toilets
Admission £3-£6 Concessions

●Producing Mainstream
A wide variety of new plays and classics are staged by the resident company most of the year round. A mainly middle class audience is attracted by the star names such as Kenneth Branagh, Margaret Tyzack and Maria Aitkin, and playwrights like Peter Nichols, Michael Frayn and Alan Ayckbourn. Several shows have transferred to the West End. They hope to celebrate the thirtieth anniversary of John Osborne's 'Look Back in Anger' with a new production of the play. The theatre was originally a music hall and much of the Victorian flavour has been retained despite extensive rebuilding over the years. The ghost of an unknown actress called the White Lady is reputed to tread the boards of the former stage now just below the ceiling of the restaurant. But don't let this spoil your appetite: she only comes out in the small hours of the morning when there's just one person working alone in the building! There's also an art gallery (see Art), and if you fancy jazz with your lunch then go along there on a Sunday. The theatre runs a subscription system which means you get priority booking and cheaper seats. There are similar privileges for the Friends of Greenwich Theatre at a membership fee of £7.50 a year for adults and 75p for those under eighteen.

Group 64 Theatre
203 Upper Richmond Road
Putney   SW15
Tel 788 6943/688 7788 ext 510
Wheelchair access to both theatres
Admission £2.50 Concessions
Membership £12(over 25) £6(under 25)
●Amateur Theatre Workshops
The centre, which is based in a converted church, takes its name from the year in which it was established. Since those early days it has managed to get funding from the MSC (for

rebuilding works) and from the borough of Wandsworth. It's adventurous in its programming: for instance Athol Fugard and David Edgar are two of the playwrights whose work they have chosen to produce. They also perform Shakespeare and other classics. The youth theatre performs two or three plays a year, and if you want to act with them you have to go through an audition and pay the membership fee of £6 a year. The 15-25 year olds also perform in other productions with the adult members who also have to go through auditions. There are close links with theatre professionals including a weekly drama workshop where people can test the water before they commit themselves to paying the full membership fee. With two performance areas, the main stage and a studio, there is plenty of opportunity to play in front of an audience.

La Bonne Crepe
539 Battersea Park Road
Battersea   SW11
Tel 228 5070
Wheelchair access to theatre bar
Admission £3.75(show only)
Membership 25p per day
●Fringe Theatre
Cafe theatre resident company offering a mix of musicals and comedy theatre while you eat a crepe with the filling of your choice.

Latchmere Theatre
503 Battersea Park Road
Battersea   SW11
Tel 228 2620
Wheelchair access none
Admission £2.50-£4.50 Concessions
Membership 25p per day £2.50pa
●Fringe Theatre Workshops
Visiting companies offer a varied programme of new plays, classics -

including adaptations - and cabaret in a pub and cafe environment. There are lunchtime plays as well, and dance and drama workshops are held on Saturday mornings.

Lewisham Theatre
Rushey Green
Catford   SE6
Tel 690 3431
Wheelchair access to theatre bar toilets
Admission £3-£9.50 Concessions
●Council run
There's a five week panto at Christmas, a jazz festival and concerts of light and classical music. The rest of the year it's amateur groups and various one-off bookings.

Morley College Theatre
61 Westminster Bridge Road
Lambeth North   SE1
Tel 928 8501 ext 46
Wheelchair access to bar concert hall
Admission £2 (for courses see Adult Education)
●Adult Institute
The 100 seater theatre is mainly for the students of the college to air the plays they've been working on over the term. There are drama workshops for both professional and amateur actors. (See Adult Education)

The National Theatre
Upper Ground South Bank
Southbank   SE1
Tel 928 2252
Wheelchair access to theatres bar cafe
For restaurant phone in advance
Admission £4.50-£11.50 Concessions
●Mainstream
The flagship of the established British theatre with three auditoriums - the Olivier, the Lyttleton and the Cottesloe - staging classical and new plays with artists considered to be at the peak of their careers. If the concrete jungle of the South Bank complex puts you off, simply turn your back on it and you will be confronted by one of the most outstanding views in the whole of London. You can see the river Thames stretching as far as St Paul's on your right and to the Houses of Parliament on your left. Watching the sun go down and the city lights come up is as good an entertainment as theatre any day. This is not to decry what goes on at the National Theatre, however, which on the whole lives up to its name as a 'centre of excellence' worthy of its world-wide acclaim and state subsidy of £8 million. Its privileged position does not mean that it has escaped the 'cuts'. At the time of going to press the smallest of the National's three theatres, the Cottesloe, is due to close in March 1986 unless funding can be found. And the number of company members has been cut back which is unfortunate especially for the Olivier Theatre, the biggest of the National's performance areas, which was built specially for large-scale productions. The National is one of the few subsidised theatres where an audience can enjoy large-cast shows and special theatrical effects which by definition cost money. It would be a real loss if these were no longer possible. The Lyttleton Theatre with its proscenium arch is taylor-made for nineteenth century plays, but is by no means confined to these. Platform performances - low budget readings and stagings with few props and costumes - are also held. Apart from the three theatres there are several bars and cafes. And there's an exhibition area and book shop in the main foyer where, if you're lucky, you may hit upon a concert too, which is free.

Nettlefold Hall
West Norwood Library
Norwood High Street
West Norwood   SE27
Tel 670 6212

Wheelchair access to bar cafe
Admission £1.75-£5 Concessions
●Council run
As with so many council-run large
entertainment centres like this, the
financial strains show, and apart
from some popular music concerts
and the occasional play, the hall is
very much for hire by private
individuals.

North Peckham Civic Centre
600-608 Old Kent Road
North Peckham   SE15
Tel 703 2917

Wheelchair access to bar cafe
Admission 50p-£15
●Council run
Light entertainment in the way of
plays, pantomime, cabaret and dance
by visiting companies, and there's a
dance and drama festival January to
March (see Arts Festivals below).
You can usually get a bite to eat here
and a hot drink.

The Old Vic

The Old Vic Theatre
Waterloo Road (The Cut)
Waterloo   SE1
Tel 928 7616
Wheelchair access to theatre toilets
Admission £2-£13.50 Concessions
●Mainstream

Before the impresario Ed Murvish
bought the Old Vic in 1982 for the sum
of £550,000, the theatre looked
doomed. The previous owners went
bankrupt and were forced to sell to
the highest bidder, which annoyed
the composer Andrew Lloyd-Webber
no end. He had already put in an offer
of half a million and, thinking the
deal was pretty well sewn up, rashly
divulged the figure to the Press. So
what did Honest Ed do but top this by
just £50,000 to win the deal. He has
since spent over two and a half
million on a complete refurbishment
of the building, reverting it to the
style of the 1870s. The place is worth a
visit just for its own sake, quite apart
from the shows. It's an experience just
eating and drinking in such
surroundings. Visiting companies
from the UK and abroad stage
established musicals and straight
plays.

The Old White Horse
261 Brixton Road
Brixton   SW9
Tel 274 5537
Wheelchair access to theatre bar
Admission £2.50-£3 Concessions
Cabaret
The resident company Cast do non-
sexist, non-racist cabaret.

The Oval House
52-54 Kennington Oval
Oval   SE11
Tel 582 7680
Wheelchair access to theatre
downstairs cafe toilets
Admission £2.50(downstairs)
£1.80(upstairs) Concessions
Membership 50p(6 mths)
●Arts centre Workshops
A multi-cultural centre with two
performance areas showing mainly
new plays often by young and
emerging theatre companies which
are encouraged in a deliberately

supportive atmosphere. Successful companies such as Burnt Bridges, Scarlet Harlets and Theatre of Black Women were virtually sporned here. This policy continues still, and many of the visiting companies are young, staging new work which often challenges existing power structures and explores themes such as sexism, racism and class prejudice. There is a lively writers' workshop and the results often get rehearsed readings in front of an audience and sometimes even a full production. Lots of other workshops are held and the aim is to encourage the community to do its own thing. There's also a cafe.

Polka Children's Theatre
Wimbledon Broadway
Wimbledon SW19
Tel 543 4888
Wheelchair access to theatre cafe toilets playground toyshop exhibition area
Admission £1.20-£3.80(children) £2-£5.80(adults)
●Producing Children's Theatre Workshops
The moment you enter the theatre you are in a dream world with characters from well-known fairy tales in the foyer. This is total environmental theatre even before the show starts. Polka has its own company which tours nationally. Their productions make full use of puppetry, masks, mime, magic and music. Outside companies also perform here and there are workshops for children, a toyshop, playground, a museum and cafe (see Children and Museums).

Rookery Open Air Theatre
Streatham Common
Streatham SW16
Tel 622 6655 ext 359
Wheelchair access with parking close by
Admission free-£3 Concessions

●Council run
Very much a summertime only theatre but even so bring warm clothing and a cushion to sit on if you can't afford one of the deckchairs provided. The shows goes on whatever the weather. So bring an umbrella too. Still, it's nice to console yourself, if the heavens do open, that Shakespeare's audiences also got wet watching his plays. Apart from Shakespeare's work you can also catch folk music here.

The South London Theatre Centre
2a Norwood High Street
Norwood SE27
Tel 670 3474
Wheelchair access to both theatres phone beforehand
Admission £1.50(members) £2(non-members)
Membership £20pa(single) £35pa(joint) £10pa(concessions)
●Amateur Theatre Workshops
Amateur theatre companies seem to have either a very long life or a very short one because the enthusiasm of volunteers seems to know no half way house. Anyway, this company has over 400 members and two theatre spaces (the Bell Theatre and Prompt Corner) and has been going since 1968. They survive through their membership fees and the profit made in the Clanger bar, not to mention ticket sales. It is quite amazing to think that while professional companies are struggling to get bums on seats the amateur sector has no problems in achieving full houses. Long live mums and dads and aunties and uncles who come to see their loved ones in the lime light! The centre also runs workshops for children and young people, and a general acting skills session.

Stanley Halls
South Norwood Hill
South Norwood SE25

Tel 653 3630
Wheelchair access to theatre bar toilets
Admission £1-£3 Concessions
●Council run
The place is kept open by the Christmas pantomime, amateur companies and old tyme music hall. Occasionally visiting theatre and dance companies are invited for short runs. Otherwise it's open for social evenings and other one off events.

National Theatre

Tara Arts Centre
356 Garratt Lane
Wandsworth　　　　　　SW18
Tel 871 1458
Wheelchair access theatre cafe
Admission £3 Concessions
Membership £5pa(single)
£7.50pa(family)
●Producing Fringe Theatre
Workshops
Theatre-in-Education
The Tara Arts Group was formed in 1976 in direct response to the murder of a young Asian, Gurdip Singh Chaggar, during racist unrest in London in the Summer of that year. Like many emerging theatre companies Tara Arts worked on a shoestring for several years, but now have two professional touring companies, a theatre-in-education

team which tours local schools and a national touring group. Both companies perform at the Arts Centre before taking a show out.
The plays, nearly all company-devised, explore Asian relations with the host society and also with its own community. Professionals from this country and the Indian sub-continent are invited to perform and run workshops at the centre in all fields of Asian arts, especially dance, music, theatre and Asian history. Workshops in theatre skills such as directing, writing and lighting are also held. The centre was recently refurbished spoiling the original features of the Victorian building, but providing a cafe, and performance and workshop area, with offices on the floor above.

The Tramshed Theatre
51 Woolwich New Road
Woolwich　　　　　　SE18
Tel 855 3371
Wheelchair access to theatre bar toilets
Admission £1-£5 Concessions
Membership £5pa(single)
£7.50pa(joint)
●Cabaret
Mostly cabaret designed to make you laugh, children's pantomime and jazz, folk and rock – all while you eat and drink.

Wimbledon Theatre
The Broadway
Wimbledon　　　　　　SW19
Tel 540 0362
Wheelchair access phone in advance
Admission £4.50-£8 Concessions
●Mainstream
Popular plays, musicals and the annual pantomime run between September and March with the occasional ballet. And there are concerts on Sunday evenings and a bar if you need a drink.

The Young Vic
66 The Cut
Waterloo SE1
Tel 928 6363
Wheelchair access to theatre bar cafe
toilets
Admission £4.95 Concessions
●Producing Fringe Theatre
A professional company presenting
modern dress Shakespeare and other
plays for a mainly youth audience.
There are two theatre spaces, the
larger one horseshoe shaped, the
other a studio.

Companies

Fringe theatre companies come and go
and by the time you read this, many
will have done just that - come and
gone. But the ones that do manage
against the odds to get regular
funding, and, with this, a strong
administrative base, usually go from
strength to strength creating a
following in their wake. Below are
some of the more long-lasting
companies most of which have
managed to get funding though not
always on a regular basis. Where
companies are building-based these
have been mentioned in Theatre
Venues above.

Afrosax
Dick Sheppard Youth Centre
Tulse Hill SW2
Tel 674 2168
●Youth Theatre Workshops
The company runs workshops many
of which culminate in a production
using music and dance as well as
drama. Professionals and non-
professionals work closely together
in this multi-cultural company.

Age Exchange Theatre Company
15 Camden Road
SE3

Tel 852 9293
●Fringe Theatre
One of the few professional theatre
companies performing specifically for
elderly people. Their shows are
devised from taped interviews with
pensioners and usually stick faithfully
to the original words, sometimes to
the theatrical detriment of the piece.
There's always an enjoyable musical
content to the plays.

The All Day Suckers
27 Wingmore Road
SE24
Tel 733 5270
●Children's Theatre
Clowning, puppets and audience
participation are what make this
children's company tick. They used to
be called the Lambeth Children's
Theatre before they named
themselves after a gigantic American
type of lollipop. Some people who book
them insist on getting the Lambeth
Children's Theatre, saying they don't
want that other lot!

Apples and Snakes
24 Worsley House
Shackleton Close
SE23
Tel 699 5265
●Cabaret
Working mainly in pubs, small fringe
theatres and sometimes bookshops,
poets enact their own words often
with music.

The Bubble Theatre Company
3-5 Elephant Lane
SE16
Tel 485 3420
●Fringe Theatre Workshops
The company promotes a 'theatre can
be fun' image with classic and new
plays for all ages. They pitch their
own theatre wherever they go. It's an
enormous tent which takes an army of
people to put up each time they play.
Watch out for them in parks and
other open spaces in South London.

Their programme is varied: shows for children, the Classics, specially commissioned plays and their own devised work. They play in repetoire, which means if you don't particularly want to see one show you won't have too long to wait till the next one. An important part of the Bubble's activites are the workshops they run in schools and community centres in certain boroughs.

The Buckmaster Puppets
72 Heythorpe Street
SW18
Tel 874 2290
● Puppet Theatre
A husband and wife team using string puppets to amuse all ages with starring characters such as Boy George. But strictly entertainment only and definitely no satire.

Burnt Bridges
4 Birdhurst Road
SW19
Tel 540 9080
● Fringe Theatre
A women's company promoting sexual equality with a sense of humour but you know they're serious.

Buster Young People's Theatre
Borough Community Centre
56 Southwark Bridge Road
Southwark　　　　　　SE1
Tel 261 0440
● Children's and Young People's Theatre
They perform mainly in schools tackling such subjects as relationships, sexism and other topics which many teachers prefer to leave to other people.

Clown Cavalcade
57 Pelham Road
Wimbledon　　　　　　SW19
Tel 540 3513
● Children's Theatre
Lots of clowning and circus skills

with a chance for the children to join in.

Common Lore
47 Evans Road
Catford　　　　　　SE6
Tel 461 1402
● Children's Theatre
Story telling is one of the oldest forms of theatre and it's enjoying a revival now. How significant is it that another expression for telling stories is telling fibs? Still they do say it's not what you tell it's the way you tell 'em. And with this company that means with traditional songs, music and dance. They work mainly with primary school children and there's a chance for lots of participation. Workshops for teachers and youth workers are also held.

Confederacy of Fools
29 Lynn House
Green Hundred Road
SE15
Tel 732 6229
● Fringe Theatre
A national touring company performing both new work and classics.

Donna Maria's Children's Theatre Company
16 Bell Meadow
Dulwich Wood Avenue
SE19

Tel 670 7814
● Professional Young People's
Theatre
A song and dance company made up of
children and young people aged 5-25.
They tour abroad with established
musicals and offer training
scholarships to young people of
exceptional talent.

Emergency Exit Arts
13 Rowley House
Watergate Street
SE8
Tel 691 7088
● Fringe Theatre
This company creates theatrical
spectaculars, for instance, a giant
puppet eighty-two feet high which
had to be brought on by crane. You
can understand, then, that they avoid
the conventional theatre venues and
often work outdoors, though they are
also to be seen in community centres,
coaches and other rather more
confined spaces.

Fireflies of the Boulevard
22 Prideaux Road
SW9
Tel 733 6634
● Fringe Theatre
Theatre of the spectacular and
unexpected which uses mixed media
and lots of music. Expect to be
surprised.

Floorboards Theatre Company
70-72 Verney Road
SE16
Tel 231 2494
● Fringe Theatre Workshops
A varied programme of new plays,
modern classics and adaptations of
well-known texts. The company also
runs workshops in schools.

Fooled Again Puppets
51 Heston House
Tanners Hill
SE8
Tel 692 1432

● Puppet Theatre Workshops
A three-woman company which
performs and runs workshops with
children and mother and toddler
groups. One of their puppet shows is
called Judy And Punch in which
Punch loses his stick.

Foot and Mouth
122 Edgeley Road
SW4
Tel 691 7149
● Cabaret
Two-man satire, though they must
have had an off-day when they chose
their name.

Greenwich Young People's Theatre
Burrage Road
SE18
Tel 854 1316
● Theatre in Education Workshops
The professional theatre in education
team tours primary and secondary
schools in Southwark, Lewisham and
Greenwich. The shows are true TIE,
that is specially created to involve the
young audiences who may be asked to
play a role, to question, and to make
decisions about issues brought up
during the performance. Workshops
in all sorts of arts are run for local
young people including sessions with
unemployed people and those with
special needs. There are two youth
theatre groups which tour nationally
once a year and visiting professional
companies occasionally perform here.

Hotfoot Community Theatre
62 Shooters Hill Road
SE3
Tel 691 5955
They run performance-based
workshops for under sevens at one
o'clock clubs and mother and toddler
groups.

Harmony Theatre Project
St Matthew's Meeting Place
Brixton Hill

SW2
Tel 274 3233
●Workshops
Workshops for 16-30 year olds,
including deaf and partially hearing
people, in mime, improvisation,
technical skills, stage fighting and
writing.

Ian and Friends
35 Hibernia Point
Wolvercote Road
SE2
Tel 310 4376
●Puppet Theatre
Ian Thom's friends are puppets and
they perform for children.

Isosceles
4B Grosvenor Hill
SW19
Tel 946 3905
●Cabaret
Two-man musical revue team with
what they call 'global' comedy. In
other words their sketches contain
characters from all over the world
recognisable by their exaggerated
accents.

John Mowat
56 Kestrel Avenue
SE24
Tel 274 3821
●Mime

Well-known stories are told through
mime by this one-man company.

Justin Case
21 Victoria Terrace
SW8
Tel 622 7484
●Cabaret
Solo comedy act.

The Little People's Theatre
15 Effingham House
Larkhall Estate
SW8
Tel 720 7029
●Children's Theatre
A one-man band using puppets and
fairy stories.

Livestock Theatre Company
41 Rosenthal Road
SE6
Tel 698 1962
●Theatre in Education
Defunct as a performing company, but
still writing plays for other theatre in
education companies.

L'Ouverture Theatre Trust
The Angell Centre
Wiltshire Road
Brixton   SW9
Tel 737 2472
●Fringe Theatre Workshops
Originally set up specifically to
provide work for black actors and
writers, though now a culturally
mixed company according to the
requirements of the plays they put on.
A reggae Shakespeare, a reggae Mac
The Knife and a Black Mikado are
just three examples of their work.
They also hold children's and young
people's workshops in dance, drama
and singing. And there's a project for
unemployed people where they write,
rehearse and perform their own plays
from start to finish.

Lumiere and Son
70 Silverthorne Road
SW8

Tel 622 4865
●Fringe Theatre
A company that makes the visual
spectacular. Unfortunately their
special effects have now grown so big
that not many venues in South
London can accommodate them
anymore.

The National Youth Music Theatre
178 Grand Drive
SW20
Tel 542 1247
●Youth Theatre
Professionals do the backstage work
and directing while the young people
aged 11-16 do the acting. They
describe their productions, which
tour internationally, as new music
theatre work, which apparently has
nothing to do with musicals.

Omelette Broadcasting Company
21 Victoria Terrace
SW8
Tel 622 7484
●Fringe Theatre
A comedy improvisation company
which basically means anything can
happen. Avoid sitting in the front row
if you don't want it to happen to you.

Resisters Theatre Group
5 Eccleston House
Tulse Hill Estate
SW2
Tel 671 0338
●Fringe Theatre Workshops
Their plays which they devise are
about women. If the members of the
company haven't had the experiences
they want to portray they go out and
research the subject. Past shows have
been about a women's self-defence
class, a women's refuge and a miners'
wives' support group. They also run
workshops on the theme of women's
strength. 'We did a show with a man
once' they said. This is feminist
theatre putting women where they
belong - at the top!

Roots Theatre Company
2 Parker Court
Studley Road
SW4
Tel 720 2707
●Fringe Theatre Workshops
A black company formed to promote
racial harmony and which deals with
such issues as women's rights and
drugs. They incorporate live music in
many of their productions and hold
workshops as well.

Sass Theatre Company
9 Churchmead
234 Camberwell Grove
SE5
Tel 708 3135
●Fringe Theatre
A black women's company formed to
give members a chance to play good
roles and thus to put across the
experience of black women.

The Smallest Theatre in the World
11 Sprules Road
SE4
Tel 635 9047
●Fringe Theatre
This one-man company lives up to its
name by performing from the side car
of a motorbike. While it means there
are few problems moving props and
scenery around it does make things
rather cramped when there's a full
house - of two!

Staunch Poets and Players
Manor House
58 Clapham Common North Side
SW4
Tel 228 2015 ext 222
●Fringe Theatre Workshops
A group of poets, musicians, dancers,
writers and directors using their
theatrical talents to present the Black
experience, past and current.

Street Theatre Trust
69 Bonnington Square
SW8
Tel 735 8268

●Children's Theatre Cabaret
Workshops
Clowning for children with Crumbs
the Clown and a chance to do some
face painting and other circus skills.
The company performs mainly in the
open air during festivals and summer
playschemes. Sometimes a character
called Arnold T Nosebag joins Crumbs
the Clown for adult cabaret with fire-
eating, escapology and mime.

Temba Theatre Company
Room 208
Dominion House
101 Southwark Street
SE1
Tel 261 0991
●Fringe Theatre Workshops
A company founded in 1972 to give
artistic expression to Black culture in
Britain and the Afro-Caribbean. They
perform mainly in schools and
community centres where they also
run workshops.

The Two Reel Company
Apt 21
154 Queenstown Road
SW8
Tel 622 7484
●Cabaret
Two-man company who play movie-
makers of the nineteen twenties.

Umoja
St Michael's Vicarage Annexe
Thompson's Avenue
Bethwin Road
SE5
Tel 701 6396
●Fringe Theatre
A young Black company formed to
promote racial harmony and
understanding through plays which
explore the Black experience in
Britain and the Afro-Caribbean.

Upstream Children's Theatre
St Andrews
Short Street
SE1

The Smallest Theatre in the World

Tel 633 9819
●Children's Theatre Workshops
A team of three performers run
projects for 4-11 year olds in
conjunction with schools in Lambeth
and Southwark. They also run
workshops for children at their home
base in story-telling, make up, music
and improvisation, and will devise
one-off workshops if given enough
warning.

Wandsworth Theatre Project
Old Chesterton School
110-115 Battersea Park Road
SW11
Tel 627 4613
●Theatre In Education
The company works mainly with
people on Youth Training Schemes.
One memorable production was based
on the theme of health and safety at
work!

Whirligig Theatre
14 Belvedere Road
Wimbledon   SW19
Tel 947 1732
●Children's Theatre
David Wood is the whirlwind behind
this company. He writes the plays and
directs them, and children love them.
He manages to get the right mixture
of adventure, suspense, comedy and
(whether you approve or not) violence
which can totally change the
atmosphere in any primary school.
The company tours nationally and
estimates 100,000 children a year see
its shows.

Witsend Theatre Company
83b South Worple Way
SW14
Tel 878 8194
●Fringe Theatre
Poetry and prose using theatrical
techniques and music.

Zuriya
38 Brixton Road
SW9
Tel 582 9479
●Fringe Theatre Workshops
The company specialises in
introducing African and Caribbean
cultures through story telling,
drumming, dancing and singing. The
plays they perform, while
highlighting the traditions of the
country they come from, have
relevance to audiences in Britain
today.

Arts Festivals

Greenwich Festival
25 Woolwich New Road
SE18
Tel 317 8687(BO)
854 8888 ext 2314(general enquiries)
Dates 30 May-15 June 1986
A major festival which takes place all
over the borough of Greenwich.
Theatre, poetry, dance, films, music,
sports, exhibitions and workshops for
all ages and all tastes. Though
participating theatre companies have
yet to be finalised some South London
companies which have performed
during the festival in the past are the
Bubble Theatre, Age Exchange, and
Lumiere and Son.

Live Arts Festival
North Peckham Civic Centre
600-608 Old Kent Road
SE15
Tel 703 2917(BO)
703 6311 ext 2330(general enquiries)
Dates 24 Jan-29 March

Local drama and dance groups as well
as those from further afield.

**The London International Festival
of Theatre (LIFT)**
Tel 736 3428
Dates Summer 1987 (to be finalised)
Since this festival was formed in 1981
it has created a name for itself as one
of the major international theatre
events in Britain. It takes place every
two years - the next one is in 1987 -
and gives a chance for audiences in
Britain to see theatre from all over
the world. The shows are specially
selected for their accessibility to a
largely English-speaking audience. At
the time of going to press the
organisers of the festival are still
travelling the world seeking out
suitable theatre companies and plans
are not yet finalised. In past years
Battersea Arts Centre in South
London has been a major venue for
visiting companies.

South Bank Splash
Tel 633 0880
Dates 4 weeks July-Aug to be finalised
The National Theatre runs this four-
week festival of free events which
takes place outside on the terraces of
the South Bank of the Thames.
There's theatre, clowning, music,
dance and puppets. The daytime is
taken up with children's events
giving ample opportunity for them to
participate as well as spectate, and the
evening is given over to music - jazz,
classical and pop.

**Southwark Community Arts
Festival**
Tel 703 6311 ext 2330
Dates 17-29 Nov 1986
This is the third annual community
arts festival run by Southwark
borough council. Theatre, dance,
workshops, poetry, films, exhibitions,
including plenty of events for
children, are held at venues
throughout the borough.

Other Organisations

This section deals with bodies which give information and advice, make policy and fund theatre in South London. As well as the national organisations such as the Arts Council of Great Britain (see below), the Borough Councils and the Greater London Council have special funds to promote theatre in South London. If you are looking for funding for a relatively new theatre company you are more likely to be successful with an application to the Arts and Entertainments department of your local borough - some have local Arts Councils (see Art introduction) - than with an application to the Arts Council of Great Britain. Or if your company has a specialism, for instance workshops with physically handicapped children, then other specialist organisation may be willing to give financial help. However, it goes without saying that any company looking for funding has to prove itself first, and that usually means working for at least a year with no financial help at all, and there are still lots of small theatre groups doing worthwhile work which never get funding at all.

Artsline
5 Crowndale Road
Mornington Crescent
NW1
Tel 388 2227/8
Open 10-4(Mon-Fri) 10-2(Sat)
A telephone arts information service for people with disabilities covering the Greater London area. They also send out useful information sheets about transport, concessions and so on.

The Arts Council of Great Britain
105 Piccadilly

W1
Piccadilly
Tel 629 9495
A national funding and policy making body for the Arts.

The Black Theatre Alliance
Lyndhurst Hall
Lyndhurst Road
Hampstead
NW3
Tel 431 1800
A campaigning group made up of representatives of Black Theatre companies in London, including Tara Arts, Umoja, Staunch Poets and Players and L'Ouverture. Its eventual aim is to attract a membership throughout the country in order to lobby funding bodies, to improve their publicity machine and to prevent what they call the 'ghetto-ising' of Black Theatre.

British Theatre Association
9 Fitzroy Square
Fitzrovia
W1
Tel 387 2666
Owns the largest theatre library in Britain. Membership costs £20 a year which entitles you to borrow books, use the reference library and take out playsets. The organisation has a large amateur theatre membership. Workshops in theatre skills are held regularly for professionals and amateurs.

The Greater London Arts
25-31 Tavistock Place
Bloomsbury
WC1
Tel 388 2211
Arts funding body for the greater London area.

The Greater London Council
County Hall
South Bank
SE1
Tel 633 5000

633 1707(arts information office)
Promotes and funds arts projects in
the greater London area (to be
abolished in March 1986).

**The Manders and Mitchenson
Theatre Collection**
5 Venner Road
Sydenham   SE26
Tel 778 6730
Open by appointment only
Theatre memorabilia put together by
two old hands of the theatre, Joe
Mitchenson and Raymond Mander,
who both started collecting
independently, then got together, and
in 1946 founded this collection of
photographs, posters, programmes and
detailed research on all aspects of
London theatre, ballet, opera and
music hall. Over the years the
Collection has got too big for its
premises and is in the process of being
moved to The Mansion, Beckenham
Place, Beckenham.

The Puppet Centre
Battersea Arts Centre
Old Town Hall
Clapham Junction   SW11
Tel 228 5335
Open 2-6(Mon-Fri)
The Centre advises organisations and
individuals on all aspects of puppetry.
There's a bookshop, library and
permanent exhibition area, and also a
fully-equipped workshop which, by
prior arrangement, you may be able to
use for puppet making. The Education
and Therapy Unit promotes an
awareness of puppet theatre in schools
to both teachers and pupils through
demonstrations and workshops which
are free. They also publish a magazine
called 'Animations' which comes out
every two months.

Puppet Centre, Battersea Arts Centre

WOMEN

Provision for women in South London varies enormously depending on which borough you live in. A good indication of the attitude of local councils towards women and women's issues is whether or not they have a Women's Equality Unit. These have been set up in Lewisham, Lambeth, Southwark and Greenwich to promote women's interests in all areas of council policy. Whether the units have been entirely successful in finding out what women in the community really require is a matter which is still being debated. But it's probably true that women living in boroughs which do not provide such a unit are having to fight even harder for those basic freedoms which women have been denied for so long. The GLC, through its Women's Committee funds over 500 women's groups. There are many people who believe that the very fact the GLC supports so many women's groups is one very good reason why the Council should be abolished. However there are many others who believe that the abolition of the GLC will lead to a serious

deterioration of facilities for women in South London. At the time of going to press only a few groups which receive grant aid from the GLC know for certain that they will be funded beyond March 1986. The existence of many women's groups is, therefore, seriously threatened.

Women's Centres

These provide an opportunity for women to meet in a friendly and informal environment. Most offer advice, information and help according to the needs of the women who use them. Although there are now many women's centres in South London there are still not enough to meet demand, and many women have to travel several miles to get to one. The Southwark Women's Bus and Women in Greenwich provide their own answer to this problem by going out to meet women nearer their homes. Hopefully the Bus is one method of finding out and fulfilling the needs of women who would not normally seek out a women's centre. There is increasing pressure from Black and ethnic minority women for centres which will more truly reflect the community, and as a result more centres for Black and ethnic minority women have been set up. The Black Women's Centre in Stockwell was the first of its kind (see below).

Asha

Asian Women's Co-operative
378 Coldharbour Lane
Brixton   SW9
Tel 278 8854/737 5901
A centre for Asian women living in Lambeth which provides support, information and advice on issues such as welfare rights, immigration, and rights at work and in the home.

Asian Women's Group

c/o Asian Resource Centre
LEB Buildings
Macbean Street
Woolwich   SE18
Tel 854 1188
A resource, information and advice centre for Asian women. It aims to eliminate the isolation and deprivation suffered by many Asian women by providing information on rights at work and in the home. It also runs advice sessions on welfare rights, health, immigration and nationality.

Battersea Black Women's Group

248 Lavender Hill
Battersea   SW11
Tel none
The group meets on Sundays 4-6.

Black Women's Centre

41A Stockwell Green
Stockwell   SW9
Tel 274 9220
A place where Black women can meet for support, advice and information. Individual counselling is available, there are arts and crafts workshops (with creche facilities) and a library. Other women's groups use the centre as a base, for instance, Brixton Black

Women's Group and the Black Women's Library (see below).

Deptford & Lewisham Women's Centre

74 Deptford High Street
Deptford   SE8
Tel 692 1851
A drop-in for all women – a common room, meeting room, office space and a kitchen are provided. Advice on a variety of issues is available – legal, domestic, welfare, sexual and health. Yoga sessions are held on Monday mornings and Wednesday afternoons, percussion on Thursday afternoons. Creche facilities are available for anyone taking part in these sessions. A hysterectomy support group meets here, and many other women's groups use the centre. There's a lending library and a cheap lunch is available on Mondays.

Greenwich Women's Place (GAGOU)

Macbean Street
Woolwich   SE18
Tel 856 3808/854 4989
Between 12 and 3 the centre is open to women for discussion on any topic. Free pregnancy testing is available, workshops in photography and on coping with pre-menstrual tension.

Older Women's Project

Pensioners' Link
Old Town Hall
Polytechnic Street
Woolwich   SE18
Tel 854 2835
Provides support, information, advice and social occasions for women pensioners (see Elderly).

South London Women's Centre

55 Acre Lane
Brixton   SW2
Tel 274 7215
A drop-in for all women. It offers advice, information, a meeting place for women's groups, a television and video room, pool room, workshop

facilities and use of the centre's mini-bus. Workshops include jewellery making, dress-making, massage and relaxation, keep-fit, video and crafts. A creche is often available, but times are not specific, so check beforehand. The snack bar is open all day and hot lunches are served between 12.30 and 2.

The Mobile Womens' Centre, Southwark

Southwark Women's Bus
c/o Southwark Women's Centre
2-6 Peckham High Street
Peckham   SE15
Tel 701 2564
The bus will visit anywhere in the borough. It's basically a women's centre on wheels providing a meeting place, information and advice to all women. It helps women to set up their own groups and activities. If you want the bus to visit your area, then contact them at the above address or phone.

Southwark Women's Centre
2-6 Peckham High Street
Peckham   SE15
Tel 701 2564
Open to all women and women's groups in Southwark. It provides a general information, advice and referral service. Other women's groups can be contacted through the Centre. There's a drop-in with creche facilities (creche information packs are available for hire for anyone thinking of setting up their own group – see Children) office equipment, including typewriters

with foreign language heads, are available, and there's a small exhibition area for use by women's groups. There is also free pregnancy testing.

Wandsworth Women's Centre
This doesn't exist at the moment, but efforts are being made to set a women's centre up in the borough. If you want to take part in starting up a centre in Wandsworth, then phone Alison on 223 5878.

A Woman's Place
Hungerford House
Victoria Embankment
WC2
Tel 836 6081
Advice and information on all issues of interest to women. Upstairs is the Feminist Library (930 0715) with books, pamphlets and magazines on the women's movement. There's also a feminist bookshop which sells non-sexist children's books, badges and posters. You can book a room for meetings and use their typewriter.

Women in Greenwich (WIG)
14 Ebdon Way
Ferrier Estate
Kidbrooke   SE3
Tel 856 3808
A mobile women's centre which travels to estates in Greenwich offering advice, information and support on such topics as welfare rights, local activities, training and others. The five women workers will help you set up your own group or put you in touch with other women's organisations in the borough. At the moment they are compiling a skills register to help women to share their skills and experience. You can find out when the bus is visiting your area by phoning the above number. WIG also run workshops for girls in schools to explore such issues as sexism, racism, drugs, sexuality and body image. If you would like to arrange a workshop in the school where you work or study, then contact the

centre on the above number.

General and Legal Advice Centres

All the law centres listed below provide legal advice, but some specialise in certain areas. You need to contact them first to make an appointment and this is a good time to make sure your particular query or problem can be dealt with by that centre. If not ask them which is the best place for you to go. As well as law centres, many women's centres (see above) provide legal and general advice, and so do Citizens' Advice Bureaux (see Community Services).

Brixton Law Centre
506 Brixton Road
Brixton SW9
Tel 733 4245
Will arrange for you to see a woman solicitor.

National Council for Civil Liberties
21 Tabard Street
Borough SE1
Tel 403 3888
The women's rights officer deals mainly with employment and sexual harrassment of women, ensures employers observe the Equal Pay Act of 1976 and helps women take cases of alleged unfair dismissal and sexual harassment to the courts.

North Lambeth Law Centre
381 Kennington Lane
Kennington SE11
Tel 582 4425
Will arrange for you to see a woman solicitor.

North Lewisham Law Centre
28 Deptford High Street
Deptford SE8
Tel 692 5355
Will arrange for you to see a woman solicitor.

Southwark Law Centre
29 Lordship Lane
East Dulwich SE22
Tel 299 1024
Will arrange for you to see a woman solicitor.

Stockwell and Clapham Law Centre
337 Wandsworth Road
Clapham SW8
Tel 720 6231
Will arrange for you to see a woman solicitor.

Wandsworth Law Centre
248 Lavender Hill
Battersea SW11
Tel 228 9462
Although the Centre does not run women only sessions you can make an appointment to talk specifically with a woman solicitor if you wish.

Women's Advice & Counselling Service
The Albany Centre
Douglas Way
Deptford SE8
Tel 692 0231 ext 62(day) 692 6268(24 hr answering service)
Free and confidential advisory service for women in Lewisham and Greenwich. Counselling, discussion groups on a wide range of subjects, legal and welfare rights advice, pregnancy testing, advice on contraception and women's health in general. Sessions are held on Monday nights between 7 and 10.

Women's Information and Advice
c/o Law Centre
105 High Street
Plumstead   SE18
Tel 855 9817
Free confidential advice on matters
such as housing, divorce, custody,
benefits, violence and sex
discrimination. Women only advice
sessions take place on a Thursday
evening between 6.30 and 8. Transport
or home visits can be arranged within
the borough of Greenwich.

Domestic Violence

An increasing number of women who
have survived physical, mental or
sexual abuse from men are making the
choice, albeit under impossible
circumstances, to leave the often
violent situations they find
themselves in. Other women do not
make the choice to leave their homes,
but are forced into doing so through
fear for their own safety or that of
their children. Women's Aid refuges
provide accommodation and support
both for women who have already
made this choice and for women who
need a safe place in order to make a
decision about their future. There are
over thirty women's refuges in
London which offer temporary and
permanent housing and also lobby
local councils to rehouse women. But
this is not enough to meet the demand
as more and more women need a safe
place where they can go for practical
and emotional support. For security
reasons we cannot publish names and
addresses of refuges, but the
organisation listed below will advise
you about where to go if you need a
refuge.

Asha
Asian Women's Aid
PO Box 484
Camberwell   SE5

A refuge specifically set up to meet
the demands of Asian women who are
in violent situations. Emergency
accommodation and protection is
provided, with advice on a wide range
of issues such as housing, legal
matters, welfare rights and children's
education. In an emergency phone
London Women's Aid (see below)
anytime day or night.

London Women's Aid
Tel 251 6537 (24 hr answering service)
Co-ordinates the work of women's
refuges in London and refers women
to refuges both in and outside of
London. A Black women's group
operates within Women's Aid.

Women's Aid Federation
Tel 251 6537 (24 hr answering service)
Offers advice and will put you in
touch with other women's
organisations including refuges.

Incest and Rape

There are many groups which offer
free and confidential advice and
counselling for women and girls who
have been raped or who have survived
incest. You may be a woman who was
sexually abused as a child or a mother
who fears that your child is being
sexually abused. If you would like to
contact a counselling support group
or need to talk to someone who has
been through a similar experience,
then phone A Woman's Place (836
6081) or your local women's centre
(see Women's Centres above). In an
emergency you can phone Women's
Aid (251 6537), the London Rape Crisis
Centre (see below) or Incest Crisis
Line (see below).

Incest Crisis Line
Tel 890 4732 (speak to Shirley)
302 0570 (speak to Ann)
422 5100 (speak to Richard)
Shirley, Ann and Richard offer
emotional and practical support to
incest victims and will arrange

medical referrals if necessary. For boys who have been abused contact Richard on the above number.

Incest Survivors Campaign

c/o A Woman's Place
Tel 737 1354
Meetings first and third Sundays of month.

Lambeth Incest Survivors Group

c/o The South London Women's Centre
55 Acre Lane
Brixton SW2
Tel 737 1354
A self-help group for survivors of incest.

London Rape Crisis Centre

PO Box 69
WC1
Tel 278 3956/837 1600(24 hr answering service)
Offers emotional support and legal and medical advice. They are committed to making the public more aware of the reality of rape.

Women's Anti-Violence Campaign

Tel 326 1203
An advice, counselling and support centre for all women who have been assaulted or abused by men. Drop in between 10 and 5 or make an appointment. They are in contact with a number of groups and women's refuges in Lambeth and will help you to take a case of rape or assault to the courts if you wish.

Housing

Below we give information on where to go for advice and help where women's particular housing needs and difficulties are dealt with. If you need re-housing urgently because of mental or physical abuse at home contact Women's Aid (see Domestic Violence above). If you are a council tenant and you are breaking up with your partner, you or your partner may be able to get re-housed, but you need to be able to prove that 'the relationship was an established one and that the breakdown of the relationship is permanent'. Contact your neighbourhood management officer whose address you can get from the housing department of your borough council (see Housing). If you are are not a council tenant and you are breaking up with your partner or you are about to become homeless, contact the Housing Advice Centre (see Housing). Law centres (see General and Legal Advice Centres above) will also give advice on housing. If you need somewhere to stay straight away because you are homeless, then phone the Housing Advice Switchboard any time day or night on 434 2522.

Asian Girls' Hostel

c/o Asha
378 Coldharbour Lane
Brixton SW9
Tel 278 8854/737 5901
Emergency accommodation for young Asian women who have left home because of conflict with parents. Provides advice and support on financial, health, welfare, educational, nationality and housing matters.

Homeless Action

Tel 251 6783
The organisation runs hostels for women in Lambeth, Southwark and Lewisham as well as other parts of London. You always have your own room. Contact the headquarters above for an interview.

Ifeoma Hostel
2 Gauden Road
Clapham   SW4
Tel 627 4005
Black single parents can stay here for
up to nine months. There will soon be
accommodation for pregnant single
women who need help. Most residents
are referred by social services, but it's
worth phoning direct for information
if you are pregnant and need help.

London Housing Aid Centre
Tel 373 7841/373 7276
They produce a booklet called A
Woman's Place about housing rights
and family break-up.

National Women's Federation
Tel 251 6429
Offers housing advice.

Rights of Women
Tel 251 6577
Line open 7-9(Tue Thur) for general &
legal advice 10-5(Mon-Fri) for referral
to solicitors
A telephone service only offering legal
advice and referrals for women on
housing rights relating to break up of
marriage.

St Michael's Hostel
52 Palace Road
Tulse Hill   SW2
Tel 671 1252
For single mothers mainly aged 16-18
who can stay here for up to two years.
Photography and computer sessions
are run for mothers, friends and ex-
residents.

Education & Training

There are many courses specially for
women in South London. Some lead to
exams, others are work
apprenticeships, and some are purely
for pleasure. Adult Education
Institutes run what are called Fresh
Start courses, some of them for women
only. These are designed to build up
your confidence and improve your
study skills, especially useful if you
have spent many years away from the
world of employment and study while
looking after your children. Adult
Education Institutes also run courses
specially for women in such subjects
as yoga, assertion, women and
writing, women's history and self-
defence (see Self-Defence &
Assertiveness below). Many courses
are run in local community centres or
tenants' associations. Creches are
often available, though you will have
to book in advance. For details of
these contact the community
education workers at the Adult
Education Institutes (see Adult
Education for more information about
courses). There are also various
training schemes for women who
want to move into less traditional ·
areas of work and training. The
boroughs of Greenwich, Lewisham
and Southwark actively encourage
women to train in areas traditionally
seen as men's. They participate in the
Women and Work Project and jointly
fund a women's training advisor.
Lambeth runs its own Women and
Work Project (see below). There are
good opportunities for women as
apprentices with some borough
councils. Greenwich encourages
women to train in carpentry,
plumbing and electrical engineering.
Contact your borough council for
more details. Some boroughs have
women's workshops or skills centres,
or at least women only sessions in
mixed centres where women can learn
a skilled trade.

Black Action Group
53 Bedford Hill
Balham   SW12
Tel 673 6430
Offers help on employment and
training for Black people. There are
courses for women in painting and
decorating, sewing and fashion, and
non-traditional women's skills.

Charlton Training Centre
Ferranti Close
Westminster Industrial Estate
Charlton   SE18
Tel 317 9636
A variety of courses are available for
women.

**Greenwich Employment Resource
Unit (GERU)**
311 High Street
Plumstead   SE18
Tel 311 0522
Short courses with a creche available.
Not exclusively for women but of
particular interest to women. The
Unit aims to further the education,
training and employment of
individuals and community groups.
They have a policy of working with
people from disadvantaged groups
including women.

Greenwich Homeworking Project
Ground Floor Clayhill House
Raglan Road
Woolwich   SE18
Tel 854 9841
Aims to give support and advice, and
improve conditions for homeworkers,
most of whom are women from ethnic
minority groups especially Asian.

**Greenwich Training and Advice
(GRETA)**
12-14 Wellington Street
Woolwich   SE18
Tel 854 2993
Offers advice on training and work
opportunities for women and is
particularly helpful if you have been
out of paid employment for some time.

Inset
175 Rye Lane
Peckham   SE15
Tel none
Provides information on education
and training on a national and local
level.

**Lambeth Educational
Opportunities (LEO)**
Strand Centre
Elm Park
Brixton   SW2
Tel 671 2961
Advice on all aspects of post-school
education and training, including
information on grants, childcare,
effect on benefits if you become a
student.

Lambeth Girls' Project
Lambeth Women's Workshop Unit
C22 Park Hall Road Trading Estate
Martell Road
West Norwood   SE21
Tel 677 4870/232 1691
Wednesday evening class in carpentry
for girls aged 12 and upwards. You
pay for materials used only.

Lambeth Institute
Lambeth Women's Workshop Unit
C22 Park Hall Road Trading Estate
Martell road
West Norwood   SE21
Tel 677 4870/670 0339
Classes in carpentry for all women on
Thursday evenings between 7 and 9
and Friday afternoons between 3 and
6.

Lambeth Women & Work Project
460 Wandsworth Road
Clapham   SW8
Tel 622 9208
Aims to promote economic justice for
women in Lambeth and offers
comprehensive information on
training courses for women.

Lambeth Women's Workshop Unit
C22 Park Hall Road Trading Estate
Martell Road
West Norwood   SE21
Tel 670 0339

A carpentry and joinery course for women over 25. It's two days a week and lasts for 16 weeks. You are entitled to travel, training and childcare allowance.

The Lee Centre
1 Aislibie Road
Lee   SE12
Tel 852 4700
A part-time study course for women called New Horizons. It lasts two terms, and starting from every day experience looks at you and society and at the work of writers.

Lewisham Women's Employment Project
179 High Street
Deptford   SE8
Tel 691 3550
Advice and information on employment, training, childcare and setting up a co-operative. They produce a monthly newsletter.

Southwark Women's Training Workshop
164-180 Union Street
Southwark   SE1
Tel 261 0575
Workshops where women can train in carpentry and joinery leading to first year City and Guilds examinations. All childcare is paid for and there is a training allowance.

Thames Polytechnic
Wellington Street

Woolwich   SE18
Tel 854 2030 ext 501
The college runs a New Opportunities for Women course designed for those who have been away from employment for some time. It's 21 hours a week to fit in with school hours and combines counselling, advice and education with communication and study skills.

Wandsworth Education Shop
86 Battersea Rise
Clapham Junction   SW11
Tel 350 1790
Free education advice for adults who live or work in the borough of Wandsworth. No need to make an appointment if you drop in on Wednesday between 2 and 6 or Friday between 10 and 2.

Women into Manual Skills Course
Deptford Skills Centre
Church Street
Deptford   SE8
Tel 691 5012
A ten week introductory course for women over 19 who would like to try out a range of manual skills to find out what suits them best. A woman counsellor is based there offering guidance and support. You are entitled to childcare, travel and training allowances.

Women's Mechanics Project
Bay R
1-3 Brixton Road
Kennington   SW9
Tel 582 2574
A part-time course (21 hours a week) lasting six months and starting from basics. You are entitled to childcare, travel and equipment allowances.

Women's Training and Employment Advice & Information
460 Wandsworth Road
Battersea   SW8
Tel 622 9208
Comprehensive information on

employment, training and childcare provision in Lambeth.

Young Lewisham Project
Motor Vehicle Workshop
346 High Street
Lewisham   SE13
Tel 690 4957
A well-equipped workshop aimed primarily at young unemployed people. There are sessions on Thursdays for women between 10 and 12 (introductory course) and 2-4.30 (repairs and motor mechanics).

Health

Good health is much more than the absence of illness. It is also freedom from anxiety, depression and dependence on drugs, alcohol tranquilisers or other artificial forms of stimulant. Unfortunately there are very few places where women can go if they are not ill but simply want to discuss health issues. We could do with a lot more Well Women's Centres where women can meet other women in an informal atmosphere for advice, information and counselling, or just to discuss their general health. Often our worries and problems about health seem too insignificant to take to the doctor   who we are told is always terribly busy. So where can we go instead? Well Women's centres are one solution, and if you would like to visit your nearest one, then contact your Community Health Council (see Health).

Association of Breast Feeding Mothers
131 Mayow Road
Lower Sydenham   SE26
Tel 778 4769(24 hr answering service)
A self-help organisation offering advice and counselling by letter, personal contact or phone. There are also informal group meetings for women who have no particular problems with breast feeding, but wish to discuss this and related topics with other women.

British Pregnancy Advisory Service
58 Pettyfrance
Westminster   SW1
Tel 222 0985
Offers advice and information on abortion, contraception, infertility and pregnancy. A charge is made for services.

The Brook Advisory Centre
Head Office
153a East Street
Walworth   SE17
Tel 708 1234/1390
(For addresses and telephone numbers of centres in South London see Youth).
Provide a free and confidential information service for young people aged up to 25 on birth control, pregnancy, and sexual and emotional problems.

Endometriosis Society
65 Holmdene Avenue
Herne Hill   SE24
Tel none
Please write in for information and advice.

Greenwich Black Women's Health Project
39 Wellington Street
Woolwich   SE18
Tel 854 3766
For Afro-Caribbean women who want to discuss health issues. Home visits can be arranged. Contact the community development worker on the above number.

Greenwich Mind
Ormiston Road Centre
54 Ormiston Road
Greenwich   SE10
Tel 853 1735
An opportunity for women to come together to discuss issues that interest them. Come along on Friday afternoons between 1.30 and 4 if you want to meet other women, or if you feel isolated, depressed or anxious.

Hysterectomy Support Group
Deptford and Lewisham Women's
Centre
74 Deptford High Street
Deptford SE8
Tel 692 1851
Information and support for women
who have had a hysterectomy or are
about to have one.

Lewisham Support Group
Voluntary Action Lewisham
120 Rushey Green
Catford SE6
Tel 690 4343 ext 328
For women who have had or will be
having hysterectomies.

National Childbirth Trust
9 Queensborough Terrace
W2
Tel 221 3833
Advice and information on childbirth.
They hold ante natal classes and post
natal support groups. There is a
breast-feeding adviser and you can
hire breast-feeding pumps. South
London branches are in Lewisham
(699 6926/698 7892), Streatham (672
1790), Clapham (870 7656) and
Wimbledon (874 4262 after 4pm).

**South London Feminist Therapy
Centre**
Pellin Centre
43 Killyon Road
Clapham SW8
Tel 622 0148
Counselling and therapy for women
and men. There are training sessions
and weekend workshops.

Waterloo Health Project
14 Baylis Road
Waterloo SE1
Tel 261 1404
A variety of health related activities
including yoga, first aid, a women's
health group, relaxation and exercise
and information on children's health.

**Women's Health Information
Centre**
52-54 Featherstone Street
EC1
Tel 251 6580
Information on many aspects of
women's health and well-being. They
will put you in touch with self-help
health groups.

Women's Health Group
Lee Centre
1 Aislibie Road
Lewisham SE12
Tel 852 4700
This is a multi-racial community
education centre, a department of
Goldsmith's College. Contact Sheila
Collins the health course tutor for
further information. All kinds of
courses for women take place (see
Education and Training in this
section). A creche is provided.

**Women's Reproductive Rights
Centre**
Tel 251 6332
Campaigns for women's rights to
decide if and when to have children

regardless of age, race, class,
sexuality, disability or status. It also
provides a meeting place, organises
speakers and puts women in touch
with other groups for support and
advice on issues such as pregnancy
testing, contraception, abortion,
infertility, donor insemination,
sterilisation and reproductive
technology. They also provide a
variety of information pamphlets.

Arts

Albany Centre
Douglas Way
Deptford   SE8
Tel 691 1367
The Centre has a women's night on
Mondays with sessions in dance,
dress-making, singing, percussion, a
women's history course, hair-plaiting,
patchwork and a writers' workshop.

Asian Women's Arts Group
c/o Asian Resource Centre
LEB Buildings
Macbean Street
Woolwich   SE18
Tel 854 1188
Fosters the development of Asian
women's arts in order to break down
the isolation that so many Asian
women feel in a racist environment.
There are dance, drama and video
workshops, women only discos, and a
slide library for use in schools is being
built up.

Battersea Arts Centre
Old Town Hall
Lavender Hill
Battersea   SW11
Tel 223 8413
A varied programme of one-off
women's workshops and regular
sessions in self-defence, dance,
photography. There is jazz by women
every second Sunday.

Feminist Photography Group
Deptford & Lewisham Women's
Centre

74 High Street
Deptford   SE8
Tel 732 4921
Group of feminists who aim to change
the image of women through their
photography.

Pictures of Women
245A Coldharbour Lane
Brixton   SW9
Tel 733 7207/274 9370
Co-op of film-makers specialising in
films about women.

Speak Out
c/o Black Women's Centre
41A Stockwell Green
Stockwell   SW9
Tel 274 9220
A magazine for and by Black women,

Women Artists' Slide Library
Battersea Arts Centre
Old Town Hall
Lavender Hill
Battersea   SW11
Tel 228 5771
A reference library of British women
artists, past and contemporary. There
is also a growing collection of theses
by students who have produced work
on women artists (see Libraries).

Childcare for Under 5s

Though there are many different
kinds of childcare provision in South
London, there is nowhere near
enough especially since more and
more women are going out to work or
would do so if only there were
someone to look after the children.
(For details of the kinds of childcare
facilities available in South London
see Children).

Single Parents

One in eight families in Britain is a
one-parent family and 90% of single
parents are women.

Gingerbread Association for One Parent Families
35 Wellington Street
WC2
Tel 240 0953
A national self-help organisation for single parents. Phone them for details about your nearest local branch.

Greenwich One Parent Project (GRIPP)
St Mary's Church
Greenlaw Street
Woolwich   SE18
Tel 316 0061
Offer advice and information for one parent families and help in campaigns for better services.

National Council for One Parent Families
255 Kentish Town Road
NW5
Tel 267 1361
Works to improve the position of single parents and their children by offering advice and information to single parents and pregnant single women, making the public aware of the plight of single parents and acting as a pressure group for policies and services which single parent families need. The Council produces several publications including Double Struggle – Sex Discrimination and One Parent Families by Penny Letts. You can get a list of all their publications from them.

Wel-Care
St Mary's Church
Greenlaw Street
Woolwich   SE18
Tel 317 8747/854 3865
A Christian organisation which offers advice and information to single pregnant women and single parents. This includes advice on abortion and adoption if required. They also run ante-natal classes and a mother and toddler group 10.30-12 on Tuesdays.

Transport

Stockwell Women's Lift Service
46 Kepler Road
Brixton   SW4
Tel 274 4641
Open 6.30-12.30(Mon-Thur) 6.30-1.30 (Fri) 9.30-1.30(Sat)
Phone during the day to book a lift. A free evening service which provides safe transport for women by women in and around the Lambeth area. Donations are welcome, and women volunteers are needed especially on Fridays and Saturdays to do the driving and answer the telephone.

Lewisham Women's Lift Service
The Albany Centre
Douglas Way
Deptford   SE8
Tel 692 6009
Open 6.30-11.30(Mon-Fri)
Phone during the day to book a lift. Flat fee of 75p, or 35p for OAPs and children.

Self-Defence & Assertiveness

Being able to defend yourself both physically and mentally means you have more freedom to do what you want when you want. Self-defence classes and assertiveness courses are both geared to this end. Most Adult Education Institutes run short courses in assertiveness training (usually 8-10 weeks). You can find out more about them by contacting the institutes direct (see Adult Education). Below we have listed some of the major self-defence classes available for women in South London.

Affirm
44 Holdenby Road
Brockley　　　　　SE4
Tel 692 4089
Assertion sessions for women only.

Albany Centre
Douglas Way
Deptford SE8
Tel 691 1367
Women's self-defence classes and self-defence for Black and ethnic minorities.

Battersea Arts Centre
Old Town Hall
Lavender Hill
Battersea　　　　　SW11
Tel 223 8413
Self-defence for women.

Kidbrooke House
Mycenae Road
Greenwich　　　　　SE3
Tel 317 9928
Self-defence for women.

London Borough of Southwark
Warwick Hall
Camberwell　　　　　SE5
Tel 639 1178
You will be able to find out about this and other women's self-defence classes by phoning the above number.

Martial Arts Commission Broadway House
15-16 Deptford Broadway
Deptford　　　　　SE8
Tel 691 3433
Information for all on martial arts including self-defence.

Simba Project
39 Wellington Street
Woolwich　　　　　SE18
Tel 317 0451
Self-defence for women.

St Michael's Community Centre
Desmond Street
New Cross　　　　　SE14
Tel None
Women's self-defence on Wednesdays 10-12.30.

Waterfield Adult Centre
Waterfield Close
Thamesmead　　　　　SE28
Tel None
Women's self-defence on Wednesdays 10-12.30.

YOUNG PEOPLE

This chapter is about what's on tap for young people in South London. At 16 you can (by law) leave school. Decision time looms. Do you stay at school, go to college, try to find a job, go on a training scheme, do voluntary service here or someplace or what? Parents and friends will have some ideas and may help you to sort out what you want to do but there are also loads of places you can go to where you can have a chat and be given practical advice. We outline the general areas you might need to know about and then go borough by borough through what is available locally, covering main contact addresses, advice centres and information on some projects. A lot of books and packs have been devised to guide you through the maze of relevant issues so be sure to look out for them (often found at Unemployment Project Information Services). It's worth remembering too that a lot of groups and projects produce leaflets in order to tell you where they are and what they do. We haven't mentioned any sports facilities here – see the chapter on

Sport. For information on where your local DHSS offices and job centres are see Local Services. Other chapters that might be useful to you are Art Galleries, Festivals, Dance, Ethnic Minorities, and Theatre.

The first part of this chapter – **How the Network Works** – has information on the following: The Youth Service, the ILEA Careers Service, Unemployment, Experience in Work, Starting a Business, Family Planning, Resource Centres. The second part – **Your Local Network** – is arranged borough by borough telling you where you can go locally for the things we told you about in the fiist section. The final section tells you about Awards and Adventure and Travel.

How the Network Works

The Youth Service

There are spaces and places set aside in each borough for use by you and your friends. The way to find out about these is by contacting the main area youth office in your borough. They can tell you where your nearest centres, clubs, projects and advice centres are (this includes statutory as well as voluntary organisations). It's best to speak to a youth worker. Youth centres are organised at secondary schools and are usually well equipped for sports, recreation and education programmes. For information contact the head of the centre.

Youth clubs vary a lot but are usually places where you can meet people. There are some organised facilities and advice is often available. Clubs often have a membership fee and a small charge for each session. Contact the leader of the club for details. Some clubs and centres are more structured than others but most are really open to your suggestions. Word gets out about which clubs are good for what but if you're not part of the local network yet then find out more from your youth office or local library. You can find out about unemployment projects here too. The following is a quote from a youth worker about the youth service and unemployment projects:

'A lot of reshaping has been happening to the old dinosaur. Quite a few youth clubs have a pool table with no cloth and the tips missing from the cues and many have no idea what to provide for young women. Things are changing to try to meet the needs of today's young people. The keyword for these changes rests on participation. The desire is to encourage young people to organise their own projects and entertainment. The great shame is that many people don't realise how to get something for themselves out of the system. None of these projects is going to shower you with cash, equipment or trinkets as you walk through the door but if you have just a quarter of a good idea about what you'd like to do then the workers would be all ears. Many youth workers walk the streets looking for the young unemployed (outreach work) so if you come to them they are more than overjoyed. If your brain is numb from months of dole-queue shuffling then drop in and have a coffee and check them out.'

The ILEA Careers Service

Careers offices listed in the borough by borough descriptions are helpful if you're having problems unravelling a future plan for yourself. No doubt you've come across careers officers already as they work in schools, colleges, and polytechnics giving information on education, employment and training opportunities. The Advanced Further Education Information Service is run in August/September every year to give advice to school-leavers. Also, in December, there are a series of careers lectures for sixth form and college students covering a wide range of careers. If you've left school and need help or advice go to the careers office nearest to you. There are specialist careers officers who visit disabled people. If you're unemployed and want to do some training you can get help to find the right kind for you (on YTS schemes and the Community Programme). They can give guidance on plans you might have for self-employment as well as help with problems you might be having with benefits and grants as well. Go to them if it's the first time that you're signing on as a full explanation of the whole process can save you time and trouble. Try to get to your local office if you're feeling unmotivated as they will talk to you about many different possibilities. There is also a computer-linked vacancy information service for training and employment.

Unemployment

The following figures come from the GLC and were produced in July 1985.

The rates are for the number of unemployed people expressed as a percentage of the number of people in work or seeking work.

Greater London all ages	11.6%
Greater London 16-24yrs	19.7%
Greenwich 16-24yrs	23.8%
Lambeth 16-24yrs	34.7%
Lewisham 16-24yrs	24.7%
Merton 16-24yrs	14.4%
Southwark 16-24yrs	31.9%
Wandsworth 16-24yrs	21.3%

A lot of work with young unemployed people is happening in each borough. To quote from the same youth worker, 'Unemployment projects are another kettle of fish altogether. These places have been set up to assist young people to broaden their interests and skills and prospects. They are usually staffed by committed individuals who are keen to involve and encourage young unemployed women and men. The best help they give is advice and information about what is going on, and many of them set up groups of young people with a similar aim. Money is, as always, the major hang-up but there are a number of ways to get round this problem.' They do offer a wide range of counselling, activities and support for those who are feeling hopeless at the lack of job prospects. There is a general feeling amongst many people that the term 'unemployed' should be changed to 'unwaged', acknowledging the fact that you don't have to have a job to be 'employed'. Help is at hand if you want to find out how to start a venture of any kind from a small group within a project to your own business or co-operative. Youth workers at the many unemployment projects can help you organise and co-ordinate these ideas as well as help you try to get grants or put you touch with people who could help. Drop-in centres provide a place to go where you can meet other people or do a variety of things.

Capital Jobmate
8 Strutton Ground
SW1
Tel 222 0222
Open 9-6(Mon-Thur) 9-5.30(Fri) answerphone at other times
Jobmate works for young unemployed people. Try it if you're between 16 and 21 and unemployed. It's a London-wide youth unemployment project that links unemployed people with a jobmate who is a local person who will understand the sort of problems and anger unemployed people feel. A jobmate is friendly, concerned and can give you help with ideas on where to look for jobs and training. Help can also be given with interviews, job applications and social security difficulties. Jobmates can also give you ideas on how to use your time. The project has helped thousands of young people since it started in 1979. A jobmate kit is free and contains information and advice on looking for work. If you feel you would like to be a jobmate then apply too. There are now over 100 jobmates in South London and they are looking for more volunteers. Initially each jobmate sees two or three young people a week on a one to one basis. The period of support could last up to six months. So if you're over 21 and feel you could provide a few young people with support, confidence and friendship then phone or write to find out more.

Work Experience

Voluntary Work
A large variety of voluntary work is organised in each borough. This gives you a chance to get some work experience and learn about a field you're interested in. It also gives you something to do for a while if you're unsure what path you want to take. The organisations you will be working with will often pay fares and lunch and you could find yourself doing gardening, painting and decorating, helping elderly, or

housebound people, or helping out on a city farm. For further information of this kind of work in your area phone the Volunteer Bureau listed under your borough or ask at your local youth office.

The Community Programme

This offers you the chance to work full or part-time for up to a year on a project in the local community. You will be paid at the local hourly rate. To qualify for a position if you're not yet eighteen you have to have been unemployed for the last two months. If you're between eighteen and twenty-four years old you should have been unemployed for a total of six out of nine months and if you're over twenty-five you should have been unemployed for twelve out of the last fifteen months. The schemes are run from your local job centre and employment offices so contact them for further information.

Youth Training Schemes(YTS)

Funded by the Manpower Services Commission this scheme offers a planned programme of training, education and work experience to 16 and 17 year old school-leavers and disabled school- leavers up to the age of 21. It is designed for both those who don't have jobs (trainees) and those who do (employees). Schemes vary and you can get full information and guidance from careers offices and job centres. The working week is the same as for other employees at your place of training but will generally not be more than forty hours excluding lunch breaks. The duration of the training is usually one year although in certain cases this can stretch to two. You will get about eighteen days holiday per year to be agreed in advance with your supervisor. Payment for trainees is £27.30 per week and fares over £3 will be paid. Employees will get a salary. If you're not living at home and are paying rent you should see what

supplementary benefits you can get by going along to your local DHSS office. Do the same if you have a disability. Schemes are provided by employers, training workshops, community projects and information technology centres. YTS schemes aren't compulsory and they don't promise a job at the end but they do offer work experience. You may be lucky and find one that suits you.

Training Opportunities Programme(TOPS)

This scheme is aimed at people who are 19 years old and over and who have been away from full time education for at least 2 years. There are a wide variety of courses and you can get full information from the training adviser at any employment office or job centre. You will be paid £38.50 per week with a meal allowance and fares over 5 miles compensated.

Starting a Business

Enterprise Allowance Scheme

Run by the MSC, this scheme will help you to set up a small business. If you have £1,000 to put down and have

been unemployed and claiming benefits continuously for the last thirteen weeks, you will receive £40.00 per week plus help with rent and rates. The business you set up must be new, independent, and 'suitable for public support'. You must not employ more than twenty people in the first three months. If a group of people want to start a business together up to ten are entitled to claim on the scheme as long as they satisfy the conditions. Ask at your local job centre or employment office for details.

Setting up your own business/co-op isn't easy. It takes a lot of effort and research to work out if your scheme will succeed. Local offices giving advice on business inititative are listed under each borough (advice). The following list of borough-wide agencies have been set up to help:
Greater London Enterprise Board
Tel 430 0300
Project Fullemploy
Tel 253 7380
Instant Muscle
Tel 672 8384
National Federation of Self-Employed and Small Businessmen
Tel 928 9292
Youth Business Initiative
Tel 930 9811
Youth Enterprise scheme
Tel 222 3341/2

Work with Young Women

Many projects have set up a group or a day or evening for girls and young women. These cover most aspects from education, counselling and advice, to learning skills and sport. Some projects provide childcare facilities so do phone to find out.

Family Planning

Brook Advisory Centres
A service provided to anyone under 26. You can get prescriptions and be advised on all methods of birth control including the morning after pill and get prescriptions. They can also provide pregnancy testing and advice. There are counsellors to discuss emotional, sexual and relationship problems. Your local area office is listed under your borough.

Resource Centres

These are places which have equipment you can use. Various places throughout your borough have typewriters, photocopiers, printing facilities, photographic equipment, video cameras, sound recording equipment and slide projectors. If you would like to use any of these things find out which projects have what resources through your area youth office or an unemployment project.

Your Local Network

Within each borough we list important contact addresses, some advice centres and then some local activities. Where we mention *wheelchair access* it means that there is access to the building but that there are no other special facilities unless these are mentioned.

Greenwich

Youth Service

Greenwich Area Youth Office
20 Passey Place
Eltham   SE9
Tel 859 4236
Wheelchair access none
Open 9.30-4.30(Mon-Fri)

Careers Offices

Eltham Careers Office
20 Passey Place
Eltham   SE9
Tel 850 0918
Wheelchair access none
Open 9-12.30 1.30-4.30(Mon-Fri)

Woolwich Careers Office
25 Wellington Street
Plumstead   SE18
Tel 854 2895
Wheelchair access none
Open 10-4.30(Mon-Fri)

South East London College
Tel 692 1117
Careers Officer (by appointment)

Thames Polytechnic and Avery Hill College
Tel 854 2030 x300
Careers Centre (by appointment)

Woolwich College
Tel 855 0322
Careers Officer (by appointment)

Voluntary Workers Bureau
Macbean Centre
Macbean Street
Woolwich   SE18
Tel 854 5499
Wheelchair access
Open 9.30-4.30(Mon-Fri)
A variety of voluntary projects to get involved in (such as gardening and decorating). Travel and lunch allowance. Phone for more information.

Community Industry (Greenwich)
Algernon Road
Lewisham   SE13
Tel 692 1005
Wheelchair access none but can be arranged
Open 8.30-5(Mon-Thur) 8.30-4(Fri)
Provide a year's work experience for people with educational or social disadvantages. A chance to try building, carpentry, painting and decorating, sewing workshops, running a drop-in canteen in a local community centre, creches and some office work. You are an employee rather than a trainee and day release courses for further study can be arranged. Apply through the Careers Office or Job Centres.

Advice

Greenwich Action Group on Unemployment(GAGOU)
Macbean Street
Woolwich   SE18
Tel 854 8494

Wheelchair access none
Open 10.30-5.30(Mon-Fri) 12-3(Sat for women only)
An active group of people who are involved in publicising all aspects of unemployment. They produce a free newsletter highlighting many current issues and organise campaigns against cuts, high fuel prices et al. You can go along to the centre and do art classes (materials provided), learn Tai Chi, get advice on pregnancy, join discussions on unemployment, racism and sexism, or meet people at social evenings. They also organise day trips to the seaside, galleries, museums and places of interest locally. There is a children's corner with toys and a telly so people with children are welcome. Women only on Saturday afternoons for talks, photography, haircutting and pregnancy testing.

Greenwich Council for Racial Equality
115-123 Powis Street
Woolwich   SE18
Tel 855 7191
Wheelchair access none
Open 9.30-5.30(Mon-Fri)
There is a full-time youth worker who can offer advice and counselling. Information is available for people from ethnic minorities on welfare and housing rights as well as employment issues. There is a campaign against racial discrimination. The employment unit has training workshops and runs a building and restoration scheme. Classes are organised to teach English as a second language. Some recreational activities (music events) are also organised.

Greenwich Education and Training Advice Centre
12-14 Wellington Street
Woolwich   SE18
Tel 854 2993
Wheelchair access
Open 10-4(Mon-Fri) 10-12(Sat)

There is a couselling service for education and training for those who are 19 years or older. A specialist worker runs sessions for disabled young people on Thursday. There are also some workshops for women. A 24 hour answerphone service is provided to deal with queries.

Greenwich Employment Resource Unit
311 Plumstead High Street
Plumstead   SE18
Tel 310 6695
Wheelchair access
Open 10-5(Mon-Fri)
Gives advice on education, basic skills and runs cultural courses. Also advises workers co-operatives and those setting up in business and applying for loans and grants. People on YTS schemes are given advice and support and local training facilities like the Charlton Training Consortium are being studied.

Thames Technet
16 Warren Lane
Woolwich   SE18
Tel 854 2511
Wheelchair access
Open 8.30-7.30pm(Mon-Thur)
If you have an idea for a business and need some guidance the staff of this organisation can help you to set up a plan, convince someone to fund your idea, and even help with getting premises. There are innovation centre workshops which cover subjects like electronics, mechanics and computers. They work with unwaged people, people with experience but no skills, people with skills but no experience, small businesses, individuals and community groups. They offer help, support and advice to further the development of ideas for useful products and services.

Some Local Activities

Archway Project
Harrow Manorway
Thamesmead   SE28
Tel 310 1730
Wheelchair access
Open 7-9(Mon) 6-8(Tue)
There are motor cycle repair and maintenance workshops. Riding skills are taught and you can do courses on road safety. Scrambling on off-road motor cycle tracks is organised once a month at weekends.

Greenwich Young People's Theatre
Burrage Road
Greenwich   SE18
Tel 854 1316
A really lively contribution from this professional theatre group which tours primary and secondary schools. The audience participate in these presentations. There are also youth theatre groups which tour nationally. Professional companies sometimes visit and a lot of interesting and exciting work is generated. They run workshops in drama, music, dance, photography and screen printing. A much needed place which gives you the time to develop creativity and explore your own potential instead of watching it all on the Telly. Go along and do it yourself.

Greenwich Youth Unemployment Project
Woolwich Dockyard
Woolwich   SE18
Tel 317 7594

If you feel your area is lacking facilities for you then contact the resource centre which is being set up to try to find out the needs of young people in the borough. (They were starting the project at the time of going to press.)

Greenwich Youth Aid
Plumcroft School
Genesta Road
Plumstead   SE18
Tel 854 3794
Wheelchair access phone in advance
Open 9.30-4.30(Tue Thur)
Many things to draw from this project. Drop-in on Tuesday or Thursday if you're unemployed. You can get advice on housing, benefits, personal matters and training. There is a girls group on Friday from 11.30 to 3. On Wednesdays they have recreational outings like going bowling or to the cinema. Life and social skills courses are organised and they arrange work experience for you if that's what you want. Phone to find out about the variety of things they do for waged or unwaged people and for single parents and children.

Simba Project
48-50 Artillery Place
Woolwich   SE18
Tel 317 0451
Wheelchair access none
Open phone for details
Activities include car mechanics, photography, keep fit, weight training and there is a recording studio from which workshops are run. Working within the music project is a reggae group called Ras Messengers who often do benefits. They also train sound engineers which is a skill that is not often taught at college. There is a drop-in centre, a canteen, a creche and a housing project. Lots of advice and counselling is available including free legal advice. They are concentrating at present on educational training for the Black community and run Turning Point in

conjunction with Goldsmiths College which is for the training of Black youth workers. A varied and interesting project.

Women in Greenwich
14 Ebdon Way
Ferrier Estate
Kidbrooke   SE3
Tel 856 3808
Open phone for details
This organisation run the Girls in Greenwich Project. They have workshops (mostly in schools) which tackle subjects like equal opportunities, sexuality, racism, relationships and training.

Lambeth

Youth Service

Lambeth Area Youth Office
1-2 Brixton Road
Brixton   SW9
Tel 582 5656
Wheelchair access none
Open 9.30-5(Mon-Fri)

Careers Offices

Brixton Careers Office
56 Brixton Hill
Oval   SW2
Tel 737 3221
Wheelchair access assisted
Open 9-12 1.30-4.30(Mon-Fri)

Vauxhall Careers Office
Belmore Street
Wandsworth Road
Vauxhall   SW8
Tel 622 7123
Wheelchair access by prior arrangement
Open 9-12 1.30-4.30(Mon-Fri)

Community Industry
18 Somerleyton Road
Stockwell   SW9
Tel 737 0037
Wheelchair access none
Open 9.30-5(Mon-Fri)

Schemes to provide work experience for 17-19 year olds in painting and decorating, woodwork, gardening, landscaping and signwriting. Weekly wage of £36 if you're 17, £45.30 if you're 18 and £49.90 if you're 19.

Advice

Brixton Circle Project
33 Effra Road
Brixton   SW2
Tel 737 2888/274 2513
Wheelchair access none
Open 2-7(Wed)
Advice on housing and benefits for single homeless people. They also have counselling sessions at other times and some leisure activities.

Melting Pot Foundation
361 Clapham Road
Stockwell   SW9
Tel 274 9566
Wheelchair access none
Open 10-5(Mon-Fri)
Counselling and advice on housing and legal matters. There is a also a boys hostel.

Lambeth Business Advisory Service
Courtenay House
9-15 New Park Road
Brixton   SW2
Tel 674 9844
Wheelchair access
Open 9-5(_on-Fri)
Advice and help with starting up your own business. Free service to anyone in the borough. If you have a good

Decisions...

idea, but haven't a clue what to do about it go along and they will tell you how to draw up a business and financial plan. Take as much basic information as you have with you. Phone to make an appointment or write to them at the above address.

Lambeth Women and Work Project
460 Wandsworth Road
Vauxhall   SW8
Tel 622 9208
Wheelchair access
The Training Owl is a booklet about training opportunities for women in Lambeth. You can ask for a copy for free if you're unemployed or a community group and they sell them at £2 per copy to others. Its aimed at women over 19 who want to do some training or who wish to change their job. There is information for people with no skills or formal qualifications, those wishing to improve skills, and those who want to go into further education. There is no information about YTS. The project also has two advice sessions per week, on Tuesday from 2 to 4 at the Springfields Community Centre, Wandsworth Road, SW8 and on Wednesday at the Tate Library in Brixton from 1 to 3.

Some Local Activities

The Abeng Centre
7 Gresham Road
Brixton   SW9
Tel 737 1628/274 5621
Open (phone for opening times)
Gives advice on homelessness, problems at home and unemployment. Liaises with skill centres throughout London and offers sports facilities, photography, video, woodwork, silk screening and discussion groups. Girls-only activities like photography, video, woodwork, table tennis and pool on Tuesdays from 10 to 3.

Brixton Music Development(BMD)
46 Kepler Road
Brixton   SW4
Tel 737 3237/8
Wheelchair access none
Open 11-6(Mon-Fri)
A community organisation which
provides facilities for people to make,
record and listen to many kinds of
music. There is a 24 track studio for
hire. Charges vary for members(£6 per
hour), community groups(£12 per
hour) and for others(£18 per hour). To
become a member you have to go
along to a meeting held on the last
Tuesday of every month and fill out
an application form. You will be given
provisional membership for six
months. BMD works mainly with
young people, women and the

unemployed. The Hip Hop Alliance
has already begun to 'hit the
headlines, rock the air-waves and
explode the tube.' It has been set up to
develop bodypopping, breaking,
rapping, scratch Dj-ing and human
beatboxing. They do events at the
Brixton Recreation Centre and have a
monthly club in Camden. All rappers
and reggae MCs should get in touch if
they want to perform at events, so
should anyone who would like to
contribute to the BMD newsletter.
The graffitti mural project is in hot
demand and is underway. They also
run the mobile music course which is
designed to train sound engineers.

The course covers the basic principles
of recording technique based on a 4
track system using drum computers,
synthesisers, bass guitars, guitars and
audio microphones. Mixers and
mixing techniques are also explained.
Black Market Enterprises was started
to promote and find employment for
artists who have difficulties
attracting mainstream support due to
ethnic origin or lack of funds. They
concentrate on projects which bring
people of various ethnic groups
together. The aim is to co-operate and
work towards successful results by
non-racist means. Plans are afoot for
BMD to be involved in a community
radio station so keep your ears
pinned. This place is brimming over
with action and vitality so go along
and show them what you can do.

Cave
3a & 4a Rectory Grove
Clapham   SW4
Tel 622 7186
Wheelchair access to 3a(literacy club
and school)
assisted to 4a(16-19 classes)
Open Mon-Fri(phone for opening
times)
A voluntary organisation running
three community education projects.
All have a concern for the difficulties
faced by teenagers and young adults
who haven't benefitted fully from
schooling. The literacy club is for 14-
25 year olds who wish to improve
reading, writing, spelling and maths.
Across the road at 4a Rectory Grove
there are courses for 16-19 year olds
who wish to improve their English
and maths and who need guidance
and support in planning their
immediate future. There is also a
small school for 14-16 year olds who
are long-term truants.

Central Lambeth Project
Beehive Place
Brixton Road
Brixton   SW9
Tel 737 1417

Wheelchair access none
Open phone for details
Serves the Ferndale, Stockwell,
Loughborough and Town Hall areas.
They work with mobile and jobless
young people between the ages of 11 to
25 who have no regular ties with the
youth service. Facilities are available
at the centre for counselling, advice,
information and group work. At the
moment they're doing street work
(which includes collating and
collecting information), outreach
work during the summer holidays,
community based projects on local
housing estates and on youth
exchanges. They work with many of
the local Lambeth advice agencies so
go along if you want to join in any of
their projects or need some help or
guidance.

Chestnut Lodge AM Project
Chestnut Lodge
48 Palace Road
Brixton   SW2
Tel 671 8342
Wheelchair access none
Open 1-4(Mon Wed Thur)
On Monday and Thursday they have
workshops for those who are between
16 and 19 years old. On Wednesdays
there are support groups and advice is
given on careers and benefits. The
young women's group meets on
Thursday and there is a creche
provided for this.

Cowley Unemployment Project
Marcus Lipton Youth Centre
Minet Road
Brixton   SW2
Tel 737 2849
Wheelchair access to building and
toilets
Open 2-5(Mon-Fri for enquiries)
A place to go to where you can do
drama, music, boxing, art,
photography and keep fit. Wednesday
night is women's night. The courses
they run are for school leavers as well
as the longer term unemployed.

Lambeth Women's Workshop
Unit C22
Park Hall Trading Estate
Martell Road
West Norwood   SE21
Tel 670 0339
Open phone for details
A carpentry/joinery workshop run for
and by women. Free courses are
offered to women who want to learn
these skills. The course is two days a
week and lasts for four months. They
are able to pay a childminding fee, and
you get a small training allowance
and some help with travel costs. Help
is offered to find further training,
with job applications and interview
tecniques.

Lambeth Youth Aid
16 Thornton Street
Brixton   SW9
Tel 274 6760
Wheelchair access none
Open phone for details
This is an active unemployment
project in the borough which has
resources and an information worker.
They mostly do group work within
the project as a result of having
located a need. There is an active girls
group and GiroScope workshops have
been run over the past two years. £1
entitles you to do as many workshops
as you want and you can keep
working with Lambeth Youth Aid for
a year. A free creche is available on
request and courses are offered in
computers, photography, fashion
design/fabric printing, furniture
repair, video, keyboards, singing,
drumming, acoustic guitar and
general musicianship. They usually
start in September and take place at
the above address or the Strand
Centre or the Lansdowne Youth Club.
Leaflets and further information can
be obtained from the office.

Oval House
52-54 Kennington Oval
Oval   SE11
Tel 735 2786/582 0080

Wheelchair access to theatre building
Open 9-10pm(Mon-Fri) 10-1(Sat)
Besides the vast array of courses and
workshops this active centre has
daytime support groups for the young
unemployed. These groups involve
themselves with voluntary work in
the community. There are good
evening workshops in drama, dance
and music.

Vauxhall City Farm
24 St Oswalds Place
Vauxhall   SE11
Tel 582 4204
Open 10.30-5(Tue Wed Thur Sat Sun)
Membership £2(over 16)
There are sheep, goats, rabbits,
donkeys and ponies. If you would like
to help with work on the farm go
along and volunteer. You could find
out about working with animals as
you help to clean, feed and look after
the animals.

Lewisham

Youth Service

Lewisham Area Youth Office
Capital House
47 Rushey Green
Catford   SE6
Tel 697 7031
Wheelchair access none
Open 9-5(Mon-Fri)

Careers Service

Catford Careers Office
5 Rosenthal Road
Catford   SE6
Tel 697 8431
Wheelchair access phone first
Open 9.30-12.30 1.30-4.30(Mon-Fri)

Lewisham Careers Office
208 Lewisham Way
Lewisham   SE14
Tel 692 1117
Wheelchair access none
Open 9.30-12.30 1.30-4.30(Mon-Fri)

Lewisham Volunteer Bureau
120 Rushey Green
Catford   SE6
Tel 690 4343
Wheelchair access
Open 10-5(Mon-Fri)

Advice

Brook Advisory Centre
Central Lewisham Health Centre
410 Lewisham High Street
Lewisham   SE13
Tel 708 1234/1390
Wheelchair access
Open 5.30-8(Tue)
Free birth control and other advice as
described under Family Planning.

**Lewisham Unemployed Action
Group**
The Albany Empire
Douglas Way
Deptford   SE8
Tel 692 0231
Wheelchair access
Open 12-4.30(Mon-Fri)
Information on welfare rights and
benefits. Also a women's advice and
counselling service and a women only
night on Monday from 7 to 10. Lots of
activities to join in with such as art,
drama, video and music. Driving
lessons and resources like a
typewriter and a phone. Two young
peoples theatres are based at the
Albany – The Combination Theatre
and the Basement Theatre. Deptford
Community Printshop has its home
here too and has silkscreen facilities
for community groups to use.
Altogether a good meeting place and
somewhere to see theatre, music and
go to discos.

Steve Biko Organisation
8 Walnut House
Clyde Street
Deptford   SE8
Tel 692 7568
Wheelchair access none
Open 10-5(Mon-Fri)
Advice, information and training

workshops in computers and new technology generally.

Hearsay
Youth Aid Lewisham
17 Brownhill Road
Catford   SE6
Tel 697 2152/7435
Wheelchair access
Open 10-1(Mon) 10.30-1.30 4-7(Tue Thur)
The service provides advice, counselling and group work. Work covers housing too and they will help you liaise with other advice centres in the borough to sort out any problems you may have. There is a young Black people's group, a young women's unemployment group, a who cares group and befrienders. Drop-in on Monday, Tuesday or Thursday and have a cup of tea and a chat. Join any of the groups or ask them to start one you're interested in. The South London Gay group use their premises and facilities.

Some Local Activities

Catford Link Enterprise Group
53-55 Silvermore Road
Catford   SE6
Tel 690 0961
Wheelchair access
Open 10-5(Mon-Fri
A self help unemployment project run by and for unwaged people. Counselling, advice and information are all available and there are activities and resources for arts and crafts and printing facilities.

Laban Centre for Movement and Dance
Goldsmiths College
New Cross   SE14
Tel 692 4070
Open 6.30-8.30(Wed) 10.30-12.15(Sun)
Some free classes are run at the Laban dance centre for local young people. The South East London Youth Dance Group has started as a result. If you're interested in dance and especially in

jazz and contemporary dance go along to one of their sessions. People who have never danced before join up and although they may find it gruelling at first could find their way into a performing dance troupe. On Sundays after the session there is a rehearsal for the group. If you have been in good form in the lessons you may be asked to go along to these. Performances take place in schools and at venues like the Albany.

Lee Centre
1 Aislibie Road
Catford   SE6
Tel 852 4700
Wheelcahir access
Open 10-9.30(Mon-Fri)
Membership £6 £1 unwaged
A community education centre where there are classes all week with a strong emphasis on literacy and maths. The young womens group on Fridays from 1-3 has typing, sewing, cooking, trips out, photography and discussions. ⬚ A creche is provided.

Lewisham Academy of Music
77 Watson Street
Deptford   SE8
Tel 691 0307
Wheelchair access none
Open 1-9(Mon) 4.30-9(Tue-Thur) 5-8(Fri)
A very popular place where you can go to learn to play an instrument. There are classes for singing, vocal groups to join, practice space and recording faculities.

Lewisham Unemployment Project
Hut 5
Granville Youth Centre
Granville Park
Lewisham   SE13
Tel 318 0526
Open 10.30-1(Mon-Fri)
An overall project for the borough which co-ordinates different kinds of groups according to local need. At the moment they are specialising in work with young women and young people from ethnic minorities.

Lewisham Way Centre
136 Lewisham Way
Lewisham   SE13
Tel 692 1190
Wheelchair access prior arrangement
Open 10-5(Mon-Fri)
There is a support group for the unwaged on Wednesday from 12.30-5.30 and you can drop-in at other times for tea, a chat, games or to discuss any problems. Daytime classes and help with training schemes and work experience.

New Cross Unemployment Project
170 New Cross Road
New Cross   SE14
Tel 639 1125
Wheelchair access assisted
Open 1-4(Tue-Thur)
Part of the New Cross Youth Project. There is a drop-in for fun and friendship and some advice if you need it. The girls-only night is on Tuesday and caters for the 14 to 20 year age group.

Platform One
Forest Hill Youth Project
2-4 Devonshire Road
Forest Hill   SE23
Tel 291 2928
Wheelchair access none
Open 12-4(Mon Tue Thur)
Drop-in for activities, advice or information. Out of Focus Films is a video workshop which is run on Tuesday afternoon. On Wednesday there is a young mothers group. The

Black Arts project is also based here and you can partake in dance, drama and music in the evenings. Phone for full details.

Telegraph Hill Unemployment Project
Kitto Road
New Cross   SE14
Tel 639 0214
Wheelchair access none
Open 1-4(Wed-Fri)
There is a drop-in for advice, and counselling. Other activities are being planned so ring for details or make some suggestions.

South London Young Gay Peoples Group
c/o Hearsay
17 Brownhill Road
Lewisham   SE6
Tel 697 7435
Wheelchair access none
Open Mon Tue(phone for opening times)
This organisation if concerned about the needs of young lesbians and gays. A mixed group meets on Monday and a women only group meets on Tuesday. They also organise outings to discos, films, Brighton, the zoo and camping trips.

Young Lewisham Motor Vehicle Workshop
346 Lewisham High Street
Lewisham   SE13
Tel 690 4957
Open 9.30-4.30 6-9(Tue-Fri)
This project is open to all young people who want to learn about motor mechanics. Most people using the workshops are unwaged but some who have jobs come in the evenings. People who have difficulty meeting garage bills for the repair of their vehicles bring them in to the workshops to be fixed. The scheme involves motor cycles as well as cars. Those who work do so on a voluntary basis and are supervised as they carry out the repair work. Thursday is for

women to learn about motor mechanics. After going through an introductory course you can work on repairs. An excellent mutually beneficial idea that works well.

Merton

Facilities for those of you who live in Merton are different from neighbouring areas because Merton is not part of ILEA. ILEA plays a big part in the organising of youth services in the other South London boroughs. There are people in Merton who are in the process of setting up more projects but none of these had taken off at the time of going to press. Phone the Youth Office for further details. Neighbouring Wandsworth facilities might prove useful for those of you who live close enough.

Youth Service

London Borough of Merton Education Department
(Principle Youth Officer)
Crown House
London Road
Morden
Tel 543 2222
Write or phone for a copy of the youth service handbook which outlines the sorts of facilities available to you in your area. There are also lists of youth organisations which offer chess clubs, model railway clubs, philatelic societies, camera clubs and a host of other small locally organised groups.

The Careers Service

London Borough of Merton Careers Office
Crown house
London Road
Morden Surrey
Tel 543 2222
Wheelchair access none
Open 9-5(Mon Wed Thur Fri) 9-7.30(Tue)

Merton Volunteer Bureau
114 London Raod
Morden
Tel 543 0099
Wheelchair access
Open 10.30-2.30(Mon-Fri)

Advice and Some Local Activities

Merton Resource Centre
240 Merton Road
Wimbledon   SW19
Tel 542 6223
Wheelchair access difficult
Open 10-5(Tue Thur Fri) 10-8(Wed) 10-2(Sat)
Affiliation rates 50p unwaged £1 individual £5 organisation
A busy centre providing research, advice on welfare benefits and other matters and support to individuals and community groups. You can enrol for workshops which cover subjects like computers, graphics, and video. The three workers at the centre work together on issues like employment, unemployment, welfare rights, womens issues, housing and community development. Resources available to you or your group are typewriters, photocopiers, lettering machines, duplicators and a small A4 printing press. You must book in advance as the equipment is in great demand. Also available for hire is a portable typewriter, the Centre's

premises for meetings, a badge-maker and video equipment.

Merton Legal Advice Centre
240 Merton Road
Wimbledon   SW19
Tel 542 6223
Wheelchair access difficult
Open 7-8.30pm(Tue)
A free legal advice group which uses the premises of the Merton Resource centre.

Merton Young Peoples Association
Edco House
10-12 High Street
Colliers Wood   SW19
Tel 543 8251
Wheelchair access none
Open 9.30-5(Mon-Fri)
Information and advice for young people and particularly for the Black community. There are educational and recreational facilities such as martial arts, dance, keep fit, crafts, writers workshops and cultural studies which include Black history. There is a drop-in centre as well so go along to find out how they can help you. Every Wednesday from 10.30-2 there is a single mothers drop-in project which includes discussions, relaxation and the learning of new skills.

Youth Centres

John Innes Youth Centre
61 Kingston Road
Wimbledon   SW19
Tel 542 3579
Open 7-9.30(Mon Tue Thur) 6.30-8.30(Fri)
Sports like judo and other martial arts, basketball and volleyball. There is a gymnasium, a games room and a lounge. There is judo on Monday, martial arts on Tuesday and Thursday, a senior club on Monday and Thursday and a junior club on Friday. Phone for details of future arts and crafts projects.

Raynes Park Youth Centre
Raynes Park High School
Bushey Road
Raynes Park   SW20
Tel 947 3842
Open phone for details
Mainly for those who are between 13 and 20 years old. Activities include table tennis, pool, darts, football badminton. There is a coffee bar and lounge with colour TV. At the time of going to press there was a junior club on Tuesday and there were plans to start a senior club so phone for further details.

YMCA
200 The Broadway
Wimbledon   SW19
Tel 542 3129/540 7255
Wheelchair access
Open 2-10(daily)
Membership £15.50(16-21yrs) £21(over 21yrs)
A wide range of interesting activities on offer here such as badminton, basketball, bridge, chess, circuit training, table tennis, volleyball, yoga, judo, keep fit, board games, drama, films, weight training, and a theatre workshop.

Deen City Farm
Corner of Church Road
Batsworth Road
Mitcham
Tel 648 1461
Open 9-4(daily)
Admission 10p
There are hamsters, rabbits, chickens, geese, ducks, goats, pigs, calves, horses, sheep and bees. Some land is being developed to start organic farming and they run a farm shop. Go along if you would like to help with work on the farm as they welcome volunteers, especially on weekends. Classes on spinning are run once a week and there is a programme of events for schools.

Southwark

The Youth Service

Area Youth Office
83 Peckham Road
Peckham SE5
Tel 701 8559
Open 9.30-4.30(Mon-Fri)

The Careers Service

Bermondsey Careers Office
68B Old Kent Road
Old Kent Road SE1
Tel 701 7171
Wheelchair access none
Open 9-12.30 1.30-5(Mon-Thur)

Elephant & Castle Careers Office
Castle House
2 Walworth Road
Elephant & Castle SE1
Tel 701 6276
Wheelchair access
Open 9-12.30 1.30-5(Mon-Thur)

Peckham Careers Office
55 Nigel Road
Peckham SE15
Tel 732 2161
Wheelchair access assisted
Open 9-12.30 1.30-4.30(Mon-Fri)

Southwark Voluntary Workers Bureau
135 Rye Lane
Peckham SE15
Tel 732 5729

Advice

Brook Advisory Centre
153a East Street
Walworth SE17
Tel 708 1234/1390
Wheelchair access
Open 9.30-7(Mon-Thur) 9.30-2.30(Fri) 9.30-12(Sat)
Free birth control advice and counselling as described under Family Planning.

Teenage Information Network(TIN)
102 Harper Road
Southwark SE1
Tel 403 2444
Wheelchair access
Open 2-6(Mon Wed Thur) 10-2(Tue Fri)
Definitely the place to go to for all sorts of advice, information, counselling, and a resources. They have been in existence for the last five years. The information bank covers housing, law, social security benefits and local facilities. They will put you in touch with what you want and need. There are drop-ins at the times stated above and groups involved in video, photography, art and craft, reading and counselling at other times. The resources on offer are silk screen printing, a photocopier, video equipment and games. Buy their Young Peoples Southwark Poster (40p) as it gives you addresses and phone numbers of youth centres, sports places, daytime places, clubs for mentally handicapped people, girls and young womens facilities, and places for health and counselling. Southwark is lucky to have this organisation.

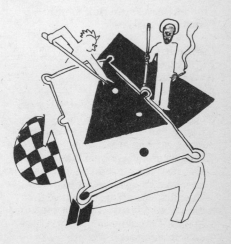

Co-op Development Agency

135 Rye Lane
Peckham   SE5
Tel 639 0134
Wheelchair access none
Open 9-5(Mon-Fri)
Comprehensive information here
about setting up a co-op. Also some
business training. There are
typewriters available and they can try
to get finance for you from other
bodies. They also allocate some small
grants.

Some Local Activities

Club of Dance and Self Defence

Paragon School
Searles Road
Old Kent Road   SE1
Tel 703 3360
Wheelchair access none
Admission 50p per day
Membership £5pa
Open 12-10pm(Mon-Fri)
Daytime and evening activities like
keep fit, martial arts, dance and
drama. There is a pool and leisure
space. The Newington Detached
Youth Project has a drop-in centre
here which runs from Monday to
Friday from 10 to 3 with space
available for unsupervised activities,
such as rehearsals.

Roundabout Unemployment Group

Roundabout Youth Club
Webber Street
Waterloo   SE1
Tel 928 7377
Wheelchair access
Open 12-6(Tue Wed Thur)
If you've been unemployed for a while
and need somewhere to go to meet
people, go on outings or share your
latest brilliant idea then go here on
Tuesday. If you're a school leaver join
one of their groups on Thursday.
Drop-in at other times for advice and
information.

Southwark Unemployed Youth Project

56 Comber Grove
Camberwell   SE5
Tel 701 0952/701 8559
At the time of going to press a new
project was being set up. Phone for
further details.

Squires Youth Club

Harper Road
Elephant & Castle   SE1
Tel 407 3949
Wheelchair access
Open 12-6(Tue) 12-3(Wed Thur)
This club runs workshops and works
actively with young women. They do
typing, dressmaking, and upholstery.

Surrey Docks Farm

Commercial Dock Passage
Gulliver Street
Surrey Docks   SE16
Tel 231 1010
Open 10-5(Tue-Sun) Closed on Fridays
during school holidays
A city farm with goats, chickens, bees,
donkeys, pigs and sheep. If you would
like work experience on a farm go
along and volunteer your services.
You can join in with looking after the
animals and helping with building
and small repairs. They also have a
farm shop.

Tustin Drop-in
Tustin Youth Club
328 Ilderton Road
Peckham   SE15
Tel 732 9366
Wheelchair access assisted
Open 10-12(Mon-Thur helpline) 11-
1.30(Mon Wed) 1-3.30(Tue Thur)
Somewhere to go to if you want to
have a chat and a coffee. On Monday
and Wednesday they have drop-in for
everybody and on Tuesday and
Thursday afternoon facilities for
young women. There is a helpline
from Monday to Thursday which is
open from 10 to 12.

**Walworth & Aylesbury
Community Arts Trust(WACAT)**
1a Wendover
Thurlow Street
Walworth   SE17
Tel 703 0415(Administration)
Wheelchair access to radio, music and
drama courses
Open 10-6(Mon-Fri)
Workshops in drama, music,
photography, print and radio. Mostly
for local people.

Elephant Enterprises
Tress House
3-7 Stamford Street
Southwark   SE1
Tel 261 0216
Wheelchair access none
Open 10-5(Mon-Fri)
Aims to help people turn their talents
and ideas into small businesses. They
provide free use of workshop space
and equipment for up to six months.
Free advice and support is available
from two experienced full-time
workers for up to a year. Ventures so
far have included painting and
decorating, design, photography,
hand-tufted carpet-making, camper
van extensions, pottery, contract
cleaning and telephone sterilisation.
After the six month testing period
you can start paying towards the cost
of the facilities or move to your own
premises. Run by Elephant Jobs Ltd

(928 2726) which also runs Elephant
Jobs YTS.

Wandsworth

Youth Service

Area youth Office
92 St Johns Hill
Clapham Junction   SW11
Tel 228 6693
Wheelchair access none
Open 9-5(Mon-Fri)

Careers Service

Balham Careers Office
2 Ravenstone Street
Balham   SW12
Tel 673 0033
Open 9-12.30 1.30-4.30(Mon-Fri)

Clapham Junction Careers Office
1 Plough Terrace
St John's Hill
Clapham Junction   SW11
Tel 228 0083
Open 9.12.30 1.30-4.30(Mon-Fri)

Putney Careers Office
50 Putney Hill
Putney   SW15
Tel 789 0201
Open 9-12.30 1.30-4.30(Mon-Fri)

Wandsworth Volunteer Bureau
170 Garratt Lane
Wandsworth   SW18
Tel 870 4319
Wheelchair access
Open 9.30-5(Mon-Fri)

Community Industry
11 Abercrombie Street
Battersea   SW11
Tel 228 5024
Wheelchair access
Open 9-5(Mon-Fri)
One year's experience for 17 to 19
year olds working in groups of 8 to 10
with a supervisor. There are
workshops in pottery, joinery and

textiles. Also groups who do general community work. See your Careers Office about joining.

Advice

Apex Charitable Trust
168-170 Battersea Park Road
Clapham junction　　　　SW11
Tel 627 3726/3882
Wheelchair access assisted
Open 10-4(Mon-Thur) 10-1(Fri)
Advice centre for the unwaged especially for those of you who have had some setbacks and are having difficulties with training schemes or need help with presenting yourself on application forms or at interviews. Counselling is also given on other problems you might be having like homelessness.

Brook Advisory Centre
St Christophers Health Centre
Wheeler Court
Plough Road
Wandsworth　　　　SW11
Tel 703 9660(ask for an appointment at the Wandsworth branch)
Wheelchair access by arrangement
Open 4.30-7(Tue) 4.30-7(Fri)
Free birth control and advice as described under Family Planning.

Central Wandsworth Youth Advisory Service
97 East Hill
Wandsworth　　　　SW18
Tel 870 5818
Wheelchair access assisted
Open 2-6(Tue Thur) 3-7(Wed)
All kinds of advice and counselling for those who are aged 15-21. You are welcome to drop in at the above times or make an appointment, or leave a message on the answerphone. You will be welcomed with a cup of tea, a friendly ear and any possible practical help. Anything from personal difficulties to problems with accommodation or benefits can be shared with a counsellor who is

trained to listen when you need someone to talk to. There is a big collection of books and leaflets which cover subjects from finding a flat to ideas for coping with unemployment. They call this the Information System so go along and find out more.

Instant Muscle
26 Montana Road
Tooting Bec　　　　SW17
Tel 672 8384
Originally formed by four teenagers who offered their services for all the jobs you meant to do but hadn't had time for. They prospered and the idea has been developed and promoted. Now they help you if you're skilled or unskilled and you have an idea you feel can be a commercial success. The learning while earning goes in three stages – a feasibility study and business plan, then starting up and, finally, keeping going. You must have the ideas, the will to succeed and the committment to make it work and they will help you to set up. There is a nationwide network of local and independent businesses all owned and managed by the young people who work in them.

Threshold Centre
101a Tooting High Street
Tooting　　　　SW17
Tel 767 2121/2162
Wheelchair access
Open 10-12.30 1.30-4(Mon Wed Fri) 4-7(Thur)
A housing advice centre for people without children who live in or have recently arrived in Wandsworth. Advice is free and deals with all aspects of housing from temporary, emergency accomodation to private rentals, co-ops, housing associations and housing benefit problems.

Wandsworth Business Resource
3rd Floor Park House
South Bank Business Centre
140 Battersea Park Road
Battersea　　　　SW11

Tel 720 7052
Open 9-5(Mon-Fri)
An excellent service with free advice on starting a new business, running a co-op, raising finance, marketing and sales, employing people, finding premises, legal matters, local authority matters and any general enquiries you may have as you dream up your new scheme. They produce a pack which contains reading lists, useful courses, some guidelines and hints on where to go for premises. They talk to people about new and established businesses.

Wandsworth Education Shop
86 Battersea Rise
Clapham Junction   SW11
Tel 350 1790
Wheelchair access
Open 12-6(Wed) 10-2(Fri) or by appointment
Offer free information and advice on the range of education and training opportunities available. Works mainly with those who are over 19 years old and will be able to help you sort out financial effects of studying, grant applications and childcare facilities. Drop in times are above and appointments can be made for the rest of the week.

Wandsworth Youth Development
The Katherine Baird Hall
Orville Road
Battersea   SW11
Wheelchair access assisted
Open 9-5(Mon-Fri)
A project that has looked carefully at the future of the world of work in order to provide an appropriate response to local people who have no jobs. There aim is to help young unwaged people to develop and carry out an idea or project of their own. They work with individuals as well as groups. If you approach them you can expect, help organising an idea, suggestions of people in the area who might be helpful, where to go if you need some further training and

perhaps some funding (grants up to £500).

Some Local Activities

Battersea Arts Centre
Old Town Hall
Lavender Hill
Clapham Junction   SW11
Tel 223 6557
Wheelchair access
Open 10-8.30(Mon-Sat)
BAC has opportunities in a wide range of activities you can watch or take part in, like theatre, dance, music, photography, film, sculpture, cabaret, painting, drawing and mime. There is a new youth theatre to join if your interest lies in drama. They plan about three major productions a year, starting with Aladdin in December 1985.

Battersea Project
Old Chesterton School
110-116 Battersea Park Road
Battersea   SW11
Tel 622 9231
Wheelchair access none
Open 9-5(Mon-Fri)
A youth and community project which is involved in girls work and helping other community groups who work with young people. They organise many projects with young unwaged people which include a daytime project for young women and courses at York Gardens Community Centre.

Battersea Boatyard
Old Chesterton School
110-116 Battersea Park Road
Battersea   SW11
Tel 622 9231
This scheme has finally started to
take shape after three years'
planning. Based at the Wandle Basin,
work is underway on clearing the
land and converting five railway
arches. Two boat projects are
proposed with large boats in one, and
smaller boats in the other. The large
boats' project will concentrate on the
restoration of historic river vessels
and will hopefully begin to provide
the embryo of a small river museum.
There will be a floating dry-dock.
Those working on the small boats
project will find themselves involved
in boat repair work and maintenance.
The boatyard will have to generate an
income and the plan is to rent out
moorings. Many groups from schools,
youth clubs, and projects as well as
boat enthusiasts will be involved. The
initial work is being carried out by
people recruited from the community
programme. Future plans include
getting a Thames sailing barge on
which they aim to take sail training
trips to the east coast and Holland,
and they would really like to build a
community narrowboat for
Wandsworth.

Elm Farm
Gladstone Terrace
Battersea   SW8
Tel 627 1130
Wheelchair access
Open Tue-Fri by appointment
A thriving community city farm in
the middle of Wandsworth which has
goats, hens, ducks and land to plant
and harvest. If you are interested in
finding out what life is like in the
countryside or how to look after
animals and plants go along to help
out. Things to learn are building,
fencing, sign making, milking a goat,
taking plant cuttings, growing

vegetables and generally helping to
run a farm.

Group 64
203 Upper Richmond Road
Putney   SW15
Tel 788 6943
Wheelchair access
Admission £2.50 Concessions
Membership £6(under 25)
If you fancy being in a play there is a
youth theatre based in this converted
church. You will have to be a member
and go through an audition. Once
established you will have the
opportunity of performing in two or
three plays and perhaps get a chance
to be in some of the other
productions put on by the (adult)
theatre company. There is a weekly
drama workshop so you can go along
and see if its what you're after.

Tooting Project
St Peter's Church Hall
Beechcroft Road
Tooting   SW17
Tel 672 9643/9562
Wheelchair access
Open 11-6(Mon-Fri)
Caters specially but not exclusively
for Black young people and its aim
and objective is to serve and develop
the Afro-Caribbean community. There
are many special interest groups
which include girls groups, an Afro
Caribbean writers workshop, a
computer group and a skills exchange.
The skills exchange is a collection of
people prepared to give their skills
and labours freely and benefit from
the skills and labour of others in
exchange. The sort of things available
are guitar and piano tutors, bicycle
repair and maintenance workshops,
badminton, yoga, typing and
photocopying, and maths or English
sessions. There is also a youth club
where you can relax and play games.

Wandsworth Photo Co-op
61 Webbs Road
Clapham Junction   SW11

Tel 228 8949
Wheelchair access none
Open 2-5(Tue drop-in)
For unwaged people on Tuesday the
co-op hold a drop-in. Both for those
who know a bit about photography
and for those who have never tried it
before. Some courses cost 50p while
others are free.

Wandsworth Unemployed Youth Project
92 St Johns Hill
Battersea   SW11
Tel 228 7136
Wheelchair access none
Open 9.30-5.30
Come here to find a forward thinking
and active bunch who can get you
involved in many activities*
throughout the borough. Their
information service is comprehensive
and produces helpful booklets like 'A
Register of Unemployment Projects',
and 'Put Your Own Ideas into action'
which gives helpful hints on filling
out application forms, writing a cv,
approaching an interview, and
working for yourself. They also
produce an amusing, informative,
imaginative monthly magazine called
Tips for the Enthusiast (well worth a
read). Participation by young people
has been encouraged for some years
now. Groups that have been set up are
video and media, music, girls work,
and a gay group. Watch out for the
Crack, which is becoming a yearly
event, and is a large selection of free
taster workshops for young (16-25)
unwaged men and women to try.
Research by street interview locates
what activities to put on so if you
have an idea remember to tell them.
The 1985 Crack was run in September
and had things like music, sounds
building, painting, graffiti, body
popping, dance, Black history, Black
art, computer programming, go-
karting, video, photography, football,
weight training and more.

Awards

Duke of Edinburgh's Award Scheme
35 Elm Road
New Malden   Surrey
Tel 949 2777
Open 9-5(Mon-Fri)
This is the London head office. The
Award Scheme provides a programme
of leisure activities offering a wide
range of choices to all young people
between the ages of 14 and 25. With
the voluntary assistance of adults as
leaders, instructors and assessors, you
can attain one or all of the three
awards (bronze, silver and gold). For
each of these you must successfully
complete four sections: service,
expeditions, skills and physical
recreation. The scheme is operated in
schools, youth organisations, firms
and through award centres and local
committees in the UK and in many
Commonwealth countries overseas.
Since the Scheme started in 1956,
nearly two million young people have
taken part, including an increasing
number who have some disability. For
more information phone your area
youth office and ask to speak to the
awards officer.

Adventure and Travel

Country Wings
Inter-Action Group
15 Wilkin Street
NW5
Tel 267 9421
Open 9.30-7.30(Mon-Fri)
Country Wings help organise groups
to visit the countryside. They have
information on over 800 venues
throughout Britain ranging from full
board to self-catering, including
camping. They can also advise
organisations who want to find
permanent accommodation in the
country. They especially help
disadvantaged groups.

The Drake Fellowship
c/o The Buffalo
Broomhouse Dock
Broomhouse Lane
SW6
Tel 736 2015
Open 9-5(Mon-Fri)
Run a 10 day initial training course.
You must be between 16 and 24 and
unemployed. The first three days are
spent at your local centre and you
learn something about living in the
wild. The next seven days are spent in
a wilderness area (like the Lake
District, Dartmoor). You will do
activities like hill walking,
navigation, climbing, water skills and
skiing. Each small group has three
instructors and you live in tents and
cook your own food. Specialist
clothing and kit can be borrowed.
After this basic training you can take
part in other projects. This can
include learning to sail with a sailing
team and if you have any particular
interest (say climbing or diving) they
will try to arrange this for you. Some
projects are in aid of a local
community (like forestry
conservation). Get in touch with
them if you're after something
challenging and out of the ordinary.

Interchange
Lloyds Bank Chambers
186 Streatham High Road
Streatham   SW16
Tel 677 9598
Wheelchair access none
Open 9-5(Mon-Fri)
Any youth group wanting to go
abroad can contact Interchange. If
you want information or help with
funding and fundraising they will
advise and also put you in touch with
others in your area who might have
done something similar. If you wish to
go somewhere as a performance group
(singing, dancing, acting) then they
can arrange for you to perform at
certain venues and meet similar
groups in other countries.

Sail Training Association
2a The Hard
Portsmouth
Tel 0705 832055
Open 9-5(Mon-Fri)
The STA run courses on two
schooners. There are some especially
for young people aged between 16 and
24 and each cruise lasts for two weeks.
During your training you and 38
other trainees will take a large sailing
ship across 800 to 1,000 miles of
mysterious water. You take an active
part in the ships company and have to
learn how to tie certain knots, raise
and lower sails and other aspects of
sailing such as navigation. There is
expert leadership and guidance from
skilled and experienced mariners. The
cruises do cost but it is possible to get
help to pay for your berth. A
programme throughout the year
includes those for boys (16-24), girls
(16-24) and adults of both sexes (21-69).
If you always dreamed of sailing
here's an opportunity.

Youth Hostels Association
58 Streatham High Road
Streatham   SW16
Tel 769 1498
Open 9-4(Mon-Fri)
This organisation aim's 'To help all,
especially young people of limited
means to a greater knowledge, love
and care of the countryside,
particularly by providing hostels or
other simple accommodation for them
in their travels and thus promote
their health rest and education.' The
YHA has 250 hostels in England and
Wales. Ask for their guide.
●Postellers
Tel 441 8126
A London hostelling Club which
organises a weekend away every
month and longer holidays at Easter
and in the summer. There is a
newsletter and a membership scheme.
You may find it easier to join an
organised weekend initially which
can give you an idea of what
hostelling can be like.

WHOOPS!

Last-minute jottings . . .

Adult Education
● There is considerable insecurity about what will be happening to ILEA's adult education rates when the GLC is wound up.

Art
● Brixton Recreation Centre has started running courses in drawing, painting, printmaking and batik.
● We forgot to mention the Dance Attic Gallery at 214 Putney Bridge Road, Putney, SW15. Tel 785 2055. The gallery space is in the main wide corridor of the building. Shows include Arts Council exhibitions and the work of individual artists, who are charged a fee of £50 for a three-week show (no commission is charged). Past Arts Council shows have included David Hockney and Giacometti lithographs. There is wheelchair access to the gallery space.

Children
● Special Needs: A useful, easy-to-read booklet for parents called Help Starts Here is available from The Voluntary Council for Handicapped Children, 8 Wakley Street, EC1. Price 50p.
● Exploring Parenthood (Tel 607 9647) is a national organisation well worth knowing about. It was founded in '82 to explore the problems and pleasures of parenthood and to provide a preventative service to stop minor problems becoming major complications. Although as yet there is no South London branch, they will help any parent get a local group off the ground. They also run workshops and will provide speakers whenever asked.

Festivals and Events
● For a few days from about 5 March Battersea Arts Centre will be celebrating International Women's Day with women's theatre, dance, literature, film, cabaret and other events.
● At the end of September, Battersea Arts Centre will be having a two-week literature festival, probably called Write On, featuring lots of different styles of prose and poetry (dub, rap and traditional) and many local poets and writers.
● The dates of the 1986 London Film Festival are now fixed for 13-30 November.

Film and Video
● Unfortunately our piece on the Ronald Grant Archive for this chapter got lost at the typesetters. Take a look at the entry in the Museums chapter.

Lesbian and Gay
● The GLC's Changing The World — a London Charter for Gay and Lesbian Rights was published just after we had gone to press. It is a serious and carefully considered document that covers all aspects of Gay life. It examines the current situation and makes over a hundred recommendations including certain changes in the law. It offers guidelines in relation to local authorities and employers, social services and the police, and covers education, health and many other issues. It has been distributed to advice centres, interested groups and local councils. It is a beautifully produced, illustrated, often witty publication which deals with some vitally important issues.

Local Services
● Lewisham Citizens' Advice Bureau at Christ Church in Bellingham Green is no longer at this address.

Museums
● We forgot Tower Bridge, which is open to the public and has a number of displays tracing the history of the bridge, other London bridges and the Thames since 1176. One of the Victorian engines which was built in 1894 and once operated the bridge can be seen in working order.

Poetry and Prose
● Bladestock Publications have a wonderful catalogue of multi-cultural and multi-ethnic poetry. You can read about this company near the beginning of the Ethnic Minorities chapter under Books.
● We forgot to mention the Signal Poetry Collection at The Centre for Children's Books in Wandsworth. (See section on Specialist Libraries in the chapter called Libraries.)

Young People
● The Steve Biko Organisation (see Lewisham) has moved to 144 Evelyn Street, Deptford, SE8. It has kept the same phone number.
● Voluntary Service Overseas (VSO) provides volunteer workers to 41 countries throughout Africa, Asia, the Caribbean and the Pacific. You have to be over 21 and willing to work in a developing country for at least two years. Give them a ring (Tel 235 5191) and see what kinds of skills they require, remembering that personal qualities and adaptability are just as important.
● International Voluntary Service (IVS) offers short-term (2-3 week) voluntary work in Europe. You don't have to have any particular skills but you must be over 18 and have done some voluntary work before.

EMERGENCY

Police Fire Ambulance
Dial 999

Medical Emergencies

Hospitals (24hr casualty depts)

Brook Hospital
Shooters Hill Road
Woolwich   SE18
Tel 856 5555

Greenwich District Hospital
Vanburgh Hill
Greenwich   SE10
Tel 858 8141

Guy's Hospital
St Thomas Street
London Bridge   SE1
Tel 407 7600

King's College Hospital
Denmark Hill
Camberwell   SE5
Tel 274 6222

Lewisham Hospital
Lewisham High Street
Lewisham   SE13
Tel 690 4311

Queen Mary's Hospital
Roehampton Lane
Roehampton   SW15
Tel 789 6611

St George's Hospital
Blackshore Road
Tooting   SW17
Tel 672 1255

St James' Hospital
Farfield Road
Balham   SW12
Tel 672 1222

St Helier Hospital
Wrythe Lane
Carshalton
Tel 644 4343

St Thomas' Hospital
Lambeth Palace Road
Waterloo   SE1
Tel 928 9292

Sydenham Children's Hospital
Sydenham Road
Sydenham   SE26
Tel 778 7031
Children only

Dental Emergencies

All the above hospitals have details of emergency dental services (some are NHS, others private), or you can turn up at casualty and be given a painkiller. The following hospitals have a dental emergency service at certain times:

Guy's Hospital
St Thomas Street
London Bridge   SE1
Tel 407 7600
Open 9-3.30(Mon-Fri dental dept)
24hrs(Sat-Sun casualty dept)

King's College Hospital
Denmark Hill   SE5
Tel 274 6222
Open 9 or 2(Mon-Fri clinics)
9-1(Sat morning clinic)

Psychiatric Emergencies
(24hrs)

Maudsley Emergency Clinic
Denmark Hill   SE5
Tel 703 6333

Emergency Prescriptions

Ring your local police station or
doctor for details of local late-night
chemists (usually open till 9) or go to
one of the following:

Bliss Chemist
50 Willesden Lane
Kilburn   NW6
Tel 624 8000
Open 24 hrs all week

Bliss Chemist
5 Marble Arch
Marble Arch   W1
Tel 723 6116
Open till midnight all week

Churchill Pharmacy
268 Oxford Street
Oxford Circus   W1
Tel 499 1517
Open till midnight all week

Homelessness

Council Emergency Homeless Person
Units:

Greenwich
Tel 858 7178
Contact a police station outside office
hours

Lambeth
Tel 274 7722
No service 5-6pm
Lewisham
Tel 690 8211

Merton
Tel 543 2222
Contact a police station outside office
hours.

Southwark
Tel 703 6311 (night line)
During office hours go to a local
district housing office (see Council
Housing section of Housing chapter).

Wandsworth
Tel 871 6000
No service 5-6pm
Housing Advice Switchboard
Tel 434 2522
Gives names of hostels (on
answerphone outside office hours).

See also chapters on Housing (section
on Homelessness) and Women (section
on Housing).

Legal Emergencies

Only Lambeth and Wandsworth have
24 hour legal services (see below).
They will help people from other areas
and refer them to daytime centres but
can't offer a full legal service.

Lambeth

Brixton Law Centre
Tel 733 4245

North Lambeth Law Centre
Tel 582 4445

Stockwell & Clapham Law Centre
Tel 720 6231

Wandsworth

Wandsworth Legal Resource
Project
Tel 228 9462

Londonwide

Release
Tel 603 8654

Racial Harrassment

Greenwich

CARA
Tel 855 4343

Lambeth
(see Legal Emergency Advice above)

Lewisham

Action on Policing
Tel 692 1312

Merton

Racial Harrassment Unit
Tel 228 9462

Southwark

Southwark Police Minority Service
Tel 703 1906

Wandsworth

Racial Harrassment Unit
Tel 228 9462

Emergency Social Services

Greenwich
Tel 854 0396

Lambeth
Tel 274 7722

Lewisham
Tel 690 4343

Merton
Tel 661 5000

Southwark
Tel 407 5522

Wandsworth
Tel 871 6000

NSPCC
Tel 778 3222
24hr Londonwide service for children
at risk

Household Emergencies

Council Services

Greenwich
Tel 854 0396

Lambeth
Tel 733 7922

Lewisham
Tel 690 4343

Merton
Tel 545 3749

Southwark
Tel 407 5522

Wandsworth
Tel 871 6000

Gas Emergencies

Greenwich
Tel 778 8090

Lambeth
Tel 733 5533

Lewisham
Tel 778 6444

Merton
Tel 640 3311

Southwark
Tel 639 2030

Wandsworth
Tel 773 5533 or 640 3311

Electricity Emergencies

Greenwich
Tel 737 2688(day) 304 7144(night)

Lambeth
Tel 733 5611(day) 701 1285(night)

Lewisham
Tel 737 2688(day) 304 7144(night)

Merton
Tel 733 5611(day) 701 1285(night)

Southwark
Tel 733 5611(day) 701 1285(night)

Wandsworth
Tel 733 5611(day) 701 1285(night)

Water Emergencies

Council tenants should contact their
Council Services number above.
Others should contact their local
number below:

Greenwich
Tel 692 0333

Lambeth
Tel 674 9888

Lewisham
Tel 692 0333

Merton
Tel 674 9888

Southwark
Tel 674 9888 (if you live in SE5 SE15
SE17 or any part of SE1 except
Bermondsey)
Tel 692 0333 (if you live in SE16 or
Bermondsey part of SE1)

Wandsworth
Tel 674 9888

24hr Helplines

All the following (except Alcoholics
Anonymous) offer a 24hr service.
Your call may be answered personally
or by an answering machine which
will refer you to someone you can talk
to on another number.

Suicide and Despair

Samaritans

Greenwich
Tel 692 5228

Lambeth
Tel 626 9000

Lewisham
Tel 692 5228

Merton
Tel 399 6676 or 399 6677

Southwark
Tel 692 5228

Wandsworth
Tel 789 9121

Rape and Incest

Incest Crisis Line
Tel 302 0572 (Ann)
Tel 890 4732 (Shirley)
Tel 422 5100 (Richard)

London Rape Crisis Centre
Tel 278 3956 or 837 1600

Rape Crisis Centre
Tel 340 6145

Women's Aid
Tel 251 6537

Children at Risk

NSPCC
Tel 778 3222

Domestic Violence

Women's Aid
Tel 251 6537

Parental Crisis

Parents Anonymous
Tel 668 4805

Lesbian and Gay

Gay Switchboard
Tel 837 7324

Drug Addiction

Release
Tel 603 8654

Alcoholism

Alcoholics Anonymous
Tel 834 8202
Line open 10am-10pm. At other times leave a message on the answerphone and you will be rung back when the office re-opens.

Al-Anon
Tel 403 0888

Gambling

Gamblers Anonymous
Tel 352 3060

Immigration

Release
Tel 603 8654

Shoplifting

Crisis Counselling for Alleged Shoplifters
Tel 202 5787 or 722 3685